ADVANCED CALCULUS

An Introduction to Analysis

Watson Fulks

Professor of Mathematics
Oregon State University

John Wiley & Sons, Inc., New York · London · Sydney

ADVANCED

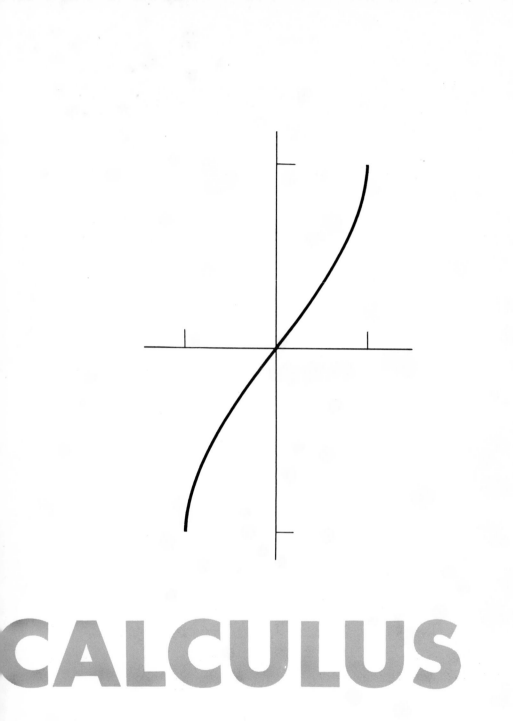

CALCULUS

An Introduction to Analysis

10

Library of Congress Catalog Card Number: 61–11255

Printed in the United States of America

to my Father

to the Student

In using this book, you should give first attention to the definitions, for they describe the terminology of mathematics; and you can no more hope to understand mathematics without learning the vocabulary than you can hope to understand any other foreign language without learning its vocabulary. As with any other language, mathematics grows partly by acquiring terms from neighboring languages (in this case primarily English), modifying their meanings, and appropriating them into itself. These form the technical terms of the subject. Since mathematics, in this country, is imbedded in the English language, it is important to distinguish between technical and nontechnical usage.

A word or phrase being defined is set in boldface type, as for example **uniform convergence**. Theorems which have names, such as the **fundamental theorem of calculus,** will have these names set in boldface. A triple-barred equal sign ($\equiv$) is used in two ways. It will mean identity, as for instance

$$x^2 - y^2 \equiv (x - y)(x + y).$$

It will also mean "defines" or "is defined by." For example,

$$f(x) \equiv 2x^2 + 3 \qquad \{-1 \leqslant x \leqslant 7\}$$

means that the function f is being defined in the designated interval. There is, I believe, little cause for confusion arising from the ambiguous uses here indicated.

In the body of the text, occasional reference is made to exercises by number. For instance, parenthetical remarks such as (see Exercise B7) frequently occur. Unless a section number is indicated, the exercise in question will be found in the first set of exercises *following* the reference.

A few more words about study: in trying to understand a proof, you should look for the driving force behind it. You should try to analyze the proof and decide that a certain idea (or ideas) involved is critical, that the proof turns on this, and that the remaining parts are secondary calculations whose presence is clearly understood once the significant point is seen.

It is desirable to understand the role each proposition plays in the construction of a chapter. Which ones, you should ask yourself, are in the nature of preliminary or secondary results, which are of prime importance, and which are anticlimactic? The names — lemma, theorem, corollary — provide a rough rule of thumb, but by no means an accurate one.

Finally, after all this talk, let it be said that no amount of directions on how to study can begin to replace a real and growing interest in the material.

WATSON FULKS

Corvallis, Oregon
March 1961

to the Teacher

This book is designed to serve as an introduction to analysis. To this end I have made an effort to present analytical proofs backed by geometrical intuition, and to place a minimum of reliance on geometrical arguments. In fact, some stress is laid on this in the body of the text. I have not succeeded completely in avoiding some essential use of intuition in the proofs, but I have localized my serious transgressions to Chapter 13 wherein are located Green's, Gauss', and Stokes' theorems and some of their consequences.

Like most who stray from the narrow path of virtue, I seek to rationalize my action. My defense is simply that to avoid such geometrical arguments would involve more difficult work than I feel is advisable. In attempting to hold to a course between the heuristics of elementary calculus on the one hand, and the rigor of function theory and topology on the other, I have chosen to err in the direction of heuristics in Chapter 13. The motivation for this is, of course, that what I sacrifice in logic I hope to gain in pedagogy.

So much for apologies.

The book is divided into three parts, beginning with calculus of functions of a single real variable. In this part I delineate some of the more significant aspects of the theory. The most novel feature is perhaps the proof of the existence of the integral of a continuous function without the use of uniform continuity. This makes possible postponement of the discussion of the more difficult properties of continuous functions until the students have gained some maturity.

The middle part is concerned with the calculus of several variables. It begins with a chapter on vectors, and uses vector terminology and vector notation consistently and, I hope, effectively. Chapter 11, which is concerned with inverse functions and transformations, contains a proof of the inversion theorem which is an adaptation of a new proof by Professor H. Yamabe (*American Mathematical Monthly* LXIV, 1957, pages 725–726), a proof which can be carried over to certain types of infinite dimensional spaces.

The third and last part of the book is concerned with a treatment of the theory of convergence as applied to infinite series and improper integrals. The Cauchy criterion forms the basis for a unified treatment of these topics.

The problems in each set are classified as A, B, or C Exercises. This classification is to be taken as an approximate grading of the difficulty of the problems. The A Exercises are straightforward applications of the theory, though the computations in some of them may be a little long. The B Exercises are somewhat deeper, and the C Exercises in general are intended to challenge the better students.

I present no bibliography, though I must of course acknowledge the influence of many books, old and new, upon the shape this one has assumed.

I gratefully acknowledge the influence of colleagues with whom I discussed the manuscript. In particular, I must mention Professor Warren Stenberg, with whom I held a number of conversations; and Professor Jack Indritz, who read critically large portions of the manuscript.

WATSON FULKS

Contents

part I

CALCULUS OF ONE VARIABLE

I

The Number System

1.1 THE PEANO AXIOMS

Any study of mathematical analysis has its basis in the number system. It is therefore important for students of analysis to understand how the arithmetic can be developed from the natural numbers (another name for the positive integers). It is not our intention to carry out that development here, as that is more properly a part of a course in function theory. However, we do want to make some comments about the logical structure of that development.

The usual starting point in the development of the real numbers is a certain set of axioms which were first formulated by the Italian mathematician Peano. These axioms state that the natural numbers satisfy certain properties. From only these properties, making appropriate definitions as we proceed, we can develop all the usual rules of arithmetic. In the terminology of formal logic, we have a set of undefined objects which we choose to name the **natural numbers**, satisfying Peano's axioms. This means merely the natural numbers are taken as the basic "atoms" of our mathematical system in terms of which we express the other mathematical concepts, but which are themselves not expressed in more fundamental terms.

Perhaps an easier way to visualize the situation, since after all you cannot claim that you never heard of arithmetic or rational numbers, etc., is this: We can verify that the positive integers are a system of objects which do satisfy the Peano axioms. We can now proceed to recapture all we know of arithmetic, using only those properties stated explicitly in the axioms.

The five Peano axioms follow:

Axiom I. 1 is a natural number.

Axiom 2. To every natural number n there is associated in a unique way another natural number n' called the **successor** of n.

Axiom 3. The number 1 is not a successor of any natural number.

Axiom 4. If two natural numbers have equal successors they are themselves equal. That is, if $n' = m'$, then $n = m$.

Axiom 5. Suppose M is a collection or set of natural numbers with the properties
(i) 1 is in M.
(ii) n' is in M whenever n is in M.
Then the collection M consists of all natural numbers.

Here equality is used in the sense of numerical identity; that is, $m = n$ means that m and n are symbols standing for the same number. Thus we take
(i) $m = m$,
(ii) $m = n$ implies that $n = m$,
(iii) $m = n$, $n = k$ implies that $m = k$,
as part of the underlying logic and do not list these as part of our set of numerical axioms.

Notice that this list of properties does not contain any explicit statement of the linear ordering of numbers. There is a "first" one, namely 1, distinguished by not being a successor. The successor n' of a natural number n turns out to be $n + 1$ after addition has been defined. In fact, this is essentially the way addition is defined. We can then proceed to show that the natural numbers must line up after 1 in their familiar order: 1, 2, 3, 4, ... (Since 2, 3, 4, . . . are not given in the axioms, they are defined by $2 = 1' = 1 + 1$, $3 = 2' = 2 + 1$, ...)

Axiom 5 is precisely the principle of mathematical induction. It is an important tool in the technical development of the properties of the number system which we have been discussing. We will have occasional use for this principle later, and we will see that the statement of Axiom 5 is equivalent to the more familiar one given in elementary texts.

As indicated earlier, we can start with the natural numbers and, knowing only the properties and relationships stated by the axioms, derive all of arithmetic. Why do you suppose mathematicians are interested starting from such primitive beginnings? Are $m + n = n + m$ and $m \cdot n = n \cdot m$ any truer because they can be derived as a consequence of the axioms? In one sense it is quite the other way around. The axioms are "true" or valid because from them we can derive $m + n = n + m$ and $m \cdot n = n \cdot m$ (after defining addition and multiplication), and all the other standard rules of arithmetic. One aspect of such an approach is aesthetic: it gives a clean, beautiful development of a well-known and useful body of knowledge from simple precisely stated foundations. There is an artistic beauty to such a structure.

Another somewhat more pragmatic purpose is that it serves to help answer the question, "What is a proof?" If we try to do mathematics without a precise foundation, a 'proof" may be any convincing argument, based on what one "knows." But since this knowledge is not well formulated, this may lead to circular arguments: Theorem A may be based eventually on Theorem B, Theorem B may be based on Theorem C, and Theorem C finally based on A again. If the proofs are long and involved, it may be difficult to spot such circular arguments. Having a well-formulated axiom system reduces the possibility of such mistakes. A proof becomes a logical argument based directly on the axioms, or on previous theorems based on the axioms. Of course there is always the possibility of human error, for everyone makes mistakes; but at least this approach gives a clearer idea of what we seek in a proof.

In any case, it is an example of what is called the **axiomatic approach** to the study of mathematics. By this we mean merely that the whole of a certain section of mathematics has been reduced to a few statements, and the complete structure can then be unfolded from these by a logical study of the consequences of these statements.

1.2 **RATIONAL NUMBERS AND ARITHMETIC**

After the salient properties of the natural numbers have been developed, the next step is the introduction and study of **rational numbers**. Rational numbers, you will recall, are those numbers which can be represented as ratios of whole numbers; in other words, rational numbers are common fractions. We list below certain properties of rationals which can be deduced in the course of their development from the natural numbers. Thus these properties of rational numbers are actually consequences of the Peano axioms.

The sign $\geqslant$, read "is greater than or equal to," means that one of the two stated possibilities holds. Thus $a \geqslant b$ means that a is either (1) greater than b or (2) equal to b. The sign $\leqslant$, read "less than or equal to," is similarly defined.

I. Order Properties of Rational Numbers

   1. For any two rationals a and b, exactly one of $a > b$, $a = b$, $a < b$ is true. This is the trichotomy law.

   2. From $a \leqslant b$ and $b < c$ we have $a < c$. Similarly, $a < b$ and $b \leqslant c$ implies that $a < c$. This says that inequality is transitive.

II. Arithmetical Properties of Rational Numbers
1. Addition
   (*a*) For each rational *a* and *b* there is a unique rational *c*, called the **sum** of *a* and *b* and written $c = a + b$.
   (*b*) Addition is commutative:
$$a + b = b + a.$$
   (*c*) Addition is associative:
$$(a + b) + c = a + (b + c).$$
   (*d*) $a < b$ implies that $a + c < b + c$ for each *c*.
   (*e*) There is a unique number 0 such that $a + 0 = a$ for each *a*.
2. Subtraction
   (*a*) For each rational *a* and *b*, there is a unique rational *d* for which $a + d = b$. The number *d* is called the **difference** of *a* and *b* and is denoted by $b - a$.

On the basis of II 2(*a*) we define the **negative** of a number. By II 2(*a*) we see that for each rational *a* there is a rational *x* for which
$$a + x = 0.$$
That number we call $(-a)$. Thus $(-a)$ is defined by
$$(-a) = 0 - a.$$
Frequently we write $-a$ instead of $(-a)$.
3. Multiplication
   (*a*) For each rational *a* and *b*, there is a unique rational *p* called the **product** of *a* and *b*, and is written $p = a \cdot b$ or $p = ab$.
   (*b*) Multiplication is commutative:
$$a \cdot b = b \cdot a.$$
   (*c*) Multiplication is associative:
$$a \cdot (b \cdot c) = (a \cdot b) \cdot c.$$
   (*d*) Multiplication is distributive:
$$a \cdot (b + c) = a \cdot b + a \cdot c$$
   (*e*) $a > b$, $c > 0$ implies that $ac > bc$.
   (*f*) $a \cdot 1 = a$ for every *a*.
4. Division
   (*a*) For each rational *a* and *b* with $b \neq 0$, there is a unique number *q* for which $b \cdot q = a$. The number *q* is called the **quotient** of *a* and *b*, and is written $q = a/b$.

As stated in the first paragraph of this section, these properties follow from the axioms of Section 1.1. Furthermore, from the statements listed here we can derive all other elementary rules of arithmetic. Thus this list could itself be taken as an axiom system for the description of arithmetic. We now give a few examples of the derivation of these rules from the properties listed under I and II.

EXAMPLE 1. Show that $a \cdot 0 = 0$ for every rational a.

Solution. By II 1(*e*),

$$b + 0 = b \qquad \text{for every } b.$$

Thus $\qquad\qquad a \cdot (b + 0) = a \cdot b$

or, by II 3(d), $\qquad a \cdot b + a \cdot 0 = a \cdot b = a \cdot b + 0.$

Thus, by the uniqueness of the difference [II 2(*a*)], we have

$$a \cdot 0 = 0.$$

EXAMPLE 2. Show that $(-1) \cdot a = -a$.

Solution. By the definition of (-1), we have

$$1 + (-1) = 0.$$

Multiplying both sides by a, using the distributive law and Example 1, we get

$$a + (-1) \cdot a = 0.$$

Hence $(-1) \cdot a$ is a solution of

$$a + x = 0.$$

By II 2(*a*) there is only one solution, namely $(-a)$. Thus

$$(-1) \cdot a = -a.$$

B EXERCISES

I. The following set of problems consists of some rules of arithmetic to be established on the basis of properties listed under I and II of this section. In general, though not always, the earlier rules are useful in establishing the later ones. The two examples may also be used:

(*a*) $b + (-a) = b - a$ $\qquad$ (*b*) $b(-a) = -(a \cdot b)$ $\qquad$ (*c*) $-(-a) = a$

(*d*) $(-a)(-b) = a \cdot b$ $\qquad\qquad$ (*e*) $a > 0$ implies that $-a < 0$

(*f*) $a \neq 0$ implies that $a^2 > 0$ $\qquad$ (*g*) $1 > 0$

(*h*) $a \cdot b = 0$ implies that $a = 0$ or $b = 0$

(*i*) $a > 0$ implies that $1/a > 0$

(*j*) $a > 0, b > 0$ implies that $a \cdot b > 0$

(*k*) $a > 0, b < 0$ implies that $a \cdot b < 0$

(*l*) $a < 0, b < 0$ implies that $a \cdot b > 0$

(*m*) $a \geqslant 0, b \geqslant 0$ implies that $a + b \geqslant 0$

(*n*) $\left(\dfrac{x}{y}\right) \cdot \left(\dfrac{u}{v}\right) = \dfrac{xu}{yv}$ $\qquad\qquad$ (*o*) $\left(\dfrac{x}{y}\right) + \left(\dfrac{u}{v}\right) = \dfrac{(xv) + (yu)}{yv}$

1.3   THE REAL NUMBERS: COMPLETENESS

We have listed a few of the properties of rational numbers. So long as we want to perform only arithmetic, this set of numbers and the rules (and their consequences) listed under I and II are quite adequate. However, if we venture into algebra—that is, if we want to extract roots as well as add, subtract, multiply, and divide—then our number system is not sufficient to provide a solution to all our problems. For example, if we seek a solution to the equation

$$x^2 = 2,$$

we will not find one among the rationals. By this we mean that there is no rational number x whose square is 2. You have probably seen a proof of this fact before, but we review that argument here.

1.3a   Theorem. There is no rational number whose square is 2.

Proof (by contradiction). Suppose there were such a number, x. Then x could be written as p/q, where we may suppose that the fraction is in lowest terms. Thus p and q have no common factors. Then

$$p^2/q^2 = 2$$

or
$$q^2 = p^2/2.$$

Since q^2 is an integer, p^2 must be divisible by 2. But if p^2 is divisible by 2, then p is divisible by 2, so that there is an integer k for which $p = 2k$. Then

$$q^2 = p^2/2 = (2k)^2/2 = 2k^2$$

or
$$k^2 = q^2/2.$$

By the same argument, q is divisible by 2. This contradiction completes the proof.   ∎ *

You are, of course, familiar with the geometrical interpretation of numbers as points on a line. For the purpose of emphasizing certain aspects of this interpretation, we review its main features here. On a straight line we choose a point which we mark O and call the origin. We take a convenient unit of length, and to each number x we make correspond the point whose distance from O is x measured to the right if x is positive and to the left if x is negative. Let us note that the arithmetical law

$$a > b, \qquad b > c \qquad \text{implies} \qquad a > c$$

finds its geometrical counterpart in the following statement about points

---

* The symbol ∎ will be used to denote the end of a proof. It replaces Q.E.D.

P_1, P_2, P_3 on a line: If P_1 lies to the right of P_2 and P_2 to the right of P_3, then P_1 lies to the right of P_3.

Now if x is any rational number, then all rational numbers fall into two classes associated with x, namely, the classes U and L (upper and lower), where U consists of all rationals greater than x and L consists of all rationals less than x. The number x itself may be assigned to either U or L. Such a separation or cut in the rationals produced by a definite rational x divides the rationals into two classes such that each member of the first class, U, is greater than every member of the second class, L.

Similarly, if P is any point on the line, then all the points of the line fall into two classes R and L (right and left) associated with P, where R consists of all points to the right of P and L all points to the left of P. The point P itself may be put into either class. But for all points P the separation or cut leads to a partition of the points of the line into two classes such that each point in the first class, R, is to the right of every point in the second class, L.

Now there are points on the line which do not correspond to any rational number. For if we mark the point whose distance from 0 is $\sqrt{2}$, we see by Theorem 1.3a that there can be no rational number corresponding to it. In fact, it is not very difficult to show that there are infinitely many points which correspond to no rational number. This means that if we mark all points on the line which correspond to rational numbers, there are infinitely many unmarked points left over. In fact, in every interval of the line there are points corresponding to rational numbers and points which correspond to no rational numbers. (See Exercises C3 and C4 in Section 1.7.)

These considerations lead to the recognition of the existence of gaps or a lack of continuity or completeness in the distribution of rational numbers as compared with the distribution of points on a line. We accept as a basic fact of geometry that points are continuously distributed on a line; that is, that there are no gaps or incompletenesses in the line. For this we offer no proof, but take it as a geometric axiom.

While we offer no proof of this concept of the continuous distribution of points on a line, we do want to formulate it in a precise form which we can use in our discussion of the number system. The formulation we use is due to the German mathematician Dedekind, whose treatment we are following closely. Dedekind uses the **separation** or **cut** described earlier to characterize the completeness of the line. His formulation is as follows:

Suppose that all points on the line are separated into two non-empty classes R and L so that each point in R is to the right of every point in L. Then there is exactly one point P which produces this cut, and P itself is either the rightmost point of L or the leftmost point of R.

We offer no proof for this statement, any more than we do for the statement that points are continuously distributed on the line. We take this to be merely a precise statement of that continuity or completeness, a formulation which is adapted for the purpose of considering the analogous questions for the distribution of numbers.

The analogous statement for rational numbers cannot be true. To see this, we need only give one example where it fails, and this example we now describe.

Let the upper class U, corresponding to R for the line, be the set of all positive rationals whose squares are greater than 2, and let L be all the other rationals. Suppose the cut is produced by a rational number x. Then it is possible to show (the technical proof will be omitted) that $x^2 = 2$. But this contradicts Theorem 1.3a. Thus we see that the analogue for rationals, of the completeness axiom of the line, is not correct.

The final big step in the development of the number system is to define numbers to fill the gaps displayed by the previous remarks. These new numbers are called **irrational numbers**. The system of numbers consisting of the rationals and irrationals together is called the **real-number system**. Thus a real number can be either rational or irrational.

The details involved in carrying out the definition of the new numbers will be omitted. We want to emphasize two important facts about the real-number system. First, the notions of addition and multiplication can be defined for real numbers so as to satisfy the properties listed for rationals under I and II of Section 1.2; that is, if we read "real number" in place of "rational number," the conclusions stated there remain true. Second, and very important, the real-number system is complete; that is, the analogue of the geometrical axiom on the completeness of the line can be proved as a theorem.

III. Dedekind's Theorem

Suppose that all real numbers are divided into two non-empty classes, R and L, so that each number in R is greater than every number in L. Then there is a real number x such that x is greater than or equal to every number in L and less than or equal to every number in R.

We designate this by the numeral III for the following reason: the statements listed under I and II of Section 1.2, together with III of the present section, can be taken as an axiom system for the descriptions of the real numbers. That is, all properties of the real numbers can be developed from these statements alone.

The scientific importance of the development of the real-number system outlined here is, of course, that it puts a large body of useful knowledge in a cleanly laid out, logical form. We also want to emphasize that it strengthens the analogy between real numbers and points on a line, yet at the same time removes analysis from any logical dependence on geometry. All the basic theorems of calculus can now be given purely arithmetical proofs.

1.4 GEOMETRY AND THE NUMBER SYSTEM

Analysis is that branch of mathematics which is concerned with limits and with limiting operations. Mathematicians, as you may have surmised in the last section, like to base their study of analysis on arithmetic, with no logical dependence on geometry. However, as you already know, geometrical pictures can be very enlightening when you are attempting to solve many types of problems. There is no objection to using such devices; indeed you should be encouraged to use them. But use them as guides which give insight, and not, if you can possibly avoid it, as essential parts of an argument.

Geometrical language with its highly suggestive power can also be very useful and can be given arithmetical meaning. We shall define a few geometrical terms here, and others will occur intermittently throughout the rest of the book. This, of course, is an attempt to exploit the geometric analogy we have pointed out. We will thus rely heavily on geometry for our inspiration, but where possible we will avoid any essential use of geometry in our arguments. In this we succeed reasonably well, except in Chapter 13. When we do lean on geometry in any essential way, we will be careful to point this out.

We proceed to define a number of geometrical terms. Since there are quite a few of these, you will want to refer back to this section until you become familiar with all these terms.

We will speak of the real-number system as a **one-dimensional space**, and of course we will visualize it as a line.

In one-dimensional space we will use the word **point** to mean "number."

A **point set** is a collection of points.

An **interval** is a point set described by inequalities of one of the following types:

$$\{a \leqslant x \leqslant b\} \qquad \text{closed interval}$$
$$\{a \leqslant x < b\} \qquad \begin{cases} \text{half-open or half-} \\ \text{closed intervals} \end{cases}$$
$$\{a < x \leqslant b\}$$
$$\{a < x < b\} \qquad \text{open interval}$$

In general, a point set will be represented by placing its description in braces. Thus we will speak of "the interval $\{a \leqslant x < b\}$" rather than "the interval described by $\{a \leqslant x < b\}$."

The **end points** of the interval are a and b; a is the left-end point, b the right-end point. The **length** of the interval is $b - a$.

A **neighborhood** of a point x_0 is an open interval centered at x_0: $\{x_0 - h < x < x_0 + h\}$.

A **deleted neighborhood** of a point x_0 is a neighborhood from which the point x_0 itself has been removed. Thus it consists of two open intervals abutting at the point x_0: $\{x_0 - h < x < x_0\}$ and $\{x_0 < x < x_0 + h\}$.

A number x_0 is an **interior point** of a point set S if there is a neighborhood of x_0 which is entirely contained in S. For example, if S is the interval $\{-1/2 < x \leqslant 1\}$, then $x_0 = 3/4$ is an interior point but $x_0 = 1$ is not.

A number is said to be an **element** of a point set if it is a member of the set.

It is also convenient to say a few words here about the geometry of the higher dimensional spaces. Just as one-dimensional space is the collection of all real numbers, so **two-dimensional space** is the collection of all ordered pairs (x, y) of real numbers. These ordered pairs are called **points** in the two-dimensional space. We visualize this geometrically as a plane wherein points are plotted in the usual manner in a rectangular Cartesian coordinate system. Similarly, **three-dimensional space** is the collection of ordered triples (x, y, z), again visualized in terms of a rectangular coordinate system. In discussing these spaces, the term **point set** means a collection of ordered pairs, triples, etc. of real numbers.

1.5 BOUNDED SETS

It should be noted that the word "set" covers complicated, scattered collections of points as well as simple collections of points such as intervals. Indeed, much of what follows would appear trivial and uninteresting if this were not so. While the procedure being developed is intended primarily to handle complicated sets, it applies equally well to simple ones.

A set S will be said to be **bounded above** if there is a number M with the property that

$$x \leqslant M \qquad \text{if } x \text{ is in } S.$$

Similarly, S is **bounded below** if there is a number m with the property that

$$x \geqslant m \qquad \text{if } x \text{ is in } S.$$

If S is bounded above and below, then we say that it is **bounded**. In this case there is a number N such that

$$-N \leqslant x \leqslant N \qquad \text{if } x \text{ is in } S.$$

The numbers M, m, and N are called **bounds** of the set S. For example, if S is the interval $\{-1/2 < x \leqslant 1\}$, then $M = 2$ and $m = -3$ are bounds for S. $M = 2$ is an upper bound and $m = -3$ is a lower bound. These are quite obviously *not* the most precise bounds, for there are smaller upper bounds than 2 and larger lower bounds than -3—for example, $3/2$ and -1. But these are still not the most precise bounds. We can easily see that $M = 1$ is the least upper bound, and $m = -1/2$ the greatest lower bound. We define these terms precisely:

Suppose S is a set bounded above, and suppose that M_0 is an upper bound of S which is smaller than or equal to any other upper bound. Then M_0 is called the **least upper bound** or **supremum** of S and is denoted by

$$M_0 = \sup_S x.$$

Clearly, if S has a maximum or largest element, then that element is the supremum (see Exercise B6). If S has no maximum, then its supremum is designed to replace that maximum in calculations.

Similarly if m_0 is a lower bound of S, and is greater than or equal to any other lower bound, then it is called the **greatest lower bound** or **infimum** of S and is denoted by

$$m_0 = \inf_S x.$$

Of course, the infimum bears the same relationship to the minimum that the supremum does to the maximum.

To reinforce our statement that the supremum replaces the maximum, we prove the following.

1.5a   Theorem. If S is bounded above and $M_0 = \sup_S x$, then for each $y < M_0$ there is an x in S for which

$$y < x \leqslant M_0.$$

Proof. (Note that it doesn't matter whether y is in S or not.) Let $y < M_0$ be given. Suppose, for contradiction, that there are no members of S which satisfy $y < x \leqslant M_0$. We then have

$$x \leqslant y \qquad \text{for all } x \text{ in } S.$$

Thus y is an upper bound for S and is smaller than M_0. This is the contradiction we sought. ∎

Not every set which is bounded above has a maximum (can you give an example?), and not every set bounded below has a minimum. Thus it makes sense to ask: "Does every set bounded above have a supremum?" The answer is "Yes," and this fact is another statement of the completeness of the real numbers. That is, in the presence of properties I and II of Section 1.2 the existence of the supremum is a consequence of the Dedekind theorem, III of Section 1.3, and conversely the Dedekind theorem can be proved if we assume that every bounded set has a supremum. This form of the statement of the completeness of the real numbers is much easier to use than Dedekind's Theorem. We take this without proof as a fundamental property of the real-number system.

Fundamental Property. Each non-empty set which is bounded above has a supremum.

With the statement of this principle, we end the survey of the number system. From now on we shall make a serious effort to supply proofs for our statements.

1.6 SOME POINTS OF LOGIC

In the previous sections, we gave some proofs by contradiction. The logic behind this is of course that not both a statement and its negation can be true, and even more, that there is no third possibility: either the statement or its negation must be true. Consequently, a proof that the negation is false is taken as a proof that the statement itself is true.

We will frequently have occasion to state that "A is necessary and sufficient for B," where A and B are mathematical propositions. This means that they are logically equivalent: that A implies B, and B implies A. The statement "A is necessary for B" means that A follows from B; that if B is true, than A necessarily follows. The statement "A is sufficient for B" means that A implies B; in other words, the assumption of A is sufficient to prove B.

Axiom 5 of Peano's axioms is a somewhat different formulation of the principle of mathematical induction than the form usually given in elementary texts. The more familiar formulation is easily deduced from Axiom 5.

1.6a Theorem. Suppose a proposition $P(n)$ (that is, a statement) about positive integers has the following properties:
  (i) it is true for $n = 1$—that is, $P(1)$ is true,
  (ii) whenever $P(n)$ holds, so does $P(n + 1)$.
  Then $P(n)$ is true for all n.

Proof. By a proof here we mean that this is a consequence of Axiom 5. Let M be the set of integers for which $P(n)$ is true. Then by (i) above, 1 is a member of M, and by (ii) above, $n + 1 = n'$ is in M whenever n is in M. Thus (i) and (ii) of Axiom 5 are satisfied. Thus M is the set of all positive integers (natural numbers).   ∎

As an example of mathematical induction, we will prove **Bernoulli's inequality**.

1.6b   Theorem. If $x \geqslant -1$, and n is a positive integer, then

$$(1 + x)^n \geqslant 1 + nx.$$

Proof. Let $P(n)$ be the statement "$(1 + x)^n \geqslant 1 + nx$ holds provided $x \geqslant -1$".

(i) $P(1)$ is true. In fact, we have

$$(1 + x)^1 = 1 + x.$$

(ii) Suppose $P(n)$ is true—that is, suppose

$$(1 + x)^n \geqslant 1 + nx.$$

Multiplying both sides by $1 + x$ we have

$$(1 + x)^{n+1} \geqslant (1 + nx)(1 + x) = 1 + (n + 1)x + nx^2$$
$$\geqslant 1 + (n + 1)x.$$ ∎

Where did we use the hypothesis that $x \geqslant -1$?

1.7   ABSOLUTE VALUE

read

If x is a real number, then the absolute value of x, denoted by $|x|$, is defined by

$$|x| = \begin{cases} x & \text{if } x \geqslant 0 \\ -x & \text{if } x < 0. \end{cases}$$

The main properties of absolute value are given in the following theorems.

1.7a   Theorem. $|x| = |-x|$.

1.7b   Theorem. $|1/x| = 1/|x|$, if $x \neq 0$.

These statements are clear from the definition.

1.7c   Theorem. $|xy| = |x|\,|y|$.

Proof:

(i) If $x > 0$, $y > 0$, then $xy > 0$ and

$$|xy| = xy = |x|\,|y|.$$

(ii) If $x < 0$, $y < 0$, then $xy > 0$ and

$$|xy| = xy = (-x)(-y) = |x|\,|y|.$$

(iii) If $x < 0$, $y > 0$, then $xy < 0$ and

$$|xy| = -xy = (-x)y = |x|\,|y|.$$

(iv) If $x > 0$, $y < 0$, then $xy < 0$ and

$$|xy| = -xy = x(-y) = |x|\,|y|. \qquad \blacksquare$$

1.7d   Theorem. $|x/y| = |x|/|y|$, if $y \neq 0$.

Proof. Write $x/y = x \cdot (1/y)$ and apply Theorems 1.7c and 1.7b. $\qquad \blacksquare$

1.7e   Theorem. $\big||x| - |y|\big| \leq |x + y| \leq |x| + |y|$.

Proof. First, we prove the right-hand inequality. Clearly

$$-|x| \leq x \leq |x|$$
$$-|y| \leq y \leq |y|.$$

Adding, we get

$$-(|x| + |y|) = -|x| - |y| \leq x + y \leq |x| + |y|.$$

Hence both $(x + y)$ and $-(x + y)$ are not greater than $|x| + |y|$; that is

$$|x + y| \leq |x| + |y|.$$

To prove the left side of (1.7e), set $a = x + y$, $b = -y$. Then

$$|a + b| \leq |a| + |b|$$

or $\qquad\qquad |x| \leq |x + y| + |-y| = |x + y| + |y|.$

Thus $\qquad\qquad |x| - |y| \leq |x + y|.$

Set $a = x + y$, $b = -x$ and repeat to get

$$|y| - |x| \leq |x + y|$$

These two inequalities are equivalent to the left side of Theorem 1.7e. $\qquad \blacksquare$

1.7f Theorem. $|x_1 + x_2 + \cdots + x_n| \leqslant |x_1| + |x_2| + \cdots + |x_n|$.

Proof (by induction). Let $P(n)$ be the statement that

$$|x_1 + x_2 + \cdots + x_n| \leqslant |x_1| + |x_2| + \cdots + |x_n|.$$

(i) $P(1)$ is true:

$$|x_1| = |x_1|$$

(ii) Suppose $P(n)$ holds. Then

$$|x_1 + x_2 + \cdots + x_n + x_{n+1}| = |(x_1 + x_2 + \cdots + x_n) + x_{n+1}|$$
$$\leqslant |x_1 + x_2 + \cdots + x_n| + |x_{n+1}|$$

by Theorem 1.7e. Then, since $P(n)$ holds, this is less than or equal to

$$|x_1| + |x_2| + \cdots + |x_n| + |x_{n+1}|. \qquad \blacksquare$$

The result of Theorem 1.7f is easily remembered in words as: The absolute value of a sum is less than or equal to the sum of the absolute values.

A EXERCISES

1. Prove by induction:

(a) $1 + 2 + 3 + \cdots + n = n(n + 1)/2$

(b) $1 + 3 + 5 + \cdots + (2n - 1) = n^2$

(c) $1 + 2^2 + 3^2 + \cdots + n^2 = n(n + 1)(2n + 1)/6$

(d) $1 + 1/2 + 1/2^2 + \cdots + 1/2^n = 2 - 1/2^{n-1}$

(e) $1^3 + 2^3 + 3^3 + \cdots + n^3 = (1 + 2 + 3 + \cdots + n)^2$

2. Denote by S the set of points described in braces. Determine by inspection $\sup_S x$ and $\inf_S x$ when they exist, and state when they belong to S:

(a) $\{x^2 - 2x < 8\}$

(b) $\{x + 4 > 3x + 15\}$

(c) $\{1/(1 - x) \leqslant 1 + 2x\}$

(d) $\{(1 + x) < 1/(1 - x)\}$

(e) $\{\sqrt{4 + x} > x\}$

(f) $\{|x| + |x + 1| < 2\}$

(g) $\{|x| \cdot |x + 1| < 2\}$

(h) $\{(x + 2)(x - 1)(x + 5) > 0\}$

(i) $\{(-1)^n(2 - 4/2^n)\}$, $n = 1, 2, 3, \ldots$

(j) $\{1 - 1/n\}$, $n = 1, 2, 3, \ldots$

3. (a) Show that $\frac{1}{2}(a + b + |a - b|) = \max(a, b) =$ larger of a and b.

(b) Evaluate $\frac{1}{2}(a + b - |a - b|)$.

B EXERCISES

1. Prove by induction that:

(a) $(1 + x)^n \geqslant 1 + nx + \dfrac{n(n - 1)}{2} x^2$, $\quad x \geqslant 0$

(b) $(1 - x)^n \leqslant 1 - nx + \dfrac{n(n - 1)}{2} x^2$, $\quad 0 \leqslant x < 1$

(c) $(1 + a_1)(1 + a_2) \cdots (1 + a_n) \geqslant 1 + a_1 + a_2 + \cdots + a_n$, if all the a's are non-negative.

2. Find the error: "All positive integers are equal to each other."

"*Proof*":

(i) $1 = 1$ *Let* $n = 1$ $1 = 1 - 1 \neq 0$

(ii) Suppose all integers up to and including n are equal. Then $n = n - 1$. Adding 1 to both sides, we get $n + 1 = n$. Since n is equal to all lower numbers, so is $n + 1$. $1 + 1 \neq 1$

3. Establish that the suprema and infima found in Exercise A2 satisfy the definitions of suprema and infima.

4. When does the strict inequality hold in Bernoulli's inequality?

5. Prove that $\left(1 - \dfrac{1}{n^2}\right)^n \geq 1 - \dfrac{1}{n}$, and deduce that $\left(1 + \dfrac{1}{n-1}\right)^{n-1} \leq \left(1 + \dfrac{1}{n}\right)^n$.

6. Prove that if a set S has a maximal element—that is, if there is an x_0 in S such that $x_0 \geqslant x$ for every other x in S—then $x_0 = \sup\limits_{S} x$.

7. Show that every non-empty set S which is bounded below has an infimum.

8. Show that if S is bounded below and $m_0 = \inf S$, then for each $y > m_0$ there is an x in S for which $y > x \geqslant m_0$.

9. Show that if x_0 is an interior point of a set S, then there are interior points of S on each side of x_0.

C EXERCISES

1. Show that if $a > 0$ and $b > 0$, there is an n such that $na > b$. This is the theorem of Eudoxus, or the theorem of Archimedes.

2. By C1 show that if $\epsilon > 0$ is given then there is an N such that $N > 1/\epsilon$ and hence $1/N < \epsilon$.

3. Show that in any interval of real numbers there are rational numbers.

4. Show that in any interval of real numbers there are irrational numbers.

5. Show that Peano's fifth axiom can be deduced from Theorem 1.6a, thus completing the proof of the equivalence of the two statements of mathematical induction.

2

Functions, Sequences, and Limits

2.1 MAPPINGS, FUNCTIONS, AND SEQUENCES

Let us consider two sets S_1 and S_2. By a **mapping** of S_1 to S_2 we will mean a correspondence whereby to each point x in S_1 exactly one point y in S_2 is associated. The totality of all ordered pairs (x, y), where y is the point in S_2 corresponding to x in S_1, will be called a **function** and will be denoted by a single letter such as f. The number y in S_2 corresponding to x in S_1 will be called the **value** of the function f at x and will be denoted by $f(x)$.

Note that a function as we have defined it is a so-called **single-valued function**, that is, for each x in S_1, there is exactly one y in S_2. However, some, or for that matter all, values of y may correspond to two or more x's.

We will say the function is **defined** on S_1 and **has values** in S_2, and we will also say it is a function from S_1 to S_2. Since x is free to take any value in S_1, it is called the **independent variable**; and since the value of y is determined by x, it is called the **dependent variable**. The independent variable is also sometimes called the **argument** of the function.

If all of S_2 is covered by the mapping—that is, if for every value of y in S_2 there is at least one x in S_1 for which $y = f(x)$—we say the mapping is **onto** S_2. Otherwise we say it is **into** S_2. The set S_1 on which the function is defined is called the **domain** of the function and will in general be denoted by D. The sub-set of S_2 onto which D is mapped is called the **range** of f and is denoted by R.

By the **graph** of a function we mean simply the two-dimensional picture of the point set given by (x, y) where x is in D and y is the corresponding value. In other words, the graph is the locus of points in two dimensions given by

$$[x, f(x)] \qquad x \text{ in } D.$$

The single-valuedness of the function is reflected by the fact that each vertical line through a point x of D meets the graph in exactly one point. However, each horizontal line through a point of R meets the graph in at least one point, but it might meet it in even infinitely many points.

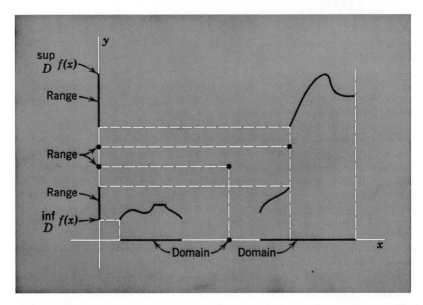

It is perhaps appropriate to say a few words here about the so-called **multivalued functions** and **implicit functions**. We begin by studying a familiar example. The equation

(1) $$x^2 + y^2 = 25$$

is satisfied by certain pairs of numbers, but as it stands it does not determine a function in the sense of our definition. There are certain functions whose independent and dependent variables do satisfy this relation. The two most likely to come to mind are given by

$$y = +\sqrt{25 - x^2} \qquad \{|x| \leqslant 5\}$$

and $$y = -\sqrt{25 - x^2} \qquad \{|x| \leqslant 5\}.$$

Equally good are

$$y = \begin{cases} +\sqrt{25 - x^2} & \{0 \leqslant x \leqslant 5\} \\ -\sqrt{25 - x^2} & \{-5 \leqslant x < 0\}, \end{cases}$$

and
$$y = \begin{cases} +\sqrt{25 - x^2} & \text{for } x \text{ rational} \\ -\sqrt{25 - x^2} & \text{for } x \text{ irrational} \end{cases} \{|x| \leqslant 5\}.$$

Of course, when one says that the equation (1) implicitly defines a function, he usually means one of the first two. What we want to point out is that in order to specify a function one needs more than the relation $x^2 + y^2 = 25$. For example, if we ask that the function be continuous,* then we are forced to choose one of the first two.

Similarly, such a formula as

$$y = \text{arc sin } x \qquad D: \{-1 \leqslant x \leqslant 1\}$$

does not yet define a function, as there are infinitely many angles y whose sine is x. But the principal value defined by

$$y = \text{arc sin } x \qquad \begin{cases} D: \{-1 \leqslant x \leqslant 1\} \\ R: \{-\pi/2 \leqslant y \leqslant \pi/2\} \end{cases}$$

is a function.

Two functions useful for stating certain problems are the **greatest integer** function $[x]$, and the **signum** function. First

$$[x] = \text{the greatest integer less than or equal to } x.$$

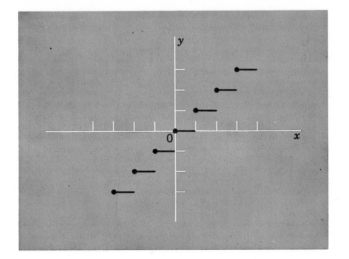

The figure gives an indication of how this function varies with x.

* We are a little ahead of ourselves here, but you have some idea of continuity already.

The signum function is given by

$$\operatorname{sgn} x = \begin{cases} +1 & \text{if } x > 0 \\ 0 & \text{if } x = 0 \\ -1 & \text{if } x < 0. \end{cases}$$

For $x \neq 0$, we can represent $\operatorname{sgn} x$ by

$$\operatorname{sgn} x = \frac{|x|}{x} = \frac{x}{|x|} \qquad x \neq 0.$$

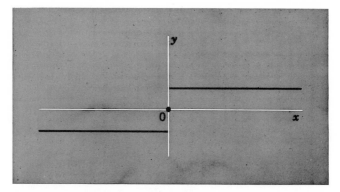

For $x = 0$, these quotients are meaningless.

We are most interested in the cases where D, the domain of the function, is the whole line, an interval, a finite collection of intervals, or a semi-infinite interval. However, there is one important exception to this, which leads us to the concept of a sequence.

Let f be a function defined on a domain D consisting of all integers n beyond (that is, greater than or equal to) some integer n_0. Such a function will be called a **sequence**. We will make the change of notation

$$f(n) = a_n,$$

so that the **terms** of the sequence appear in a more familiar form. We will indicate the sequence by putting a typical term in braces: $\{a_n\}$. The integer n_0 with which the sequence begins will usually be either 0 or 1, and will be stated or implied. But certainly n_0 must be so chosen that the formula (if there is one) for a_n makes sense for all $n \geqslant n_0$. For example, the sequence $\{1/n\}$ cannot have $n_0 = 0$, and the sequence $\{1/[n(n-1)(n-2)]\}$ must have n_0 at least three.

Let f be defined on a set D with range R. By $\sup_D f$, we mean $\sup_R y$; and similarly $\inf_D f$ means $\inf R$. This applies in particular to sequences in which case we write $\sup a_n$ instead of $\sup_D f$ and $\inf a_n$ instead of $\inf_D f$.

2.2 LIMITS

Suppose we have a function f defined on a set D which includes arbitrarily large numbers; that is, for every number M, however large, there is an x in D for which $x \geqslant M$. In actual practice, we will be interested in two cases; (a) D contains a semi-infinite interval $\{x \geqslant x_0\}$; and (b) D consists of all integers beyond some fixed integer: $\{n \geqslant n_0\}$—that is, in this case we are interested in sequences. We can inquire about the behavior of $f(x)$ for large x. In particular, we can ask if the values $f(x)$ get close to some fixed number A if x becomes very large. If it is true that there is a number A such that $f(x)$ is as close as we please to A for all sufficiently large x's (that is, all sufficiently large x's in D), we say that $f(x)$ tends to the limit A as x tends to infinity.

More precisely, a number A will be called the **limit** of f as x **tends to infinity** if for each $\epsilon > 0$, there is a number X (depending on ϵ, and hence sometimes written $X(\epsilon)$) for which

$$|f(x) - A| < \epsilon \qquad \text{if } x > X \text{ and } x \text{ in } D.$$

We express this symbolically by

$$\lim_{x \to \infty} f(x) = A$$

or $\qquad\qquad f(x) \to A \qquad \text{as} \qquad x \to \infty.$

A similar definition holds for $\lim_{x \to -\infty} f(x)$. (See Exercise A4.) In the case of sequences, this becomes

$$\lim_{n \to \infty} a_n = A$$

or $\qquad\qquad a_n \to A \qquad \text{as} \qquad n \to \infty.$

In this case we sometimes simplify our notation by just writing

$$\lim a_n = A$$

or $\qquad\qquad a_n \to A,$

for in the case of sequences these are the only kinds of limits we will be concerned with.

If $\lim a_n$ exists for a certain sequence, we say that the sequence **converges**. Otherwise we say that it **diverges**.

When a limit exists (for either functions or sequences), it is unique; that is, no two distinct numbers can both be limits of the same sequence or function. (See Exercise B5.)

EXAMPLE 1. Suppose $f(x) = 1/(x^2 + 2x - 4)$ D: $\{x \geqslant 2\}$

or $a_n = 1/(n^2 + 2n - 4)$ $n \geqslant 2$.

Then let us observe that

$$x^2 + 2x - 4 \geqslant x^2 > x$$

Thus if we take X to be the larger of 2 and $1/\epsilon$, then for $x > X$

$$0 < f(x) \leqslant 1/x < 1/X \leqslant \epsilon,$$

from which we see that

$$\lim_{x \to \infty} f(x) = 0.$$

The same calculations prove that

$$\lim a_n = 0.$$

EXAMPLE 2. Let $a_n = [2^n - (-1)^n]/2^n$.

Solution. Here $\lim a_n = 1$, for

$$|a_n - 1| = |\{[2^n - (-1)^n]/2^n\} - 1| = 1/2^n.$$

Now we could find an $N(\epsilon)$ [in the case of sequences we use $N(\epsilon)$ instead of $X(\epsilon)$] in terms of $\log_2 \epsilon$, but we can get a simpler, if cruder, N as follows:

$$2^n = (1 + 1)^n = 1 + n + n(n - 1)/2 \cdots + 1 > n$$

(the second equality is by the binomial theorem). Hence, if we choose $N = 1/\epsilon$ or larger, we have for $n > N$

$$|a_n - 1| = 1/2^n < 1/n < 1/N \leqslant \epsilon.$$

This completes the solution.

EXAMPLE 3. $f(x) = \sqrt{x}(\sqrt{x + 1} - \sqrt{x})$ D: $\{x > 0\}$.

Solution. We assume that for every $x > 0$ there is a unique positive square root; that is, there is a unique positive number y for which $y^2 = x$. This will be proved in a later chapter (see Section 3.4).

It will also be convenient to know that if $a > 1$,

$$a^2 > a > \sqrt{a} > 1,$$

which we leave as an exercise.

Now

$$f(x) = \sqrt{x}(\sqrt{x+1} - \sqrt{x}) = \frac{\sqrt{x}(\sqrt{x+1} - \sqrt{x})(\sqrt{x+1} + \sqrt{x})}{\sqrt{x+1} + \sqrt{x}}$$

$$= \frac{\sqrt{x}}{\sqrt{x+1} + \sqrt{x}} = \frac{1}{\sqrt{1 + (1/x)} + 1},$$

from which it seems clear that the limit is $\frac{1}{2}$. Hence we consider

$$\left| f(x) - \frac{1}{2} \right| = \left| \frac{1}{\sqrt{1 + (1/x)} + 1} - \frac{1}{2} \right| = \frac{1}{2} - \frac{1}{\sqrt{1 + (1/x)} + 1}$$

$$= \frac{\sqrt{1 + (1/x)} - 1}{2(\sqrt{1 + (1/x)} + 1)} < \frac{1 + 1/x - 1}{2(1 + 1)} = \frac{1}{4x}.$$

So if we take X to be $1/4\epsilon$ or larger, and $x > X$, then

$$| f(x) - \tfrac{1}{2} | < \frac{1}{4x} < \frac{1}{4X} \leqslant \epsilon.$$

We close with a theorem which establishes a limit very useful for comparison purposes.

2.2a   Theorem. If $0 < a < 1$, then $a^n \to 0$.

Proof. Let $x = 1/a - 1$. Then $x > 0$ and

$$a = \frac{1}{1 + x}$$

so for $n \geqslant 1$,

$$a^n = \frac{1}{(1 + x)^n} = \frac{1}{1 + nx + \dfrac{n(n-1)}{2} x^2 + \cdots + x^n} < \frac{1}{nx}.$$

Thus $\qquad\qquad |a^n| = a^n < \epsilon \qquad$ if $n > \dfrac{1}{x\epsilon} = N(\epsilon).$ ∎

A   EXERCISES

I. Determine whether the following sequences have limits. In each case where a limit A exists, determine an $N(\epsilon)$ such that

$$|a_n - A| < \epsilon \qquad \text{if } n > N,$$

where a_n is given below:

(a) $\dfrac{n+1}{n}$

(b) $\dfrac{n^2+n}{2n^2+1}$ $\dfrac{n^2+n}{2n^2} \to \frac{1}{2}$

(c) $\dfrac{6n^3+4n-1}{n^3+5n}$

(d) $\dfrac{n^2+1}{n+1}$

(e) $\dfrac{1}{n^2}+\dfrac{2}{n^2}+\cdots+\dfrac{n}{n^2}$

(f) $1-n^{(-1)^n}$ *add nos. to l* *pos. nos. to* $-\infty$ *does not converge*

(g) $\left(1-\dfrac{1}{2}\right)\left(1-\dfrac{1}{3}\right)\left(1-\dfrac{1}{4}\right)\cdots\left(1-\dfrac{1}{n}\right)$

2. Determine whether the following functions have limits at infinity. In each case where a limit A exists determine an $X(\epsilon)$ such that

$$|f(x) - A| < \epsilon \qquad \text{if } x > X.$$

(a) $\sin x$

(b) $\dfrac{\sin x}{x}$

(c) $\dfrac{x^3-4x^2+3x}{x^3-x+1}$

(d) $\cos x\left(\dfrac{x^2+2}{2x^2+3x-1}\right)$

(e) $\sin\dfrac{1}{x}$

3. Prove that if $a > 1$, then $a^2 > a > \sqrt{a} > 1$.

4. Define $\lim\limits_{x\to-\infty} f(x)$.

B   EXERCISES

1. Examine these sequences and functions as in the A exercises.

(a) $\left(1-\dfrac{1}{2^2}\right)\left(1-\dfrac{1}{3^2}\right)\cdots\left(1-\dfrac{1}{n^2}\right)$

(b) $\dfrac{1-(1-1/n)^3}{1-(1-1/n)^2}$

(c) $\dfrac{2^n}{n}$

(d) $x\left[1-\left(1-\dfrac{2}{x}\right)^5\right]$

(e) $\sqrt[n]{1+\dfrac{1}{2n}}$

(f) $\left(\dfrac{1}{4}\sin^2\dfrac{n^{100}}{n+2}+\dfrac{1}{3}\cos^2\dfrac{n^{100}}{n+2}\right)^n$

2. Suppose there is a number q, $0 < q < 1$ such that $|a_{n+1}| \leqslant q|a_n|$. Examine the sequence $\{a_n\}$.

3. Calculate $\sup a_n$ and $\inf a_n$ when they exist. In each case determine whether or not the extreme value (i.e., sup or inf) is attained.

(a) $\left\{(-1)^n\left(2-\dfrac{4}{2^n}\right)\right\}$

(b) $\left\{\dfrac{1}{n}+\cos\dfrac{\pi n}{2}+(-1)^n\right\}$

(c) $\{n^{\cos(\pi n/2)}\}$

(d) $\left\{(-1)^n n^{\sin(\pi n/2)}+\dfrac{1}{n}\right\}$

4. Calculate $\sup\limits_{D} f(x)$ and $\inf\limits_{D} f(x)$ when they exist. In each case determine whether or not the extreme value is attained.

(a) $x - [x]$ D: all x
(b) x D: $\{0 < x \leqslant 1\}$
(c) arc tan x (principal value) D: $\{0 \leqslant x\}$
(d) arc tan $1/x$ D: $\{x \neq 0\}$
(e) $e^{-1/x}$ D: $\{x > 0\}$

5. Prove the uniqueness of the limit; that is, prove that if $\lim a_n = A$ and $\lim a_n = A'$, then $A = A'$.

C EXERCISES

1. Suppose $a_n \to A$, $c_n \to A$, and $a_n \leqslant b_n \leqslant c_n$. Show that $b_n \to A$.

2. Suppose $f(x) \to A$, $h(x) \to A$ as $x \to \infty$, and $f(x) \leqslant g(x) \leqslant h(x)$. Show that $g(x) \to A$ as $x \to \infty$.

3. Show that $n^2/2^n \to 0$, $n^3/2^n \to 0$, $n^4/2^n \to 0$. (*Hint:* See Example 2.)

4. Show that $n^2 a^n \to 0$, $n^3 a^n \to 0$, and $n^4 a^n \to 0$ if $0 < a < 1$. (Compare Exercise 3 above and see the proof of Theorem 2.2a.)

5. (*a*) Let $f(x)$ and $g(x)$ have the same domain D. Show that

$$\sup_D [f(x) + g(x)] \leqslant \sup_D f(x) + \sup_D g(x)$$

$$\inf_D [f(x) + g(x)] \geqslant \inf_D f(x) + \inf_D g(x).$$

In particular for sequences, this becomes

$$\sup (a_n + b_n) \leqslant \sup a_n + \sup b_n$$

$$\inf (a_n + b_n) \geqslant \inf a_n + \inf b_n.$$

(*b*) Show that for $f(x) \geqslant 0$ and $g(x) \geqslant 0$

$$\sup_D f(x) \cdot g(x) \leqslant \sup_D f(x) \cdot \sup_D g(x)$$

$$\inf_D f(x) \cdot g(x) \geqslant \inf_D f(x) \cdot \inf_D g(x).$$

2.3 OPERATIONS WITH LIMITS (SEQUENCES)

Here are a number of useful theorems about limits. They are mostly theorems about how to operate or compute with limits. We begin however with a simple but very useful theorem on sub-sequences. But first we must define a sub-sequence.

A sequence $\{a_n\}$ is a function on the integers; that is,

$$a_n = f(n) \qquad \text{for all } n \geqslant n_0.$$

Now suppose we consider the function restricted to a sub-set of the integers. Let us choose an integer greater than or equal to n_0 and denote it by n_1, another greater than n_1 and denote it by n_2, another greater than n_2 and denote it by n_3, and so forth. Then the new sequence, defined by

$$b_k = a_{n_k} = f(n_k) \qquad k = 0, 1, 2, \ldots,$$

we call a **sub-sequence** of $\{a_n\}$. It is clear that there are many sub-sequences of a given sequence, and that in each case $n_k \geqslant k$. (Why?) The theorem we want to prove is the following.

2.3a   Theorem. Suppose $\{a_n\}$ converges, then any sub-sequence $\{a_{n_k}\}$ also converges and has the same limit.

Proof. Let A be the limit of the sequence $\{a_n\}$. We know that for each $\epsilon > 0$ there is an N for which

$$|a_{n_k} - A| < \epsilon \qquad \text{if } n_k > N.$$

But $n_k \geqslant k$; hence $\qquad\qquad n_k > N \qquad \text{if } k > N.$

Thus $\qquad\qquad |b_k - A| = |a_{n_k} - A| < \epsilon \qquad \text{if } k > N.$ ∎

The following are a collection of standard operational theorems with which you should become familiar.

2.3b   Theorem. If $\lim a_n$ exists then $\{a_n\}$ forms a bounded set. (That is there is a constant M for which $|a_n| \leqslant M$ for all n.)

Proof. Let $a = \lim a_n$. Then there is an N such that

$$|a_n - a| < 1 \qquad \text{if } n > N. \qquad \text{(Why?)}$$

Then $\qquad\qquad 1 > |a_n - a| \geqslant |a_n| - |a|. \qquad \text{(Why?)}$

Thus

(1) $\qquad\qquad |a_n| < |a| + 1 \equiv M_1 \qquad \text{if } n > N.$

Now we look among the numbers $|a_1|, |a_2|, \ldots, |a_N|$, and choose the largest, calling it M_2. Then

(2) $\qquad\qquad |a_n| \leqslant M_2 \qquad \text{if } n \leqslant N.$

It is now clear that if we take M to be the larger of M_1 and M_2, then by (1) and (2)

$$|a_n| < M \qquad \text{for all } n. \qquad\qquad$$ ∎

In the remaining theorems in this section, we assume that the sequences $\{a_n\}$ and $\{b_n\}$ converge and that their limits are a and b respectively, and we conclude the existence of the other limits which occur.

2.3c   Theorem. $\lim (a_n \pm b_n) = \lim a_n \pm \lim b_n$

Proof. The proof of this theorem is left as an exercise (Exercise B). Note that, by induction, this theorem extends to any finite number of sequences.

2.3d   Theorem. $\lim (a_n b_n) = (\lim a_n)(\lim b_n)$

Proof. We examine

$$|a_n b_n - ab| = |(a_n b_n - ab_n) + (ab_n - ab)|$$
$$\leqslant |a_n b_n - ab_n| + |ab_n - ab|.$$

Thus

$$|a_n b_n - ab| \leqslant |b_n| \cdot |a_n - a| + |a| \, |b_n - b|.$$

By Theorem 2.3b, we have that $|b_n|$ is bounded. Suppose $|b_n| \leqslant M$; then

(3) $$|a_n b_n - ab| \leqslant M|a_n - a| + |a| \, |b_n - b|.$$

Now we see that by making $|a_n - a|$ and $|b_n - b|$ small, we can make $|a_n b_n - ab|$ small. Let $\epsilon > 0$ be given, and take $\epsilon_1 = \epsilon/2(M + 1)$ and $\epsilon_2 = \epsilon/2(|a| + 1)$. Then there are N_1 and N_2 such that

$$|a_n - a| < \epsilon_1 \qquad \text{if } n > N_1,$$

and $$|b_n - b| < \epsilon_2 \qquad \text{if } n > N_2.$$

Thus if $n > N \equiv \max(N_1, N_2)$, we have from (3)

$$|a_n b_n - ab| \leqslant M\epsilon_1 + |a|\epsilon_2 = \epsilon[M/2(M + 1) + |a|/2(|a| + 1)] < \epsilon. \quad \blacksquare$$

From this proof, it follows that

$$\lim cb_n = c \lim b_n. \qquad \text{(Why?)}$$

2.3e Theorem. $\lim(a_n/b_n) = (\lim a_n)/(\lim b_n) \qquad$ if $\lim b_n \neq 0$.

Proof. Proof of this theorem follows from Theorem 2.3d, provided we can show that

(4) $$\lim 1/b_n = 1/\lim b_n.$$

To prove (4), we note first that, since $b = \lim b_n \neq 0$, there is an N_1 so large that

$$|b_n - b| < (\tfrac{1}{2})|b| \qquad \text{if } n > N_1. \qquad \text{(Why?)}$$

Then $$|b_n| > (\tfrac{1}{2})|b| \qquad \text{if } n > N_1. \qquad \text{(Why?)}$$

Hence, for $n > N_1$,

$$\left| \frac{1}{b_n} - \frac{1}{b} \right| = \left| \frac{b_n - b}{b_n b} \right| \leqslant \left| \frac{b_n - b}{(\tfrac{1}{2})|b|^2} \right| = \frac{2}{|b|^2} |b_n - b|$$

Now given that $\epsilon > 0$, let $\epsilon_1 = |b|^2 \epsilon/2$ and N_2 be such that

$$|b_n - b| < \epsilon_1 \qquad \text{if } n > N_2$$

Then if $n > N = \max[N_1, N_2]$,

$$\left| \frac{1}{b_n} - \frac{1}{b} \right| \leqslant \frac{2}{|b|^2} |b_n - b| < \frac{2}{|b|^2} \epsilon_1 = \frac{2}{|b|^2} \cdot \frac{|b|^2 \epsilon}{2} = \epsilon. \qquad \blacksquare$$

2.3f   Theorem. $\lim |a_n| = |\lim a_n|$.

Proof. The proof of this theorem follows directly from

$$\big| \, |a_n| - |a| \, \big| \leqslant |a_n - a|. \qquad \text{(How?)} \qquad \blacksquare$$

2.3g   Theorem. If $a_n \geqslant 0$, then $\lim a_n \geqslant 0$.

Proof. Suppose $\lim a_n = a < 0$. Then there is an N such that

$$|a_n - a| < -\tfrac{1}{2}a \qquad \text{for all } n > N \qquad (\text{remember } a < 0).$$

Thus in particular, for such n, we have

$$a_n - a < -(\tfrac{1}{2})a,$$

or
$$a_n < (\tfrac{1}{2})a < 0.$$

This contradiction completes the proof. $\blacksquare$

2.3h   Theorem. If $a_n \geqslant b_n$, then $\lim a_n \geqslant \lim b_n$.

Proof. By Theorems 2.3c and 2.3g,

$$\lim a_n - \lim b_n = \lim (a_n - b_n) \geqslant 0. \qquad \blacksquare$$

2.3i   Theorem. If $a_n \geqslant 0$, then $\lim \sqrt{a_n} = \sqrt{\lim a_n}$.

Proof. Again we assume the existence and uniqueness of positive square roots of positive numbers (see Section 3.4). We consider two cases according as $\lim a_n = a > 0$ or $a = 0$.

CASE 1. $a > 0$.

Here there is an N_1 such that

$$a_n > \tfrac{1}{2}a \qquad \text{if } n > N_1. \qquad \text{(Why?)}$$

Thus for $n > N_1$

$$|\sqrt{a_n} - \sqrt{a}| = \frac{|\sqrt{a_n} - \sqrt{a}| \, |\sqrt{a_n} + \sqrt{a}|}{|\sqrt{a_n} + \sqrt{a}|} = \left| \frac{a_n - a}{\sqrt{a_n} + \sqrt{a}} \right| \leqslant \frac{|a_n - a|}{\sqrt{a}}.$$

This is the basic inequality. The completion of the proof is left as an exercise.

CASE 2. $a = 0$.

Given $\epsilon > 0$, choose n so large that $a_n < \epsilon^2$.

Then
$$\sqrt{a_n} < \epsilon. \qquad \blacksquare$$

EXAMPLE. Compute $\lim \sqrt{\dfrac{4n^2 + 6n + 3}{n^2 - 5}}$.

Solution:

$$\lim \sqrt{\frac{4n^2 + 6n + 3}{n^2 - 5}} = \sqrt{\lim \frac{4n^2 + 6n + 3}{n^2 - 5}}$$

$$= \sqrt{\lim \frac{4 + (6/n) + (3/n^2)}{1 - (5/n^2)}} = \sqrt{\frac{\lim [4 + (6/n) + (3/n^2)]}{\lim [1 - (5/n^2)]}}$$

$$= \sqrt{\frac{\lim 4 + \lim (6/n) + \lim (3/n^2)}{\lim 1 - \lim (5/n^2)}} = \sqrt{\frac{4 + 0 + 0}{1 - 0}}$$

$$= \sqrt{4} = 2.$$

A word of explanation about the computations in this example: Each step in the solution is a provisional argument which depends, for its validity, on the existence of the limits involved. Thus the first step wherein we interchange the limit sign and root sign is valid only if we know the existence of the limit of the quotient under the root sign. Similarly each of the other steps is a tentative one, predicated on the existence of the limits involved. The final justification for all these provisional steps is that we do arrive at an expression which does have a limit.

A EXERCISES

1. Determine whether the following have limits. Calculate the limit in each case where it exists: use theorems

(a) $\sqrt{n + 1} - \sqrt{n}$

(b) $\sqrt{\dfrac{n^3 + 4n^2 + 5n + 16}{n^2 + 3n + 2}}$

(c) $\dfrac{\sqrt{n}}{1 + \sqrt{n}}$

(d) $\sqrt{1 + a/n}$

(e) $\dfrac{\frac{1}{2}n^3 - n^2 + 1/n}{3n^3 - n + 800/n}$

(f) $\dfrac{1 + 2 + 3 + \cdots + n}{n + 2} - \dfrac{n}{2}$

(g) $n(1 - \sqrt{1 - a/n})$

(h) $n[(a + 1/n)^5 - a^5]$

(i) $\dfrac{\log n + 1}{\log n - 1}$

B EXERCISES

1. (a) Prove Theorem 2.3c.
   (b) Complete the proof of Theorem 2.3i.

$a_n = (-1)^n$

2. Show by examples that if $|a_n| \to |a|$, then a_n does not necessarily converge; and that if it does converge, it doesn't necessarily converge to a.

3. Show that $|a_n| \to 0$ if and only if $a_n \to 0$.

4. Show that if $a_n \to a$, then $\sqrt[3]{a_n} \to \sqrt[3]{a}$.

5. Show that $\lim \sqrt[n]{a} = 1$ if $a > 0$. Consider first the case where $a > 1$. (*Hint:* Set $\sqrt[n]{a} = 1 + h_n$, and apply Bernoulli's inequality.)

6. Calculate the limit of each of the following sequences:

(a) $\left\{ n\left(1 - \sqrt[3]{1 - \dfrac{a}{n}} \right) \right\}$.

(b) $\left\{ \dfrac{1}{n^2 + 1} + \dfrac{1}{n^2 + 2} + \cdots + \dfrac{1}{n^2 + n} \right\}$.

(c) $\left\{ \dfrac{1}{\sqrt{n^2 + 1}} + \dfrac{1}{\sqrt{n^2 + 2}} + \cdots + \dfrac{1}{\sqrt{n^2 + n}} \right\}$.

7. Show by examples that for a convergent sequence $\{a_n\}$ the condition $a_n > 0$ does not imply $\lim a_n > 0$.

8. Show by examples that if $\{a_n\}$ and $\{b_n\}$ are divergent sequences, then $\{a_n + b_n\}$ is not necessarily divergent. Do the same for $\{a_n - b_n\}$ and $\{a_n/b_n\}$.

C   EXERCISES

1. Show that if $\{a_n\}$ converges to zero and $\{b_n\}$ is bounded, then $\{a_n b_n\}$ converges to zero.

2. Evaluate the limit of each of the following sequences:

(a) $\left\{ \left(\dfrac{x^n + y^n}{2} \right)^{1/n} \right\}$ $x \geqslant y > 0$.

(b) $\left\{ \left(\dfrac{1}{k} \sum_1^k a_j{}^n \right)^{1/n} \right\}$ $a_j > 0, j = 1, 2, \ldots k$.

(c) $\left\{ \left(\dfrac{x^{-n} + y^{-n}}{2} \right)^{-1/n} \right\}$.

(d) $\left\{ \left(\dfrac{1}{k} \sum_1^k a_j{}^{-n} \right)^{-1/n} \right\}$ $a_j > 0, j = 1, 2, \ldots k$

3. Show that $\sqrt[n]{n} \to 1$. (*Hint:* Set $\sqrt[n]{n} = 1 + h_n$, and use the binomial theorem.)

4. (a) Suppose that $\lim a_n = a$. Set $\sigma_n = \dfrac{1}{n} \sum_1^n a_j$, and show that $\lim \sigma_n = a$.

(b) Show by examples that the converse of (a) is not true; that is, there are sequences $\{a_n\}$ such that $\lim \sigma_n = a$, but $\lim a_n$ does not exist.

2.4 LIMITS OF FUNCTIONS

For some positive h, let $f(x)$ be defined in the interval I: $\{a - h < x < a + h\}$, except possibly at the point a itself. That is, $f(x)$ is defined in a deleted neighborhood of a. Then a number A will be called the **limit** of $f(x)$ as x tends to a (or as x approaches a), if for each $\epsilon > 0$ there is a number δ, $0 < \delta \leqslant h$ (δ of course depends on ϵ, and so is frequently written $\delta(\epsilon)$) for which

$$|f(x) - A| < \epsilon \qquad \text{if } 0 < |x - a| < \delta.$$

We express this formally as

$$\lim_{x \to a} f(x) = A$$

or

$$f(x) \to A \quad \text{as} \quad x \to a.$$

Consider, for example, $f(x) = x^2 + 2$. We will show that $\lim_{x \to 2} f(x) = 6$. Clearly, f is defined in $0 < x < 4$; that is, we can take $h = 2$. In this interval,

$$|f(x) - 6| = |x^2 - 4| = |x - 2|\,|x + 2| < 6 \cdot |x - 2|.$$

Hence if $\delta = \epsilon/6$ or smaller, then

$$|f(x) - 6| < 6|x - 2| < 6 \cdot \frac{\epsilon}{6} \leqslant \epsilon \qquad \text{if } 0 < |x - 2| < \delta = \epsilon/6.$$

Of course, if there is no number A which meets the requirements of the definition, then we say that the limit does not exist. A function may fail to have a limit for any of several reasons. We give a few examples at finite points and at infinity.

EXAMPLE 1. The function may oscillate boundedly, as does the function

$$f(x) = \sin 1/x \qquad \text{as } x \to 0.$$

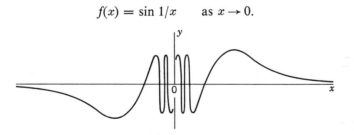

EXAMPLE 2. The function may oscillate unboundedly, as does the function

$$f(x) = x \sin x \qquad \text{as } x \to \infty,$$

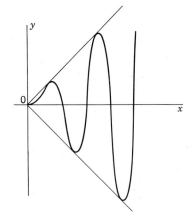

or as does

$$f(x) = x(1 + \sin x) \qquad \text{as } x \to \infty.$$

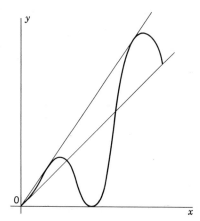

EXAMPLE 3. The function may grow large without bound, as does

$$f(x) = \frac{1}{(x - 2)^2} \qquad \text{as } x \to 2.$$

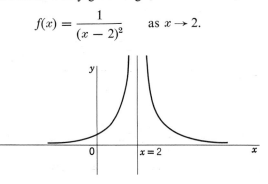

EXAMPLE 4. The function may decrease without bound, as does

$$f(x) = -2 + 3x - x^2 \qquad \text{as } x \to \infty.$$

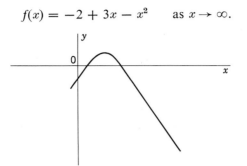

In situations such as Examples 3 and 4, where a function increases or decreases without bound, we sometimes say that the limit is $+\infty$ or $-\infty$, as the case might be.

We say that the limit of $f(x)$ as x tends to a is $+\infty$ if for each M there is a $\delta(M)$ for which

$$f(x) > M \qquad \text{if } 0 < |x - a| < \delta.$$

We express this formally as

$$\lim_{x \to a} f(x) = +\infty$$

or $\qquad\qquad f(x) \to +\infty \qquad$ as $x \to a$.

Similar definitions are made to cover the cases $\lim_{x \to a} f(x) = -\infty$ and $\lim_{x \to +\infty} f(x) = \pm\infty$. Similar definitions are also made for sequences.

It should be clearly stated that we have in no way defined either $+\infty$ or $-\infty$. We have defined certain expressions, such as $\lim_{x \to a} f(x) = +\infty$. But the word "infinity" or the symbol ∞ standing alone are not defined. In particular, $\lim_{x \to a} f(x) = +\infty$ means $f(x)$ grows without bound as x approaches a, and this in turn is made precise by the definition itself.

When we say that $\lim_{x \to a} f(x)$ exists, we will in general mean that it exists in the sense of our first definition, that is, as a finite number. For emphasis, we may sometimes say that $\lim_{x \to a} f(x)$ exists and is finite. Whenever we have occasion to use the latter definition—that is, $\lim_{x \to a} f(x) = \pm\infty$—we will make it clear that it is in this extended or improper sense that we use it.

Before leaving this section, we prove the following theorem, which is valid for either limits taken in either the proper or improper sense.

2.4a **Theorem.** Suppose that $\lim\limits_{x \to a} f(x) = A$, and that $\{x_n\}$ is a sequence of points converging to a, with $x_n \neq a$ for all n. Denote $f(x_n)$ by y_n. Then

$$\lim y_n = A.$$

Proof. We give the proof for the case where a and A are both finite. Let $\epsilon > 0$ be given. Then, by the definition of $\lim\limits_{x \to a} f(x)$, there is a δ for which

$$|f(x) - A| < \epsilon \quad \text{if } 0 < |x - a| < \delta.$$

And, since $x_n \to a$, there is an N such that

$$|x_n - a| < \delta \quad \text{if } n > N.$$

Thus for all such n's,

$$|y_n - A| = |f(x_n) - A| < \epsilon$$

since

$$0 < |x_n - a| < \delta.$$

That is,

$$|y_n - A| < \epsilon \quad \text{if } n > N. \qquad \blacksquare$$

One-sided limits sometimes exist when a limit does not. By a one-sided limit we mean that the approximating point x should stay on one side of the point a. Precisely, we will say that A is the **limit from the right** of $f(x)$ as x tends to a if for each $\epsilon > 0$ there is a $\delta > 0$ such that

$$|f(x) - A| < \epsilon \quad \text{if } a < x < a + \delta.$$

The concept of **limit from the left** requires that $a - \delta < x < a$. These limits are denoted by

$$\lim_{x \to a+} f(x)$$

and

$$\lim_{x \to a-} f(x)$$

for the right-hand and left-hand limits, respectively. A more convenient notation is given by

$$f(a + 0) = \lim_{x \to a+} f(x)$$

and

$$f(a - 0) = \lim_{x \to a-} f(x).$$

2.5 OPERATIONS WITH LIMITS (FUNCTIONS)

In this section, we reproduce for functions the theorems proved in Section 2.3 for sequences. The theorems will be proved for the case where the limit is a finite limit at a finite point. This is purely a matter of convenience, as they are true for limits at $\pm \infty$, and for one-sided limits. The modifications in the proofs to handle these cases are all simple, so they are omitted to keep the length of the section from getting out of hand. Further, since the proofs are naturally very similar to those of Section 2.3, they are frequently omitted entirely or only the significant portions are sketched. One more simplification: we will write only $\lim f(x)$ rather than $\lim_{x \to a} f(x)$, leaving this as implied. We assume the existence of $\lim f(x)$ and $\lim g(x)$, and conclude the existence of all other limits involved.

2.5a Theorem. If $\lim f(x) = A$, then there is a deleted neighborhood of a in which $f(x)$ is bounded.

Proof. There is a $\delta > 0$ such that

$$|f(x) - A| < 1 \qquad \text{if } 0 < |x - a| < \delta. \quad \textit{Test \#1:4.}$$

For such x's,

$$|f(x)| - |A| \leqslant |f(x) - A| < 1.$$

Thus

$$|f(x)| < |A| + 1 \equiv M \qquad \text{for } 0 < |x - a| < \delta. \qquad \blacksquare$$

2.5b Theorem. $\lim [f(x) \pm g(x)] = \lim f(x) \pm \lim g(x)$.

2.5c Theorem. $\lim [f(x) \cdot g(x)] = \lim f(x) \cdot \lim g(x)$.

Proof. Let $\lim f(x) = A$, $\lim g(x) = B$. Then

$$
\begin{aligned}
|f(x) \cdot g(x) - A \cdot B| &= |f(x)g(x) - f(x)B + f(x)B - AB| \\
&\leqslant |f(x)g(x) - f(x)B| + |f(x)B - AB| \\
&\leqslant |f(x)| \cdot |g(x) - B| + |B| \cdot |f(x) - A| \\
&\leqslant M|g(x) - B| + |B| \cdot |f(x) - A|. \qquad \blacksquare
\end{aligned}
$$

2.5d Theorem. $\lim [f(x)/g(x)] = (\lim f(x))/(\lim g(x))$ if $\lim g(x) \neq 0$.

Proof. As before, it is sufficient to show that

$$\lim 1/g(x) = 1/\lim g(x).$$

First, there is a deleted neighborhood in which

$$|g(x)| > (\tfrac{1}{2})|B|. \qquad \text{(Why?)}$$

Then $\left| \dfrac{1}{g(x)} - \dfrac{1}{B} \right| = \left| \dfrac{g(x) - B}{g(x) \cdot B} \right| \leqslant \dfrac{|g(x) - B|}{(\tfrac{1}{2})|B|^2} = \dfrac{2|g(x) - B|}{|B|^2}.$ $\qquad \blacksquare$

2.5e Theorem. $\lim |f(x)| = |\lim f(x)|$.

2.5f Theorem. If $f(x) \geqslant 0$, then $\lim f(x) \geqslant 0$.

2.5g Theorem. If $f(x) \geqslant g(x)$, then $\lim f(x) \geqslant \lim g(x)$.

2.5h Theorem. If $f(x) \geq 0$, then $\lim \sqrt{f(x)} = \sqrt{\lim f(x)}$.

EXAMPLE:

$$\lim_{x \to 2} \sqrt{\frac{4 - x^2 + \sqrt{x + 2} + 5x^3}{x^2 + 15}} = \sqrt{\lim_{x \to 2} \frac{4 - x^2 + \sqrt{x + 2} + 5x^3}{x^2 + 15}}$$

$$= \sqrt{\frac{\lim_{x \to 2} (4 - x^2 + \sqrt{x + 2} + 5x^3)}{\lim (x^2 + 15)}}$$

$$= \sqrt{\frac{4 - 4 + \sqrt{4 + 40}}{4 + 15}}$$

$$= \sqrt{\frac{42}{19}}.$$

The comments made after the example in Section 2.3 are equally appropriate here: the steps are tentative with the final justification being that we do get an expression which does have a limit.

A EXERCISES

1. Evaluate the following limits:

(a) $\lim\limits_{x \to 1} \dfrac{x^m - 1}{x - 1}$

(b) $\lim\limits_{x \to 1} \dfrac{x^m - 1}{x^n - 1}$

(c) $\lim\limits_{x \to 2} \dfrac{x^2 - 4}{x - 2}$

(d) $\lim\limits_{h \to 0} \dfrac{1}{h}\left[\dfrac{1}{(x + h)^2} - \dfrac{1}{x^2}\right]$

(e) $\lim\limits_{h \to 0} \dfrac{1}{h}[\sqrt{x + h} - \sqrt{x}]$

(f) $\lim\limits_{x \to 0} \dfrac{\sqrt[3]{1 + x} - 1}{x}$

(g) $\lim\limits_{x \to 0} \dfrac{\sqrt{1 + x} - \sqrt{1 - x}}{x}$

2. Evaluate the following, assuming you know that $\lim\limits_{x \to 0} \dfrac{\sin x}{x} = 1$:

(a) $\lim\limits_{x \to 0} \dfrac{\sin 3x}{x}$

(b) $\lim\limits_{x \to 0} \dfrac{\sin x^2}{x}$

(c) $\lim\limits_{x \to 0} \dfrac{\tan x}{x}$

(d) $\lim\limits_{x \to 0} \log \dfrac{\sin x}{x}$

(e) $\lim\limits_{x \to 0} \dfrac{1 - \cos x}{x}$

(f) $\lim\limits_{x \to 0} \dfrac{1 - \cos x}{x^2}$

(g) $\lim\limits_{x \to 0} \dfrac{\sin 4x^2}{1 - \cos x}$

(h) $\lim\limits_{x \to \pi} \dfrac{\sin x}{\pi - x}$

(i) $\lim\limits_{x \to 2\pi} \left[\dfrac{1 - \cos x}{(x - 2\pi)^2}\right]$

(j) $\lim\limits_{x \to \alpha} \dfrac{\sin (x - \alpha)}{x^2 - \alpha^2}$

(k) $\lim\limits_{x \to 0} x \sin \dfrac{1}{x}$

(l) $\lim\limits_{x \to \infty} x \sin \dfrac{1}{x}$

B EXERCISES

1. Evaluate $\lim\limits_{x \to 0} \dfrac{\sqrt{(1 + ax)(1 + bx)} - 1}{x}$.

2. Evaluate $\lim\limits_{x \to \infty} \left[\sqrt{x + \sqrt{x}} - \sqrt{x - \sqrt{x}} \right]$.

3. If $ax - x^2 \leqslant x$ for all $x > 0$, show that $a \leqslant 1$.

4. If $axy + by^2 \leqslant 0$ for all x, y, show that $a = 0$, $b \leqslant 0$.

5. Recall (Section 2.1) the definition of $[x]$. Show that for $a > 0$, $b > 0$,

$$\lim_{x \to 0+} \frac{x}{a}\left[\frac{b}{x}\right] = \frac{b}{a}, \quad \lim_{x \to 0+} \left[\frac{x}{a}\right]\frac{b}{x} = 0.$$ Discuss the left-hand limits of these functions.

6. Set $f(x) = e^{1/x}$ for $x \neq 0$ and discuss the one-sided limits of f at $x = 0$.

7. Set $f(x) = \dfrac{e^{1/x}}{e^{1/x} - 1}$ for $x \neq 0$ and discuss the one-sided limits of f and of $xf(x)$ at $x = 0$.

8. Discuss the one-sided limits at $x = 0$ of arc tan $1/x$.

9. Prove that a necessary and sufficient condition that $\lim\limits_{x \to a} f(x)$ exist is that $f(a + 0)$ and $f(a - 0)$ exist and be equal.

C EXERCISES

1. Prove that $^{[x]}\sqrt{x} \to 1$ as $x \to \infty$. (See Exercise C3 of Section 2.3.)

2. Evaluate $\lim\limits_{x \to 0} \left[\sqrt[n]{(1 + a_1 x)(1 + a_2 x) \cdots (1 + a_n x)} - 1 \right]/x$.

3. Let x_a be the root of $ax^2 + bx + c = 0$ which has smallest absolute value. Show that if $b \neq 0$, then $\lim\limits_{a \to 0} x_a = -c/b =$ the root of the limit equation. What happens to the other root?

4. Prove the "converse" of Theorem 2.4a: If $f(x_n) \to A$ for every sequence $\{x_n\}$ such that $x_n \to a$, then $\lim\limits_{x \to a} f(x) = A$.

2.6 MONOTONE SEQUENCES

A very important class of sequences are monotone or monotonic sequences, those which steadily increase or decrease. More precisely, a sequence $\{a_n\}$ is monotone-increasing if its elements a_n satisfy an inequality of the form

$$a_{n+1} \geqslant a_n \quad \text{or} \quad a_{n+1} > a_n \qquad n = 1, 2, \ldots .$$

In the first case, we say that the sequence is **weakly monotone-increasing** or that it is **non-decreasing.** In the second case, we say the sequence is **strictly increasing. Monotone-decreasing** or **non-increasing** sequences are defined by reversing the inequalities.

In particular, if a sequence is strictly increasing—that is, $a_{n+1} > a_n$—then it is weakly increasing; but the converse is of course not necessarily true. Thus any theorems established for weakly increasing sequences apply to strictly increasing ones.

We establish the following theorem, which is a consequence of our fundamental principle of the continuity of the number system. (See Section 1.5.)

2.6a   Theorem. Let $\{a_n\}$ be a non-decreasing sequence which is bounded above. Then $\lim a_n$ exists and

$$\lim a_n = \sup a_n.$$

Proof. Since $\{a_n\}$ is a set of numbers which is bounded above, $\sup a_n$ exists by our fundamental principle. Let

$$A = \sup a_n.$$

We want to show that A satisfies the definition of a limit.

Let $\epsilon > 0$ be given. By Theorem 1.5a, there is an N for which

$$a_N > A - \epsilon.$$

Hence, for $n > N$ $\quad A \geqslant a_n \geqslant a_N > A - \epsilon,$

or $\quad A \geqslant a_n > A - \epsilon,$

or, finally, $\quad 0 \leqslant A - a_n < \epsilon \quad$ if $n > N.$

Hence certainly $\quad |A - a_n| < \epsilon \quad$ if $n > N.$ ∎

2.6b   Corollary. Let $\{a_n\}$ be a non-increasing sequence bounded below. Then $\lim a_n$ exists and

$$\lim a_n = \inf a_n.$$

Proof. The proof of this theorem is similar to that of Theorem 2.6a. ∎

These simple but important results supply us with a powerful tool which we will use throughout this book. As an example, let us consider the sequence given by

$$a_n = 1 + 1 + \frac{1}{2!} + \frac{1}{3!} + \cdots + \frac{1}{n!} = \sum_{k=0}^{n} 1/k!$$

(You will see that we are really discussing the convergence of the infinite series $\sum_{1}^{\infty} 1/k!$.)

Clearly

$$a_{n+1} - a_n = \frac{1}{(n+1)!} > 0.$$

Hence $a_{n+1} > a_n$, so that the sequence is monotone-increasing. Let us now show that it is bounded above:

$$a_n = 1 + 1 + \frac{1}{2!} + \frac{1}{3!} + \frac{1}{4!} + \cdots + \frac{1}{n!}$$

$$< 1 + 1 + \frac{1}{2} + \frac{1}{2^2} + \frac{1}{2^3} + \cdots + \frac{1}{2^{n-1}} = 1 + \frac{1 - 1/2^n}{1 - 1/2} \quad \text{(how?)}$$

$$< 1 + \frac{1}{1 - 1/2} = 3.$$

Thus the sequence $\{a_n\}$ is monotone-increasing and bounded; hence the limit exists. Let us designate it by e' for the present.

Let us consider another example:

$$e \equiv \lim (1 + 1/n)^n \text{ exists.}$$

In fact $e' = e$, but the proof of this will be postponed until we discuss infinite series. For the present, we will show that $e \leqslant e'$.

Let $b_n = (1 + 1/n)^n$. Then, by the binomial theorem,

$$b_n = 1 + n \cdot \frac{1}{n} + \frac{n(n-1)}{2!}\left(\frac{1}{n}\right)^2 + \cdots + \frac{n(n-1)\cdots(n-k+1)}{k!}\left(\frac{1}{n}\right)^k$$

$$+ \cdots + \frac{n!}{n!} \cdot \left(\frac{1}{n}\right)^n$$

$$= 1 + 1 + \frac{1}{2!}\left(1 - \frac{1}{n}\right) + \cdots + \frac{1}{k!}\left(1 - \frac{1}{n}\right)\left(1 - \frac{2}{n}\right)\cdots\left(1 - \frac{k-1}{n}\right)$$

$$+ \cdots + \frac{1}{n!}\left(1 - \frac{1}{n}\right)\cdots\left(1 - \frac{n-1}{n}\right)$$

$$< 1 + 1 + \frac{1}{2!} + \cdots + \frac{1}{k!} + \cdots + \frac{1}{n!} < e'$$

Hence $\{b_n\}$ is bounded above by e'.

It is also clear that the kth term of the expansion for b_n is smaller than that for b_{n+1}:

$$\frac{1}{k!}\left(1 - \frac{1}{n}\right)\left(1 - \frac{2}{n}\right)\cdots\left(1 - \frac{k-1}{n}\right)$$

$$< \frac{1}{k!}\left(1 - \frac{1}{n+1}\right)\left(1 - \frac{2}{n+1}\right)\cdots\left(1 - \frac{k-1}{n+1}\right).$$

This is true because

$$\left(1 - \frac{j}{n}\right) < \left(1 - \frac{j}{n+1}\right) \qquad j = 1, 2, \ldots (k-1) \leqslant n-1,$$

and b_{n+1} contains one more positive term than b_n.
Hence $e = \lim (1 + 1/n)^n$ exists and

$$e \leqslant e',$$

since e' is an upper bound for $\{b_n\}$ and e is the least upper bound for $\{b_n\}$.

2.7 MONOTONE FUNCTIONS

A function f defined on an interval is said to be **monotone-increasing** if, for x_1 and x_2 in the interval, $x_1 > x_2$ implies that $f(x_1) \geqslant f(x_2)$ or $f(x_1) > f(x_2)$. In the first case, the function is **weakly monotone-increasing** (or **non-decreasing**). In the latter case, it is **strictly increasing**. A function is **monotone-decreasing** if $x_1 > x_2$ implies that $f(x_1) \leqslant f(x_2)$ or $f(x_1) < f(x_2)$. Again, the two cases distinguish weak

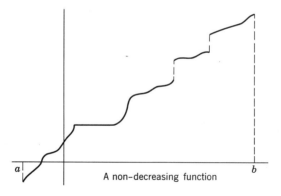

A non–decreasing function

and strict monotonicity (maybe "monotoneity," but definitely not "monotony"). As with sequences, an important consequence of monotonicity is the existence of limits:

2.7a   Theorem. Let $f(x)$ be monotone on an interval $\{a \leqslant x \leqslant b\}$. Then the limits $f(b - 0)$ and $f(a + 0)$ exist. At all interior points x, the limits $f(x + 0)$ and $f(x - 0)$ exist.

Proof. We recall that $f(x + 0)$ refers to the right-hand limit and $f(x - 0)$ to the left-hand limit. Our proof is for the left-hand limit, with f non-decreasing. The proof would be similar for other cases.

Let x_0 be any point in $\{a \leqslant x \leqslant b\}$ except a itself. We examine f near this point. Let

$$x_n = x_0 - \frac{1}{n}$$

and

$$y_n = f\left(x_0 - \frac{1}{n}\right).$$

Since $f(x)$ is monotone,

$$y_n \leqslant y_{n+1} \leqslant f(x_0).$$

Thus y_n is monotone and bounded. Hence there is a number A such that

$$\lim y_n = A \leqslant f(x_0)$$

Now given $\epsilon > 0$, there is an $N(\epsilon)$ such that

$$0 \leqslant A - f(x_N) < \epsilon.$$

Choose $\delta(\epsilon) = 1/N(\epsilon)$. Then for $x_N = x_0 - \delta < x < x_0$ we have, by monotonicity,

$$f(x_N) \leqslant f(x) \leqslant A$$

or

$$\epsilon \geqslant A - f(x_N) \geqslant A - f(x) \geqslant 0,$$

which proves the theorem. It proves even more, for if $f(x)$ is non-decreasing, then

$$f(x_0 - 0) \leqslant f(x_0).$$

It should be clear that a similar argument will prove $f(x_0 + 0)$ exists and that

$$f(x_0) \leqslant f(x_0 + 0). \qquad \blacksquare$$

For non-increasing functions, we have

$$f(x_0 + 0) \leqslant f(x_0) \leqslant f(x_0 - 0).$$

A EXERCISES

1. Examine Exercise B5 of 1.7. What does it establish about the sequence $(1 + 1/n)^n$?

2. Establish the following limits:

(a) $\left(1 + \dfrac{1}{3n + 1}\right)^{3n+1} \to e.$

(b) $\left(1 + \dfrac{1}{n + 4}\right)^n \to e.$

(c) $\left(1 + \dfrac{1}{2n}\right)^n \to \sqrt{e}.$

(d) $\left(1 + \dfrac{1}{n + 1}\right)^{6n} \to e^6.$

(e) $\left(1 + \dfrac{1}{n^2}\right)^{n^2} \to e.$

(f) $\left(1 + \dfrac{1}{n!}\right)^{n!} \to e.$

(g) $\left(1 + \dfrac{2}{n}\right)^{n} \to e^2.$ $\left[\textit{Hint: } \text{Show that } \left(1 + \dfrac{2}{n}\right) = \left(1 + \dfrac{1}{n+1}\right)\left(1 + \dfrac{1}{n}\right).\right]$

(h) $\left(1 + \dfrac{3}{n}\right)^{n} \to e^3.$

B EXERCISES

1. Prove that $(1 - 1/n)^n \to 1/e$. Evaluate $\lim [1 - 1/(n - 2)]^{n+7}$.

2. Suppose a sequence $\{a_n\}$ is defined by

$$a_1 = \sqrt{2}, \qquad a_2 = \sqrt{2 + \sqrt{2}}, \qquad a_3 = \sqrt{2 + \sqrt{2 + \sqrt{2}}}, \ldots.$$

In general, $a_{n+1} = \sqrt{2 + a_n}$. Show that the sequence is monotone and bounded, and compute the limit. (*Hint:* By induction, show that $a_n < 2$.)

3. Do the same for the sequence $\{a_n\}$ given by $a_1 = \sqrt{2}$, $a_{n+1} = \sqrt{2a_n}$.

4. Show that $a^n/n! \to 0$. Is the convergence monotone?

5. Show that $n^n/(n!\, e^n)$ tends to a limit.

6. Show that if $a_n > 0$ and $(a_{n+1}/a_n) \to q < 1$, then $a_n \to 0$.

7. Let $x_n = (1 + a)(1 + a^2) \cdots (1 + a^n)$. Show that $\lim x_n$ exists if $0 \leqslant a < 1$. (*Hint:* Use $1 + x \leqslant e^x$.)

C EXERCISES

1. Let $0 < x_1 < y_1$. For $n > 1$, set $x_{n+1} = \sqrt{x_n y_n}$, $y_{n+1} = \frac{1}{2}(x_n + y_n)$. Show that $\lim x_n = \lim y_n$.

2. Let $x_1 > 0$ be given. For $n > 1$, set $x_n = 1/(1 + x_{n-1})$. Show that $\lim x_n$ exists and evaluate.

3. Let $a_1, a_2, a_3, \ldots$ be a sequence of digits; that is, each $a_k = 0, 1, 2, \ldots, 8$, or 9. Consider the sequence of decimal fractions b_n given by

$$b_1 = 0.\, a_1$$
$$b_2 = 0.\, a_1 a_2$$
$$b_3 = 0.\, a_1 a_2 a_3$$
$$\cdots \cdots$$
$$b_n = 0.\, a_1 a_2 a_3 \cdots a_n.$$

Show that $\{b_n\}$ has a limit b between 0 and 1. We designate this number by the "infinite" decimal expansion:

$$b = 0.\, a_1 a_2 a_3 \cdots a_n \cdots.$$

4. Show that any number between 0 and 1 has a decimal expansion of the form discussed in Exercise 3 and that this representation is unique, except that numbers of the form

$$0. a_1 a_2 \cdots a_n \, 9 \, 9 \, 9 \cdots 9 \cdots$$

and $$0. a_1 a_2 \cdots (a_n + 1) \, 0 \, 0 \, 0 \, 0 \cdots,$$

where $a_n \neq 9$, are equal.

5. Suppose a function f is locally monotone on an interval I; that is, at each point x in I, there is a neighborhood in which f is monotone. Show that it is then monotone over the whole interval I.

3

Continuity
and Differentiability

3.1 CONTINUITY. UNIFORM CONTINUITY

Roughly speaking, when we say that a function f is continuous at a point a in its domain, we mean that its values at near-by points are near to its value at a. Our precise definition is:

A function f, defined in a neighborhood of a point a is **continuous** at a if

$$\lim_{x \to a} f(x) = f(a).$$

This, of course, is an idea with which you are already familiar in a primitive form from your earliest concept of a function, because most of the functions with which you are familiar are continuous, except possibly at a few points.

A function may fail to be continuous at a point a for any of three reasons: f may not be defined there; the limit may not exist; or if f is defined at a and the limit exists, then the two may not be equal.

If f is not continuous at a point a, it may still happen that it is **left-continuous** or **right-continuous** at a. That is, it may be that

$$\lim_{x \to a-} f(x) = f(a)$$

or

$$\lim_{x \to a+} f(x) = f(a).$$

In other symbols,

$$f(a - 0) = f(a)$$

or

$$f(a + 0) = f(a).$$

For example, let

$$f(x) = \begin{cases} \dfrac{|x|}{x} & \text{if } x \neq 0 \\ -1 & \text{if } x = 0. \end{cases}$$

That is,

$$f(x) = \begin{cases} -1 & \text{if } x \leqslant 0 \\ +1 & \text{if } x > 0. \end{cases}$$

Clearly $f(x)$ is left-continuous. If we had taken $f(0) = +1$, it would be right-continuous. If we take $f(0)$ as anything else, then $f(x)$ has neither left nor right continuity, though it has left- and right-hand limits, namely -1 and $+1$ respectively.

In particular, for the function $f(x) = \text{sgn } x$ (see 2.1) we have $f(0-0) = -1$, $f(0) = 0$, $f(0+0) = +1$. It should be clear that a necessary and sufficient condition that f be continuous at $x = a$ is that it be both left- and right-continuous. (See Exercise B9, Section 2.5.)

The definition of continuity depends on the concept of a limit, which has been defined in ϵ, δ terms. We can phrase our definition in such terms, and for many purposes it is better to do so. The statement is as follows:

A function f, defined in $\{x_0 - h < x < x_0 + h\}$, is **continuous** at x_0 if for each $\epsilon > 0$ there is a δ, $0 < \delta \leqslant h$ for which

$$|f(x) - f(x_0)| < \epsilon \qquad \text{if } |x - x_0| < \delta.$$

Now the number δ, as we know, depends in general on ϵ; but here it may also depend on the point x_0. Hence we sometimes write $\delta (\epsilon, x_0)$.

We will say that a function f is continuous on an open interval I if it is continuous at each point in I. If I is semi-closed or closed (that is, contains one or both end points) we say it is continuous on I if it is continuous at each interior point (Section 1.4) and has the appropriate one-sided continuity at each end point which is included. Thus if I is given by $\{a \leqslant x < b\}$, then for f to be continuous in I it must be right-continuous at a as well as continuous at all other points x in I.

If a function f fails to be continuous at a point x_0 of its domain, it is said to be **discontinuous** there. The point x_0 is called a **point of discontinuity**—or, more briefly, simply a **discontinuity**—of f.

EXAMPLE. Show that $f(x) = x^2$ is continuous at x_0. We choose any h we please, say $h = 1$. We consider f, then, in the interval I: $\{x_0 - 1 < x < x_0 + 1\}$. Here $|x - x_0| < 1$. From which we see that

$$|x| \leqslant |x_0| + 1.$$

Now for x in I we consider

$$|f(x) - f(x_0)| = |x^2 - x_0^2| = |x - x_0| \, |x + x_0|$$
$$\leqslant |x - x_0|(|x| + |x_0|) \leqslant |x - x_0|(2|x_0| + 1).$$

Consequently, we see that choosing $|x - x_0| < \epsilon/(2 |x_0| + 1)$ gives us

$$|x^2 - x_0^2| < \epsilon.$$

To achieve this inequality, we have imposed two conditions on x:

(1) $\qquad\qquad\qquad |x - x_0| < 1 \qquad$ (that is, x is in I)

(2) $\qquad\qquad\qquad |x - x_0| < \epsilon/(2|x_0| + 1).$

Thus if we choose $\delta = \min [1, \epsilon/(2|x_0| + 1)]$, our definition is satisfied. Note that the dependence of δ on x_0 is quite explicit.

EXAMPLE. Show that the function defined by $f(x) = 1/x$ is continuous in the set D: $\{|x| \geqslant \frac{1}{2}\}$. We have

$$|f(x) - f(x_0)| = \left| \frac{1}{x} - \frac{1}{x_0} \right| = \frac{|x - x_0|}{|xx_0|}.$$

Hence if we take x and x_0 in D, and choose $\delta = |x_0|\epsilon/2$, we get

$$|f(x) - f(x_0)| \leqslant \frac{2|x - x_0|}{|x_0|} \leqslant \frac{2\epsilon|x_0|}{2|x_0|} = \epsilon \qquad \text{if } |x - x_0| < \delta.$$

Now, as in any limit, if δ satisfies the conditions of the definition, so will any smaller number, say $\delta' \leqslant \delta$. In the previous example we have $\delta = |x_0|\epsilon/2$, where $|x_0| \geqslant \frac{1}{2}$. Hence $\delta' = \epsilon/4$ is no larger than δ, and therefore

$$|f(x) - f(x_0)| < \epsilon \qquad \text{if } |x - x_0| < \delta' = \frac{\epsilon}{4}$$

for x_0 in D.

The significance of our new choice, δ', is that it will work for any arbitrary choice of x_0 in D; that is, δ' is independent of x_0 in D. It depends only upon the set D itself, but not on the individual point x_0 in D. Such a δ is called uniform and we say that $f(x)$ is uniformly continuous in D.

Precisely, we say that a function f is **uniformly continuous** on a set D if for each $\epsilon > 0$ there is a δ [depending only on ϵ and D, and hence sometimes written $\delta \, (\epsilon, D)$], so that for x and x' in D we have

$$|f(x) - f(x')| < \epsilon \qquad \text{if } |x - x'| < \delta.$$

It follows immediately that if f is uniformly continuous on a set D, then it is continuous at each point of D.

EXAMPLE. Show that the function f defined by $f(x) = \sin x$ is uniformly continuous for all x. Observe that

$$\sin x - \sin x' = 2 \sin \left(\frac{x - x'}{2} \right) \cos \left(\frac{x + x'}{2} \right),$$

so that $|\sin x - \sin x'| \leqslant 2\left|\sin \dfrac{x - x'}{2}\right| \leqslant 2 \cdot \left|\dfrac{x - x'}{2}\right| = |x - x'|.$

Hence $|\sin x - \sin x'| < \epsilon$ whenever $|x - x'| < \epsilon.$

That is, we can take $\delta = \epsilon$. We have therefore shown that $\sin x$ is uniformly continuous over the whole one-dimensional space.

Now it is not true that every function which is continuous on a set is uniformly continuous there. Consider, for example, $f(x) = \sin 1/x$, $\{0 < x < 1\}$. That this is continuous on $\{0 < x < 1\}$ can be easily seen. We see that it is not uniformly continuous there by considering two points,

$x_n = \dfrac{1}{n\pi}$ and $x_n' = \dfrac{1}{(n + \frac{1}{2})\pi}$. We have

$$f(x_n) = \sin n\pi = 0$$

and $$f(x_n') = \sin (n + \tfrac{1}{2})\pi = \pm 1.$$

Thus

$$|f(x_n) - f(x_n')| = 1 \qquad \text{while } |x_n - x_n'| = \frac{1}{n(2n + 1)\pi}$$

can be made as small as we please by taking n sufficiently large.

It is true, however, that if f is continuous on a closed bounded interval, it is uniformly continuous there. This is a rather deep theorem which will be proved in Section 6.4, along with other deep properties of continuous functions.

3.2 OPERATIONS WITH CONTINUOUS FUNCTIONS

If f and g are two continuous functions defined on a domain D, then we define the function $f + g$ on D to be the function which assigns to each point x in D the function value $f(x) + g(x)$. Similarly, we define $f - g$, $f \cdot g$ (f times g); and if g never takes the value zero, we define f/g. If g is zero for certain x's and not for others, then the function f/g is defined for a sub-set, D', of D on which g does not vanish. And if f is non-negative, $\sqrt{f}$ is defined in the obvious way. Our immediate interest in these functions is that their continuity follows from that of f and g.

3.2a   Theorem. Let f and g be two functions defined in a neighborhood of x_0, which are both continuous at x_0.

(i) $f + g, f - g$, and $f \cdot g$ are continuous at x_0;

(ii) if $g(x_0) \neq 0, f/g$ is continuous at x_0;

(iii) if $f \geqslant 0, \sqrt{f}$ is continuous at x_0;

(iv) $|f|$ is continuous at x_0.

This theorem is an immediate consequence of the theorems on limits of Chapter 2.

Part (iii) of Theorem 3.2a is a special case of a more general theorem which asserts that, if f and g are continuous, then the composite function F, given by $F(x) = g[f(x)]$, is continuous. But first a word about such functions.

Let $f(x)$ be defined on a set D with a range R, and let $g(y)$ be defined on a set D' which contains R. Thus if x is in D, then $f(x)$ is in D' so that $g[f(x)]$ is defined. The resulting function is called the **composition** of g with f. We can now prove our theorem.

3.2b Theorem. Let f and g satisfy the conditions of the previous paragraph. If f and g are continuous, so is the composite function F, given by $F(x) = g[f(x)]$.

Proof. Let x_0 be a point of D. Then $y_0 = f(x_0)$ is in D'. For each $\epsilon > 0$, there is a $\delta_1(\epsilon, y_0)$ such that

$$|g(y) - g(y_0)| < \epsilon \quad \text{if } |y - y_0| < \delta_1.$$

Now that δ_1 is determined, there is a $\delta_2(\delta_1, x_0)$ such that

$$|f(x) - y_0| = |f(x) - f(x_0)| < \delta_1 \quad \text{if } |x - x_0| < \delta_2.$$

Thus if $|x - x_0| < \delta_2$,

$$|F(x) - F(x_0)| = |g[f(x)] - g[f(x_0)]| = |g(y) - g(y_0)| < \epsilon. \quad \blacksquare$$

Notice that the proof did not use the fact that f and g were continuous throughout D and D'. Only the continuity at x_0 and y_0, respectively, was used.

Another important property of a continuous function is that it will maintain its sign for a sufficiently small interval.

3.2c Theorem. If f is continuous at x_0 and $f(x_0) > 0$, then there is a neighborhood about x_0 in which $f(x) > (\tfrac{1}{2})f(x_0) > 0$.

Proof. Since f is continuous at x_0, choose $\epsilon = (\tfrac{1}{2})f(x_0)$ and apply the definition of continuity. There is a δ such that

$$|f(x) - f(x_0)| < (\tfrac{1}{2})f(x_0) \quad \text{if } |x - x_0| < \delta.$$

Thus

$$-(\tfrac{1}{2})f(x_0) < f(x) - f(x_0)$$

or

$$f(x) > \tfrac{1}{2}f(x_0) \quad \text{if } |x - x_0| < \delta. \quad \blacksquare$$

3.3 THE INTERMEDIATE-VALUE PROPERTY

A continuous function has the property that it takes all values between any two which it achieves. This is made precise by the following theorem.

3.3a   Theorem. Suppose f is continuous on a closed interval I: $\{a \leqslant x \leqslant b\}$, $f(a) = A$, $f(b) = B$, and $A \neq B$. Then, for each C between A and B, there is a point x_0 in $\{a < x < b\}$ for which

$$f(x_0) = C.$$

Proof. The truth of this theorem seems obvious, and indeed it is obvious geometrically. However, the point is to give a proof based on the arithmetical properties of numbers rather than on the geometrical picture. This turns out to be just a little difficult.

For the sake of definiteness, let us suppose that $A > B$. The function $f - C$ is positive at a; and hence, by Theorem 3.2c, it is positive immediately to the right of a. But it is not positive all the way, for at b it is negative; and hence, by the same theorem, it must be negative for a short interval before b. Thus the sub-set S of I with the property that the values of $f - C$ are positive on S is a bounded set. It therefore has a supremum $x_0 = \sup_S x$, where clearly, by our previous remarks,

$$a < x_0 < b.$$

We want to show that $f(x_0) = C$.

By Theorem 1.5a, for each n there is an x_n satisfying $x_0 - 1/n < x_n \leqslant x_0$ for which

$$f(x_n) > C.$$

By Theorem 2.4a,

$$\lim f(x_n) = f(x_0);$$

and by Theorem 2.3g,

$$\lim f(x_n) \geqslant C.$$

Thus

(1) $$f(x_0) \geqslant C.$$

For any $x > x_0$, $f(x) \leqslant C$. Thus taking the limit from the right and applying the same two theorems, we get

(2) $$f(x_0) \leqslant C.$$

Combining (1) and (2) gives us our result.   ∎

The theorem asserts the existence of at least one point for which $f(x) = C$. Clearly, there may be many such points. In one important situation, we can assert that there is exactly one point x_0 for which $f(x_0) = C$.

3.3b   Theorem. Let f satisfy the hypotheses of Theorem 3.3a, and suppose also that it is strictly monotone. Then there is exactly one x_0 for which $f(x_0) = C$.

Proof. For definiteness, suppose f is increasing. And suppose, for contradiction, that there were two such points x_0 and $x_0{}'$, say with $x_0 > x_0{}'$. Then

$$C = f(x_0) > f(x_0{}') = C,$$

which is a contradiction. ∎

3.4 INVERSE FUNCTIONS

Let f be a function defined on a domain D and having range R, and let ϕ be a function defined on R with range D. If f and ϕ are so related that $f[\phi(y)] = y$ for every y in R, and $\phi[f(x)] = x$ for every x in D, then ϕ is said to be the **inverse function** of f. The basic inverse-function theorem is the following.

3.4a Theorem. If f is a strictly increasing continuous function on $\{a \leqslant x \leqslant b\}$, with $f(a) = \alpha$, and $f(b) = \beta$, then there is a unique inverse function of f, which we will call ϕ, defined on $\{\alpha \leqslant y \leqslant \beta\}$, which is strictly increasing and continuous there.

Proof. By Theorem 3.3b, for each y in $\{\alpha \leqslant y \leqslant \beta\}$ there is exactly one x for which $f(x) = y$. This x depends on the chosen y, and will be denoted by $\phi(y)$. Thus, by definition,

$$\phi[f(x)] \equiv \phi(y) = x.$$

Taking f of both sides, we get

$$f[\phi(y)] = f(x) = y.$$

Hence the unique function $\phi(y)$ is the inverse of f.

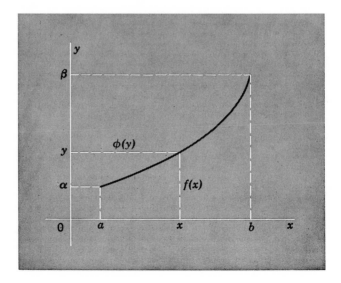

We can see that ϕ is strictly increasing, as follows: Choose y_1 and y_2, say $y_1 > y_2$, and let x_1 and x_2 respectively be the corresponding x's. Then suppose, for contradiction, that

$$x_1 = \phi(y_1) \leqslant \phi(y_2) = x_2.$$

Taking f of both sides, and using the monotonicity of f, we have

$$y_1 = f(x_1) \leqslant f(x_2) = y_2.$$

This is a contradiction, and hence establishes the strict monotonicity of ϕ.

To prove the continuity, we use a contradiction argument again. Suppose ϕ were discontinuous at some point y_0 in $\{\alpha \leqslant y \leqslant \beta\}$. Then either $\phi(y_0 - 0) < \phi(y_0)$ or $\phi(y_0) < \phi(y_0 + 0)$. For definiteness, suppose it is the first of these two which holds. Then let

$$\phi(y_0 - 0) = \phi(y_0) - d \qquad \text{where } d > 0.$$

Let x_0 be the x value corresponding to y_0. Then

$$f(x_0) = y_0$$

and

$$\phi(y_0) = x_0.$$

For every δ, $0 < \delta < y_0 - \alpha$ we have

$$\phi(y_0 - \delta) < \phi(y_0 - \delta/2) < \phi(y_0 - 0) = \phi(y_0) - d = x_0 - d,$$

the inequality holding since ϕ is strictly monotone. Now taking f of the two ends of this inequality and using the strict monotonicity of f, we get

$$y_0 - \delta = f(\phi(y_0 - \delta)) < f(x_0 - d)$$

or

$$f(x_0) - \delta < f(x_0 - d) < f(x_0).$$

If we let $\delta \to 0$ (for δ was arbitrary), we get

$$f(x_0) \leqslant f(x_0 - d) < f(x_0).$$

But this is a contradiction. ∎

We have frequently used square roots with an occasional remark that their existence would be established later. We are now in a position to give that proof. What we want to show is the following.

3.4b Theorem. For each non-negative number y, there is a unique $x \geqslant 0$ for which $x^2 = y$.

Proof. Let any y_0 be given. Consider the function f, given by $f(x) = x^2$ on a large interval, say $\{0 \leqslant x \leqslant b\}$ where $b^2 > y_0$. (How can we be sure such a b exists? See Exercise A4.) Now on this interval f is strictly increasing: Suppose $x_1 > x_2$, then

$$x_1{}^2 - x_2{}^2 = (x_1 - x_2)(x_1 + x_2) > 0$$

since $x_1 - x_2 > 0$. It is also continuous; hence a unique inverse exists. This means that for every y in $\{0 \leqslant y \leqslant b^2\}$ there is a unique x such that $x^2 = y$. This holds in particular for the given y_0. ∎

By the same type of argument, we can prove the existence of a unique n^{th} root of any non-negative number. Since integral powers are also defined, we can now define what we mean by $a^{n/m}$, namely $\sqrt[m]{a^n}$. It is easy to see that

$$\sqrt[n]{a^m} = (\sqrt[n]{a})^m \qquad \text{(Exercise B9)}.$$

It is somewhat more difficult to define a^x for arbitrary x. This will be postponed to the chapter on the elementary transcendental functions.

A EXERCISES

1. Determine whether the following functions are continuous in the domains indicated. In each case where the function is continuous, determine whether it is uniformly continuous.

(a) $$f(x) = \begin{cases} x^2, & \{\ 0 < x < 1\}. \\ x, & \{-1 < x \leqslant 0\}. \end{cases}$$ (b) $$f(x) = \begin{cases} x^2, & \{\ 0 \leqslant x \leqslant 1\}. \\ e^x, & \{-1 \leqslant x < 0\}. \end{cases}$$

(c) $f(x) = x^2$, $|x| \leqslant a$, for arbitrary $a > 0$. Is x^2 uniformly continuous for all x?

2. Where are $x - [x]$ and $[x] + [-x]$ discontinuous?

3. Show graphically why the function f given by $f(x) = 1/x$ is not uniformly continuous in $\{0 < x \leqslant 1\}$ (see Exercise B3).

4. Show that for any positive y_0 there is a b so that $b^2 > y_0$.

5. Set $f(x) = \sqrt{a^2 + x^2}$. Determine how close to take x and x' to each other to insure that $|f(x) - f(x')| < 10^{-100}$.

6. Suppose that f is continuous in an interval and does not take the value 0 there. Show that f has one sign on this interval.

7. Let $f(x) = x/(x + 1)$, $x > -1$. Find an inverse function for f. Where is it defined? Illustrate graphically.

8. Let $f(x) = x^2 - 2x + 4$. Find an inverse function (a) for $x \geqslant 1$, (b) for $x \leqslant 1$. Where is each defined? Illustrate graphically.

B EXERCISES

1. Set

$$f(x) = \begin{cases} x & x \text{ rational} \\ 1 - x & x \text{ irrational} \end{cases} \qquad \{0 \leqslant x \leqslant 1\}.$$

Show that f is continuous only at $x = \frac{1}{2}$.

2. Let f be defined as in Exercise B1. Define g by $g(x) = f(x)f(1 - x)$. Where is g continuous?

3. Prove that $1/x$ is not uniformly continuous in $\{0 < x \leqslant 1\}$ (see Exercise A3).

4. Prove that $\dfrac{x^4 + 2x^2 + 5}{x - 1} + \dfrac{x^6 + 2x^4 + 6}{x - 7} = 0$ has a solution between 1 and 7.

5. Show that $\dfrac{5}{x - 1} + \dfrac{7}{x - 2} + \dfrac{16}{x - 3} = 0$ has a solution between 1 and 2,

(ex) $x = \frac{3}{2}$ $x = 6\frac{1}{2}$ $f(x)$ changes from

pos. to neg. or vice-versa

and another between 2 and 3.

6. Prove that if $y > 0$, then y has a unique negative square root.

7. Prove that any real number y has a unique real cube root and that $\operatorname{sgn} \sqrt[3]{y} = \operatorname{sgn} y$.

8. Suppose f is continuous on an interval, and at the rational points of that interval it has the values given by $f(x) = x^2 - 3x + 5$. What values has it on the irrational points? $f(x) = x^2 - 3x + 5$

9. Prove that $\sqrt[m]{a^n} = (\sqrt[m]{a})^n$.

10. Suppose f is strictly increasing, continuous and bounded on $\{a < x < b\}$. Show that it can be defined at a and at b so as to be strictly increasing, continuous, and bounded in $\{a \leqslant x \leqslant b\}$.

C EXERCISES

1. Show that if f is uniformly continuous in D_1 and also in D_2, then it is uniformly continuous in the set D consisting of both D_1 and D_2.

2. Show that $\sqrt{x}$ and $x \sin \dfrac{1}{x}$ are uniformly continuous in $\{0 < x \leqslant 1\}$ by finding for each function a uniform δ.

3. Show that if f is continuous on an interval and assumes no value more than once, then it is strictly monotone there.

4. Suppose f and g are increasing and continuous in an interval I, and $f(x) > g(x)$ in I. Let ϕ and ψ be the inverse functions of f and g, respectively, and let their intervals of definition overlap. Show that $\phi(y) < \psi(y)$ in this common part.

3.5 THE DERIVATIVE. CHAIN RULE

It is assumed that you are familiar with the elementary differentiation formulas. A list of these can be found in the back of the book. Very likely your exposure to formulas involving the logarithm, the exponential, and the trigonometric functions was based on elementary and somewhat unsatisfactory definitions of these functions. In Chapter 5 we define these functions and put their properties on a firmer foundation. In the meantime we will not hesitate to continue to use these functions as examples.

Let f be a function defined in a neighborhood of a point x_0. The ratio

$$\frac{\Delta f}{\Delta x} = \frac{f(x_0 + h) - f(x_0)}{h} = \frac{f(x) - f(x_0)}{x - x_0} \qquad (\Delta x = x - x_0 = h)$$

is called the **difference quotient** of f at x_0. If

$$\lim_{h \to 0} \frac{f(x_0 + h) - f(x_0)}{h} = \lim_{x \to x_0} \frac{f(x) - f(x_0)}{x - x_0}$$

exists, it is called the **derivative** of f at x_0 and is written

$$f'(x_0), \ Df(x_0)$$

or sometimes, recalling the common notation $y = f(x)$,

$$\frac{dy}{dx}$$

where the point x_0 is indicated by $(dy/dx)_{x_0}$ or is implied by the setting of the problem.

If $f'(x)$ exists for all points x in some sub-set D' of the domain D of f (an interval perhaps), it defines there a function which will be denoted by f'. It is called the **derived function** or the **derivative** of f.

If f has a derivative at a point x_0, it is said to be **differentiable** there. If it has a derivative at every point of a set D, it is said to be differentiable on D. If f' is continuous on a set D, we say that f is **continuously differentiable** there.

If the derivative fails to exist at a point x_0, the **one-sided derivatives** may still exist. They can be defined by

$$(1) \qquad \lim_{h \to 0+} \frac{f(x_0 + h) - f(x_0)}{h}, \qquad \lim_{h \to 0-} \frac{f(x_0 + h) - f(x_0)}{h}.$$

And if these fail to exist, then a weaker type is given by

$$(2) \qquad \lim_{h \to 0+} \frac{f(x_0 + h) - f(x_0 + 0)}{h}, \qquad \lim_{h \to 0-} \frac{f(x_0 + h) - f(x_0 - 0)}{h}.$$

There is no standard notation for these one-sided derivatives. When we have occasion to use a one-sided derivative, we will state explicitly which we mean.

An important property of differentiable functions is their continuity.

3.5a   Theorem. If a function f is differentiable at a point x_0, then it is continuous at x_0.

Proof. Let $A = f'(x_0)$. Then

$$\frac{f(x_0 + h) - f(x_0)}{h} = A + \eta$$

where $\eta \to 0$ as $h \to 0$. Hence there is a δ so that $|\eta| < 1$ if $|h| < \delta$. Then setting $M = |A| + 1$ we have

$$|f(x_0 + h) - f(x_0)| \leq |A + \eta| \cdot |h| \leq M|h|. \qquad \blacksquare$$

Similarly, the existence of a one-sided derivative of type (1) would imply one-sided continuity—from the same side, of course.

If f is a function which is differentiable in an interval, the derived function f' is well defined there. We can then inquire about the existence of the derivative of f'. If this exists at a point x_0, it is called the **second derivative** of f at x_0 and is denoted by

$$f''(x_0), \frac{d^2f(x_0)}{dx^2}, \frac{d^2f}{dx^2}\bigg|_{x_0}, \frac{d^2y}{dx^2}, \dots$$

If $f''(x)$ exists for every point of an interval, it defines a function there which we will denote by f''.

We can next inquire about the existence of the third and higher derivatives. If n is a definite but unspecified integer, the derivative of order n is denoted by

$$f^{(n)}, \frac{d^nf}{dx^n}, \dots$$

The next result is usually known as the **chain rule**. It is the formula for differentiating a composite function (Section 3.2).

3.5b Theorem. Let f and g satisfy the conditions of 3.2b and be differentiable. Then if $y_0 = f(x_0)$, we have

$$\frac{d}{dx} g[f(x)]\bigg|_{x_0} = F'(x_0) = g'(y_0)f'(x_0).$$

Proof. Let $y = f(x)$. Then

$$\begin{aligned}
F(x) - F(x_0) &= g[f(x)] - g[f(x_0)] \\
&= g(y) - g(y_0) \\
&= g'(y_0)(y - y_0) + \eta(y - y_0)
\end{aligned}$$

where $\eta \to 0$ as $y \to y_0$. Thus

$$\begin{aligned}
\frac{F(x) - F(x_0)}{x - x_0} &= g'(y_0)\frac{y - y_0}{x - x_0} + \eta\frac{y - y_0}{x - x_0} \\
&= g'(y_0)\frac{f(x) - f(x_0)}{x - x_0} + \eta\frac{f(x) - f(x_0)}{x - x_0}.
\end{aligned}$$

Now $y \to y_0$ as $x \to x_0$. Hence $\eta \to 0$. Thus

$$F'(x_0) = \lim_{x \to x_0} \frac{F(x) - F(x_0)}{x - x_0} = g'(y_0) f'(x_0).$$ ▮

This rule is perhaps familiar to you in the form

$$\frac{dz}{dx} = \frac{dz}{dy}\frac{dy}{dx}.$$

From the definition of a derivative and these theorems, the usual rules for differentiating a product, quotient, etc. follow quite simply. For their derivations, you are therefore referred to your elementary calculus text.

Let us remind you of the geometrical meaning of the derivative. Let $\mathbf{P} = (x_0, y_0)$ be a point on the graph of $y = f(x)$, and $\mathbf{Q}$ be a near-by point. The coordinates of $\mathbf{Q}$ will be $[x_0 + h, f(x_0 + h)]$. The secant line through $\mathbf{P}$ and $\mathbf{Q}$ will have its slope equal to the difference quotient at x:

$$\frac{f(x_0 + h) - f(x_0)}{h}.$$

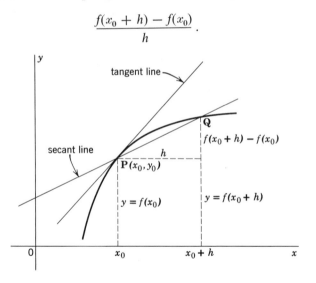

The existence of the derivative—that is, of the limit of this difference quotient—then means geometrically that as $\mathbf{Q}$ slides along the curve to coincide with $\mathbf{P}$ the secant line rotates into a limiting position. The line occupying this limiting position is called the **tangent line** to the curve given by $y = f(x)$. It passes through the point (x_0, y_0) and has slope $f'(x_0)$. Hence its equation is

(3) $\qquad y - y_0 = f'(x_0)(x - x_0) \qquad$ (tangent line).

The line perpendicular to the tangent line at (x_0, y_0) is called the **normal line**, and its equation, if $f'(x_0) \neq 0$, is

$$y - y_0 = -\frac{1}{f'(x_0)}(x - x_0)$$

or (4) $f'(x_0)(y - y_0) + (x - x_0) = 0$ (normal line).

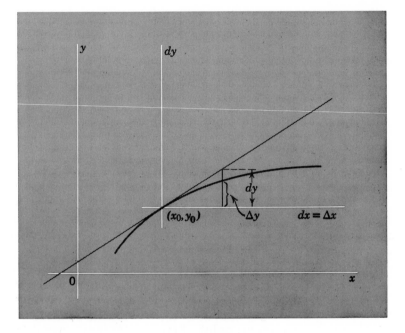

If we make a change of variable given by $dy = y - y_0$, $dx = x - x_0$, the equation of the tangent line (3) becomes

(5) $$dy = f'(x_0)\,dx.$$

This amounts to introducing new coordinate axes namely the dy-axis and the dx-axis, centered at (x_0, y_0) and parallel to the old axes.

Equation (5) then gives the change in y, namely dy, along the tangent line due to a change of dx in x. We call dx and dy **differentials**; dy is the differential of f at x_0. We see that it gives an approximation to the change in y along the curve due to a change $h = \Delta x = dx$ in x:

$$\Delta y = f(x_0 + dx) - f(x_0) = f'(x_0)\,dx + \eta\,dx$$

where $\eta \to 0$ as $dx \to 0$. That is,

$$\Delta y = dy + \eta\,dx$$

where η is small when dx is small. When the formula is used as an approximation formula, the value of η must be estimated in order to give precise information about the quality of the approximation.

However, you should understand that the equation

$$dy = f'(x_0)\, dx$$

and the corresponding

$$\frac{dy}{dx} = f'(x_0)$$

have been given meanings independent of the size of dx and dy. In particular, dx and dy need not be small. The meaning given to the preceding equations is that they describe the tangent line in the proper (that is, dx, dy) coordinate system.

3.6 THE MEAN-VALUE THEOREM

In elementary calculus, you sought maximum and minimum points of functions by solving the equation $f'(x) = 0$. A root of this equation was tested by one or the other of various tests to determine if it is at a maximum value or a minimum value, or neither. We remind you of the definitions of maxima and minima:

A function f is said to attain a **maximum value** at a point x_0 of its domain D if $f(x_0) \geqslant f(x)$ for all other values of x in D. It is a **strict maximum** if $f(x_0) > f(x)$. The function attains a **local maximum** value at x_0 if there is a neighborhood of x_0 in which $f(x) \leqslant f(x_0)$. Such a point x_0 is called a **maximum point**. Reversing the inequalities defines **minimum values** and **points**.

The justification for the method described above is provided by the following theorem.

3.6a **Theorem.** If f is defined in an interval and attains a maximum or a minimum value (maybe even a local one) at an interior point x_0, and if $f'(x_0)$ exists, then $f'(x_0) = 0$.

Proof. To prove this theorem, we examine the difference quotient $\frac{f(x_0 + h) - f(x_0)}{h}$. Let us take the case of a maximum. Even for a local maximum, the numerator is $\leqslant 0$ if h is sufficiently small. For $h < 0$, the difference quotient is then non-negative: $\frac{\Delta f}{\Delta x} \geqslant 0$. The left-hand limit of this quotient is therefore also $\geqslant 0$. But since the derivative exists, each one-sided limit is equal to the derivative. Thus $f'(x_0) \geqslant 0$. For $h > 0$, we have $\Delta f/\Delta x \leqslant 0$, and hence taking the right-hand limit we get $f'(x_0) \leqslant 0$. Thus $f'(x_0) = 0$. ∎

We now want to use a certain property of continuous functions whose proof will be postponed until a later chapter. (We will be careful not to get into a circular argument by using any consequences of this property in its proof later on.) The statement of the property follows.

3.6b Theorem. If f is continuous on a closed bounded interval I: $\{a \leqslant x \leqslant b\}$, then there is a point x_0 in I for which

$$f(x_0) \geqslant f(x) \qquad \text{for all } x \text{ in } I.$$

Proof. See Theorem 6.4b.

This means that a function continuous in a closed bounded interval has a maximum value. It follows that such a function also has a minimum value.

3.6c Theorem. If f is continuous on a closed bounded interval I: $\{a \leqslant x \leqslant b\}$, then there is a point x_0' in I for which

$$f(x_0') \leqslant f(x) \qquad \text{all } x \text{ in } I.$$

Proof. The proof of this theorem is left as an exercise (A8).

We can see by examples that the closedness is essential. For consider the function f given by $f(x) = x^2$ on $\{0 < x < 1\}$. Clearly,

$$\sup_{\{0 < x < 1\}} f(x) = 1$$

and

$$\inf_{\{0 < x < 1\}} f(x) = 0,$$

but neither is assumed by f. In fact, a function continuous on an open interval need not even be bounded, as in the case of f given by

$$f(x) = \frac{1}{x} \qquad \{0 < x < 1\}.$$

We should also point out that there may be many maximal points. The theorem asserts the existence of a least one.

On the basis of these theorems, we can prove the following theorem, known as **Rolle's theorem.**

3.6d **Theorem.** If f is continuous in a closed interval I: $\{a \leqslant x \leqslant b\}$ and differentiable in the open interval J: $\{a < x < b\}$, and if $f(a) = f(b)$, then there is a point x_0 in J for which $f'(x_0) = 0$.

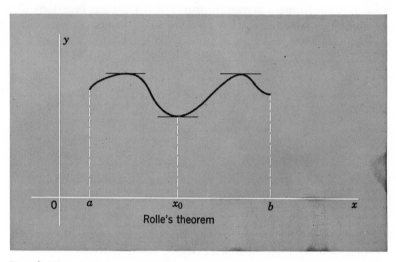

Rolle's theorem

Proof. The geometrical meaning is this: if the curve C given by $y = f(x)$, has a tangent at every point of J then between two points on C which are at the same level there is a (at least one) point between them at which the tangent line is horizontal. We proceed to the proof.

By Theorems 3.6b and 3.6c, f achieves both its maximum and its minimum in I. Let

$$M = \max_I f(x)$$

and

$$m = \min_I f(x).$$

If $M = m$, then f is a constant and $f'(x) = 0$ for every x in J. If $M \neq m$, then one of them is different from $f(a)$. Suppose it is M (the other case is similar). Then $M > f(a)$, so that the maximum cannot be assumed at $x = a$ or $x = b$. Hence there is a point x_0 in J at which $f(x)$ is a maximum. By Theorem 3.6a, then,

$$f'(x_0) = 0. \qquad \blacksquare$$

The assumption that $f'(x)$ exists for all interior points is essential, as can be seen by examining the function

$$f(x) = \begin{cases} x & \{0 \leqslant x < 1\} \\ 2 - x & \{1 \leqslant x \leqslant 2\} \end{cases}$$

This function fails to have a derivative at only one point, namely $x = 1$, and the conclusion of the theorem is false.

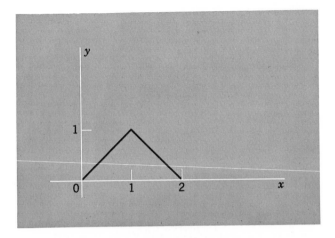

We come now to the **mean-value theorem**. This too has an easily remembered geometrical meaning. Let a curve C given by $y = f(x)$ have

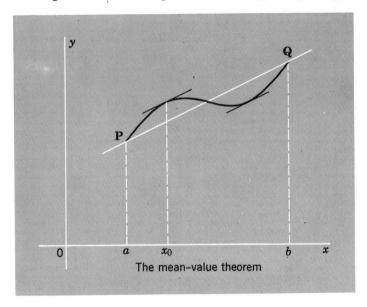

The mean–value theorem

a tangent at each point. Let **P** and **Q** be two points on C. Then there is a point between them where the slope of the tangent line is parallel to the secant line connecting them. The precise statement follows.

3.6e   Theorem. Let f be continuous on a closed interval I: $\{a \leqslant x \leqslant b\}$ and differentiable in the open interval J: $\{a < x < b\}$. Then there is a point x_0 in J at which

$$f'(x_0) = \frac{f(b) - f(a)}{b - a}.$$

Proof. By the point-slope formula, the secant line is given by

$$\frac{y - f(a)}{x - a} = \frac{f(b) - f(a)}{b - a}.$$

When solved for y, this becomes

$$y = \frac{f(b) - f(a)}{b - a}(x - a) + f(a).$$

Let F be the function given by the difference of f and the linear function describing the secant:

$$F(x) = f(x) - \frac{f(b) - f(a)}{b - a}(x - a) - f(a).$$

Certainly F is continuous in I and differentiable in J. Also $F(b) = F(a) = 0$, so that Rolle's theorem applies. Thus there is a point x_0 in J so that

$$F'(x_0) = f'(x_0) - \frac{f(b) - f(a)}{b - a} = 0. \qquad ■$$

A useful way in which to write the mean-value theorem is

$$f(x + h) = f(x) + hf'(x_0)$$

where x_0 is some point between x and $x + h$.

It is a simple result that, if two functions differ by a constant, they have the same derivative. The converse is now an easy consequence of the mean-value theorem.

3.6f   Corollary. If f_1 and f_2 are both differentiable in an interval and if $f_1'(x) = f_2'(x)$ for all x in that interval, then

$$f_1(x) = f_2(x) + c \qquad \text{where } c \text{ is a constant.}$$

Proof. Let $\phi(x) = f_1(x) - f_2(x)$. Then $\phi'(x) \equiv 0$ in the interval. Choose a fixed x_1 in the interval. For any other x, we have

$$\frac{\phi(x) - \phi(x_1)}{x - x_1} = \phi'(x_0) = 0.$$

That is, $\qquad\qquad\qquad \phi(x) = \phi(x_1) = c. \qquad\qquad ■$

Theorem 3.6e can be very useful in estimating the size of functions and in making numerical approximations. For example, let us estimate $\sqrt[3]{28}$. By the mean-value theorem with $x = 27$, $h = 1$, we have

$$\sqrt[3]{28} = 3 + \tfrac{1}{3}(x_0)^{-\frac{2}{3}} \qquad 27 < x_0 < 28$$

$$= 3 + \frac{1}{3(x_0)^{\frac{2}{3}}} < 3 + \frac{1}{3(27)^{\frac{2}{3}}} = 3 + \frac{1}{3 \cdot 9}$$

$$= 3 + \frac{1}{27}.$$

Hence we have $\qquad\qquad 3 < \sqrt[3]{28} < 3 + 1/27.$

As another example, let us examine arc tan x near $x = 0$. By the mean-value theorem,

$$\text{arc tan } x = \text{arc tan } 0 + x \frac{1}{1 + x_0^2} = \frac{x}{1 + x_0^2},$$

where x_0 is between x and zero. Hence for $x > 0$

$$\frac{x}{1 + x^2} < \text{arc tan } x < x,$$

where x_0 is replaced by 0 on the right and by x on the left.

Let us now return to discuss monotone functions when we add the additional hypothesis of differentiability.

3.6g Theorem. Let f be non-decreasing on an interval. Then at each point x_0 where f is differentiable, we have

$$f'(x_0) \geqslant 0.$$

Proof. In the difference quotient

$$\frac{f(x_0 + h) - f(x_0)}{h},$$

the numerator and denominator have the same sign. Then, passing to the limit, we get $f'(x_0) \geqslant 0$ by 2.5f. ∎

It is **not** true that, if f is strictly increasing, then $f'(x_0) > 0$. (See Exercise A9.)

3.6h   Theorem. Suppose now that f is strictly increasing and continuous on an interval, and suppose also that $f'(x_0) > 0$ for some x_0 in the interval. Then the inverse function ϕ is differentiable at the point $y_0 = f(x_0)$, and

$$\phi'(y_0) = \frac{1}{f'(x_0)}.$$

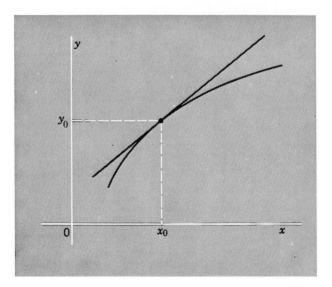

Proof. Let x be a near-by point and let y be given by $y = f(x)$, which means of course that $x = \phi(y)$. Then

$$\frac{\phi(y) - \phi(y_0)}{y - y_0} = \frac{x - x_0}{f(x) - f(x_0)} = \frac{1}{\dfrac{f(x) - f(x_0)}{x - x_0}}.$$

A passage to the limit effects the proof. ∎

It seems quite reasonable to expect that $f'(x) \geqslant 0$ should imply that f is increasing. This is made precise in the following theorem.

3.6i   Theorem. If f is differentiable on an interval and if $f'(x) \geqslant 0$ there, then f is non-decreasing; and if $f'(x) > 0$ there, then f is strictly increasing.

Proof. Let $x_1 > x_2$ be two points in the interval. Then by the mean-value theorem (3.6e)

$$\frac{f(x_1) - f(x_2)}{x_1 - x_2} = f'(x_0)$$

where $x_1 > x_0 > x_2$. Thus

$$f(x_1) - f(x_2) = f'(x_0)(x_1 - x_2).$$

Now $x_1 - x_2 > 0$, so that

$$f(x_1) - f(x_2) \geqslant 0 \qquad \text{if } f'(x_0) \geqslant 0$$

and $\qquad\qquad f(x_1) - f(x_2) > 0 \qquad \text{if } f'(x_0) > 0.$

Hence f is non-decreasing in the first case and strictly increasing in the second. ∎

A EXERCISES

I. Differentiate

(a) $x\sqrt{x + 2x^2}$

(b) $\sqrt[3]{\dfrac{4 + 5x}{4 - 5x}}$

(c) $\dfrac{x(x - 5)\sqrt{x + 3}}{(x^2 + 5)^3(1 - x)^3\sqrt{1 + x}}$

(d) $\sin \dfrac{x}{\sqrt{1 - x^2}}$

(e) $\arctan \dfrac{x}{\sqrt{1 + x^2}}$

(f) $\log \tan \sqrt{1 - x^3}$

(g) $\exp\left(\dfrac{x^2}{1 + x^3}\right)$

2. Assume in each part that there is a differentiable function given by $y = f(x)$ which satisfies the given equation. Compute its derivative:

(a) $y^{1/2} + x^{1/2} = a^{1/2}$

(b) $y^{2/3} + x^{2/3} = a^{2/3}$

(c) $x^2 + 15\sqrt{xy} + y^3 = 36$

(d) $\sin(x^2 + y^2) = e^{x^2 - y^2}$

3. Let the function f be given by

$$f(x) = \begin{cases} x^2 & \{x \leqslant 1\} \\ 2x & \{x > 1\}. \end{cases}$$

Does f have a continuous derivative?

4. Find the equations of the two tangents to the ellipse $x^2 + 4y^2 = 1$ which pass through the point $(5, 0)$.

5. Evaluate $\displaystyle\lim_{h \to 0} \dfrac{e^h - 1}{h}$.

6. Use the mean-value theorem to show that:

(a) $\sqrt{101}$ is between 10 and 10.05.

(b) $\sin 46° \sim \frac{1}{2}\sqrt{2}(1 + \pi/180)$, where $\sim$ means "approximately equal." Is this estimate high or low?

(c) $\dfrac{x}{\sqrt{1 - x^2}} \geqslant \arcsin x \geqslant x \qquad$ if $\{0 \leqslant x < 1\}$.

When does equality hold?

(d) $1 - \dfrac{x}{2} \leqslant \dfrac{1}{\sqrt{1+x}} \leqslant 1 - \dfrac{x}{2(1+x)^{3/2}}$ if $x > -1$.

When does equality hold?

(e) $\log(1 + x^2) \leqslant x^2$ if $x \geqslant 0$.

(f) $\dfrac{\pi}{6} + \dfrac{2x-1}{\sqrt{3}} < \arcsin x < \dfrac{\pi}{6} + \dfrac{2x-1}{2\sqrt{1-x^2}}$ if $x > \dfrac{1}{2}$.

(g) $\dfrac{\log x}{x} < \dfrac{\log x'}{x} + \dfrac{1}{x'}$ if $0 < x' < x$.

7. Give an example of a function which is continuous at a point, but not differentiable there.

8. Use Theorem 3.6b to prove Theorem 3.6c.

9. Show that $f(x) = x^3$ defines a strictly increasing function. Compute $f'(0)$.

B EXERCISES

1. Find the one-sided derivatives [definition (1), Section 3.5] at $x = 0$ of the function given by

$$f(x) = \begin{cases} \dfrac{x}{1 + e^{1/x}} & x \neq 0 \\ 0 & x = 0. \end{cases}$$

2. Find the one-sided derivatives [definition (2), Section 3.5] at $x = 0$ of $x|\cot x| + \operatorname{sgn} x$.

3. Define the function f by

$$f(x) = \begin{cases} e^{-1/x} & x > 0 \\ 0 & x \leqslant 0. \end{cases}$$

Compute $f'(x)$ and $f''(x)$ for all x.

4. Compute the derivative of $f_1(x) g_2(x) - f_2(x) g_1(x)$, and hence prove that

$$\frac{d}{dx} \begin{vmatrix} f_1(x) & f_2(x) \\ g_1(x) & g_2(x) \end{vmatrix} = \begin{vmatrix} f_1'(x) & f_2'(x) \\ g_1(x) & g_2(x) \end{vmatrix} + \begin{vmatrix} f_1(x) & f_2(x) \\ g_1'(x) & g_2'(x) \end{vmatrix}.$$

5. State and prove a theorem which gives a sensible meaning to

$$\frac{dy}{dt} = \frac{dy}{dz}\frac{dz}{dx}\frac{dx}{dt}.$$

6. Use Theorem 3.6h to prove that $\dfrac{d}{dx}\sqrt{x} = \dfrac{1}{2\sqrt{x}}$.

7. Let f be a monotone function on an interval I with $f'(x) > 0$ everywhere in I. Show that if $f''(x_0)$ exists at a point x_0 in I, then $\phi''(y_0)$ exists where ϕ is the inverse function of f and $y_0 = f(x_0)$. Show, too, that $\phi''(y_0) = -f''(x_0)/[f'(x_0)]^3$. Also compute a formula for ϕ''' in terms of f''', f'', and f'.

8. If f and g have n^{th} derivatives, show that

$$\frac{d^n}{dx^n}[f(x)g(x)] = f^{(n)}(x)g(x) + nf^{(n-1)}(x)g'(x)$$

$$+ \frac{n(n-1)}{2}f^{(n-2)}(x)g''(x)$$

$$\ldots\ldots\ldots$$

$$+ nf'(x)g^{(n-1)}(x) + f(x)g^{(n)}(x),$$

where the coefficients are the binomial coefficients. (This formula is known as **Leibnitz' rule**.)

9. Define f by

$$f(x) = \begin{cases} x^2 \sin \dfrac{1}{x} & x \neq 0 \\ 0 & x = 0. \end{cases}$$

Show that

(a) $f'(0) = 0$.

(b) $f'(x) = 2x \sin 1/x - \cos 1/x$ $(x \neq 0)$, so that $f'(0)$ exists but $f'(x)$ is not continuous at $x = 0$.

10. Examine the function $f(x)$ given by

$$f(x) = \begin{cases} x^2 \sin \dfrac{1}{x^2} & x \neq 0 \\ 0 & x = 0. \end{cases}$$

Show that this is an example of a function which is everywhere differentiable, but which has an unbounded derivative.

11. For what values of α is f differentiable at $x = 0$ if

$$f(x) = \begin{cases} |x|^\alpha \sin \dfrac{1}{x} & x \neq 0 \\ 0 & x = 0. \end{cases}$$

12. Define f by

$$f(x) = \begin{cases} x^2 & x \text{ rational} \\ 0 & x \text{ irrational.} \end{cases}$$

Show that f is continuous at only one point and is differentiable there.

13. Suppose f is differentiable in an interval I, and let a be a point in I. Show that there is a sequence $\{x_n\}$ in I with $x_n \to a$ for which $f'(x_n) \to f'(a)$. (Use the mean-value theorem.)

14. Suppose it is known in Exercise 13 that $\lim_{x \to a} f'(x) = A$ exists. Show that $A = f'(a)$.

15. Show that $3x^4 + 4x^3 + c = 0$ can have at most one root less than or equal to -1, no matter what the value of c.

16. Show that if f is continuous in $\{0 \leqslant x < a\}$, $f(0) = 0$, $f'(x) > 0$ and increasing, then $f(x)/x$ is increasing.

17. If f is differentiable at $x = a$, compute

$$\lim_{h \to 0} \frac{f(a + \alpha h) - f(a + \beta h)}{h}.$$

C EXERCISES

1. Show that if $f'(x_0) > 0$, there is a neighborhood of x_0 in which

$$f(x) > f(x_0) \qquad \text{if } x > x_0$$
$$f(x) < f(x_0) \qquad \text{if } x < x_0.$$

In this situation we say that f is increasing at x_0. Does this mean $f(x)$ is monotone in this neighborhood? Give an example to show that it does not.

2. Show that the function f defined in Exercise B3 is infinitely differentiable for all x; that is, all derivatives exist.

3. We have seen that a derived function need not be continuous (Exercise B9). However, it does have the intermediate value property. Suppose that f is differentiable in $\{a \leqslant x \leqslant b\}$ and $f'(a) = A$ and $f'(b) = B$. Show that for any C between A and B there is a c between a and b for which $f'(c) = C$. [*Hint:* Examine $f(x) - C(x - a)$.]

4. Suppose $f(x)g'(x) - f'(x)g(x) \neq 0$ in an interval. Show that between two consecutive solutions of $f(x) = 0$ there is exactly one solution of $g(x) = 0$.

5. Prove that

$$\frac{d}{dx} \begin{vmatrix} f_{11}(x) & f_{12}(x) & \cdots & f_{1n}(x) \\ f_{21}(x) & f_{22}(x) & \cdots & f_{2n}(x) \\ & & \\ & & \\ & & \\ & & \\ & & \\ f_{n1}(x) & f_{n2}(x) & \cdots & f_{nn}(x) \end{vmatrix} = \sum_{k=1}^{n} \begin{vmatrix} f_{11}(x) & \cdots & f_{1n}(x) \\ & & \\ & & \\ f_{k1}'(x) & \cdots & f_{kn}'(x) \\ & & \\ & & \\ f_{n1}(x) & \cdots & f_{nn}(x) \end{vmatrix}.$$

6. Suppose f is defined for all x, is continuous and $\neq 0$ at $x = 0$, is differentiable at $x = 0$, and satisfies the functional equation $f(x + y) = f(x)f(y)$ for all x and y. Show that $f(x) = e^{cx}$ where $c = f'(0)$.

4

Integration

4.1 INTRODUCTION

We will now study the **Riemann integral**, which takes its name from the German mathematician B. Riemann, who was the first to remove the integral from a geometrical basis and put it on an arithmetical one. Though we follow this lead here, we will of course appeal to geometry for our intuitive ideas.

The integral is intimately and naturally bound up with the concept of area. However, we will base our concept of area on the integral, rather than the other way round. We begin with an heuristic discussion of area.

The area of even simple geometrical figures is not easy to define. Starting with the rectangle, whose area we take to be the product of its length times its width, we progress quickly to areas of triangles, and from them to areas of general polygons. However, when we consider the areas of figures with curvilinear boundaries, we have a deep and basic difficulty in deciding precisely what we mean by the area. If you will look at almost any elementary textbook on plane geometry, you will see that its discussion of the area of a circle is obscure and perhaps even a little mystical.

Our approach—and it is the standard one—is to approximate a given figure by appropriate polygons and to define the area of the figure in terms of the areas of the approximating polygons. We begin by considering a figure bounded by the lines $x = a$, $x = b$, the x-axis, and "curve" C given by $y = f(x)$, which we will suppose to be positive. We approximate the figure by polygons in two ways. We divide the segment $\{a \leqslant x \leqslant b\}$ of the x-axis into smaller segments, and upon each of these we erect a rectangle with its base on the x-axis and whose upper side lies everywhere below the curve. The rectangles so constructed form a polygon which is entirely contained in the given figure whose area we want to define. Any reasonable

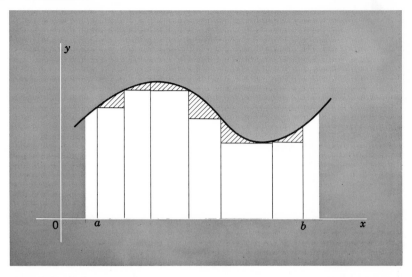

definition of area would have the area of this polygon less than the area of the figure.

Let us now construct a new polygon. On each sub-interval we place a rectangle whose upper side is always above the curve. These form a

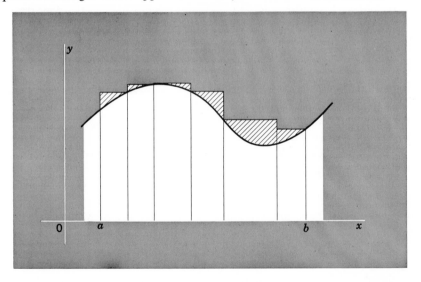

polygon which encloses the given figure, and hence we would expect it to have area larger than that of our figure under any reasonable definition ᵒf area.

If P is any polygon enclosing the figure and Q any polygon enclosed by the figure, then

$$A_P \geqslant A_Q,$$

where A_P means the area of P and A_Q the area of Q. Hence, for any Q, A_Q is a lower bound for the numbers A_P; thus

$$\bar{A} \equiv \inf A_P \geqslant A_Q$$

for every Q. Then $\bar{A}$ is an upper bound for the numbers A_Q, and hence

$$\bar{A} \geqslant \underline{A} \equiv \sup A_Q.$$

If it should turn out that $\bar{A} = \underline{A}$, then we will define the area of our figure to be their common value. If it should turn out that $\bar{A} > \underline{A}$, we do not define the area. All these things will be better understood after the formal definition of an integral.

4.2 PRELIMINARY LEMMAS

We want to lay the groundwork here for the definition of the integral of a function f defined on $\{a \leqslant x \leqslant b\}$. We proceed to set up certain standard notations and nomenclature which will be used consistently throughout the remainder of this chapter.

Our function f will be a bounded function defined on I: $\{a \leqslant x \leqslant b\}$, and M and m will be defined by

$$M = \sup_I f(x) \qquad m = \inf_I f(x).$$

By a **partition** P of I we will mean a finite sequence of numbers, $x_0, x_1, \ldots, x_n,$ where

$$a = x_0 < x_1 < \cdots < x_{n-1} < x_n = b.$$

The kth sub-interval of P, namely $\{x_{k-1} \leqslant x \leqslant x_k\}$, will be denoted by I_k; its length, $x_k - x_{k-1}$, will be denoted by $\Delta_k x$, and M_k and m_k will be defined by

$$M_k = \sup_{I_k} f(x) \qquad m_k = \inf_{I_k} f(x).$$

By the **norm** of the partition P, denoted by $\|P\|$, we will mean

$$\|P\| = \max_P \Delta_k x,$$

where this notation is to imply the maximum of all the lengths of all the sub-intervals formed by the partition P.

By a **lower sum** $\underline{S}_P(f)$ over the partition P, we shall mean

$$\underline{S}_P(f) = \sum_P m_k \Delta_k x;$$

and again this notation, $\sum\limits_P$, is meant to imply that the quantity $m_k \, \Delta_k \, x$ is computed for each I_k formed by P and then the sum of all these quantities is computed. We will sometimes suppress the f, and perhaps even sometimes the P, so that this may occur as

$$\underline{S}_P(f) \quad \text{or} \quad \underline{S}_P \quad \text{or} \quad \underline{S}.$$

The bar underneath is to signify that it is a lower sum. In case f is a positive function, a lower sum would represent geometrically the area of one of the enclosed polygons discussed in the previous section.

By an **upper sum**, $\bar{S}_P(f)$ over P we mean

$$\bar{S}_P(f) = \sum_P M_k \Delta_k x.$$

As in the case of a lower sum, the f and P may be suppressed when this may be done unambiguously. Geometrically, this represents the area of an enclosing polygon for positive f.

We now turn to a sequence of lemmas.

4.2a   Lemma. If f is bounded on I: $\{a \leqslant x \leqslant b\}$, then, for any partition P, we have

$$\bar{S}_P(f) \geqslant \underline{S}_P(f).$$

Proof. The proof follows immediately from $M_k \geqslant m_k$.   ∎

Next, we introduce the idea of a partition P' being a refinement of another partition P. We will say that P': $\{x_0', x_1', \ldots x_j'\}$ is a **refinement** of P: $\{x_0, x_1, \ldots x_n\}$ if every x_k occurring in P also occurs somewhere in P' as an x_p'; in other words, if P' can be constructed from P by distributing additional partition points between those already occurring:

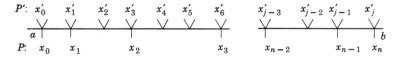

4.2b   Lemma. If f is bounded on I: $\{a \leqslant x \leqslant b\}$, and if P and P' are partitions of I, with P' a refinement of P, then

$$\bar{S}_{P'}(f) \leqslant \bar{S}_P(f)$$

and $\qquad\qquad \underline{S}_{P'}(f) \geqslant \underline{S}_P(f).$

That is, a refinement decreases upper sums and increases lower sums.

Proof. We prove the statement for upper sums, the one for lower sums being similar. To do so, we need only to look at one term in the expression for $\bar{S}_P$ which arises from a single interval I of P, and compare this term with the corresponding terms of $\bar{S}_{P'}$, that is, with those arising from I_k in the refinement. For simplicity, we suppose that there is only one P' point in I_k. The contribution to $\bar{S}_P$ from this interval is

$$M_k \, \Delta_k \, x = M_k(x_k - x_{k-1}).$$

Suppose $x_p{}' = x_k$. Then x'_{p-1} is the intermediate point and $x'_{p-2} = x_{k-1}$.

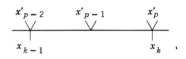

The contribution to $\bar{S}_{P'}$ arising from I_k is

$$M'_{p-1}(x'_{p-1} - x'_{p-2}) + M_p{}'(x_p{}' - x'_{p-1}),$$

where of course $M_p{}' = \sup_{I_{p'}} f(x)$ and so forth. But $M_p{}'$ and $M'_{p-1} \leqslant M_k$, since $I_p{}'$ and I'_{p-1} are both contained in I_p. Hence

$$M'_{p-1}(x'_{p-1} - x'_{p-2}) + M'_p(x_p{}' - x'_{p-1})$$
$$\leqslant M_k(x'_{p-1} - x'_{p-2}) + M_k(x_p{}' - x'_{p-1})$$
$$= M_k(x_p{}' - x'_{p-2}) = M_k(x_k - x_{k-1}).$$

Thus the contribution to $\bar{S}_{P'}$ from I_k is less than or equal to the contribution to $\bar{S}_P$. It is clear that the same will be true no matter how many intermediate points of P' occur in I_k. (We could give an induction proof.) Summing over all intervals of P, we get the desired inequality. ∎

4.2c   Lemma. If f is bounded on $I: \{a \leqslant x \leqslant b\}$, and if P and P' are any two partitions of I, then

$$\bar{S}_P(f) \geqslant \underline{S}_{P'}(f).$$

Proof. This is very easy to prove. Let P'' be the common refinement of P and P' formed by taking as partition points all points which occur in P and P'. Then

$$\bar{S}_P \geqslant \bar{S}_{P''} \geqslant \underline{S}_{P''} \geqslant \underline{S}_{P'}.$$

The first and last inequalities are by Lemma 4.2b and the middle one by Lemma 4.2a. ∎

Our series of lemmas has now established the following facts. For any bounded function f, the class of numbers formed by the upper sums has as a lower bound any lower sum, and conversely the class of lower sums has any upper sum as an upper bound. Thus

$$\inf \bar{S}_P \geqslant \underline{S}_{P'}$$

for any partition P'. Thus $\inf \bar{S}_P$ is an upper bound for the lower sums, so that

$$\inf \bar{S}_P \geqslant \sup \underline{S}_{P'}.$$

Now $\inf \bar{S}_P(f)$ is called the **upper Riemann-Darboux integral** of f over I: $\{a \leqslant x \leqslant b\}$, and $\sup \underline{S}_{P'}(f)$ the **lower Riemann-Darboux integral** of f over I. They are written

$$\inf \bar{S}_P(f) = \overline{\int_a^b} f(x)\, dx$$

$$\sup \underline{S}_P(f) = \underline{\int_a^b} f(x)\, dx.$$

We will refer to them simply as the **upper and lower integrals.** We have therefore proved the following lemma.

4.2d   Lemma. If f is a bounded function over I,

$$\overline{\int_a^b} f(x)\, dx \geqslant \underline{\int_a^b} f(x)\, dx.$$

4.2e   Lemma. If f is bounded on I: $\{a \leqslant x \leqslant b\}$, and if M and m are upper and lower bounds for f on I, then

$$m(b - a) \leqslant \underline{\int_a^b} f(x)\, dx \leqslant \overline{\int_a^b} f(x)\, dx \leqslant M(b - a).$$

Proof. The proof is left as an exercise (B5).

4.2f   Lemma. If f is bounded on I: $\{a \leqslant x \leqslant b\}$, then for any constant c

$$\overline{\int_a^b} [f(x) + c]\, dx = \overline{\int_a^b} f(x)\, dx + c(b - a)$$

and $$\underline{\int_a^b} [f(x) + c]\, dx = \underline{\int_a^b} f(x)\, dx + c(b - a).$$

Proof. For any partition P, let

$$\mathcal{M}_k = \sup_{I_k} [f(x) + c], \qquad M_k = \sup_{I_k} f(x).$$

Then $\mathcal{M}_k = M_k + c$. Multiplying by $\Delta_k x$ and summing, we get

$$\bar{S}_P(f + c) = \bar{S}_P(f) + c(b - a).$$

Taking infima of both sides gives us the result for upper integrals. A similar argument works for lower integrals.   ∎

We turn next to an addition formula for upper and lower integrals.

4.2g   Lemma. If f is a bounded function on $I: \{a \leqslant x \leqslant b\}$, and c is an intermediate point, then

$$\overline{\int_a^b} f(x)\,dx = \overline{\int_a^c} f(x)\,dx + \overline{\int_c^b} f(x)\,dx$$

and $$\underline{\int_a^b} f(x)\,dx = \underline{\int_a^c} f(x)\,dx + \underline{\int_c^b} f(x)\,dx.$$

Proof. We will give the proof for upper integrals; that for lower integrals is similar. We indicate the interval over which an upper sum is taken by writing the end points as limits on $\bar{S}$ as with integrals, so that $\bar{S}_a{}^b$ and $\bar{S}_a{}^c$ will represent, respectively, an upper sum over the interval $\{a \leqslant x \leqslant b\}$ and one over $\{a \leqslant x \leqslant c\}$.

Let P be any partition over $\{a \leqslant x \leqslant b\}$. Then it may or may not have a partition point at c. If it does, fine; if not, refine P by introducing a partition point at c. Then if P' be the new partition, it induces also partitions of $\{a \leqslant x \leqslant c\}$ and $\{c \leqslant x \leqslant b\}$. Thus

$$\bar{S}_{aP}^{b} \geqslant \bar{S}_{aP'}^{b} = \bar{S}_a{}^c + \bar{S}_c{}^b \geqslant \overline{\int_a^c} f(x)\,dx + \overline{\int_c^b} f(x)\,dx.$$

The two integrals on the right form a lower bound for all the upper sums on the left. Hence

(1) $$\overline{\int_a^b} f(x)\,dx \geqslant \overline{\int_a^c} f(x)\,dx + \overline{\int_c^b} f(x)\,dx.$$

Now for any $\epsilon > 0$, there are partitions of $\{a \leqslant x \leqslant c\}$ and $\{c \leqslant x \leqslant b\}$ for which

$$\bar{S}_a{}^c < \overline{\int_a^c} f(x)\,dx + \frac{\epsilon}{2} \quad \text{and} \quad \bar{S}_c{}^b < \overline{\int_c^b} f(x)\,dx + \frac{\epsilon}{2}$$

since the integrals are the infima of such sums. Now these two partitions together form a partition of $\{a \leqslant x \leqslant b\}$, so that for these partitions we have

$$\bar{S}_a{}^b = \bar{S}_a{}^c + \bar{S}_c{}^b < \overline{\int_a^c} f(x)\,dx + \overline{\int_c^b} f(x)\,dx + \epsilon.$$

But the sum on the left is an upper bound for the upper integral over $\{a \leqslant x \leqslant b\}$, so that

$$\overline{\int_a^b} f(x) \, dx \;\leqslant\; \overline{\int_a^c} f(x) \, dx + \overline{\int_c^b} f(x) \, dx + \epsilon.$$

Since this inequality holds for every $\epsilon > 0$, we conclude that

(2) $$\overline{\int_a^b} f(x) \, dx \;\leqslant\; \overline{\int_a^c} f(x) \, dx + \overline{\int_c^b} f(x) \, dx.$$

Inequalities (1) and (2) combine to give the conclusion. ∎

4.2h   Lemma. Suppose f is bounded on $I:\{a \leqslant x \leqslant b\}$. Let F and G be defined on I by

$$F(x) = \overline{\int_a^x} f(t) \, dt \quad \text{and} \quad G(x) = \underline{\int_a^x} f(t) \, dt \qquad \{a < x \leqslant b\},$$

and let

$$F(a) = G(a) = 0.$$

Then $$F'(x_0) = G'(x_0) = f(x_0)$$

at each point x_0 of I at which f is continuous. (At a and b, the derivatives are of course one-sided.)

Proof. At such a point x_0 we examine the difference quotient

$$\frac{\Delta F}{\Delta x} = \frac{F(x_0 + h) - F(x_0)}{h} = \begin{cases} \dfrac{1}{h} \overline{\int_{x_0}^{x_0+h}} f(t) \, dt & \text{if } h > 0 \\[2mm] -\dfrac{1}{h} \overline{\int_{x_0+h}^{x_0}} f(t) \, dt & \text{if } h < 0, \end{cases}$$

the last equality by Lemma 4.2g. For definiteness, we will assume that h is positive; the other case is quite similar. By Lemma 4.2f,

$$\frac{\Delta F}{\Delta x} - f(x_0) = \frac{1}{h} \overline{\int_{x_0}^{x_0+h}} \big[f(t) - f(x_0) \big] \, dt.$$

Then, by Lemma 4.2e,

$$\frac{1}{h} h \inf_{|t-x_0| \leqslant h} \big[f(t) - f(x_0) \big] \leqslant \frac{\Delta F}{\Delta x} - f(x_0) \leqslant \frac{1}{h} h \sup_{|t-x_0| \leqslant h} \big[f(t) - f(x_0) \big]$$

By the continuity of f at x_0, both sides go to zero as $h \to 0$.

Hence $$F'(x_0) = f(x_0).$$

Similarly, $$G'(x_0) = f(x_0). \qquad \blacksquare$$

4.3 THE RIEMANN INTEGRAL

If f is a bounded function on $I:\{a \leqslant x \leqslant b\}$ and

$$\underline{\int_a^b} f(x)\, dx = \overline{\int_a^b} f(x)\, dx,$$

then we will say that f is **Riemann-integrable** on I and the common value of the upper and lower integrals will be called the **Riemann integral** of f over I. For brevity, we will simply call it the **integral** of f over I; or, to distinguish it from the indefinite integral, we will sometimes call it the **definite integral** of f over I. We will denote its value by an integral sign without the bar. Thus, for an integrable function f, we have

$$\underline{\int_a^b} f(x)\, dx = \overline{\int_a^b} f(x)\, dx = \int_a^b f(x)\, dx.$$

It is perhaps not clear at this stage whether all functions, or for that matter whether any functions, are integrable. The situation is that some are and some are not. The following theorems and examples illustrate this.

4.3a   Theorem. If f is monotone on $I:\{a \leqslant x \leqslant b\}$, it is integrable there.

Proof. Suppose, for definiteness, that f is non-decreasing. Then, for any partition P, we have

$$0 \leqslant \overline{\int_a^b} f(x)\, dx - \underline{\int_a^b} f(x)\, dx$$

$$\leqslant \bar{S}_P - \underline{S}_P$$

$$= \sum_P (M_k - m_k)\, \Delta_k x$$

$$\leqslant \|P\| \sum_P (M_k - m_k).$$

Since f is non-decreasing, we have in each sub-interval I_k that $M_k = f(x_k)$ and $m_k = f(x_{k-1})$, so that

$$\sum_P (M_k - m_k) = \sum_P [f(x_k) - f(x_{k-1})] = f(b) - f(a).$$

If $f(b) = f(a)$, then f is constant and the integrability is clear. If $f(b) \neq f(a)$, then, given $\epsilon > 0$, choose $\delta = \epsilon/[f(b) - f(a)]$. If $\|P\| < \delta$ we have

$$0 \leqslant \overline{\int_a^b} f(x)\, dx - \underline{\int_a^b} f(x)\, dx \leqslant \epsilon.$$

This holds for every $\epsilon > 0$. Hence the two are equal, and integrability follows. ∎

4.3b Theorem. If f is continuous on $I:\{a \leqslant x \leqslant b\}$, then it is integrable there.

Proof. Define F and G as in Lemma 4.2h; that is,

$$F(x) = \overline{\int_a^x} f(t)\, dt \qquad \text{and} \qquad G(x) = \underline{\int_a^x} f(t)\, dt \qquad \{a < x \leqslant b\}.$$

and
$$F(a) = G(a) = 0.$$

By Lemma 4.2h, $\quad F'(x) = G'(x) \qquad$ for all x in I.

Then, by Corollary 3.6f (a corollary of the mean-value theorem) we have $F(x) = G(x) + c$ in I. But $F(a) = G(a)$, so that $c = 0$. Thus $F(x) = G(x)$ in I, in particular at $x = b$. Thus

$$\overline{\int_a^b} f(t)\, dt = F(b) = G(b) = \underline{\int_a^b} f(t)\, dt. \qquad \blacksquare$$

We pause now to give an example of a non-integrable function. This example depends on the fact that in every interval there are both rational numbers and irrational numbers. (See Exercises C3 and C4 of Section 1.6.) The function we examine is given by

$$f(x) = \begin{cases} 0 & \text{if } x \text{ is rational} \\ 1 & \text{if } x \text{ is irrational.} \end{cases}$$

For any partition P of $I:\{a \leqslant x \leqslant b\}$, we have

$$\bar{S}_P = \sum_P M_k \Delta_k x = \sum_P 1 \cdot \Delta_k x = b - a,$$

so that
$$\overline{\int_a^b} f(x)\, dx = (b - a).$$

And
$$\underline{S}_P = \sum_P m_k \Delta_k x = \sum_P 0 \cdot \Delta_k x = 0;$$

hence
$$\underline{\int_a^b} f(x)\, dx = 0.$$

Thus the upper and lower integrals are not equal if $b > a$, so that f is not integrable.

We now give a useful criterion for integrability which is due to Darboux.

4.3c Theorem. A necessary and sufficient condition that a function f be integrable on $I:\{a \leqslant x \leqslant b\}$ is that for each $\epsilon > 0$ there is a partition P for which

$$\bar{S}_P(f) - \underline{S}_P(f) < \epsilon.$$

Proof. Sufficiency. If the ϵ-condition holds, then

$$0 \leqslant \overline{\int_a^b} f(x)\, dx - \underline{\int_a^b} f(x)\, dx \leqslant \bar{S}_P - \underline{S}_P < \epsilon,$$

so that the upper and lower integrals are equal.

Necessity. If f is integrable, choose a P such that

(1)
$$\bar{S}_P < \int_a^b f(x)\, dx + \epsilon/2.$$

This is possible, since the integral is the infimum of the upper sums. similarly, there is a P' such that

(2)
$$\underline{S}_{P'} > \int_a^b f(x)\, dx - \epsilon/2.$$

Let P'' be the common refinement of P and P'. Then $\bar{S}_{P''}$ satisfies (1) and $\underline{S}_{P''}$ satisfies (2), so that we get

$$\bar{S}_{P''} - \underline{S}_{P''} < \epsilon. \qquad \blacksquare$$

The following lemma is to prepare the ground for another necessary and sufficient condition that the integral exist.

4.3d Lemma. If f is bounded on $I:\{a \leqslant x \leqslant b\}$, then for each $\epsilon > 0$ there is a $\delta(\epsilon)$ for which

$$\bar{S}_P(f) < \overline{\int_a^b} f(x)\, dx + \epsilon \quad \text{and} \quad \underline{S}_P(f) > \underline{\int_a^b} f(x)\, dx - \epsilon$$

for every partition P for which $\|P\| < \delta$.

Proof. We prove the first point. The second is similar.

Let $\epsilon > 0$ be given. By the definition of the upper integral, there is a partition P' for which

$$\bar{S}_{P'} < \overline{\int_a^b} f(x)\, dx + \epsilon/2.$$

Having chosen P', we count the number of partition points it has inside the interval I. Suppose this number is n. Also, let δ_1 be the least length of any of the sub-intervals of P'. Now we choose δ to be less than the smaller of the two numbers δ_1 and $\epsilon/6Mn$:

$$\delta < \min[\delta_1, \epsilon/6Mn],$$

where this time $M = \sup_I |f(x)|$.

Now let P be an arbitrarily chosen partition with $\|P\| < \delta$. We want to show that for this P the conclusion of the theorem holds. Let P'' be the common refinement of P and P'. Then, by Lemma 4.2,

$$(3) \qquad \bar{S}_{P''} \leqslant \bar{S}_{P'} < \int_a^{\overline{b}} f(x)\,dx + \epsilon/2.$$

By our choice of δ, there is at most one point of P' between any two of P. Thus we separate the sub-intervals of P into two classes: (1) those which contain a point of P'; and (2) those which do not.

The intervals of P'' are likewise separated into two classes: (1) those which arose from an interval of P by its containing a point of P'; and (2) all others, these being identical with those of class 2 above.

Thus when we compare $\bar{S}_P$ and $\bar{S}_{P''}$, we see that in the difference $\bar{S}_P - \bar{S}_{P''}$ all contributions from intervals of class 2 cancel out. What remains is the contribution to each sum from intervals of class 1. In P there are at most n intervals in class 1, since there are at most n interior points of P'. Hence there are at most $2n$ intervals in P'' in class 2. The contribution of each of these intervals is of the form $M_k\,\Delta_k\,x$ and clearly $|M_k\,\Delta_k\,x| \leqslant M\,\delta$. There are, as we have seen, at most $3n$ of these altogether. Hence

$$|\bar{S}_P - \bar{S}_{P''}| \leqslant 3nM\,\delta < \epsilon/2.$$

But P'' is a refinement of P, so that

$$(4) \qquad 0 \leqslant \bar{S}_P - \bar{S}_{P''} = |\bar{S}_P - \bar{S}_{P''}| < \epsilon/2.$$

By (3) and (4), we get

$$\bar{S}_P = \bar{S}_{P''} + (\bar{S}_P - \bar{S}_{P''}) < \int_a^{\overline{b}} f(x)\,dx + \epsilon/2 + \epsilon/2$$

or
$$\bar{S}_P < \int_a^{\overline{b}} f(x)\,dx + \epsilon. \qquad \blacksquare$$

Let us now consider a slightly different type of sum which is not necessarily either an upper sum or a lower sum, but which always lies between them. Given a partition P of an interval $I:\{a \leqslant x \leqslant b\}$, we choose a point ξ_k in each sub-interval $I_k:\{x_{k-1} \leqslant x \leqslant x_k\}$. The sum

$$S_P(f, \xi) = \sum_P f(\xi_k)\,\Delta_k\,x$$

will be called a **Riemann sum** or an **approximating sum**. We want to consider the limit of such sums as $\|P\| \to 0$. You should understand that this is a somewhat more complicated type of limit than we have dealt with before. The sum is in no sense a function of $\|P\|$, for $\|P\|$ does not even determine P itself; and after P is chosen the ξ's may then be freely chosen in the sub-intervals. However, $\|P\|$ does have some influence over the range of possible values such a sum may have. We now define this type of limit precisely.

If there is a number J such that for each $\epsilon > 0$ there is a $\delta > 0$ for which

$$|S_P(f, \xi) - J| < \epsilon$$

whenever $\|P\| < \delta$, then we say that J is the limit of these Riemann sums as $\|P\| \to 0$ and express this by

$$\lim_{\|P\| \to 0} S_P(f, \xi) = J.$$

This definition reads like the definition of a limit of a function. However, it is to be emphasized that the ϵ-condition must be satisfied for all choices of the partition points of P consistent with $\|P\| < \delta$ and for all choices of the ξ's.

We now demonstrate the connection between this limit and the Riemann integral.

4.3e   Theorem. If f is bounded on $I:\{a \leqslant x \leqslant b\}$, a necessary and sufficient condition that the integral of f over I exists and equals J is that

$$\lim_{\|P\| \to 0} S_P(f, \xi) = J.$$

Proof. Necessity. We assume that the integral exists and equals J. Then, by Lemma 4.3d, for each $\epsilon > 0$, there is a δ such that

$$-\epsilon + \bar{S}_P < J < \underline{S}_P + \epsilon$$

whenever $\|P\| < \delta$. Then for any such P and any choice of ξ's, we have

$$J - \epsilon < \underline{S}_P \leqslant S_P(f, \xi) \leqslant \bar{S}_P < J + \epsilon.$$

But this says that

$$|S_P(f, \xi) - J| < \epsilon \quad \text{if} \quad \|P\| < \delta.$$

Sufficiency. Suppose the limit exists and equals J. Then for each $\epsilon > 0$, there is a δ such that if $\|P\| < \delta$

$$(5) \qquad J - \epsilon < S_P(f, \xi) < J + \epsilon$$

for any choice of ξ's. Then in each I_k of P choose ξ_k such that

$$f(\xi_k) > M_k - \epsilon/(b - a).$$

Then

$$S_P(f, \xi) = \sum_P f(\xi_k) \Delta_k x > \sum_P M_k \Delta_k x - \epsilon.$$

By the upper inequality of (5), we then have

$$J + \epsilon > S_P(f, \xi) > \bar{S}_P - \epsilon > \overline{\int_a^b} f(x)\, dx - \epsilon$$

or

$$J > \overline{\int_a^b} f(x)\, dx - 2\epsilon \quad \text{for every } \epsilon.$$

Thus
$$J \geqslant \overline{\int_a^b} f(x)\, dx.$$

By a similar argument, we get
$$J \leqslant \underline{\int_a^b} f(x)\, dx,$$

so that
$$\underline{\int_a^b} f(x)\, dx \geqslant J \geqslant \overline{\int_a^b} f(x)\, dx.$$

Since the upper integral by definition is not less than the lower, this completes the proof. ∎

EXAMPLE. Compute $\displaystyle\int_0^a x\, dx.$

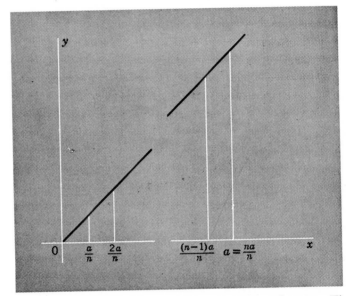

Solution. The integrand is both monotone and continuous. The existence of the integral is clear by either Theorem 4.3a or 4.3b. And since, by Theorem 4.3e, the integral is the limit of the Riemann sums, we take a simple partition $P:\{0, a/n, 2a/n, \ldots, na/n\}$. Then a Riemann sum, in fact the upper sum, is
$$S_n = \sum_{k=1}^n \left(\frac{ka}{n}\right) \cdot \left(\frac{a}{n}\right) = \frac{a^2}{n^2} \sum_1^n k = \frac{a^2}{n^2}\frac{n}{2}(n+1).$$

Now, as $\|P\| \to 0$, $n \to \infty$ and $S_n \to a^2/2$. Thus
$$\int_0^a x\, dx = a^2/2.$$

If it should happen that f is continuous in $\{a \leqslant x \leqslant b\}$ except at $x = a$, then for every c for which $a < c < b$, the integral $\int_c^b f(x)\,dx$ will exist. We can then inquire into the existence of $\lim\limits_{c \to a+0} \int_c^b f(x)\,dx$.

If this limit exists, we say that it defines the **improper integral** of f from a to b. We write this in the same way as an ordinary or proper integral. Similarly, $\int_a^\infty f(x)\,dx$ is defined as

$$\lim_{b \to \infty} \int_a^b f(x)\,dx$$

if the limit exists. If an improper integral exists, we say it **converges.** Improper integrals are discussed in some detail in Chapter 17.

Let us return briefly to the question of area. If f is a positive function on the interval $I:\{a \leqslant x \leqslant b\}$, we define the area between the "curve" $y = f(x)$, the ordinates $x = a$, $x = b$, and the x-axis to be

$$A = \int_a^b f(x)\,dx,$$

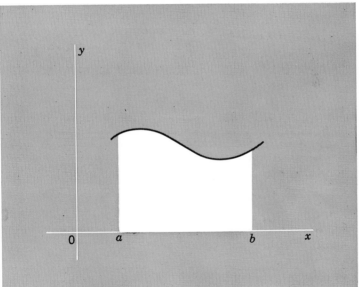

if this integral exists. In particular, we know by Theorems 4.3a and 4.3b that if f is continuous or monotone, then the area exists. Generalizing, we can interpret this $\int_a^b f(x)\,dx$ as the "net" area between $x = a$, $x = b$, the x-axis, and the "curve" $y = f(x)$, the area being taken as positive when it lies above the x-axis and negative when it lies below.

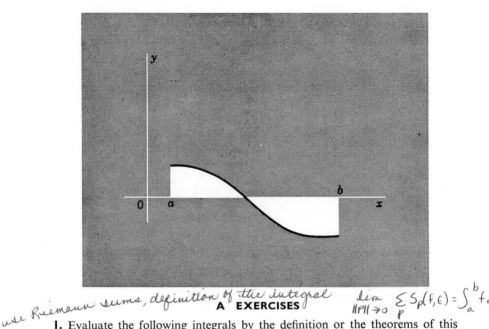

use Riemann sums, definition of the integral $\lim\limits_{\|P\| \to 0} \sum\limits_P S_P(f, \epsilon) = \int_a^b f.$

A EXERCISES

1. Evaluate the following integrals by the definition or the theorems of this section:

(a) $\displaystyle\int_a^b x \, dx$ (b) $\displaystyle\int_a^b x^2 \, dx$ (c) $\displaystyle\int_a^b e^x \, dx$

(d) $\displaystyle\int_1^2 \frac{dx}{x^2}$ (*Hint:* Show that you can choose $\xi_k = \sqrt{x_k}\sqrt{x_{k-1}}$.)

2. A function f defined on an interval $\{-a \leqslant x \leqslant a\}$ is said to be **even** if $f(-x) = f(x)$, and **odd** if $f(-x) = -f(x)$. Show that, if f is integrable, then

$$\int_{-a}^a f(x) \, dx = 2\int_0^a f(x) \, dx \qquad \text{if } f \text{ is even}$$

and $\displaystyle\int_{-a}^a f(x) \, dx = 0 \qquad \text{if } f \text{ is odd.}$

B EXERCISES

1. Suppose f is continuous on $I: \{a \leqslant x \leqslant b\}$ and $\displaystyle\int_a^x f(t) \, dt = x$ for every x in I. Find f. Also find a.

2. Evaluate $\displaystyle\lim_{x \to 0} \frac{x}{1 - e^{x^2}} \int_0^x e^{t^2} \, dt.$

3. Evaluate $\lim\limits_{n \to \infty} \sum\limits_{k=1}^{n} \dfrac{1}{n+k}$. (*Hint:* Write it as a Riemann sum, and express the answer as an integral.)

4. Evaluate $\lim\limits_{n \to \infty} \sum\limits_{k=1}^{n} \dfrac{k}{n^2 + k^2}$. *check notes for ex.*

5. Prove Lemma 4.2e.

C EXERCISES

I. Suppose f is bounded on $I : \{a \leqslant x \leqslant b\}$ and is continuous there except for one point c. Show that f is integrable on I. What if f has a finite number of such discontinuities?

2. Let f be given by

$$f(x) = \begin{cases} \sin \dfrac{1}{x} & x \neq 0, \\ 16 & x = 0. \end{cases}$$

Is f integrable on $\{-1 \leqslant x \leqslant 1\}$?

3. A function f defined on an interval $I : \{a \leqslant x \leqslant b\}$ is called a **step function** if there is a partition P of I for which f is constant on each sub-interval of P. Show that any step function is integrable and that, in particular upper sums and lower sums are integrals of step functions.

4. Suppose f is bounded on $I : \{a \leqslant x \leqslant b\}$ and is integrable on $\{c \leqslant x \leqslant b\}$ for every c between a and b. Show that it is integrable on I.

4.4 PROPERTIES OF THE DEFINITE INTEGRAL

We have not defined the definite integral when the upper limit of integration is less than or equal to the lower. Accordingly, we define

$$\int_a^a f(x)\, dx = 0$$

$$\int_b^a f(x)\, dx = -\int_a^b f(x)\, dx.$$

We now establish the certain properties of integrals and integrable functions.

4.4a Theorem. If f is integrable on $\{a \leqslant x \leqslant b\}$, then it is integrable on $\{c \leqslant x \leqslant d\}$ where $\{a \leqslant c < d \leqslant b\}$. That is, f is integrable on every sub-interval.

Proof:

$$0 \leqslant \overline{\int_c^d} f(x)\, dx - \underline{\int_c^d} f(x)\, dx \leqslant \overline{\int_a^b} f(x)\, dx - \underline{\int_a^b} f(x)\, dx = 0$$

The last equality by the definition of integrability on $\{a \leqslant x \leqslant b\}$. Explain the second inequality, (see Exercise B1). Hence the upper and lower integrals on $\{c \leqslant x \leqslant d\}$ are equal. ∎

4.4b   Theorem. If f is integrable on $\{a \leqslant x \leqslant b\}$, and c is an intermediate point, then

$$\int_a^b f(x)\,dx = \int_a^c f(x)\,dx + \int_c^b f(x)\,dx.$$

Proof. The proof of this theorem follows immediately from Lemma 4.2g. ∎

In fact, this relation is valid no matter what the order of the three points a, b, c. Why?

4.4c   Theorem. If f is integrable on $I:\{a \leqslant x \leqslant b\}$, and if c is a constant, then cf is integrable there and

$$\int_a^b cf(x)\,dx = c\int_a^b f(x)\,dx.$$

4.4d   Theorem. If f and g are integrable on $I:\{a \leqslant x \leqslant b\}$, and if $f(x) \geqslant g(x)$ there, then

$$\int_a^b f(x)\,dx \geqslant \int_a^b g(x)\,dx.$$

4.4e   Theorem. If f and g are integrable on $I:\{a \leqslant x \leqslant b\}$, so is $f \pm g$ and

$$\int_a^b [f(x) \pm g(x)]\,dx = \int_a^b f(x)\,dx \pm \int_a^b g(x)\,dx.$$

The proofs of the three previous theorems are left to the exercises (Exercise B2), since they are quite simple. Instead of using upper and lower sums, use Riemann sums to approximate the integrals.

Before proceeding to the next theorem, it will be convenient to set up some notations. Given a function f, we define the corresponding functions f^+ and f^- by

$$f^+(x) = \begin{cases} f(x) & f(x) \geqslant 0 \\ 0 & f(x) < 0 \end{cases}$$

and

$$f^-(x) = \begin{cases} 0 & f(x) \geqslant 0 \\ -f(x) & f(x) < 0. \end{cases}$$

Then clearly we have

$$f(x) = f^+(x) - f^-(x)$$

and

$$|f(x)| = f^+(x) + f^-(x).$$

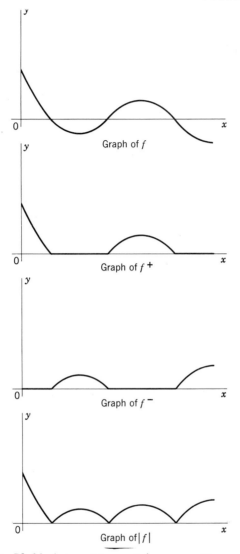

Graph of f

Graph of f^+

Graph of f^-

Graph of $|f|$

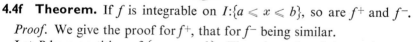

4.4f   Theorem. If f is integrable on $I:\{a \leqslant x \leqslant b\}$, so are f^+ and f^-.

Proof. We give the proof for f^+, that for f^- being similar.

Let P be a partition of $\{a \leqslant x \leqslant b\}$. Then, in each sub-interval I_k, we will set

$$M_k = \sup_{I_k} f(x) \qquad M_k{}^+ = \sup_{I_k} f^+(x)$$
$$m_k = \inf_{I_k} f(x) \qquad m_k{}^+ = \inf_{I_k} f^+(x).$$

To see that $M_k - m_k \geq M_k^+ - m_k^+$, we distinguish three cases:

(1) $M_k \geq 0$, $m_k \geq 0$. Then $M_k = M_k^+$, $m_k = m_k^+$, so that

$$M_k - m_k = M_k^+ - m_k^+.$$

(2) $M_k \geq 0$, $m_k \leq 0$. Then $M_k^+ = M_k$, $m_k \leq m_k^+$, so that

$$M_k - m_k \geq M_k^+ - m_k^+.$$

(3) $M_k \leq 0$, $m_k \leq 0$. Then $M_k^+ = m_k^+ = 0$, so that

$$M_k - m_k \geq M_k^+ - m_k^+ = 0.$$

Thus we have

$$M_k - m_k \geq M_k^+ - m_k^+.$$

If we multiply by $\Delta_k x$ and sum over P, we have for every partition P

$$\bar{S}_P(f) - \underline{S}_P(f) \geq \bar{S}_P(f^+) - \underline{S}_P(f^+).$$

Now, given $\epsilon > 0$, by Theorem 4.3c, there is a partition P for which the left-hand side of this inequality is $< \epsilon$. Then, since the right side is also $< \epsilon$, we have by Theorem 4.3c again that f^+ is integrable. ∎

4.4g Theorem. If f is integrable on $I:\{a \leq x \leq b\}$, then so is $|f|$ and

$$\left| \int_a^b f(x)\, dx \right| \leq \int_a^b |f(x)|\, dx.$$

Proof. Clearly $|f(x)| = f^+(x) + f^-(x)$, so that, by Theorem 4.4e, $|f|$ is integrable and

$$\int_a^b |f(x)|\, dx = \int_a^b f^+(x)\, dx + \int_a^b f^-(x)\, dx.$$

Since $\int_a^b f^-(x)\, dx \geq 0$ (how do we know this?), we subtract twice this value from the previous formula to get

$$\int_a^b |f(x)|\, dx \geq \int_a^b f^+(x)\, dx - \int_a^b f^-(x)\, dx = \int_a^b f(x)\, dx.$$

Similarly, subtracting $2 \int_a^b f^+(x)\, dx$, we get

$$\int_a^b |f(x)|\, dx \geq - \int_a^b f(x)\, dx.$$

These last two inequalities establish the theorem. ∎

4.4h Theorem. If f and g are integrable on $\{a \leq x \leq b\}$, so is their product $f \cdot g$.

Proof. Suppose first that both f and g are positive. Let P be any partition of I. Then, in each sub-interval I_k, we define

$$M_{fg} = \sup_{I_k} f(x)g(x) \qquad M_f = \sup_{I_k} f(x) \qquad M_g = \sup_{I_k} g(x)$$

$$m_{fg} = \inf_{I_k} f(x)g(x) \qquad m_f = \inf_{I_k} f(x) \qquad m_g = \inf_{I_k} g(x),$$

and let $B_f = \sup_I f(x)$, $B_g = \sup_I g(x)$. Then in I_k, $M_{fg} \leqslant M_f M_g$ and $m_{fg} \geqslant m_f m_g$. Thus

$$\begin{aligned}
M_{fg} - m_{fg} &\leqslant M_f M_g - m_f m_g \\
&= M_f M_g - M_f m_g + M_f m_g - m_f m_g \\
&= M_f[M_g - m_g] + m_g[M_f - m_f] \\
&\leqslant B_f[M_g - m_g] + B_g[M_f - m_f].
\end{aligned}$$

If we multiply by $\Delta_k x$ and sum, we get

$$\bar{S}_P(fg) - \underline{S}_P(fg) \leqslant B_f[\bar{S}_P(g) - \underline{S}_P(g)] + B_g[\bar{S}_P(f) - \underline{S}_P(f)].$$

From this inequality follows the integrability of fg, since the right-hand side can be made less than any given ϵ by the integrability of f and g separately.

Then, given f and g not necessarily positive, we can write

$$fg = (f^+ - f^-)(g^+ - g^-) = f^+ g^+ - f^- g^+ - f^+ g^- + f^- g^-.$$

By the first part of this theorem, each product on the right is integrable, as is the whole right-hand side by Theorem 4.4e. ∎

4.5 THE FUNDAMENTAL THEOREM OF CALCULUS

Suppose f is integrable in $I:\{a \leqslant x \leqslant b\}$. It is then an immediate consequence of Lemma 4.2h that

$$\frac{d}{dx} \int_a^x f(t)\, dt = f(x)$$

at each point x in I at which f is continuous. In particular, if f is continuous in I, then this equation holds at all points of I. A function F with the property that $F'(x) = f(x)$ at every point x of I is called a **primitive** of f or an **indefinite integral** of f. Thus, for a continuous f, we see that

$$F(x) = \int_a^x f(t)\, dt$$

is a primitive of f. We are led immediately to ask if there are other primitives. The answer is yes; for any constant c, $F + c$ is also a primitive. But, by Corollary 3.6f, this must give all primitives; for if we have two such functions, say F and G, then $F'(x) = G'(x) = f(x)$ in I and by Corollary 3.6f they differ by a constant. This is essentially the **fundamental theorem** of **calculus**, which we now state precisely.

4.5a   Theorem. If f is continuous on I, and G is a primitive (indefinite integral) of f, then

$$\int_a^b f(x)\, dx = G(b) - G(a).$$

Proof. Let F be given by

$$F(x) = \int_a^x f(t)\, dt.$$

Then, as we saw in the last paragraph, $F(x) = G(x) + c$. We can determine c. Since $F(a) = 0$, we get $c = -G(a)$, so that

$$F(x) = G(x) - G(a).$$

In particular, $F(b) = \displaystyle\int_a^b f(x)\, dx = G(b) - G(a).$ ∎

Using the common notation

$$G(x)\Big|_a^b = G(b) - G(a),$$

the fundamental theorem can then be stated as

$$\int_a^b f(x)\, dx = G(x)\Big|_a^b.$$

With this theorem as a background, it is natural to ask if all derivatives integrate back to the functions from which they were derived. The answer is no, because a derivative is not necessarily an integrable function. For example, let f be given by

$$f(x) = \begin{cases} x^2 \sin 1/x^2 & x \neq 0 \\ 0 & x = 0. \end{cases}$$

Then f' is given by

$$f'(x) = \begin{cases} 2x \sin \dfrac{1}{x^2} - \dfrac{2}{x} \cos \dfrac{1}{x^2} & x \neq 0 \\ 0 & x = 0 \end{cases}$$

Thus f' is not bounded in any neighborhood of the origin, and hence cannot be integrable in any interval containing the origin.

However, if f' is integrable, then it must integrate back to f. This is seen as a consequence of the following theorem.

4.5b   Theorem. If f is differentiable on $I:\{a \leqslant x \leqslant b\}$, and if f' is integrable, then

$$\int_a^b f'(x)\,dx = f(b) - f(a).$$

Proof. For any partition P of I, we have

$$f(b) - f(a) = \sum_P [f(x_k) - f(x_{k-1})] = \sum_P f'(\xi_k)\,\Delta_k x.$$

The last equality comes from applying the mean-value theorem to each sub-interval. Now if we let $M_k' = \sup_{I_k} f'(x)$ and $m_k' = \inf_{I_k} f'(x)$, then

$$\underline{S}_P(f') = \sum_P m_k'\,\Delta_k x \leqslant f(b) - f(a) \leqslant \sum_P M_k'\,\Delta_k x = \bar{S}_P(f).$$

And this inequality must hold for every P. Then taking the infimum of the upper sums and the supremum of the lower sums, we get

$$\underline{\int_a^b} f'(x)\,dx \leqslant f(b) - f(a) \leqslant \overline{\int_a^b} f'(x)\,dx.$$

This more general result holds if f' is merely bounded. If f' is integrable, the two ends of this inequality are equal. ∎

We have seen from our study of composite functions that

(1) $$\{g[v(x)]\}' = g'[v(x)]v'(x).$$

This formula serves as the basis of integration by substitution.

4.5c   Theorem. Let f be continuous in $\{a \leqslant y \leqslant b\}$, let v be a function with a continuous derivative v' on $\{c \leqslant x \leqslant d\}$, and let $v(c) = a$ and $v(d) = b$. Then, if $a \leqslant v \leqslant b$, we have

$$\int_a^b f(y)\,dy = \int_c^d f[v(x)]v'(x)\,dx.$$

Proof. Let $g(y) = \int_a^y f(t)\,dt$. Then, by (1) above, $g[v(x)]$ is a primitive of

$$g'[v(x)]v'(x) = f[v(x)]v'(x).$$

Then, by the fundamental theorem,

$$\int_c^d f[v(x)]v'(x)\,dx = g[v(x)]\Big|_c^d$$

$$= g[v(d)] - g[v(c)]$$

$$= g(b) - g(a)$$

$$= \int_a^b f(y)\,dy.$$ ∎

4.6 FURTHER PROPERTIES OF INTEGRALS

We have the familiar formula

(1) $$(fg)' = fg' + f'g,$$

for the differentiation of a product of differentiable functions. Integrating this formula, we get the formula for integration by parts.

4.6a Theorem. If f and g are differentiable on $\{a \leqslant x \leqslant b\}$, and if f' and g' are integrable there, then

$$\int_a^b f(x)\,g'(x)\,dx = f(x)\,g(x)\Big|_a^b - \int_a^b g(x)f'(x)\,dx.$$

Proof. Clearly $(fg)'$ is integrable, since by equation (1) it is a sum of products of integrable functions. By Theorem 4.5b,

$$\int_a^b [f(x)\,g(x)]'\,dx = f(x)\,g(x)\Big|_a^b,$$

and expanding the integrand by (1) gives us the desired result. ∎

The technique of integration by parts can be used to find primitives or indefinite integrals. This is well covered in elementary calculus and need not be stressed here, although a few related problems will occur in the exercises.

We turn now to the proofs of certain mean-value theorems for integrals. If f is integrable on $\{a \leqslant x \leqslant b\}$, it is a consequence of Lemma 4.2e that

(2) $$m \leqslant \frac{1}{b-a}\int_a^b f(x)\,dx \leqslant M,$$

where m and M are upper and lower bounds for f. The quantity

$$\frac{1}{b-a}\int_a^b f(x)\,dx$$

is called the **mean** or **average** of f over $\{a \leqslant x \leqslant b\}$. Hence the inequality (2) says that the average or mean of f lies between its largest and smallest values. This itself is a sort of a mean-value theorem. We give now several others. The following is known as the **first mean-value theorem** for integrals.

4.6b Theorem. If f is continuous on $\{a \leqslant x \leqslant b\}$, then there is a ξ in $\{a < x < b\}$ for which

$$\frac{1}{b-a} \int_a^b f(x)\, dx = f(\xi).$$

Proof. Set $F(x) = \displaystyle\int_a^x f(t)\, dt$, and apply the mean-value theorem of differential calculus (Theorem 3.6e). ∎

If $g(x) \geqslant 0$, the ratio

$$\mu = \left(\int_a^b f(x)\, g(x)\, dx \right) \Big/ \left(\int_a^b g(x)\, dx \right)$$

is called the **weighted mean** of f with respect to the **weight function** g. There is also a mean-value theorem for weighted means:

4.6c Theorem. If f is continuous on $\{a \leqslant x \leqslant b\}$, and if g is integrable there with $g(x) \geqslant 0$ and with $\displaystyle\int_a^b g(x)\, dx > 0$, then for μ as defined above there is a ξ in $\{a \leqslant x \leqslant b\}$ for which

$$\mu = f(\xi).$$

Proof. Clearly fg is integrable, by Theorem 4.4h; and if m and M have their usual meanings,

$$mg(x) \leqslant f(x)\, g(x) \leqslant Mg(x),$$

then

$$m \int_a^b g(x)\, dx \leqslant \int_a^b f(x)\, g(x)\, dx \leqslant M \int_a^b g(x)\, dx.$$

Dividing by $\displaystyle\int_a^b g(x)\, dx$, we get

$$m \leqslant \mu \leqslant M.$$

By the intermediate-value theorem for continuous functions (3.3a), there is a ξ in $\{a < x < b\}$ for which $\mu = f(\xi)$. ∎

The next theorem is known as the **second mean-value theorem**, or **Bonnet's theorem**.

4.6d   Theorem. Suppose that f is monotone and f' integrable, and that g is continuous in $\{a \leqslant x \leqslant b\}$. Then there is a ξ in $\{a \leqslant x \leqslant b\}$ for which

$$\int_a^b f(x)\, g(x)\, dx = f(a) \int_a^\xi g(x)\, dx + f(b) \int_\xi^b g(x)\, dx.$$

Proof. Let $G(x) = \int_a^x g(t)\, dt$. Then

$$\int_a^b f(x)\, g(x)\, dx = \int_a^b f(x)\, G'(x)\, dx$$

$$= f(x)\, G(x)\,\Big|_a^b - \int_a^b G(x) f'(x)\, dx$$

$$= f(b)\, G(b) - \int_a^b G(x) f'(x)\, dx.$$

We now apply the mean-value theorem for weighted means to the last integral:

$$\int_a^b f(x)\, g(x)\, dx = f(b)\, G(b) - G(\xi) \int_a^b f'(x)\, dx$$

$$= f(b)\, G(b) - G(\xi)[f(b) - f(a)]$$

$$= f(a)\, G(\xi) + f(b)[G(b) - G(\xi)]$$

$$= f(a) \int_a^\xi g(x)\, dx + f(b) \int_\xi^b g(x)\, dx. \qquad \blacksquare$$

Actually, this conclusion is valid if we only assume that f is monotone and g is integrable. However, as you might expect, the proof is more difficult under these conditions.

A   EXERCISES

I. Integrate—that is, find primitives for—the following:

(a) $\displaystyle\int \log^n x\, dx$ (b) $\displaystyle\int (x^2 - 1) \cos x\, dx$ (c) $\displaystyle\int e^{ax} \cos bx\, dx$

(d) $\displaystyle\int e^{ax} \sin bx\, dx$ (e) $\displaystyle\int x \cos^2 x\, dx$ (f) $\displaystyle\int \sec^3 x\, dx$

(g) $\displaystyle\int \sin \sqrt{x-1}\, dx$ (h) $\displaystyle\int \frac{dx}{\sqrt{a^2 - x^2}}$ (i) $\displaystyle\int \sqrt{9 + x^2}\, dx$

(j) $\displaystyle\int \frac{x^2\, dx}{\sqrt{x^2 - a^2}}$ (k) $\displaystyle\int \frac{\sqrt{2 + x}}{x - 3}\, dx$ (l) $\displaystyle\int \frac{dx}{\sqrt{x} + \sqrt{x + 1}}$

2. Show that if f is monotonic on $I : \{a \leqslant x \leqslant b\}$, $\displaystyle\int_a^b f(x)\, dx$ is between $f(a)\,(b - a)$ and $f(b)\,(b - a)$.

3. Show that $0 < \displaystyle\int_0^{\pi/2} \sin^{n+1} x \, dx < \int_0^{\pi/2} \sin^n x \, dx$.

4. What is wrong with $\displaystyle\int_{-1}^1 \frac{dx}{x^2} = -\frac{1}{x}\Big]_{-1}^1 = -2$?

5. Compute $\dfrac{d}{dx} \displaystyle\int_x^b f(t) \, dt$ if f is continuous.

6. Give a formula for $\dfrac{d}{dx} \displaystyle\int_{u(x)}^{v(x)} f(t) \, dt$ if f is continuous, and u and v are differentiable.

B EXERCISES

1. Explain the inequality in Theorem 4.4a.

2. Prove Theorems 4.4c, 4.4d, and 4.4e.

3. What is the geometrical meaning of the formula

$$\frac{d}{dx} \int_a^x f(t) \, dt = f(x)?$$

4. If f is integrable on $I:\{a \leqslant x \leqslant b\}$, show that $\displaystyle\int_a^x f(t) \, dt$ is continuous on I.

5. Show that if f has a continuous derivative on $I:\{a \leqslant x \leqslant b\}$, then it can be represented as the difference of two non-decreasing functions.

6. Show that there is a constant K for which $\displaystyle\sum_{k=1}^n k^{1/2} < Kn^{3/2}$.

7. What is wrong with the following "proof" of 4.4g? For any partition P:

$$|S_P(f, \xi)| = \left|\sum_P f(\xi_k) \, \Delta_k x\right| < \sum_P |f(\xi_k)| \, \Delta_k x = S_P(|f|, \xi).$$

Letting $\|P\| \to 0$, we get the conclusion of the theorem.

8. Show that if f is continuous and non-negative on $I:\{a \leqslant x \leqslant b\}$, and if there is an x_0 in I for which $f(x_0) > 0$, then $\displaystyle\int_a^b f(x) \, dx > 0$.

9. Though the function in the example in Section 4.5 has a derivative which is not integrable in any neighborhood of the origin, show that for any $b > 0$

$$\lim_{a \to 0+} \int_a^b f'(x) \, dx = f(b).$$

C EXERCISES

1. Show that if f is continuous on $I:\{a \leqslant x \leqslant b\}$ and $\displaystyle\int_a^b f(x)\phi(x) \, dx = 0$ for every integrable ϕ, then $f(x) = 0$.

2. Show that if f is integrable and non-negative on $I:\{a \leqslant x \leqslant b\}$, then $\sqrt{f}$ is integrable.

3. Show that if f is integrable on $I:\{a \leqslant x \leqslant b\}$ and there is a constant $c > 0$ for which $f(x) \geqslant c$, then $1/f$ is integrable on I.

5

The Elementary
Transcendental Functions

5.1 THE LOGARITHM

Perhaps the simplest class of functions are the **polynomials**—that is, those functions which are representable by

$$P(x) = \sum_0^n a_k x^k.$$

Next in order of increasing complexity we might place the **rational functions**, those which are expressible as ratios of polynomials. A still more complicated class of functions are the algebraic functions. A function given by $y = f(x)$ is an **algebraic function** if it satisfies an equation of the form

$$P_n y^n + P_{n-1} y^{n-1} + \cdots + P_1 y + P_0 = 0,$$

where the P's are polynomials in x.

Here we want to study a few familiar functions belonging to none of these classes, but to a different class called **transcendental functions.** We will not define this class here, since this definition is best framed in terms of the theory of complex analytic functions.

We begin with the **logarithm,** which is defined by

$$\log x = \int_1^x \frac{dt}{t} \qquad x > 0.$$

We will assume without further comment that all arguments of this function are positive.

5.1a **Theorem.** $\log 1 = 0$.

Proof. The proof of this theorem is clear.

5.1b **Theorem.** $\log 1/a = -\log a$.

Proof. In the defining integral, we make the substitution $t = 1/s$ and use Theorem 4.5c:

$$\log 1/a = \int_1^{1/a} \frac{dt}{t} = -\int_1^a \frac{ds}{s} = -\log a. \qquad \blacksquare$$

5.1c **Theorem.** $\log ab = \log a + \log b$.

Proof. In the integral defining $\log ab$, we make the substitution $t = as$

$$\log ab = \int_1^{ab} \frac{dt}{t} = \int_{1/a}^b \frac{ds}{s} = \int_{1/a}^1 \frac{ds}{s} + \int_1^b \frac{ds}{s}$$

$$= -\int_1^{1/a} \frac{ds}{s} + \int_1^b \frac{ds}{s} = -\log 1/a + \log b = \log a + \log b. \qquad \blacksquare$$

5.1d **Theorem.** $\log a/b = \log a - \log b$.

Proof. We prove this theorem by means of Theorems 5.1c and 5.1b. $\blacksquare$

5.1e **Theorem.** For any rational number r, $\log a^r = r \log a$.

Proof. In the integral defining $\log a^r$, make the substitution $t = s^r$.

$$\log a^r = \int_1^{a^r} \frac{dt}{t} = r \int_1^a \frac{ds}{s} = r \log a. \qquad \blacksquare$$

We restrict r to be rational here because we have defined a^r only for rational r (Section 3.4). It is one of the aims of this chapter to define a^x for an arbitrary real number x.

5.1f **Theorem.** $\lim\limits_{x \to 0} \dfrac{1}{x} \log (1 + x) = 1$.

Proof. From the definition of $\log (1 + x)$, we have

$$\frac{x}{1 + x} \leqslant \log (1 + x) \leqslant x.$$

We then get

$$\frac{1}{1 + x} \leqslant \frac{1}{x} \log (1 + x) \leqslant 1$$

or

$$\frac{1}{1 + x} \geqslant \frac{1}{x} \log (1 + x) \geqslant 1,$$

according as x is positive or negative. From these last two inequalities, the result is clear. $\blacksquare$

5.1g   Theorem. $\log e = 1.$

Proof. $\log e = \log \lim \left(1 + \dfrac{1}{n}\right)^n = \lim \log \left(1 + \dfrac{1}{n}\right)^n.$

This last equality is true since $\log x$ is a continuous function, which in turn is true since an integral is a continuous function of its upper limit. Then, by Theorems 5.1e and 5.1f,

$$\log e = \lim n \log \left(1 + \frac{1}{n}\right) = \lim \frac{\log (1 + 1/n)}{1/n} = 1. \qquad \blacksquare$$

5.1h   Theorem. $\log x$ is strictly increasing.

Proof. By Lemma 4.2h, we get

$$\frac{d}{dx} \log x = \frac{1}{x} > 0 \qquad \text{for } x > 0. \qquad \blacksquare$$

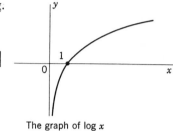

The graph of log x

5.1i   Theorem. $\lim\limits_{x \to +\infty} \log x = +\infty,$

$\lim\limits_{x \to 0+} \log x = -\infty.$

Proof. Since $\log x$ is increasing, it is sufficient to find a sequence $\{x_n\}$ such that $x_n \to +\infty$, for which $\log x_n \to +\infty$. We choose $x_n = e^n$, which does have this property (see Exercise B1). Now

$$\log e^n = n \log e = n \to +\infty,$$

which proves that $\log x \to +\infty$ as $x \to +\infty$. If $x \to 0+$, $1/x \to +\infty$, so that

$$\log x = -\log 1/x \to -\infty. \qquad \blacksquare$$

5.2   THE EXPONENTIAL FUNCTION

Having established the most important properties of the logarithm, we now turn to a discussion of the **exponential function**.   This function will be denoted by exp x until we can justify saying that

$$\exp x = e^x.$$

We have seen that $\log x$ has as its domain of definition the semi-infinite interval $\{0 < x < \infty\}$, that it is continuous and strictly increasing, and that its range is $\{-\infty < x < \infty\}$. It therefore has a unique continuous inverse function whose domain is $\{-\infty < x < \infty\}$ and whose range is $\{0 < x < \infty\}$. The values of this inverse function we denote by exp x.

We proceed to obtain the most important properties of this function.

5.2a Theorem. $\exp x > 0$ for all x.

Proof. A proof of this theorem merely reiterates the fact that the range of the exponential function is $\{0 < x < \infty\}$. ∎

5.2b Theorem. $\exp 0 = 1$.

Proof. $\log 1 = 0$. ∎

5.2c Theorem. $\exp r = e^r$ for all rational r.

Proof. $\log e^r = r \log e = r$. ∎

Again we restrict ourselves to rational r, because we do not have e^x defined for irrational x.

5.2d Theorem. $\dfrac{d}{dx} \exp x = \exp x$.

Proof. By Theorem 3.6h, on the differentiation of inverse functions, if $y = \exp x$, then

$$\frac{d}{dx}(\exp x) = \frac{1}{(d/dy)\log y} = \frac{1}{1/y} = y = \exp x. \qquad ∎$$

5.2e Theorem. $\exp(x + y) = (\exp x)(\exp y)$.

Proof. Set $a = \exp x$, $b = \exp y$. Then $x = \log a$, $y = \log b$, and

$$\log ab = \log a + \log b = x + y.$$

Taking exponentials of both sides, we get

$$ab = \exp(x + y). \qquad ∎$$

5.2f Theorem. $\exp(x - y) = (\exp x)/(\exp y)$.

Proof. The proof of this theorem is similar to that of Theorem 5.2e.

It is now clear that the function $\exp x$ is a continuous function which coincides with e^x whenever x is rational, that is, whenever e^x has a meaning. Since the function is continuous, it interpolates between the values of e^x which are defined for rational x. Graphically, this means that if we plot the points $y = e^x$ for x rational, then the curve $y = \exp x$ is a smooth curve passing through all these points. Accordingly, we define e^x for irrational x to be $\exp x$:

$$e^x = \exp x \qquad \{-\infty < x < \infty\}.$$

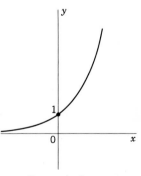

The graph of exp x

More generally, a^x, for $a > 0$, is defined only for rational x. Furthermore, for such rational x we have

$$\log a^x = x \log a,$$

and taking exponentials of both sides we get

$$a^x = \exp x \log a = e^{x \log a}.$$

But this latter function is a continuous function for all values of x. Hence $e^{x \log a}$ interpolates between the previously defined values of a^x. Accordingly, we define a^x for all x by the formula

$$a^x = e^{x \log a} \qquad \{-\infty < x < \infty\},$$

under the condition that $a > 0$.

The hyperbolic functions are defined in terms of the exponential function. Since we have the requisite properties of the exponential established, the usual study of the hyperbolic functions is quite adequate and need not be repeated here.

A EXERCISES

1. Explain why $e^{\log x} = x$ for $x > 0$ and $\log e^x = x$ for all x.

2. Show that:

(a) $a^x > 0$ (b) $a^0 = 1$ (c) $a^x \cdot a^y = a^{x+y}$

(d) $(a^x)/(a^y) = a^{x-y}$ (e) $(a^x)^y = a^{xy}$

3. Show that $\dfrac{d}{dx} a^x = a^x \log a$.

4. Show that $\dfrac{d}{dx} x^a = ax^{a-1}$ if $x > 0$ for all a.

5. Show that $\log a^x = x \log a$ if $a > 0$ for all x.

6. Show that $\lim\limits_{h \to 0} \dfrac{e^h - 1}{h} = 1$.

7. Show that $\lim\limits_{x \to 0} a^x = 1$.

8. If $f(x) > 0$ and f and g are both differentiable, derive the formula

$$\frac{d}{dx}\{[f(x)]^{g(x)}\} = [f(x)]^{g(x)}g'(x) \log f(x) + g(x)[f(x)]^{g(x)-1}f'(x).$$

9. Let $\mathbf{P}(x, y)$ be a point on the curve $y = \log x$. What is the distance from $\mathbf{P}$ to the y-axis. Express your answer in terms of y.

10. Show that $\log x \leqslant x - 1$. When does equality hold?

11. Show that $e^x \geqslant 1 + x$. When does equality hold?

B EXERCISES

1. Show that $e^n > n$, and hence complete the proof of Theorem 5.1i. (*Hint:* Write $e = 1 + h$ where $h > 1$.)

2. Evaluate the following limits. In some cases it will be useful to recognize difference quotients of the form of Exercise A6 or related forms:

(a) $\displaystyle\lim_{x\to 0} \frac{e^{x^2} - 1}{x^2}$

(b) $\displaystyle\lim_{x\to 2} (e^x - e^2)\cot(x - 2)$

(c) $\displaystyle\lim_{x\to 0} \frac{e^{x^3} - 1}{\log(1 + x^3)}$

(d) $\displaystyle\lim_{x\to 0} \frac{e^{ax} - e^{bx}}{\log(1 + x)}$

(e) $\displaystyle\lim_{x\to 0} \sqrt[4]{\frac{e^{\tan x} - e^x}{\tan x - x}}$

(f) $\displaystyle\lim_{n\to\infty} \frac{e^{nx} - 1}{e^{nx} + 1}$

(g) $\displaystyle\lim_{x\to\infty} (a + bc^x)^{1/x}$ $a > 0, b > 0, c \geqslant 1.$

(h) $\displaystyle\lim_{x\to\infty} \left[\frac{a^x + b^x}{2}\right]^{1/x}$ $a \geqslant b > 0.$

(i) Show that $\displaystyle\lim_{x\to +\infty} \left(1 + \frac{1}{x}\right)^x = e.$ (*Hint:* Consider the derivative of log x at $x = 1$.)

(j) Show that $\displaystyle\lim_{x\to +\infty} \left(1 + \frac{a}{x}\right)^x = e^a.$

C EXERCISES

1. Evaluate the following limits:

(a) $\displaystyle\lim_{x\to\infty} x^{1/x}$

(b) $\displaystyle\lim_{x\to 0} x^{1/x}$

(c) $\displaystyle\lim_{x\to 0} \frac{a^x - b^x}{x}$ $a > 0, b > 0.$

(d) $\displaystyle\lim_{x\to 0} [f(x)]^{1/x}$ $f(0) = 1, f'(0) = a.$

2. Let L be a function defined for all $x > 0$ for which $L(xy) = L(x) + L(y)$ and $\displaystyle\lim_{x\to 0} \frac{L(1 + x)}{x} = 1.$ Show that $L(x) = \log x$ for all $x > 0.$

5.3 THE CIRCULAR FUNCTIONS

In this section we do not follow the usual theorem-proof sequence, since another type of presentation seems preferable.

The circular functions—that is, the ordinary trigonometric functions—are customarily defined in elementary courses solely in geometric terms, which is not entirely satisfactory. Therefore we plan here to place these functions on a firmer arithmetical basis. We will lean heavily on geometry for our inspiration, essentially following the trigonometric development, but will take care not to resort to geometry in the proofs. The only exception will be in proving the addition formulas, and even for these a non-geometrical proof will be suggested in the exercises.

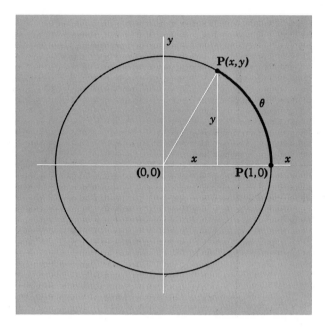

We begin by considering the circle indicated by $x^2 + y^2 = 1$. At first we are concerned only with the right-hand semicircle given by

$$x = +\sqrt{1 - \alpha^2}, \qquad y = \alpha, \qquad \{-1 \leqslant \alpha \leqslant 1\}.$$

If $\mathbf{P}(x, y)$ is a point on this right-hand semicircle, we want to discuss the arc length along the circle from $\mathbf{P}_0(1, 0)$ to $\mathbf{P}$. For this we will use the formula for arc length from elementary calculus, namely,

$$\int_0^y \sqrt{\left(\frac{dx}{d\alpha}\right)^2 + \left(\frac{dy}{d\alpha}\right)^2}\, d\alpha = \int_0^y \frac{d\alpha}{\sqrt{1 - \alpha^2}}.$$

(Arc length will be discussed and this formula established in Chapter 8.)

This defines arc length in the open interval $\{-1 < y < 1\}$, counted positive for positive y, as in the figure, and negative for negative y. Since the integrand becomes unbounded at ± 1, the integral becomes improper; but it is still convergent at both points. To see that, we argue as follows: For y near 1, we can write

$$\int_0^y \frac{d\alpha}{\sqrt{1-\alpha^2}} = \int_0^{1/\sqrt{2}} \frac{d\alpha}{\sqrt{1-\alpha^2}} + \int_{1/\sqrt{2}}^y \frac{d\alpha}{\sqrt{1-\alpha^2}} = \int_0^{1/\sqrt{2}} \frac{d\alpha}{\sqrt{1-\alpha^2}}$$

$$+ \int_{\sqrt{1-y^2}}^{1/\sqrt{2}} \frac{d\beta}{\sqrt{1-\beta^2}},$$

where we have made the substitution $\beta = +\sqrt{1-\alpha^2}$ in the last integral. This formula shows that

$$\lim_{y\to 1-0} \int_0^y \frac{d\alpha}{\sqrt{1-\alpha^2}} = 2 \int_0^{1/\sqrt{2}} \frac{d\alpha}{\sqrt{1-\alpha^2}}.$$

Similarly, the integral converges for $y = -1$. Thus the integral defines a function θ given by

$$\theta(y) = \int_0^y \frac{d\alpha}{\sqrt{1-\alpha^2}} \qquad \{-1 < y < 1\}.$$

The number θ will be called **the angle from P_0 to P.** Being guided by our geometrical picture, we define the number π by

$$\pi/2 = \theta(1) = \int_0^1 \frac{d\alpha}{\sqrt{1-\alpha^2}} = 2 \int_0^{1/\sqrt{2}} \frac{d\alpha}{\sqrt{1-\alpha^2}}.$$

The function θ, now defined and continuous on $\{-1 \leqslant y \leqslant 1\}$ is familiar to you as the **principal value of the arc sine:**

$$\text{Arc sin } y = \theta(y) = \int_0^y \frac{d\alpha}{\sqrt{1-\alpha^2}} \qquad \{-1 \leqslant y \leqslant 1\}.$$

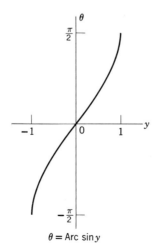

$\theta = \text{Arc sin } y$

We will not make use of any previously known properties of this function, but will use the properties that we can deduce from the integral to define the trigonometric functions.

First, it is clear that θ is an odd function

$$\theta(-y) = -\theta(y).$$

Furthermore, we observe that θ is strictly increasing on $\{-1 < y < 1\}$, since

$$\theta'(y) = 1/\sqrt{1 - y^2} > 0.$$

Then, by Exercise B10 of Section 3.4, it is also strictly increasing on $\{-1 \leqslant y \leqslant 1\}$. Therefore, by Theorem 3.4a, θ has a continuous strictly increasing inverse function defined on $\{-\pi/2 \leqslant \theta \leqslant \pi/2\}$, which increases from -1 to $+1$ as θ increases from $-\pi/2$ to $+\pi/2$. This inverse function we define to be the **sine** of θ, and use the familiar notation

$$y = \sin\theta \qquad \{-\pi/2 \leqslant \theta \leqslant \pi/2\}.$$

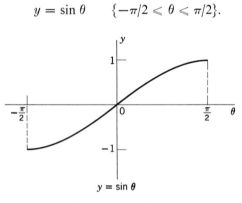

$$y = \sin\theta$$

We define the **cosine** of θ by the formula

$$x = \cos\theta = +\sqrt{1 - \sin^2\theta}, \qquad \{-\pi/2 \leqslant \theta \leqslant \pi/2\}.$$

Now since θ is differentiable in the open interval $\{-1 < y < 1\}$, $\sin\theta$ must also be differentiable in $\{-\pi/2 < \theta < \pi/2\}$. We compute the derivative there:

$$\frac{d}{d\theta}\sin\theta = \frac{1}{\dfrac{d}{dy}\theta(y)} = \frac{1}{\dfrac{d}{dy}\displaystyle\int_0^y \frac{d\alpha}{\sqrt{1-\alpha^2}}} = \frac{1}{\dfrac{1}{\sqrt{1-y^2}}}$$

$$= \sqrt{1-y^2} = \sqrt{1-\sin^2\theta} = \cos\theta \qquad \{-\pi/2 < \theta < \pi/2\}.$$

From this, we can get $\dfrac{d}{d\theta}\cos\theta$. First we observe that

$$\cos^2\theta = 1 - \sin^2\theta,$$

whence $\qquad\qquad 2\cos\theta\,\dfrac{d}{d\theta}(\cos\theta) = -2\sin\theta\cdot\cos\theta.$

Now $\cos\theta > 0$ in $\{-\pi/2 < \theta < \pi/2\}$.   (Why?)

Thus $\qquad\qquad\qquad\qquad \dfrac{d}{d\theta}\cos\theta = -\sin\theta.$

We now turn to the problem of extending the domain of definition of $\sin\theta$ and $\cos\theta$. To this end, we consider the function

$$\theta_1(y) = \pi - \int_0^y \frac{d\alpha}{\sqrt{1-\alpha^2}} \qquad \{-1 \leqslant y \leqslant 1\}.$$

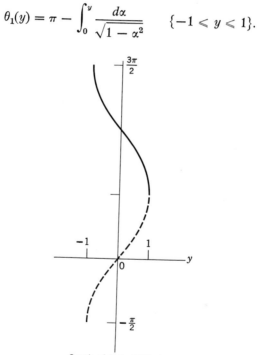

Graph of θ_1 (solid line)

Geometrically, this is again the arc length along our circle C from $\mathbf{P}_0(1, 0)$ around counterclockwise to a point $\mathbf{P}(x, y)$ on the left semicircle ($x \leqslant 0$) of C.

Clearly, θ_1 is strictly decreasing on $\{-1 \leqslant y \leqslant 1\}$ and is of course continuous there. It decreases from $3\pi/2$ at -1 to $\pi/2$ at $+1$. Hence it has a strictly decreasing inverse function on $\{\pi/2 \leqslant \theta \leqslant 3\pi/2\}$. It decreases from 1 at $\pi/2$ to -1 at $3\pi/2$. This inverse function we define to be $\sin \theta$ in the proper interval:

$$y = \sin \theta \qquad \{\pi/2 \leqslant \theta \leqslant 3\pi/2\}.$$

Note that the two definitions of $\sin \theta$ at $\pi/2$ are compatible. Hence we now have $\sin \theta$ uniquely defined as a continuous function in $\{-\pi/2 \leqslant 0 \leqslant 3\pi/2\}$. We define $\cos \theta$ in the extended interval by

$$\cos \theta = -\sqrt{1 - \sin^2 \theta} \ \{\pi/2 \leqslant \theta \leqslant 3\pi/2.\}$$

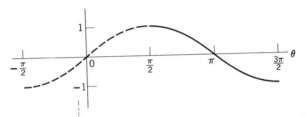

This now gives us $\cos \theta$ as a continuous function in $\{-\pi/2 \leqslant \theta \leqslant 3\pi/2\}$.

Again, let us compute the derivative of $\sin \theta$, this time in the open interval $\{+\pi/2 < \theta < 3\pi/2\}$. Here we have

$$\frac{d}{d\theta} \sin \theta = \frac{1}{\theta_1{}'(y)} = \frac{1}{-1/\sqrt{1 - y^2}} = -\sqrt{1 - y^2} = -\sqrt{1 - \sin^2\theta} = \cos \theta,$$

and again

$$\cos^2 \theta = 1 - \sin^2 \theta.$$

Thus

$$2 \cos \theta \, \frac{d}{d\theta} \cos \theta = -2 \sin \theta \cos \theta,$$

or

$$\frac{d}{d\theta} \cos \theta = -\sin \theta \qquad \{\pi/2 < \theta < 3\pi/2\}.$$

Let us note that

(1)
$$\begin{cases} \sin(-\pi/2) = \sin(+3\pi/2) = -1 \\ \cos(-\pi/2) = \cos(3\pi/2) = 0. \end{cases}$$

We define $\sin \theta$ and $\cos \theta$ for values of θ outside the interval $\{\pi/2 \leqslant \theta \leqslant 3\pi/2\}$ by periodicity with period 2π:

$$\sin(2\pi + \theta) = \sin \theta$$
$$\cos(2\pi + \theta) = \cos \theta.$$

In view of the above relationships (1), these equations serve to define $\sin \theta$ and cos θ for all values of θ and preserve the derivative formulas which now hold except at odd multiples of $\pi/2$. We now want to examine the possibility of differentiating the sine and cosine at these points.

We calculate the derivatives at only one such point, namely $\pi/2$, for the situation is similar at $-\pi/2$, and by periodicity these are the only two points we need to consider. For simplicity, we calculate at $\pi/2$ only the left-hand derivative. The calculations for the right-hand derivative are almost identical.

At $\pi/2$, $\sin \theta = 1$; and for $\theta < \pi/2$, we have $\sin \theta < 1$. Hence we can write

$$\sin (\pi/2 - h) = 1 - k,$$

where k is small and positive when h is small and positive. Then

$$\frac{\Delta \sin \theta}{\Delta \theta} = \frac{\sin (\pi/2 - h) - \sin \pi/2}{(\pi/2 - h) - \pi/2} = \frac{(1 - k) - 1}{\int_0^{1-k} \frac{d\alpha}{\sqrt{1 - \alpha^2}} - \int_0^1 \frac{d\alpha}{\sqrt{1 - \alpha^2}}}$$

$$= \frac{k}{\int_{1-k}^1 \frac{d\alpha}{\sqrt{1 - \alpha^2}}} = \frac{k}{\int_0^{\sqrt{2k-k^2}} \frac{d\beta}{\sqrt{1 - \beta^2}}},$$

the last equality coming from the substitution $\beta = +\sqrt{1 - \alpha^2}$. Thus

$$\frac{k}{\int_0^{\sqrt{2k-k^2}} \frac{d\beta}{\sqrt{1 - (2k - k^2)}}} \leqslant \frac{\Delta \sin \theta}{\Delta \theta} \leqslant \frac{k}{\int_0^{\sqrt{2k-k^2}} \frac{d\beta}{1}}$$

or

$$\frac{k(1 - k)}{\sqrt{2k - k^2}} \leqslant \frac{\Delta \sin \theta}{\Delta \theta} \leqslant \frac{k}{\sqrt{2k - k^2}}.$$

Now as $\Delta \theta = h$ tends to zero, so also k tends to zero. And as $k \to 0$ both sides of the previous inequality tend to zero. Thus we get

$$\frac{d}{d\theta} \sin \theta \bigg|_{\pi/2} = 0 = \cos \pi/2.$$

Next we examine the difference quotient of $\cos \theta$ at $\pi/2$. Again we compute only the left-hand derivative:

$$\frac{\Delta \cos \theta}{\Delta \theta} = \frac{\cos (\pi/2 - h) - \cos \pi/2}{(\pi/2 - h) - \pi/2} = \frac{\sqrt{1 - \sin^2 (\pi/2 - h)} - 0}{\int_0^{1-k} \frac{d\alpha}{\sqrt{1 - \alpha^2}} - \int_0^1 \frac{d\alpha}{\sqrt{1 - \alpha^2}}}$$

$$= - \frac{\sqrt{2k - k^2}}{\int_{1-k}^1 \frac{d\alpha}{\sqrt{1 - \alpha^2}}}.$$

Estimating exactly as before, we get

$$-1 = -\frac{\sqrt{2k - k^2}}{\sqrt{2k - k^2}} \leqslant \frac{\Delta \cos \theta}{\Delta \theta} \leqslant -\frac{\sqrt{2k - k^2}}{\sqrt{2k - k^2}}(1 - k) = -1 + k.$$

As $k \to 0$,

$$\frac{d}{d\theta} \cos \theta \Big|_{\pi/2} = -1 = -\sin \pi/2.$$

Thus

$$\frac{d}{d\theta} \sin \theta = \cos \theta, \frac{d}{d\theta} \cos \theta = -\sin \theta \qquad \{-\infty < \theta < \infty\}.$$

The other trigonometric functions are defined in terms of the sine and cosine:

$$\tan \theta = \frac{\sin \theta}{\cos \theta} \qquad \cot \theta = \frac{\cos \theta}{\sin \theta}$$

$$\sec \theta = \frac{1}{\cos \theta} \qquad \csc \theta = \frac{1}{\sin \theta}.$$

From the identity

$$\cos^2 \theta + \sin^2 \theta = 1$$

(which was part of the definition of $\cos \theta$), we get

$$\sec^2 \theta - \tan^2 \theta = 1$$

$$\csc^2 \theta - \cot^2 \theta = 1.$$

We can introduce inverse functions of the trigonometric functions in appropriate intervals. In particular, the function with which we began our discussion of this section is the principal value of the arc sine:

$$\theta(y) = \text{arc } \sin y = \int_0^y \frac{d\alpha}{\sqrt{1 - \alpha^2}} \qquad \{-1 \leqslant y \leqslant 1\}.$$

The function $\theta_1(y)$ is another **branch,** as it is called, of arc $\sin y$.

We introduce one other inverse trigonometric function, namely the principal value of arc $\tan z$. Now

$$\frac{d}{d\theta} \tan \theta = \frac{d}{dt} \frac{\sin \theta}{\cos \theta} = \frac{\cos^2 \theta + \sin^2 \theta}{\cos^2 \theta} = \sec^2 \theta > 0,$$

so that $\tan \theta$ is strictly increasing in $\{-\pi/2 < \theta < \pi/2\}$. Also

$$\tan \theta \to -\infty \quad \text{as} \quad \theta \to \pi/2 + 0$$

and

$$\tan \theta \to +\infty \quad \text{as} \quad \theta \to \pi/2 - 0.$$

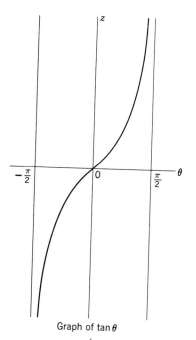

Graph of $\tan \theta$

Hence there is an inverse function which we will represent by the formula

$$\theta = \text{arc tan } z.$$

It is defined in $\{-\infty < z < \infty\}$, is monotone-increasing, and

$$\text{arc tan } z \to \pi/2 \quad \text{as} \quad z \to +\infty$$
$$\text{arc tan } z \to -\pi/2 \quad \text{as} \quad z \to -\infty \qquad \text{(Why?)}$$

Also

$$\frac{d\theta}{dz} = \frac{1}{\dfrac{dz}{d\theta}} = \frac{1}{\sec^2 \theta} = \frac{1}{1 + \tan^2 \theta} = \frac{1}{1 + z^2},$$

whence

$$\theta(z) = \text{arc tan } z = \int_0^z \frac{dt}{1 + t^2}.$$

Next we establish further identities. First, it follows from the definition that

$$\sin (-\theta) = -\sin \theta.$$

Differentiating, we get

$$\cos (-\theta) = \cos \theta.$$

Thus the sine is odd and the cosine is even. From this we get immediately that the tangent, the cotangent, and the cosecant are odd and the secant is even.

Now let θ be any number $\{-\pi/2 \leqslant \theta \leqslant 3\pi/2\}$. Then there is a y, namely $y = \sin \theta$, in $\{-1 \leqslant y \leqslant 1\}$ for which

$$\theta = \int_0^y \frac{d\alpha}{\sqrt{1 - \alpha^2}}$$

or

$$\theta = \pi - \int_0^y \frac{d\alpha}{\sqrt{1 - \alpha^2}},$$

according as θ is in $\{-\pi/2 \leqslant \theta \leqslant \pi/2\}$ or $\{\pi/2 \leqslant \theta \leqslant 3\pi/2\}$. In either case,

$$(\pi - \theta) = \pi - \int_0^y \frac{d\alpha}{\sqrt{1 - \alpha^2}}$$

or

$$(\pi - \theta) = \int_0^y \frac{d\alpha}{\sqrt{1 - \alpha^2}}.$$

Thus in either case $\sin (\pi - \theta) = y$. But y was chosen as $\sin \theta$ in the first place. Thus

$$\sin (\pi - \theta) = \sin \theta$$

holds for θ in $\{-\pi/2 \leqslant \theta \leqslant 3\pi/2\}$, and by periodicity it must hold for all θ. Differentiating with respect to θ, we get

$$\cos (\pi - \theta) = -\cos \theta.$$

Consider $\tan (\pi + \theta)$ for any θ. Set $\theta = -\psi$:

$$\tan (\pi + \theta) = \tan (\pi - \psi) = \frac{\sin (\pi - \psi)}{\cos (\pi - \psi)} = \frac{\sin \psi}{-\cos \psi} = \frac{\sin (-\psi)}{\cos (-\psi)}$$

$$= \frac{\sin \theta}{\cos \theta} = \tan \theta.$$

Thus the tangent, and hence also the cotangent, is periodic with period π.

In order to obtain the addition formulas for the circular functions, we make use of a geometrical property, namely that distances are preserved under a rotation.

Let θ and ϕ be any two numbers. Let $\mathbf{P}$ be the point on the unit circle having the angular distance θ from $\mathbf{P}_0(1, 0)$ and $\mathbf{Q}$ the point whose angular distance from $\mathbf{P}$ is ϕ (both θ and ϕ are indicated as positive in the figure). The coordinates of $\mathbf{P}$ are $(\cos \theta, \sin \theta)$ and of $\mathbf{Q}$ are $[\cos (\theta + \phi), \sin (\theta + \phi)]$. Now rotate the three points clockwise an angle θ until $\mathbf{P}_0$ goes into

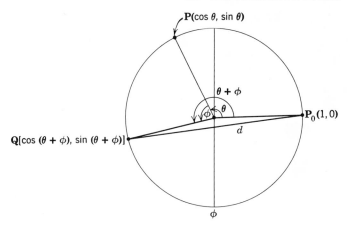

the point $\mathbf{P}'[\cos(-\theta), \sin(-\theta)]$, $\mathbf{P}$ goes into $\mathbf{P}_0(1, 0)$ and $\mathbf{Q}$ goes into $\mathbf{Q}'(\cos\phi, \sin\phi)$. Then the distance d from $\mathbf{P}_0$ to $\mathbf{Q}$ is the same as the distance from $\mathbf{P}'$ to $\mathbf{Q}'$. Thus

$$d^2 = [\cos(\theta + \phi) - 1]^2 + [\sin(\theta + \phi)]^2$$
$$= (\cos\phi - \cos\theta)^2 + (\sin\phi + \sin\theta)^2.$$

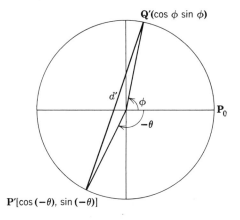

This reduces to

$$\cos(\theta + \phi) = \cos\theta\cos\phi - \sin\theta\sin\phi.$$

Then, holding ϕ fixed and differentiating with respect to θ, we get

$$\sin(\theta + \phi) = \sin\theta\cos\phi + \cos\theta\sin\phi.$$

From these two we can get the addition formulas for other trigonometric functions. Also the standard identities for double and half angles follow immediately from these.

B   EXERCISES

1. Prove that the function f, given by $f(x) = \sin x \cos(\alpha + \beta - x) + \cos x \sin(\alpha + \beta - x)$ is a constant by showing $f'(x) = 0$. Deduce a non-geometrical proof of the addition formulas.

2. Prove that
$$\sin(\pi/2 - \theta) = \sin(\pi/2 + \theta) = \cos \theta$$
$$\cos(\pi/2 - \theta) = -\cos(\pi/2 + \theta) = \sin \theta.$$

3. In expressing arc tan z as an integral, why is the lower limit taken to be zero?

4. Show that, in the interval $\{0 < \theta < \pi\}$, the cosine has an inverse function. This gives the principal value of the arc cos x. Obtain an integral formula for arc cos x.

5. Show that
$$\frac{d}{dx} \sin x \Big|_0 = 1,$$
and hence
$$\lim_{x \to 0} \frac{\sin x}{x} = 1.$$

6. Show that sin x and cos x are infinitely differentiable.

6

Limits and Continuity

6.1 CLUSTER POINTS. ACCUMULATION POINTS

We have discussed limits of sequences and of functions. The existence of a limit of a sequence demands that the nth term of the sequence become arbitrarily close to some fixed number A as n increases. If the limit does not exist, this condition does not hold. However, it is still possible that there is a number A to which the terms recurrently become close. That is, certain judiciously chosen terms may be near A, though others may be far away. For example, suppose

$$x_n = (-1)^n + 1/n \qquad n = 1, 2, 3, \ldots .$$

Clearly this sequence has no limit, for there is no one number A such that x_n is arbitrarily near A for large n. But the x_n's do cluster around two distinct points, namely $+1$ and -1, so that for any $\epsilon > 0$ there are x_n's within ϵ of $+1$ and others of -1. Such a point is called a cluster point or cluster value of the sequence. The precise definition follows:

A point A is called a **cluster point** or **cluster value** of the sequence $\{x_n\}$ if there is a sub-sequence $\{x_{n_k}\}$ converging to A:

$$x_{n_k} \to A.$$

Similarly, if f is defined in a deleted neighborhood of a, we say that A is **cluster value** of f at a if there is a sequence $\{x_n\}$ with $x_n \to a$ for which $f(x_n) \to A$.

We define a similar concept for sets: a point a is an **accumulation point** of a set S if every deleted neighborhood of a contains points of S. Note that the point a itself may or may not be a member of the set S.

We come to the basic theorem on cluster and accumulation points, namely the **Bolzano-Weierstrass theorem.**

6.1a   Theorem. A bounded infinite set has at least one accumulation point, and a bounded sequence has at least one cluster point.

We write out the first part of the proof for sets. The proof for sequences is quite similar and can be read off from the one for sets by replacing such phrases as "infinitely many members of S" by "a_n for infinitely many distinct values of n."

Proof. Let S be the set. Since S is bounded, there is an M such that S is contained in the interval

$$I_0: \{-M \leqslant x \leqslant M\}.$$

When we bisect I_0 to form the two closed intervals $\{-M \leqslant x \leqslant 0\}$ $\{0 \leqslant x \leqslant M\}$, one (or maybe both) of these contains infinitely many members of S, since S is an infinite set. Denote one such interval by I_1. Bisect I_1: one of the two intervals must contain infinitely many points of S. Call it I_2, bisect it, and continue this process ad infinitum. This constructs a sequence of intervals $I_0, I_1, I_2, \ldots, I_n, \ldots$, each contained in the preceding and each containing infinitely many members of S. The length of $I_n = M/2^n$.

If we denote the end points of I_n by a_n and b_n so that I_n is described by $\{a_n \leqslant x \leqslant b_n\}$, then $\{a_n\}$ is a non-decreasing sequence bounded above and $\{b_n\}$ is a non-increasing sequence bounded below. Hence both sequences have limits. Furthermore,

$$\lim b_n - \lim a_n = \lim (b_n - a_n) = \lim M/2^n = 0.$$

Denote the common value of the limit by A. Then clearly

$$a_n \leqslant A \leqslant b_n,$$

or A is in I_n for every n.

Now let $\epsilon > 0$ be given. Then $M/2^n < \epsilon$ if n is sufficiently large, say $n > N$. For such n's, I_n is in $\{A - \epsilon < x < A + \epsilon\}$, since no point of I_n is further from A than the length of I_n, namely $M/2^n$. Hence in this neighborhood there are infinitely many points of S.

This really completes the proof for sets. With sequences, there is one more step: to show that we have a sub-sequence converging to A. But this is now simple. There are infinitely many n's for which x_n is in $\{|A - x| < 1\}$. Hence there is an

$$n_1 \text{ for which } |A - x_{n_1}| < 1$$

There are infinitely many n's for which x_n is in $\{|A - x| < 1/2\}$. Hence there is an

$$n_2 > n_1 \text{ for which } |A - x_{n_2}| < 1/2$$

Similarly there is an

$$n_3 > n_2 \qquad \text{for which} \quad |A - x_{n_3}| < 1/3$$
.
.
.
$$n_k > n_{k-1} \quad \text{for which} \quad |A - x_{n_k}| < 1/k.$$
.
.
.

It is now clear that the sub-sequence $\{x_{n_k}\}$ converges to A.   ∎

6.2 THE CAUCHY CRITERION

From the discussion of the previous section, we can deduce a general principle of convergence known as the **Cauchy criterion.** It is very useful in establishing the existence of a limit when the value of the limit is difficult or impossible to calculate explicitly.

6.2a   Theorem. A necessary and sufficient condition that a sequence $\{x_n\}$ converges is that for each $\epsilon > 0$ there is an $N(\epsilon)$ for which

$$|x_m - x_n| < \epsilon \text{ for all } m > N, n > N.$$

We refer to the statement starting with "for each" as the ϵ-condition of the Cauchy criterion. This is an assertion about the behavior of the terms of a sequence. It says that far out in the sequence all of them are close to each other. When applied to a particular sequence, this assertion may of course be true or false. The theorem shows that those sequences for which the statement is true are precisely the convergent ones, and those for which it is untrue are the divergent ones.

Proof: Necessity. The ϵ-condition is necessary. We assume that $A = \lim x_n$ exists. Then for each $\epsilon > 0$ there is an $N(\epsilon)$ for which

$$|x_n - A| < \epsilon/2 \qquad \text{if} \quad n > N.$$

If both $n > N$ and $m > N$, then

$$|x_m - x_n| = |(x_m - A) - (x_n - A)| \leqslant |x_m - A|$$

$$+ |x_n - A| < \frac{\epsilon}{2} + \frac{\epsilon}{2} = \epsilon.$$

Sufficiency. The ϵ-condition is sufficient. We want to prove that $\lim x_n$ exists under the assumption that the ϵ-condition holds. This is more difficult, since we have no number A to serve as a candidate for $\lim x_n$. To get such an A, we apply the Bolzano-Weierstrass theorem (6.1a). In order to do this, we must show that the sequence is bounded. We apply the ϵ-condition with $\epsilon = 1$. Thus there is an N such that

$$|x_n - x_m| < 1 \quad \text{if } n > N, m > N.$$

Hence
$$|x_n| - |x_m| \leqslant \big||x_n| - |x_m|\big| \leqslant |x_n - x_m| < 1.$$

or
$$|x_n| \leqslant |x_m| + 1 = M_1.$$

Keep m fixed. M_1 is then a bound for all x_n's for $n > N$. There are only a finite number of x's not covered by this bound. Hence, by increasing M_1 if necessary, we get a number M such that

$$|x_n| < M \quad \text{for all } n.$$

Thus $\{x_n\}$ is a bounded sequence, and so has a cluster point which we will denote by A.

We have our candidate now, but have yet to show that it is a real limit. For this purpose we recall that, by Theorem 6.1a, there is a subsequence $\{x_{n_k}\}$ converging to A. Again, by the ϵ-condition applied for $\epsilon/2$, we have

$$|x_n - x_{n_k}| < \epsilon/2 \quad \text{if } n > N(\epsilon/2) \quad \text{and } n_k \geqslant k > N(\epsilon/2).$$

Now keeping n fixed and letting $k \to \infty$, we get

$$|x_n - A| \leqslant \epsilon/2 < \epsilon \quad \text{if } n > N(\epsilon/2).$$

This is the definition of a limit. ∎

The Cauchy criterion extends easily to cover the existence of a limit of a function.

6.2b   Theorem. Let $f(x)$ be defined in a deleted neighborhood of a (or in the case of one-sided limits it need be defined only on one side of a). A necessary and sufficient condition that $\lim_{x \to a} f(x)$ exist is that for each $\epsilon > 0$ there is a $\delta\,(\epsilon)$ for which

$$|f(x) - f(x')| < \epsilon \quad \text{whenever } 0 < |x - a| < \delta,$$
$$0 < |x' - a| < \delta.$$

Proof. The proof of this theorem involves basically the same ideas as the proof of the preceding one. The necessity of the ϵ-condition is left as an exercise (B1). We content ourselves by sketching an outline of the proof of the sufficiency. Choose a sequence $\{x_n\}$ so that $x_n \to a$. Then the associated sequence $\{y_n\}$, where $y_n = f(x_n)$, will satisfy the ϵ-condition of Theorem 6.2a so that $\{y_n\}$ has a limit, which we denote by A. Next we consider

$$|f(x) - f(x_n)| < \epsilon/2,$$

where

$$0 < |x - a| < \delta(\epsilon/2)$$

and

$$0 < |x_n - a| < \delta(\epsilon/2).$$

Keep x fixed and let $n \to \infty$. We then get

$$|f(x) - A| \leqslant \epsilon/2 < \epsilon \qquad \text{if } 0 < |x - a| < \delta\left(\frac{\epsilon}{2}\right). \qquad \blacksquare$$

EXAMPLE 1. Suppose $f(x)$ is defined on $\{0 < x < 1\}$, and satisfies

$$|f(x) - f(x')| < 5\sqrt{|x - x'|}.$$

Show that $\lim_{x \to 1-0} f(x)$ exists.

Solution. We show that the ϵ-condition of the Cauchy criterion (Theorem 6.2b) is satisfied. Consider two points x and x' in the interval of definition. Suppose x' is the larger. Then

$$|f(x) - f(x')| < 5\sqrt{|x - x'|} = 5\sqrt{(x' - x)} \leqslant 5\sqrt{1 - x}$$

We see that if $0 < 1 - x < \epsilon^2/25$, then

$$0 < 1 - x' < \epsilon^2/25$$

and

$$|f(x) - f(x')| < 5\sqrt{1 - x} < 5\sqrt{\epsilon^2/25} = \epsilon.$$

EXAMPLE 2. Suppose a sequence $\{x_n\}$ has the property that there is an r, $0 < r < 1$, for which

$$|x_{n+1} - x_n| < cr^n.$$

Show that $\lim x_n$ exists.

Solution. Let us first point out a trap into which we might fall. As we know, $r^n \to 0$ as $n \to \infty$, so that there is an $N(\epsilon)$ for which

$$r^n < \epsilon/c \qquad \text{if } n > N.$$

Thus

$$|x_{n+1} - x_n| < \epsilon \qquad \text{if } n > N.$$

Unfortunately, however, this does not prove that the limit exists, since the ϵ-condition must be satisfied for *every* m and $n > N$. We have only shown it for a very special m, namely $m = n + 1$. We now give a correct proof.

Consider $|x_m - x_n|$. Since one of m or n is the larger, suppose for definiteness that $m > n$. Then

$$|x_m - x_n| = |(x_m - x_{m-1}) + (x_{m-1} - x_{m-2}) + \cdots$$
$$+ (x_{n+2} - x_{n+1}) + (x_{n+1} - x_n)|$$
$$\leqslant |x_m - x_{m-1}| + |x_{m-1} - x_{m-2}| + \cdots + |x_{n+1} - x_n|$$
$$\leqslant cr^{m-1} + cr^{m-2} + \cdots + cr^n$$
$$= cr^n[1 + r + r^2 + \cdots + r^{m-n-1}]$$
$$= cr^n \frac{1 - r^{m-n}}{1 - r} < \frac{cr^n}{1 - r}.$$

Now, since $r^n \to 0$, there is an N such that $r^n < (1 - r)\epsilon/c$ if $n > N$. For such n's

$$|x_m - x_n| < \frac{cr^n}{1 - r} < \epsilon.$$

A EXERCISES

1. Find all the cluster points of the following sequences:

(a) $\{\sin n\pi/2 + (-1)^n/n\}$

✓(b) $\left\{\cos \dfrac{n\pi}{4} + \sin \dfrac{n\pi}{2} + (-1)^n + \dfrac{1}{2^n}\right\}$

2. Let r_n be the integer remainder $(0 \leqslant r_n \leqslant 9)$, when n is divided by 10. Find all the cluster points of the sequences:

(a) $\{r_n + 1/n\}$ ✓(b) $\{r_n/4 + 1/3^n\}$

3. Find all the cluster points of the following functions at $x = 0$:

(a) $\sin \dfrac{1}{x}$ ✓(b) $\operatorname{sgn} x$ pg. 22

✓(c) $\left|\cos \dfrac{1}{x}\right|$ ✓(d) $\dfrac{1}{1 + e^{1/x}}$

B EXERCISES

1. Prove the necessity part of Theorem 6.2b.

2. Let $\lim x_n = A$ for the sequence of Example 2. Give an estimate for $|x_n - A|$ in terms of n and r.

✓**3.** Use the Cauchy criterion to prove the existence of

$$\lim \left(1 + 1 + \frac{1}{2!} + \frac{1}{3!} + \cdots + \frac{1}{n!}\right).$$

4. Prove that if f is uniformly continuous on $\{a < x < b\}$, then both $f(a + 0)$ and $f(b - 0)$ exist.

use Ex.2 pg 119

5. Suppose $\{x_n\}$ is a sequence which satisfies $|x_{n+1} - x_n| \leqslant c_n$ and that $\sum_{1}^{n} c_k = S_n$ is a convergent sequence. Show that $\{x_n\}$ converges.

6. Show that if $\{a_n\}$ converges, then for each $p \geqslant 1$

$$\lim_{n \to \infty} (a_{n+p} - a_n) = 0$$

7. Suppose f is differentiable for all x and that f' is a bounded function. Show that f is uniformly continuous for all x. *M.V. Theorem*

C EXERCISES

I. Suppose $x_1 > x_0 > 0$ and that for $n \geqslant 1$ we have

$$x_{n+1} = x_n + r^n x_{n-1} \qquad \text{where } 0 < r < 1.$$

Show that $\{x_n\}$ converges. (*Hint:* Show convergence, assuming that $\{x_n\}$ is bounded. To show boundedness, prove by induction that $x_{n+1} \leqslant x_1(1 + r)$ $(1 + r^2) \cdots (1 + r^n)$, then use Exercise B7 of Section 2.6.)

2. Prove the Cauchy criterion for convergence at $+\infty$. Let $f(x)$ be defined for $x \geqslant x_0$. A necessary and sufficient condition for $\lim\limits_{x \to +\infty} f(x)$ to exist is that for each $\epsilon > 0$ there is an $X(\epsilon)$ such that

$$|f(x) - f(x')| < \epsilon \qquad \text{if } x > X \text{ and } x' > X.$$

3. Suppose $\{I_n\}$ is a sequence of non-empty, closed, bounded intervals with each contained in the preceding. Show that if the length of I_n tends to zero with n, there is exactly one point contained in all the intervals. (See the proof of Theorem 6.1a.)

6.3 LIMIT SUPERIOR AND LIMIT INFERIOR

We have seen that a sequence $\{x_n\}$ which fails to have a limit may have many cluster points. Let $\{x_n\}$ have cluster points and let C be the set of the cluster points of $\{x_n\}$. We want to examine the bounds of this set of points C. In fact, C need not be bounded (see Exercise B1), but we are primarily concerned with the cases where it is bounded, at least on one side.

Suppose a given sequence $\{x_n\}$ is bounded above and has cluster points. Then C itself is bounded above (why?), and so by Section 1.5, C has a supremum, which we will denote by Λ. This number, Λ, is called the **limit superior** of the sequence $\{x_n\}$ and will be expressed by

$$\Lambda = \limsup_{n \to \infty} x_n$$

or

$$\Lambda = \overline{\lim_{n \to \infty}} x_n.$$

As in the case of ordinary limits, we will suppress the symbols $n \to \infty$, so that the previous formulas appear as

$$\Lambda = \lim \sup x_n$$

or

$$\Lambda = \overline{\lim} \; x_n.$$

Similarly, if $\{x_n\}$ is bounded below and has cluster points, then its set C of cluster points is bounded below. Its infimum will be called the **limit inferior** of $\{x_n\}$ and will be denoted by λ:

$$\lambda = \lim \inf x_n$$

or

$$\lambda = \underline{\lim} \; x_n,$$

where $n \to \infty$ is again suppressed.

Let us recall that not every set bounded above has a maximum. Applied to the case at hand, this means that it is conceivable that Λ does not belong to C; that is, Λ may itself not be a cluster point of $\{x_n\}$. Similarly, it is not clear whether λ is a cluster point of $\{x_n\}$ or not. Actually Λ and λ are both cluster points when they exist, but these remarks are merely to point up the fact that this has to be proved. The proof will be discussed in the exercises.

For the sake of completeness, let us discuss the improper cases where the sequence may not be bounded. This is largely a matter of nomenclature; that is, we set up certain standard terms to describe such a situation. Thus:

(a) If $\{x_n\}$ is not bounded above, we say $\lim \sup x_n = +\infty$.

(b) If $\{x_n\}$ is not bounded below, we say $\lim \inf x_n = -\infty$.

(c) If $x_n \to -\infty$, we say $\lim \sup x_n = -\infty$.

(d) If $x_n \to +\infty$, we say $\lim \inf x_n = +\infty$.

Ordinarily when we say that $\lim \sup x_n$ or $\lim \inf x_n$ exists, we mean it in the sense of the first definitions. Sometimes for emphasis we may say $\lim \sup x_n$ exists and is finite. When one of the latter definitions is used, it will be specifically pointed out that the extended or improper form is being used.

Perhaps the most important property of these numbers Λ and λ is described in the following theorem. Roughly, it says that for each $\epsilon > 0$ all but a finite number of x_n's of a sequence lie below $\Lambda + \epsilon$ and above $\lambda - \epsilon$.

6.3a   Theorem. Let $\{x_n\}$ be a sequence for which Λ is finite. Then for each $\epsilon > 0$ there is an $N_1(\epsilon)$ such that

$$x_n < \Lambda + \epsilon \qquad \text{if } n > N_1$$

And if λ is finite , then there is an $N_2(\epsilon)$ such that

$$x_n > \lambda - \epsilon \qquad \text{if } n > N_2.$$

Proof. We prove the first statement. Suppose this were not so: suppose there were an exceptional $\epsilon_0 > 0$, so that no matter how large N is there is an $n > N$ for which $x_n \geqslant \Lambda + \epsilon_0$. Then there is a sub-sequence $\{x_{n_k}\}$, all of whose points lie above $\Lambda + \epsilon_0$. But this sub-sequence is also bounded above, hence by Theorem 6.1a it has a cluster point β, for which clearly $\beta \geqslant \Lambda + \epsilon_0$. But this contradicts the fact that Λ is the supremum of the set of the cluster points of $\{x_n\}$. ∎

A glance at the previous figure should convince you of the truth of the next theorem.

6.3b Theorem. In order for $\lim x_n$ to exist, it is necessary and sufficient that

$$\lim \sup x_n = \lim \inf x_n.$$

Proof: Necessity. If $\lim x_n = A$ exists, then the set of cluster points of $\{x_n\}$ contains exactly one point, namely A itself. Hence

$$\Lambda = \lambda = A.$$

Sufficiency. Suppose $\Lambda = \lambda$. Then, by Theorem 6.3a, there is an N (take N to be the larger of N_1 and N_2 of that theorem) such that

$$\lambda - \epsilon < x_n < \Lambda + \epsilon \qquad \text{if } n > N.$$

Since $\Lambda = \lambda$, this can be rewritten as

$$|x_n - \lambda| < \epsilon \qquad \text{if } n > N. \quad ∎$$

The **limit superior** of a function at a point can be defined similarly. Thus if f is bounded above in a neighborhood of a, $\lim \sup_{x \to a} f(x)$ or $\overline{\lim}_{x \to a} f(x)$ is defined as the supremum of the cluster points of f at a. If f is not bounded above in any neighborhood of a, we say that

$$\lim \sup_{x \to a} f(x) = +\infty.$$

Similarly we define $\lim \inf_{x \to a} f(x)$ or $\underline{\lim}_{x \to a} f(x)$, and $\lim \sup_{x \to \pm \infty} f(x)$ and $\lim \inf_{x \to \pm \infty} f(x)$.

The next two theorems are the analogues of the two previous ones. Their proofs are left as exercises (B2).

6.3c Theorem. Let f be bounded above in a deleted neighborhood of a. Then for each $\epsilon > 0$ there is a $\delta_1(\epsilon)$ such that

$$f(x) \leqslant \lim \sup_{x \to a} f(x) + \epsilon \qquad \text{if } 0 < |x - a| < \delta_1,$$

and if f is bounded below there is a $\delta_2(\epsilon)$ such that

$$f(x) \geqslant \lim \inf_{x \to a} f(x) - \epsilon \qquad \text{if } 0 < |x - a| < \delta_2.$$

6.3d Theorem. In order that $\lim\limits_{x \to a} f(x)$ exist, it is necessary and sufficient that

$$\limsup_{x \to a} f(x) = \liminf_{x \to a} f(x).$$

A EXERCISES

1. Compute $\limsup x_n$ and $\liminf x_n$ for the following sequences:

(a) $\left\{\sin\dfrac{n\pi}{2} + \dfrac{(-1)^n}{n}\right\}$ (b) $\left\{\cos\dfrac{n\pi}{4} + (-1)^n\right\}$

(c) $\left\{\dfrac{[1 + (-1)^{n+1}]}{2} n^{(-1)^n} + \sin\dfrac{n\pi}{6}\right\}$ (d) $\{n^{(-1)^n}\}$

(e) $\{(-1)^{n+1} n^{(-1)^n}\}$ (f) $\{(-1)^n n^{(-1)^n}\}$.

2. Compute $\limsup\limits_{x \to 0} f(x)$ and $\liminf\limits_{x \to 0} f(x)$ for the following functions:

(a) $\sin\dfrac{1}{x}$.   (b) $\left|\sin\dfrac{1}{x}\right|$.   (c) $\sin\dfrac{1}{x}\cos\dfrac{1}{x}$.

B EXERCISES

1. Show that the set of cluster points of $\dfrac{1}{x}\left|\sin\dfrac{1}{x}\right|$ at zero is not bounded above.

2. Prove Theorems 6.3c and 6.3d.

C EXERCISES

1. Letting $\{x_n\}$ be a given sequence, prove that:

(a) $\limsup x_n = \lim\limits_{n \to \infty}\left[\sup\limits_{k \geqslant n} x_k\right]$ (b) $\liminf x_n = \lim\limits_{n \to \infty}\left[\inf\limits_{k \geqslant n} x_k\right]$

2. Letting f be defined in a neighborhood of a, prove that:

(a) $\limsup\limits_{x \to a} f(x) = \lim\limits_{\delta \to 0}\left[\sup\limits_{0 < |x-a| \leqslant \delta} f(x)\right]$ (b) $\liminf\limits_{x \to a} f(x) = \lim\limits_{\delta \to 0}\left[\inf\limits_{0 < |x-a| \leqslant \delta} f(x)\right]$

6.4 DEEPER PROPERTIES OF CONTINUOUS FUNCTIONS

In this section we want to establish some properties of continuous functions defined on closed bounded intervals. These are somewhat more difficult to prove than the earlier properties established in Chapter 3, hence the title of the present section. We have here two main aims. The first is to prove Theorem 3.6b, which asserts that a continuous function on a closed bounded interval attains a maximum there. This provides the completion of the proofs of Rolle's theorem and the mean-value theorem, which were based on Theorem 3.6b. The second is to prove that continuity on a closed bounded interval implies uniform continuity. We begin with a preliminary theorem.

6.4a   Theorem. If f is continuous on a closed bounded interval I: $\{a \leqslant x \leqslant b\}$, then it is bounded there.

Proof. Suppose, for contradiction, that f is not bounded on I. Let us consider the set S of c's between a and b for which f is bounded in $\{a \leqslant x \leqslant c\}$. The set S is not empty, for by continuity at $x = a$ with $\epsilon = 1$ we have a δ, so that

$$|f(x) - f(a)| < 1 \qquad \text{if } |x - a| < \delta_1.$$

Thus $\qquad |f(x)| < |f(a)| + 1 \qquad \text{if } |x - a| < \delta_1.$

Define c_0 by

$$c_0 = \sup_S c.$$

We wish to show that $c_0 = b$. Suppose this is not so. Then also at c_0 there is an interval $\{c_0 - \delta \leqslant x \leqslant c_0 + \delta\}$ in which f is bounded by $M_1 = |f(c_0)| + 1$, by the same sort of continuity argument. And since $c_0 - \delta < c_0$, we have f bounded in $\{a \leqslant x \leqslant c_0 - \delta\}$, say by M_2. Then for $M = \max [M_1, M_2]$ we have

$$|f(x)| \leqslant M \qquad \text{in } \{a \leqslant x \leqslant c_0 + \delta\}.$$

Since $c_0 + \delta > c_0$, this contradicts the definition of c_0 as $\sup_S c$. Therefore $c_0 = b$ and f is bounded in I. ∎

We now turn to the proof that a continuous function achieves a maximum on a closed bounded interval.

6.4b   Theorem. If f is continuous on a closed bounded interval I: $\{a \leqslant x \leqslant b\}$, then there is a point x_0 in I for which

$$f(x_0) \geqslant f(x) \qquad \text{for all } x \text{ in } I.$$

Proof. By Theorem 6.4a, f is bounded in I. Hence $M = \sup_I f(x)$ exists. Suppose there is no point in I for which $f(x) = M$. Then $M - f(x)$ is everywhere positive in I and is of course continuous there. This implies, by Theorem 3.2a(ii), that $\dfrac{1}{M - f(x)}$ is continuous there. Again by Theorem 6.4a, $\dfrac{1}{M - f(x)}$ is bounded in I, say by B. Then

$$\frac{1}{M - f(x)} \leqslant B \qquad \text{for all } x \text{ in } I,$$

which implies that

$$f(x) \leqslant M - \frac{1}{B} < M \qquad \text{for all } x \text{ in } I.$$

This contradicts the fact that $M = \sup_I f(x)$.   ∎

Let us recall the definition of uniform continuity which we had in Chapter 3: A function f is uniformly continuous on a set D if for each $\epsilon > 0$ there is a δ (depending only on ϵ and D), so that for x and x' in D

$$|f(x) - f(x')| < \epsilon \qquad \text{if } |x - x'| < \delta.$$

The fundamental theorem on uniform continuity follows.

6.4c   Theorem. A function which is continuous on a closed bounded interval I: $\{a \leqslant x \leqslant b\}$ is uniformly continuous there.

Proof. Again the proof is by contradiction. Suppose the theorem were not true. This would mean that there is an exceptional ϵ, say ϵ_0, such that for every $\delta > 0$ there exists a pair of points x and x' in I with $|x - x'| < \delta$ for which $|f(x) - f(x')| \geqslant \epsilon_0$. Take δ successively to be $1, \frac{1}{2}, \frac{1}{3}, \ldots$. Thus there are

x_1, x_1' in I with $|x_1 - x_1'| < 1$ for which $|f(x_1) - f(x_1')| \geqslant \epsilon_0$

x_2, x_2' in I with $|x_2 - x_2'| < 1/2$ for which $|f(x_2) - f(x_2')| \geqslant \epsilon_0$

.

.

.

x_n, x_n' in I with $|x_n - x_n'| < 1/n$ for which $|f(x_n) - f(x_n')| \geqslant \epsilon_0$.

.

.

.

Thus we have two sequences, $\{x_n\}$ and $\{x_n'\}$, in I for which

$$|x_n - x_n'| < 1/n$$

and

$$|f(x_n) - f(x_n')| \geqslant \epsilon_0.$$

Now the sequence $\{x_n\}$ is bounded, for $a \leqslant x_n \leqslant b$, and hence has a cluster point, which we will denote by β. There is a sub-sequence $\{x_{n_k}\}$ converging to β. Thus

$$\beta = \lim x_{n_k} \geqslant a \qquad \text{since } x_{n_k} \geqslant a$$

and

$$\beta = \lim x_{n_k} \leqslant b \qquad \text{since } x_{n_k} \leqslant b.$$

This means that β is in I, and therefore f is continuous at β. Also

$$|\beta - x_{n_k}'| \leqslant |\beta - x_{n_k}| + |x_{n_k} - x_{n_k}'| \leqslant |\beta - x_{n_k}| + 1/n_k$$

As $k \to \infty$, $n_k \to \infty$ and $x_{n_k} \to \beta$, so that $|\beta - x'_{n_k}| \to 0$. This means that $x'_{n_k} \to \beta$. Then by the continuity of f at β,

$$|f(x_{n_k}) - f(x'_{n_k})| \to |f(\beta) - f(\beta)| = 0,$$

which contradicts the construction that

$$|f(x_{n_k}) - f(x'_{n_k})| \geqslant \epsilon_0. \qquad ■$$

A EXERCISES

1. Show that the following functions are uniformly continuous in the intervals indicated:

(a) $\sqrt{x}$ $\quad \{0 \leqslant x \leqslant 1.\}$ *use theorem 1 (pan. 12)*

(b) $\begin{cases} x \sin \dfrac{1}{x} & x \neq 0 \\ 0 & x = 0 \end{cases}$ $\quad \{0 \leqslant x \leqslant 1\}.$

hand in (c) $\begin{cases} \dfrac{\sin x}{x} & x \neq 0 \\ 1 & x = 0. \end{cases}$ $\quad \{-1 \leqslant x \leqslant 1\}$

(d) $\begin{cases} \dfrac{1 - \cos x}{x^2} & x \neq 0 \\ \dfrac{1}{2} & x = 0 \end{cases}$ $\quad \{-\pi \leqslant x \leqslant \pi\}$ *prove continuity quotient of 2 cont. func-tions is cont; a constant is cont.*

(e) $x^3 \operatorname{sgn} x$ $\quad \{-\pi \leqslant x \leqslant \pi\}$

2. Show that if $f(x)$ is uniformly continuous on an interval I, then it is uniformly continuous on each sub-interval of I.

B EXERCISES

hand in
1. Show that if $f(x)$ is continuous on an open interval J: $\{a < x < b\}$, and if $f(a + 0)$ and $f(b - 0)$ both exist, then $f(x)$ is uniformly continuous on J. *(Pg. 47) Theorem 1*

2. Let f be differentiable on an open interval J: $\{a < x < b\}$. Show that if f' is bounded on J, then f is uniformly continuous on J.

prove the func. has a der. to prove it cont. at 0

$$\lim_{h \to 0} \frac{f(0+h) - f(0)}{h} = \lim_{h \to 0} \frac{\frac{1-\cos h}{h^2} - \frac{1}{2}}{h} =$$

$$\lim_{h \to 0} \frac{\frac{\sin^2 h}{(1+\cos h) h^2} - \frac{1}{2}}{h} = \lim_{h \to 0} \frac{2\sin^2 h - h^2(1+\cosh)}{2h^3(1+\cosh)}$$

show: $\left| \dfrac{1-\cos x}{x^2} - \dfrac{1}{2} \right|$

$|f(x) - f(a)|$

7

Properties
of Differentiable Functions

7.1 THE CAUCHY MEAN-VALUE THEOREM

In this chapter we obtain some further properties of differentiable functions, most of which are consequences of the mean-value theorem (3.6e). We begin by establishing an extension of this theorem known as the **Cauchy mean-value theorem.**

7.1a Theorem. Suppose f and g are continuous on a closed interval $I: \{a \leqslant x \leqslant b\}$ and differentiable on the open interval $J: \{a < x < b\}$. Then there is a point β for which

$$[f(b) - f(a)]g'(\beta) = [g(b) - g(a)]f'(\beta).$$

If, in addition, $g(b) \neq g(a)$ and $f'(x)$ and $g'(x)$ are not simultaneously zero in J, then

$$\frac{f(b) - f(a)}{g(b) - g(a)} = \frac{f'(\beta)}{g'(\beta)}.$$

Proof. We apply Rolle's theorem to the function F given by

$$F(x) = g(x)[f(b) - f(a)] - f(x)[g(b) - g(a)].$$

Clearly F is continuous in I and differentiable in J, since f and g are. And it is easily verified that $F(b) = F(a)$. Thus there is a point β in J for which $F'(\beta) = 0$. This proves the first part. If $g(b) - g(a) \neq 0$, and if $f'(\beta)$ and $g'(\beta)$ are not both zero, then $g'(\beta)$ cannot be zero; for if it were, then $f'(\beta)$

128

would also be zero. Thus we can divide by $g'(\beta)$ and by $g(b) - g(a)$ to obtain the second formula.   ∎

While the above proof is simple, it depends upon writing down the correct function F. There is a geometrical interpretation of this result which helps to explain the form of F. Suppose we have a curve C given by

$$x = g(t), \quad y = f(t) \quad \{a \leqslant t \leqslant b\}.$$

The coordinates of the end points are $[g(a), f(a)]$ and $[g(b), f(b)]$. The slope of the secant line connecting these points is

$$\frac{f(b) - f(a)}{g(b) - g(a)}.$$

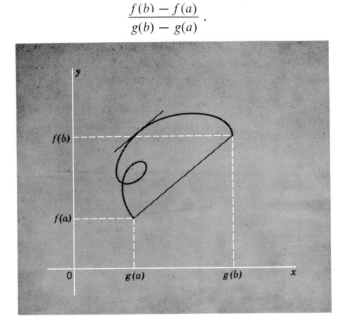

And if the functions are smooth, the slope of the tangent line at any point is given by

$$\frac{dy}{dx} = \frac{dy/dt}{dx/dt} = \frac{f'(x)}{g'(x)}.$$

The equality asserted by the theorem then reads geometrically as follows: Between any two points on a smooth curve C, there is a third point at which the tangent line is parallel to the secant line connecting the first two. Working backward, it is not difficult to guess that the function F to examine is precisely the one we wrote down.

7.2 L'HOSPITAL'S RULE

In calculating limits of ratios, our only formula is

$$\lim_{x \to a} [f(x)/g(x)] = \left[\lim_{x \to a} f(x)\right] / \left[\lim_{x \to a} g(x)\right].$$

This formula, of course, requires that both limits on the right exist, and also that the denominator not be zero. Many important and interesting limits fail to meet one or the other of these requirements, so that this formula is not available for their evaluation. A simple example is given by

$$\lim_{x \to 0} \frac{\sin x}{x} = 1,$$

which we have used before and which was established in Chapter 5.

In the following theorem f and g are defined on an open interval J, of which a is an end point. The limits are to be understood as one-sided limits as $x \to a$, with x of course being in J; and they may also be improper limits in the sense that the "value" of a limit may be $+\infty$ *or* $-\infty$. The limits may also be as $x \to +\infty$ or $-\infty$, in which case J will be a semi-infinite interval of the form $\{x > X_0\}$ or $\{x < X_0\}$. This theorem is known as **l'Hospital's rule**.

7.2a Theorem. Let J be an interval as described in the previous paragraph. Suppose also that f and g are differentiable functions in J for which

(i) neither $g(x)$ nor $g'(x)$ vanishes in J,

(ii) $\lim\limits_{x \to a} \dfrac{f'(x)}{g'(x)} = A,$

(iii) $f(x) \to 0$ and $g(x) \to 0$ as $x \to a$, or

(iii') $g(x) \to \pm\infty$ as $x \to a$.

Then
$$\lim_{x \to a} \frac{f(x)}{g(x)} = A.$$

Proof. The different cases covered by this theorem add up to quite a long argument. We will give proofs of two typical cases to illustrate the type of arguments involved:

CASE 1. a is a finite point, and condition (iii) holds rather than (iii').

Here we define $f(a) = g(a) = 0$ so that f and g are continuous at $x = a$. Then, for any x in J, we can apply the Cauchy mean-value theorem to the interval between a and x. Thus for each x in J there is a point β between a and x for which

$$\frac{f(x)}{g(x)} = \frac{f(x) - f(a)}{g(x) - g(a)} = \frac{f'(\beta)}{g'(\beta)}.$$

Now $\beta \to a$ as $x \to a$, so that

$$\lim_{x \to a} \frac{f(x)}{g(x)} = \lim_{\beta \to a} \frac{f'(\beta)}{g'(\beta)} = A.$$

CASE 2. $a = +\infty$, $A = +\infty$ $g(x) \to \pm\infty$.

Here we assume that f and g have the stated properties in $J: \{x > X_0\}$. Let $M > 1$ be given. Then there is an $X_1 \geqslant X_0$ for which

$$\frac{f'(x)}{g'(x)} \geqslant 2M + 2 \qquad \text{if } x > X_1.$$

(The meaning of the hypothesis that $A = +\infty$—that is, $\dfrac{f'(x)}{g'(x)} \to +\infty$— is that this ratio becomes larger than any preassigned number if x is sufficiently large.) We choose any $x > X_1$ and then b, so that $x > b > X_1$. Applying the Cauchy mean-value theorem to the interval from b to x, we see that there is a β between b and x such that

$$\frac{f(x) - f(b)}{g(x) - g(b)} = \frac{f'(\beta)}{g'(\beta)} \geqslant 2M + 2.$$

Thus

$$\frac{f(x)/g(x) - f(b)/g(x)}{1 - g(b)/g(x)} \geqslant 2M + 2.$$

If we keep b fixed, we see that there is an X_2 such that

$$\left| \frac{f(b)}{g(x)} \right| \leqslant 1 \quad \text{and} \quad \left| \frac{g(b)}{g(x)} \right| \leqslant \frac{1}{2} \qquad \text{if } x > X_2,$$

since $|g(x)| \to +\infty$. Thus for $x > X = \max[X_1, X_2]$ we have

$$\frac{f(x)/g(x) + 1}{1 - \frac{1}{2}} \geqslant 2M + 2,$$

or

$$\frac{f(x)}{g(x)} \geqslant M \qquad \text{if } x > X.$$

Since this is true for every $M > 1$, it is the meaning of

$$\frac{f(x)}{g(x)} \to +\infty.$$

■

Instead of writing limit symbols at each step of a calculation of a limit, by l'Hospital's rule we find it convenient to use the symbol $\sim$, which is to be read "has the same limit as." Thus the equation

$$\lim_{x \to a} \frac{f(x)}{g(x)} = \lim_{x \to a} \frac{f'(x)}{g'(x)}$$

becomes

$$\frac{f(x)}{g(x)} \sim \frac{f'(x)}{g'(x)} \qquad \text{as } x \to a.$$

The point a at which the limit is being computed will have to be explicitly stated as above or made clear in some way.

EXAMPLE 1. Compute $\displaystyle\lim_{x \to 0} \frac{a^x - b^x}{x}$ if $a > 0$, $b > 0$. [See Exercise C1(c), Section 5.2.]

Solution:

$$\frac{a^x - b^x}{x} \sim \frac{a^x \log a - b^x \log b}{1} \to \log a - \log b = \log \frac{a}{b}.$$

The symbol $\sim$ indicates here the step in which l'Hospital's rule was applied; the arrow indicates passage to the limit. We leave it for you to verify that l'Hospital's rule is applicable. Be careful to avoid such nonsense as

$$\frac{a^x - b^x}{x} = a^x \log a - b^x \log b = \log a - \log b.$$

The new symbol is also quite useful in eliminating factors having known limits, as the following example illustrates.

EXAMPLE 2. Compute $\displaystyle\lim_{x \to 0} \frac{1 - \cos x}{x^2}$.

Solution:

$$\frac{1 - \cos x}{x^2} = \frac{1 - \cos^2 x}{(1 + \cos x)x^2} = \frac{\sin^2 x}{x^2} \cdot \frac{1}{1 + \cos x} \sim \frac{1}{1 + \cos x} \to \frac{1}{2}.$$

The same limit can be evaluated by l'Hospital's rule:

$$\frac{1 - \cos x}{x^2} \sim \frac{\sin x}{2x} \to \frac{1}{2}.$$

Repeated application of the rule is sometimes necessary to evaluate some limits.

EXAMPLE 3. Compute $\displaystyle\lim_{x \to 0} \frac{\sin x - x}{x^3}$.

Solution:

$$\frac{\sin x - x}{x^3} \sim \frac{\cos x - 1}{3x^2} \sim \frac{-\sin x}{6x} \rightarrow -\frac{1}{6}.$$

The hypotheses must be satisfied for each application in order that we may apply the rule repeatedly.

EXAMPLE 4. Compute $\lim\limits_{x \to \infty} \left(1 + \dfrac{1}{x}\right)^x$.

Solution:

$$\log \left(1 + \frac{1}{x}\right)^x = x \log \left(1 + \frac{1}{x}\right) = \frac{\log (1 + 1/x)}{1/x}$$

$$\sim \frac{[x/(x + 1)](-1/x^2)}{-1/x^2} = \frac{x}{1 + x} \rightarrow 1.$$

Thus, since the logarithm is a continuous function,

$$\lim_{x \to \infty} \log \left(1 + \frac{1}{x}\right)^x = \log \lim_{x \to \infty} \left(1 + \frac{1}{x}\right)^x = 1.$$

Taking exponentials, we then get

$$\lim_{x \to \infty} \left(1 + \frac{1}{x}\right)^x = e^1 = e.$$

EXAMPLE 5. Compute $\lim\limits_{x \to 0} (\cos x)^{1/x^2}$.

Solution:

$$\log (\cos x)^{1/x^2} = \frac{\log \cos x}{x^2} \sim \frac{-\tan x}{2x} \rightarrow -\frac{1}{2}.$$

Hence, as before,

$$\lim_{x \to 0} (\cos x)^{1/x^2} = e^{-\frac{1}{2}} = 1/\sqrt{e}.$$

A EXERCISES

1. Compute the following limits:

(a) $\lim\limits_{x \to 0} \dfrac{\sin 3x}{\sin x}$

(b) $\lim\limits_{x \to \frac{1}{2}} \dfrac{\cos \pi x}{2x - 1}$

(c) $\lim\limits_{x \to 0} \dfrac{e^x - (1 + x)}{x^2}$

(d) $\lim\limits_{x \to \infty} \dfrac{\log x}{x^\alpha} \qquad \alpha > 0$

(e) $\lim\limits_{x \to \infty} x^\alpha e^{-x} \qquad \alpha > 0$

(f) $\lim\limits_{x \to 0+} \dfrac{x^\alpha}{e^x - 1} \qquad \alpha \geqslant 1$

(g) $\lim\limits_{x \to 0} \dfrac{1 - \cos kx}{a^{x^2} - b^{x^2}} \qquad a > 0, b > 0.$

(h) Is $3^x/x^{100,000,000}$ large or small for very large x?

(i) $\lim\limits_{x\to 0} \dfrac{1 - a^x}{1 - b^x}$ $\quad a > 0, b > 0$

(j) $\lim\limits_{x\to 0} \dfrac{\sin x - x}{\arcsin x - x}$

(k) $\lim\limits_{x\to 0} \left(\dfrac{1}{x} - \cot x\right)$

(l) $\lim\limits_{x\to 0+} x^x$

(m) $\lim\limits_{x\to\infty} (1 + a/x)^{bx}$

(n) $\lim\limits_{x\to\pi/2-0} (\tan x)^{\sin 2x}$

(o) $\lim\limits_{x\to\pi/2-0} (\tan x)^{\tan x}$

(p) $\lim\limits_{x\to 0} (\sec x)^{1/x^2}$

B EXERCISES

1. If f is defined in a neighborhood of a, f' is continuous there, and $f''(a)$ exists, show that

$$\lim_{h\to 0} \frac{f(a + 2h) - 2f(a + h) + f(a)}{h^2} = f''(a).$$

h and in 2. Compare the behavior of $f(x)/g(x)$ and $f'(x)/g'(x)$ in the following instances:

(a) $f(x) = x^2 \sin 1/x$, $g(x) = \tan x$ $\quad$ as $x \to 0$. $\quad$ *$f(x) = \frac{1}{x}$, $g(y) = \frac{1}{x} + \sin$* *$(x \to 0)$*

(b) $f(x) = x - \sin x$, $g(x) = x$ $\quad$ as $x \to \infty$.

Reconcile the behavior of these examples with l'Hospital's rule.

3. Suppose f and g are continuous and have continuous derivatives up to nth order in a neighborhood of a. Suppose also that f and g and their first $(n - 1)$ derivatives vanish at a, while $g^{(n)}(a) \neq 0$. Show that as $x \to a$, $f(x)/g(x) \to$ $f^{(n)}(a)/g^{(n)}(a)$.

direct application of last theorem in notes in hand in 4. Let f be differentiable in $\{x > x_0\}$, and suppose $f'(x) \to A$ as $x \to \infty$. Show that $f(x)/x \to A$ as $x \to \infty$.

5. Let f be differentiable in $\{x > x_0\}$, and suppose $f(x) \to A < \infty$ as $x \to \infty$ and $f'(x) \to B$, show that $B = 0$.

C EXERCISES

extra credit *problem is wrong (A should be restricted a* *find an ex. which proves this false*

1. If f is differentiable in $\{x > x_0\}$ and $f(x) + f'(x) \to A$ as $x \to \infty$, show that $f(x) \to A$ and $f'(x) \to 0$.

2. Let f have n continuous derivatives in $\{x > x_0\}$, and suppose that $f(x)/x^n \to A$ and $f^{(n)}(x) \to B$ as $x \to \infty$. Evaluate B in terms of A and n. Also evaluate

$$\lim_{x\to\infty} \frac{f^{(k)}(x)}{x^{n-k}} \quad \text{for } 1 \leqslant k \leqslant n.$$

7.3 TAYLOR'S FORMULA WITH REMAINDER

We know that e^x has the value 1 when $x = 0$, that is, $e^0 = 1$. Thus one might reasonably ask how close is e^x to 1 when x is small? Is the difference approximately the size of x itself, of x^2, of $\sqrt{x}$, or of $1/\log(1/x)$? The mean-value theorem supplies a clue, since it says that

$$\frac{e^x - e^0}{x - 0} = \frac{e^x - 1}{x} = e^\beta,$$

where β is between 0 and x. Thus for small x we must have β even smaller, so that e^β is near 1 and $e^x - 1$ is approximately equal to x. In fact, by l'Hospital's rule

(1) $$\frac{e^x - 1}{x} \sim e^x \to 1 \qquad \text{as } x \to 0.$$

Thus, interpreting the $\sim$ as "approximately equal," we have that e^x is approximately equal to $1 + x$ when x is small.

Again, we can ask how close are e^x and $1 + x$ for small x. Let us compare the difference with x^2. Using l'Hospital's rule again, we get

(2) $$\frac{e^x - (1 + x)}{x^2} \sim \frac{e^x - 1}{2x} \to \frac{1}{2},$$

where we used (1) in the last step of (2).

This suggests that we compare the difference between e^x and $1 + x + \frac{1}{2}x^2$ with x^3:

(3) $$\frac{e^x - (1 + x + \frac{1}{2}x^2)}{x^3} \sim \frac{e^x - (1 + x)}{3x^2} \to \frac{1}{3} \cdot \frac{1}{2} = \frac{1}{3!},$$

where we used (2) in the last step of (3). Clearly we could proceed.

We can readily repeat these calculations with any sufficiently differentiable function f at any point a. The mean-value theorem suggests we compare $f(x) - f(a)$ with $x - a$. Indeed, the existence of a derivative demands that they be comparable:

$$\frac{f(x) - f(a)}{x - a} \to f'(a).$$

From this, as above, we are lead to compare $f(x) - [f(a) + f'(a)(x - a)]$ with $(x - a)^2$:

$$\frac{f(x) - [f(a) + f'(a)(x - a)]}{(x - a)^2} \sim \frac{f'(x) - f'(a)}{2(x - a)} \to \frac{1}{2}f''(a).$$

You see how it goes. Soon we are comparing $f(x)$ with

$$f(a) + f'(a)(x - a) + \frac{1}{2!}f''(a)(x - a)^2 + \cdots + \frac{1}{n!}f^{(n)}(a)(x - a)^n.$$

The value of n with which this terminates depends upon which is exhausted first, the number of available derivatives or our patience. But at no place (unless f happens to be a polynomial) will we be able to stop the procedure and have equality between f and the approximating polynomial in an interval. Hence we have the alternatives of continuing indefinitely, as we will do when we study infinite series, or of stopping after a finite number of terms and writing in a correction term:

$$f(x) = f(a) + f'(a)(x - a) + \frac{1}{2!} f''(a)(x - a)^2$$

$$+ \cdots + \frac{1}{n!} f^{(n)}(a)(x - a)^n + R_{n+1}.$$

This is known as **Taylor's formula with remainder**, which can be written down for any function which has n derivatives. The remainder, R_{n+1}, is simply the difference between f and the approximating polynomial. It is the form and size of this remainder which concerns us now. In particular, we are interested in information about R_{n+1} that will help us determine the closeness with which the polynomial approximates f. We begin with the following theorem.

7.3a   Theorem. Let f and its first $n + 1$ derivatives be continuous in a closed interval I: $\{c \leqslant x \leqslant d\}$. Then for any x and any a in I, we have

$$f(x) = f(a) + f'(a)(x - a) + \cdots + \frac{1}{n!} f^{(n)}(a)(x - a)^n + R_{n+1},$$

where $\qquad R_{n+1} = \frac{1}{n!} \int_a^x (x - t)^n f^{(n+1)}(t)\, dt.$

Proof. By Theorem 4.5b, we have

$$f(x) = f(a) + \int_a^x f'(t)\, dt.$$

We integrate by parts, setting

$$u = f'(t) \qquad dv = dt$$
$$du = f''(t)\, dt \qquad v = -(x - t).$$

This yields

$$f(x) = f(a) - f'(t)(x - t)\Big|_a^x + \int_a^x f''(t)(x - t)\, dt$$

$$= f(a) + f'(a)(x - a) + \int_a^x f''(t)(x - t)\, dt.$$

Repeated integration by parts, each time differentiating the derivative of f and integrating the power of $(x - t)$, leads by induction to the stated formula. ∎

7.3b Corollary. Under the same hypotheses as in 7.3a,

$$R_{n+1} = \frac{1}{(n+1)!} f^{(n+1)}(\beta)(x-a)^{n+1},$$

where β lies between a and x.

Proof. By the generalized mean-value theorem for integrals, we have

$$R_{n+1} = \frac{1}{n!} \int_a^x f^{(n+1)}(t)(x-t)^n \, dt = \frac{f^{(n+1)}(\beta)}{n!} \int_a^x (x-t)^n \, dt$$

$$= -\frac{f^{(n+1)}(\beta)}{n!} \frac{(x-t)^{n+1}}{n+1} \bigg]_a^x = \frac{f^{(n+1)}(\beta)}{(n+1)!}(x-a)^{n+1}. \qquad \blacksquare$$

The application of the mean-value theorem requires continuity of $f^{(n+1)}$. However, the conclusion of the corollary is valid if we only assume its existence. The result, which is stated below, is sometimes known as the **generalized form of the mean-value theorem.**

7.3c Theorem. If f and its first n derivatives are continuous in a closed interval I: $\{a \leqslant x \leqslant b\}$, and if $f^{(n+1)}(x)$ exists at each point of the open interval J: $\{a < x < b\}$, then for each x in I there is a β in J for which

$$R_{n+1} = \frac{f^{(n+1)}(\beta)}{(n+1)!}(x-a)^{n+1}.$$

Proof. Let $x \neq a$ be a point in I. It will remain fixed throughout the remainder of the proof. In the closed interval from a to x, we define the function F by

$$F(t) = f(x) - f(t) - (x-t)f'(t) - \cdots - \frac{(x-t)^n}{n!} f^{(n)}(t) - \frac{(x-t)^{n+1}}{(n+1)!} A$$

We want to apply Rolle's theorem (3.6d) to F. For this, F must be differentiable in $\{a < t < x\}$ and continuous in $\{a \leqslant t \leqslant x\}$, which are clearly all satisfied, and $F(a)$ must equal $F(x)$. Clearly $F(x) = 0$. Now we choose A so that $F(a) = 0$ also. Thus we choose

$$A = \left\{ f(x) - f(a) - f'(a)(x-a) - \cdots - \frac{f^{(n)}(a)}{n!}(x-a)^n \right\} \frac{(n+1)!}{(x-a)^n}.$$

Then there is a β between a and x for which $F'(\beta) = 0$.

When we compute $F'(t)$, many cancellations take place. For example,

$$\frac{d}{dt} \left[(x-t)f'(t) \right] = (x-t)f''(t) - f'(t)$$

cancels with $f'(t)$ from the preceding term and with one of the terms from the succeeding one. Thus we get

$$F'(\beta) = -\frac{f^{(n+1)}(\beta)(x - \beta)^n}{n!} + \frac{(x - \beta)^n}{n!} A = 0.$$

Since $\beta \neq x$ we can divide out $(x - \beta)^n/n!$, substitute the previous value for A, and solve for $f(x)$. This yields the desired formula. ∎

In the statement of the theorem, we took point a to be the lower end of an interval. It could just as well be an upper end. Thus if a were an interior point, x could be on either side of it.

Taylor's formula is sometimes given in a slightly different notation. Setting $x - a = h$, then $x = a + h$, we get

$$f(a + h) = f(a) + f'(a)h + \frac{f''(a)h^2}{2!} + \cdots + \frac{f^{(n)}(a)h^n}{n!} + \frac{f^{(n+1)}(\beta)h^{n+1}}{(n + 1)!}.$$

Point β lies between a and $a + h$. Any such point can be represented as

$$\beta = a + \theta h \qquad \{0 < \theta < 1\}.$$

In fact,
$$\theta = \frac{\beta - a}{h} = \frac{\beta - a}{x - a}.$$

There are other forms in which the remainder can be written, some of which will be explored in the problems.

An important consequence of these formulas for the remainder is that now we can give some numerical bounds for determining how close the approximating polynomial in Taylor's formula is to the function. For example,

$$e^x = 1 + x + \frac{x^2}{2!} + \cdots + \frac{x^n}{n!} + \frac{x^{n+1}}{(n + 1)!} e^\beta$$

where β lies between 0 and x. Thus if

$$P_n(x) = 1 + x + \frac{x^2}{2!} + \cdots + \frac{x^n}{n!},$$

then
$$|e^x - P_n(x)| = \frac{|x|^{n+1}}{(n + 1)!} e^\beta.$$

In particular, if $x < 0$, then $\beta < 0$, and $e^\beta < 1$; hence

$$|e^x - P_n(x)| \leqslant \frac{|x|^{n+1}}{(n + 1)!}.$$

And if $x > 0$, then $\beta < x$, and $e^\beta < e^x$; hence

$$|e^x - P_n(x)| \leqslant \frac{|x|^{n+1}}{(n+1)!} e^x.$$

A EXERCISES

1. Write out Taylor's formula with remainder for the following functions at the points indicated. Letting $n = 6$, estimate the size of the remainder in each case:

(a) $\sin x$ 0 and $\pi/4$

(b) $\cos x$ 0 and $\pi/4$

(c) e^{-x} 0 and a

(d) e^x 0 and a

(e) $\sinh x$ 0

(f) $\cosh x$ 0

(g) $\log (1 + x)$ 0

(h) $x^5 + 3x^3 - 4x^2 + 2$ 1

(i) a^x 0

(j) $x^6 + 5x^3 + 4$ 2

Compute remainder

write out Taylor's formula

2. Write out the first three non-zero terms in Taylor's formula for the following:

(a) $\sin x^2$ 0

(b) $\sin^2 x$ 0

(c) $\sec x$ 0

(d) $\tan x$ 0

(e) $\arcsin x$ 0

(f) $\arctan x$ 0

(g) $(1 + x)^a$ 0

(h) $(1 + x^2)^a$ 0

(i) e^{x^2} 0

(j) e^{-x^2} 0

3. Show that in Taylor's formula for $\sin x$ about $x = 0$, $R_{2n} = R_{2n+1}$; and for $\cos x$, $R_{2n} = R_{2n-1}$.

B EXERCISES

1. Study the function f given by

$$f(x) = \begin{cases} x \csc x & x \neq 0 \\ 1 & x = 0, \end{cases}$$

and show that near $x = 0$, $\csc x = 1/x + x/6 + \cdots$

2. Obtain a similar formula for $\cot x$.

3. Let f be an even function defined in a neighborhood of the origin. Show that in Taylor's formula about 0 only even powers of x occur. And if f is odd, then only odd powers occur. Assume, of course, the existence of the necessary derivatives.

4. Let f have $(n + 1)$ continuous derivatives in a neighborhood N of the origin. Let its Taylor formula with remainder be

$$f(x) = P_n(x) + \frac{f^{(n+1)}(\beta)}{(n+1)!} x^{n+1}$$

Now the point β depends on x. Thus $f^{(n+1)}(\beta(x))$ is a function of x. Denote it by $\psi(x)$. Show that $\psi(x)$ has $(n + 1)$ derivatives in N except at the origin.

5. In the following functions, show that for each x in the given interval $R_{n+1} \to 0$ as $n \to \infty$ for Taylor's formula centred at $x = 0$:

(*a*) $\sin x$ $\{-\infty < x < \infty\}$ (*b*) e^x $\{-\infty < x < \infty\}$

(*c*) $\cos x$ $\{-\infty < x < \infty\}$ (*d*) $\log (1 + x)$ $\{-1 < x < 1\}$

(*e*) $\sinh x$ $\{-\infty < x < \infty\}$ (*f*) $\cosh x$ $\{-\infty < x < \infty\}$

6. Letting $n = 2$, use the formula from Exercise A1(*i*) to calculate $\lim\limits_{x \to 0} \dfrac{a^x - b^x}{x}$.

C EXERCISES

1. In Exercise B4, if f has $n + k + 1$ derivatives in N, then $\psi(x)$ has $n + k + 1$ derivatives in N except at $x = 0$, where it has k derivatives.

2. Obtain the first few terms of Taylor's formula for f at the origin if

$$f(x) = \begin{cases} (1 + x)^{1/x} & x \neq 0 \\ e & x = 0. \end{cases}$$

3. Show that, for small a, the equation $\sin x = ax$ has a root near π. Show also that $\pi(1 - a)$ and $\pi(1 - a + a^2)$ are successively better approximations to the root.

7.4 EXTREME VALUES

We have seen (Theorem 3.6a) that a necessary condition for a differentiable function to achieve a maximum or a minimum value at an interior point of an interval is that the first derivative be zero at the point. It is clear that this need not be so if the derivative fails to exist at only one point of the interval. It also need not be so for a maximum or a minimum achieved at an end point of a closed interval. For example, the function given by $f(x) = x$ on $\{0 < x < 1\}$ achieves a maximum at 1 and a minimum at 0, but at neither point does the derivative vanish.

In the exercises we will take up some cases of extreme values at end points and at interior points where the derivative is not zero. We will discuss here what further conditions will guarantee that a point at which the derivative is zero is an extreme point of the function. That is, we will give conditions sufficient to distinguish among the various kinds of points at which the derivative vanishes. Such a point is called a **critical point** of the function, and we want to know how to tell whether a critical point is a maximum, a minimum, or neither. We begin by establishing a test used in elementary calculus.

7.4a Theorem. Let $f(x)$ be differentiable in an open interval J: $\{a < x < b\}$ and $f'(\beta) = 0$ for some point β in J, and suppose that $f'(x) \geqslant 0$ for $x < \beta$ and $f'(x) \leqslant 0$ for $x > \beta$. Then

$$f(\beta) \geqslant f(x) \qquad \text{for all } x \text{ in } J.$$

And if $f'(x) > 0$ for $x < \beta$ and $f'(x) < (0)$ for $x > \beta$, then

$$f(\beta) > f(x) \qquad \text{for all } x \neq \beta \text{ in } J.$$

By reversing the inequalities on the derivatives, we get a weak minimum or a strict minimum according as we have the weak or strict inequalities.

Proof. Let us consider the case of a maximum. Choose any x in J, $x \neq \beta$. Suppose $x < \beta$. Then by the mean-value theorem (3.6e), there is a point α with $x < \alpha < \beta$ such that

$$f(\beta) - f(x) = f'(\alpha)(\beta - x) \geqslant 0 \qquad \text{or} > 0$$

according as $f'(\alpha) \geqslant 0$ or > 0. If $x > \beta$, then

$$f(\beta) - f(x) = f'(\alpha)(\beta - x) \geqslant 0 \qquad \text{or} > 0$$

according as $f'(\alpha) \leqslant 0$ or < 0. The case of a minimum is clearly similar. ∎

From this we can deduce the usual second-derivative test for extreme points. However, we will pass this up and go directly to the nth derivative test.

7.4b Theorem. Let f have n continuous derivatives in an open interval J: $\{a < x < b\}$. And suppose that there is a point β in J at which we have $f'(\beta) = 0, \ldots f^{(n-1)}(\beta) = 0$ and $f^{(n)}(\beta) \neq 0$. Then, if n is even, there is a neighborhood N of β in which

$$f(\beta) > f(x) \text{ for all } x \neq \beta \text{ in } N \qquad \text{if } f^{(n)}(\beta) < 0$$
$$f(\beta) < f(x) \text{ for all } x \neq \beta \text{ in } N \qquad \text{if } f^{(n)}(\beta) > 0.$$

If n is odd, there is no neighborhood of β in which f attains an extreme value at β.

In terms of testing the critical points, the implication of this theorem is as follows: We locate the critical points β as solutions of the equation $f'(x) = 0$—not necessarily an easy thing to do, of course—and having located one at β, say, we proceed to examine the higher derivatives of f at β. If the first non-zero one is of odd order, we have neither a maximum nor a minimum; if it is of even order, then there is a local maximum at β if it is negative and a local minimum if it is positive.

Proof. Since $f^{(n)}(x)$ is continuous and non-zero at β, there is a neighborhood N of β in which it is not zero and in which its sign is the same as the sign of $f^{(n)}(\beta)$. Now let x be any point in N different from β. Then, by Taylor's formula, we get

$$f(x) = f(\beta) + \frac{f^{(n)}(z)}{n!}(x - \beta)^n,$$

where z is between β and x, and hence lies in N. All intermediate terms drop out, since all derivatives up to order n vanish at β.

We can now read off the proof of our theorem from this formula as follows: Suppose n is odd. Then $f(x) - f(\beta)$ changes sign whenever $(x - \beta)$ changes sign—that is, when x crosses from one side of β to the other. Hence $f(x) - f(\beta)$ is positive on one side and negative on the other, or $f(x)$ is larger than $f(\beta)$ on one side and smaller on the other. Which way it goes—that is, on which side $f(x) > f(\beta)$—depends upon the sign of $f^{(n)}(z)$ and hence upon the sign of $f^{(n)}(\beta)$.

Suppose now that n is even. This implies that the sign of $(x - \beta)^n$ is always positive, and therefore the sign of $f(x) - f(\beta)$ depends on the sign of $f^{(n)}(z)$, and thus on $f^{(n)}(\beta)$. In particular, $f(x) - f(\beta) > 0$ if $f^{(n)}(\beta) > 0$, and hence we have a local minimum. And if $f^{(n)}(\beta) < 0$, we have a local minimum.   ∎

The theorem remains true under the weaker hypotheses that $(n - 1)$ derivatives exist in a neighborhood of β, and the nth exists at β. The proof, however, involves a more careful examination of the situation (see Exercise C1).

A   EXERCISES

I. Locate and test the critical points of the following functions:

(a) $\dfrac{1}{x} - \dfrac{1}{x-1}$ (b) $\dfrac{4}{x} - \dfrac{1}{x-1}$ (c) $\dfrac{x^4 + 4}{x^4 + 2}$

(d) $-\dfrac{1}{x} - \log x$ (e) $\sin x - \tan x$ (f) $\sin x^4$

(g) $e^{x^2} + e^{-x^2}$ (h) $\dfrac{x}{\log x}$ (i) $\dfrac{x^2}{\log x}$

(j) $x^n e^{-x^2}$ $(n > 0)$ (k) x^x (l) $x^{1/x}$

2. What is the area of the rectangle of largest area that can be inscribed in a semicircle, with one side of the rectangle lying along the diameter of the semicircle?

3. A cup in the form of a right circular cone of opening 2θ and depth D is filled with fluid. Into this a ball of radius r is gently placed. Find r such that the volume of fluid displaced by the ball will be the largest.

B EXERCISES

1. Locate and identify all extreme points of $\sqrt[75]{e^{(x^2-x)^{132}}}$.

2. Let f be continuous in $\{a \leqslant x \leqslant b\}$ and have one-sided derivatives at each point. Let $Rf'(x)$ be the right and $Lf'(x)$ be the left derivatives. Show that $Rf'(x) \leqslant 0$ and $Lf'(x) \geqslant 0$ at a maximum, and that the inequalities are reversed at a minimum. Describe the situation at end points a and b.

3. Let $f(x)$ be continuous in a neighborhood N of β. Show that a necessary and sufficient condition that f attain a maximum at β is that

$$\frac{f(\beta + h) - f(\beta)}{h} \begin{cases} \geqslant 0 & \text{if } h < 0 \\ \leqslant 0 & \text{if } h > 0, \end{cases}$$

and that for a minimum the inequalities on the difference quotient are reversed. In particular, show that if $Rf'(\beta) = -\infty$ and $Lf'(\beta) = +\infty$, then f attains a maximum at β. (See Exercise 2 above for the definitions of $Rf'(\beta)$ and $Lf'(\beta)$.

4. Use the previous problem to discuss the extreme values of f and g at the origin where

$$f(x = \begin{cases} \dfrac{e^{1/x} - 1}{e^{1/x} + 1} & x \neq 0 \\ 0 & x = 0 \end{cases}$$

and

$$g(x) = \begin{cases} e^{-1/x^2} & x \neq 0 \\ 0 & x = 0. \end{cases}$$

C EXERCISES

1. Prove Theorem 7.4b, assuming that $f^{(n)}(x)$ exists only at β.

part **11**

VECTOR CALCULUS

8

Vectors and Curves

8.I INTRODUCTION AND DEFINITIONS

The concept of a vector is a very useful one. This utility arises from two important aspects of vectors, namely that they engender a highly geometrical insight, which is of course much to be desired, and that vector notation permits many complicated formulas to be written in a very compact form. With this economy of notation comes a greater ease in handling difficult problems.

We begin with a physico-geometrical description of vectors and some of their more obvious properties, and turn later to precise definitions and proofs. Physically, we view a vector as a "directed magnitude" and geometrically as "directed segment." We represent vectors pictorially by a line segment drawn with an arrow head on one end, which points in the direction of the vector, while the length of the segment represents its magnitude. Force, the physicists tell us, has magnitude (pounds, say) and direction, and thus can be represented as a vector.

Displacements are geometrical quantities represented by vectors. In fact, in a non-technical sense, the word vector means carrier. Thus geometrically a vector is a displacement which "carries" one point to another. The displacement from the point (x, y, z) to the point (ξ, η, ζ) is represented by the segment connecting these points with the arrowhead at (ξ, η, ζ). Velocity and acceleration are also vectors, since they are respectively the first and second derivatives of a displacement.

A vector $\mathbf{a}$ and a vector $\mathbf{b}$ (boldface type will be used to denote vectors) are called equal ($\mathbf{a} = \mathbf{b}$) if they have the same magnitude and direction. Thus the vector $\mathbf{a}$ from (x, y, z) to (ξ, η, ζ) is the same as the vector $\mathbf{b}$ from (x', y', z') to (ξ', η', ζ') if $\xi - x = \xi' - x'$, $\eta - y = \eta' - y'$, and $\zeta - z = \zeta' - z'$, because they would then have the same

147

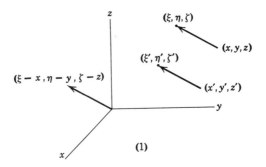

(1)

length and direction. This enables us to view all vectors as emanating from the origin, if we so desire, in fact, we may also consider any vector as having any initial point which seems convenient, and having a terminal point determined by its length and direction.

If α is a real number and **a** is a displacement vector, then α**a** is the displacement which has magnitude $|\alpha|$ times that of **a** and is in the direction of **a** if $\alpha > 0$, and is in the direction opposite that of **a** if $\alpha < 0$. We say that α**a** is a **scalar** multiple of **a**, real numbers being called **scalars** when used as multipliers of vectors.

Graphical addition of vectors is suggested by their interpretation as displacements. If **a** is one displacement from a point **P** to a point **Q**, and **b** is a second displacement from **Q** to **R** then this should be equivalent to the displacement from **P** to **R**. This is equivalent to the parallelogram rule: if **a** and **b** have a common initial point, then **a** + **b** is the diagonal of the parallelogram determined having **a** and **b** as adjacent sides.

This geometrical picture of a vector is one which we will never lose sight of. It will serve as a guide to our more formal discussion which now follows. Most of our attention will be directed toward three dimensional vectors. There is, however, only one concept which does not carry over to n dimensions where n may be any positive integer. That one is the cross or vector product. We will formulate all definitions and theorems

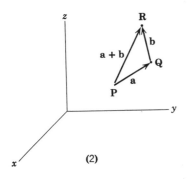

(2)

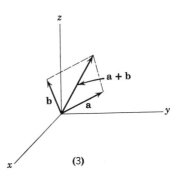

(3)

for three dimensions, and comment later about the other dimensions. But it would be well to keep in mind, as you study this chapter, that the dimensions being 3 is essential only in discussing vector products.

An ordered triple of real numbers (a_1, a_2, a_3) will be called a **vector a**, and the number a_n will be called the nth **component** of **a**. The collection of all ordered triples with the following rules will be called **three-dimensional vector space**.

RULES. If **a** is (a_1, a_2, a_3) and **b** is (b_1, b_2, b_3), then

(1) $\mathbf{a} = \mathbf{b}$ means $a_1 = b_1$, $a_2 = b_2$, $a_3 = b_3$.

(2) $\mathbf{a} + \mathbf{b} = (a_1 + b_1, a_2 + b_2, a_3 + b_3)$

(3) If α is real, then $\alpha\mathbf{a} = (\alpha a_1, \alpha a_2, \alpha a_3)$.

(4) $-\mathbf{a}$ means $(-1)\mathbf{a} = (-a_1, -a_2, -a_3)$.

(5) $\mathbf{O} = (0, 0, 0)$.

Rules 1, 2, 3, and 4 are the definitions of vector equality, of vector addition, of multiplication of a vector by a scalar, and of the negative of a vector, respectively. Rule 5 is to set up notation; it introduces a special symbol for a special vector.

Let us note that the following properties hold for our vector space.

8.1a Theorem.

(i) Addition of vectors is commutative: $\mathbf{a} + \mathbf{b} = \mathbf{b} + \mathbf{a}$.

(ii) Addition of vectors is associative: $(\mathbf{a} + \mathbf{b}) + \mathbf{c} = \mathbf{a} + (\mathbf{b} + \mathbf{c})$.

(iii) There is a unique vector $\mathbf{O}$ for which $\mathbf{a} + \mathbf{O} = \mathbf{a}$, for every $\mathbf{a}$.

(iv) For each $\mathbf{a}$, there is a unique vector $-\mathbf{a}$ for which $\mathbf{a} + (-\mathbf{a}) = \mathbf{O}$.

8.1b Theorem. For every scalar α and every vector $\mathbf{a}$, there is a vector called the product of α and $\mathbf{a}$, and written $\alpha\mathbf{a}$, with the properties:

(i) Multiplication by scalars is distributive:

$$\alpha(\mathbf{a} + \mathbf{b}) = \alpha\mathbf{a} + \alpha\mathbf{b}.$$

(ii) Multiplication of scalars by vectors is distributive:

$$(\alpha + \beta)\mathbf{a} = \alpha\mathbf{a} + \beta\mathbf{a},$$

(iii) Multiplication is associative:

$$(\alpha\beta)\mathbf{a} = \alpha(\beta\mathbf{a})$$

(iv) $0\mathbf{a} = \mathbf{O}$, $1\mathbf{a} = \mathbf{a}$.

The proofs of these theorems are quite easy. For example, we prove part (i) of Theorem 8.1a thus:

$$\mathbf{a} + \mathbf{b} = (a_1 + b_1, a_2 + b_2, a_3 + b_3)$$
$$= (b_1 + a_1, b_2 + a_2, b_3 + a_3)$$
$$= \mathbf{b} + \mathbf{a}.$$

The middle equality comes from the commutativity of real numbers; the other two equalities come from the definition of vector addition. The remaining proofs are equally simple and are left to the problems.

The reason for singling out just these rather simple properties is this: Theorem 8.1a says that vectors form what is called an **Abelian group** under addition, and Theorem 8.1b says that they form a **linear space** over the field of real numbers. (These terms may be unfamiliar to you, but you will learn them in other courses.)

Further, and more important for our present interests, any set of objects (that is, mathematical objects) for which addition and scalar multiplication are defined and which satisfy Theorems 8.1a and 8.1b is called a **vector space**. This is the abstract approach to the study of vector spaces. Some surprising things turn out to be vector spaces under this definition, as we shall see.

There are many ways in which we could measure the size of a vector. For example, we could use the absolute value of the largest component. This measure of size gives rise to a so-called **Minkowski vector space** (see Exercise C1, Section 8.3). However, we will use a more familiar measure of size, namely the **Euclidean length** of a vector $\mathbf{a}$, denoted by $|\mathbf{a}|$ and defined by

$$|\mathbf{a}| = \sqrt{a_1{}^2 + a_2{}^2 + a_3{}^2}.$$

A vector of length 1 is called a **unit vector**.

With this definition of length appended to the set of rules concerning vector spaces, ours becomes a **three-dimensional Euclidean vector space** and is denoted by E_3.

8.1c   Theorem. $\mathbf{a} = \mathbf{O}$ if and only if $|\mathbf{a}| = 0$.

Proof. If $\mathbf{a} = \mathbf{O}$, then

$$a_1 = a_2 = a_3 = 0,$$

and so
$$|\mathbf{a}| = 0.$$

Conversely, if $|\mathbf{a}| = 0$, then

$$a_1{}^2 = a_2{}^2 = a_3{}^2 = 0.$$

Consequently
$$a_1 = a_2 = a_3 = 0 \quad \text{(why?)}$$

and so
$$\mathbf{a} = \mathbf{O}. \qquad \blacksquare$$

Let us return briefly to the connection between geometry and vectors. Sometimes we will denote the components of a vector by x, y, and z respectively. Thus the point (x, y, z) and the vector $\mathbf{P}$ with components x, y, and z are really the same object, namely the ordered triple of numbers (x, y, z). The distinction between the two is largely one of intent. We use the word "point" when we are primarily interested in describing position, and the word "vector" when the triple is likely to be involved in one or another of the types of vector calculations whose description is the main object of this chapter, though we frequently combine these two outlooks. The vector $\mathbf{P} = (x, y, z)$ is called the **position vector** of the point $\mathbf{P} = (x, y, z)$.

Thus "point" and "vector" will be used interchangeably, though generally the choice of term prejudices our outlook, in the sense described above. In particular, if $\mathbf{P}$ and $\mathbf{Q}$ are points (that is, vectors) with coordinates (that is, components) (x, y, z) and (ξ, η, ζ) respectively, then $\mathbf{Q} - \mathbf{P}$ is the vector $(\xi - x, \eta - y, \zeta - z)$ and may be visualized as the vector connecting $\mathbf{P}$ to $\mathbf{Q}$ and pointing at $\mathbf{Q}$.

Vector notation frequently simplifies the proofs of elementary geometrical propositions, as is now illustrated.

EXAMPLE. Let $\mathbf{P}_1$, $\mathbf{P}_2$, $\mathbf{P}_3$ and $\mathbf{P}_4$ be four points in space. Show that the midpoints of the segments $\mathbf{P}_1$ to $\mathbf{P}_2$, $\mathbf{P}_2$ to $\mathbf{P}_3$, $\mathbf{P}_3$ to $\mathbf{P}_4$, $\mathbf{P}_4$ to $\mathbf{P}_1$ are the corners of a parallelogram.

Let the midpoints be $\mathbf{Q}_1$, $\mathbf{Q}_2$, $\mathbf{Q}_3$, and $\mathbf{Q}_4$, respectively. Then we can see (how?) that

$$\mathbf{Q}_1 = (\mathbf{P}_1 + \mathbf{P}_2)/2 \qquad \mathbf{Q}_2 = (\mathbf{P}_2 + \mathbf{P}_3)/2$$
$$\mathbf{Q}_3 = (\mathbf{P}_3 + \mathbf{P}_4)/2 \qquad \mathbf{Q}_4 = (\mathbf{P}_4 + \mathbf{P}_1)/2.$$

Thus the vector from $\mathbf{Q}_1$ to $\mathbf{Q}_2$ is given by

$$\mathbf{Q}_2 - \mathbf{Q}_1 = (\mathbf{P}_3 - \mathbf{P}_1)/2,$$

and the vector from $\mathbf{Q}_4$ to $\mathbf{Q}_3$ by

$$\mathbf{Q}_3 - \mathbf{Q}_4 = (\mathbf{P}_3 - \mathbf{P}_1)/2.$$

Hence the segments from $\mathbf{Q}_2$ to $\mathbf{Q}_1$ and from $\mathbf{Q}_3$ to $\mathbf{Q}_4$ are parallel and equal. The other two sides are similarly parallel and equal, so that the figure is a parallelogram.

A EXERCISES

I. Find a unit vector in the direction of each of the following:

(a) $(2, 4, -1)$ (b) $(1, 1, 1)$ (c) $(3, -1, 0)$

2. A 141.4 pound weight is suspended as shown in the figure. Find the tension T. Use the physical law that forces balance in a state of equilibrium.

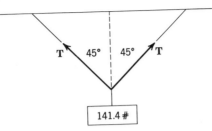

3. Prove that the medians of a triangle meet in a point which divides each median in a $2 : 1$ ratio.

4. Prove that the diagonals of a parallelogram bisect each other.

5. Prove that the angle bisectors of a triangle meet in a point.

6. Does Rule 2 for the addition of vectors give rise to the parallelogram rule?

B EXERCISES

I. Let **a** be a given non-zero vector. Show that the set of vectors of the form α**a**, where α is a scalar, forms a vector space in the sense that it satisfies the conclusions of Theorems 8.1a and 8.1b. Geometrically, what does this set of vectors represent? (This is called a **one-dimensional sub-space** of E_3.)

2. Let **a** and **b** be two non-zero vectors, neither of which is a scalar multiple of the other. Show that the set of vectors of the form α**a** $+ \beta$**b** forms a vector space. What does this set of vectors represent geometrically? (This is called a **two-dimensional sub-space** of E_3.)

C EXERCISES

I. Show that the set of functions defined on $\{0 \leqslant x \leqslant 1\}$ forms a vector space, where the individual vectors are functions and scalars are real numbers.

8.2 VECTOR MULTIPLICATIONS

It is convenient now to introduce three distinguished unit vectors in terms of which every vector can be expressed in a unique way. We define **i**, **j**, **k** by

$$\mathbf{i} = (1, 0, 0)$$
$$\mathbf{j} = (0, 1, 0)$$
$$\mathbf{k} = (0, 0, 1).$$

8.2a   Theorem. If $\mathbf{a} = (a_1, a_2, a_3)$,

$$\mathbf{a} = a_1\mathbf{i} + a_2\mathbf{j} + a_3\mathbf{k}.$$

Conversely, if $\mathbf{a} = a_1\mathbf{i} + a_2\mathbf{j} + a_3\mathbf{k}$,

$$\mathbf{a} = (a_1, a_2, a_3).$$

Proof. Clearly,

$$(a_1, a_2, a_3) = (a_1, 0, 0) + (0, a_2, 0) + (0, 0, a_3)$$
$$= a_1(1, 0, 0) + a_2(0, 1, 0) + a_3(0, 0, 1)$$
$$= a_1\mathbf{i} + a_2\mathbf{j} + a_3\mathbf{k}.$$

Reading these equations forward proves the first part; reading them backward proves the second part. ∎

The first type of product of two vectors which we define is the **inner** or **scalar** or **dot product**. It is denoted by $\mathbf{a} \cdot \mathbf{b}$ and is defined by

$$\mathbf{a} \cdot \mathbf{b} = a_1 b_1 + a_2 b_2 + a_3 b_3.$$

8.2b   Theorem. The inner product satisfies the following rules:

(i) $\mathbf{a} \cdot \mathbf{b} = \mathbf{b} \cdot \mathbf{a}$ (commutative law).

(ii) $\mathbf{a} \cdot (\mathbf{b} + \mathbf{c}) = \mathbf{a} \cdot \mathbf{b} + \mathbf{a} \cdot \mathbf{c}$ (distributive law).

(iii) $(\alpha\mathbf{a}) \cdot \mathbf{b} = \alpha(\mathbf{a} \cdot \mathbf{b})$ (associative law).

(iv) $\mathbf{a} \cdot \mathbf{a} = |\mathbf{a}|^2$.

The proof is quite trivial and is left to the exercises. We note that our special vectors $\mathbf{i}, \mathbf{j}, \mathbf{k}$ satisfy the following relationships:

$$\mathbf{i} \cdot \mathbf{i} = \mathbf{j} \cdot \mathbf{j} = \mathbf{k} \cdot \mathbf{k} = 1$$
$$\mathbf{i} \cdot \mathbf{j} = \mathbf{j} \cdot \mathbf{k} = \mathbf{k} \cdot \mathbf{i} = 0.$$

The size of $\mathbf{a} \cdot \mathbf{b}$ can be estimated in terms of $|\mathbf{a}|$ and $|\mathbf{b}|$. This result is known as the **Cauchy-Schwarz inequality**.

8.2c   Theorem. $|\mathbf{a} \cdot \mathbf{b}| \leqslant |\mathbf{a}|\,|\mathbf{b}|$, and equality holds if, and only if, one of the vectors is a scalar multiple of the other.

Proof. If either $\mathbf{a} = \mathbf{O}$ or $\mathbf{b} = \mathbf{O}$, then both sides of the inequality are 0 and equality holds (and also one is then 0 times the other). Hence we assume for the remainder of the proof that $\mathbf{a} \neq \mathbf{O}$.

For all real numbers x, define the function q by

(1) $$q(x) = |x\mathbf{a} + \mathbf{b}|^2.$$

Then we get

$$q(x) = (x\mathbf{a} + \mathbf{b}) \cdot (x\mathbf{a} + \mathbf{b}) = x^2|\mathbf{a}|^2 + 2\mathbf{a} \cdot \mathbf{b}x + |\mathbf{b}|^2.$$

On completing the square, this becomes

(2) $$q(x) = |\mathbf{a}|^2(x + \mathbf{a} \cdot \mathbf{b}/|\mathbf{a}|^2)^2 + [|\mathbf{a}|^2|\mathbf{b}|^2 - (\mathbf{a} \cdot \mathbf{b})^2]/|\mathbf{a}|^2.$$

It is clear from (1) that $q(x) \geqslant 0$, and from (2) that the minimum value of q is the last term in (2). Hence

$$|\mathbf{a}|^2|\mathbf{b}|^2 - (\mathbf{a} \cdot \mathbf{b})^2 \geqslant 0.$$

Transposing and taking roots, we get

$$|\mathbf{a} \cdot \mathbf{b}| \leqslant |\mathbf{a}|\,|\mathbf{b}|.$$

Now equality holds if, and only if, the minimum value of q is zero. By Theorem 8.1c, q can be zero if, and only if, there is an x_0 for which $x_0\mathbf{a} + \mathbf{b} = \mathbf{O}$—that is, $\mathbf{b} = (-x_0)\mathbf{a}$.   ∎

The Cauchy-Schwarz inequality can be rewritten

$$-1 \leqslant \mathbf{a} \cdot \mathbf{b}/|\mathbf{a}|\,|\mathbf{b}| \leqslant 1.$$

From this it is clear that there is a unique angle θ in $\{0 \leqslant \theta \leqslant \pi\}$ for which $\cos \theta = \mathbf{a} \cdot \mathbf{b}/|\mathbf{a}|\,|\mathbf{b}|$. We define this angle θ to be **the angle between a and b**. Now we can interpret $\mathbf{a} \cdot \mathbf{b}$ geometrically: $\mathbf{a} \cdot \mathbf{b} = |\mathbf{a}|\,|\mathbf{b}| \cos \theta =$ the length of the projection of $\mathbf{a}$ onto $\mathbf{b}$ times the length of $\mathbf{b}$; or, alternatively, $|\mathbf{a}|\,|\mathbf{b}| \cos \theta =$ the length of the projection of $\mathbf{b}$ onto $\mathbf{a}$ times the length of $\mathbf{a}$, the sign being positive or negative according as $\theta > \pi/2$ or $\theta < \pi/2$. The projection of $\mathbf{a}$ on $\mathbf{b}$ is called the **component** of $\mathbf{a}$ in the direction of $\mathbf{b}$.

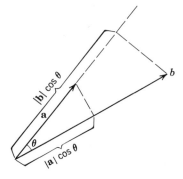

Let us note that it makes geometrical sense to define θ as we did, for by the cosine law,

$$|\mathbf{a} - \mathbf{b}|^2 = |\mathbf{a}|^2 + |\mathbf{b}|^2 - 2|\mathbf{a}|\,|\mathbf{b}| \cos \theta,$$

and by vector calculations,

$$|\mathbf{a} - \mathbf{b}|^2 = (\mathbf{a} - \mathbf{b}) \cdot (\mathbf{a} - \mathbf{b}) = |\mathbf{a}|^2 + |\mathbf{b}|^2 - 2\mathbf{a} \cdot \mathbf{b},$$

from which we see immediately that

$$\mathbf{a} \cdot \mathbf{b} = |\mathbf{a}|\,|\mathbf{b}| \cos \theta.$$

In fact, we could have used this approach in the first place to prove the Cauchy-Schwarz inequality. However, we preferred to use an algebraic proof which is independent of dimension, leaving geometry to enter only as interpretation.

If $\mathbf{a} \cdot \mathbf{b} = 0$, we conclude that either one of the vectors is zero or that $\theta = \pi/2$. In either case we say the vectors are **orthogonal**, another word for "perpendicular." If a set of vectors has the property that every pair of vectors in it is orthogonal, then it is called an **orthogonal set of vectors**.

8.2d   Corollary. The set $\mathbf{i}$, $\mathbf{j}$, $\mathbf{k}$ forms an orthogonal set of vectors.

Proof:
$$\mathbf{i} \cdot \mathbf{j} = (1, 0, 0) \cdot (0, 1, 0) = 0 + 0 + 0 = 0.$$
Similarly, $\mathbf{i} \cdot \mathbf{k} = \mathbf{k} \cdot \mathbf{j} = 0.$ ∎

From the Cauchy-Schwarz inequality, we can prove another very useful inequality. Geometrically, $\mathbf{a} + \mathbf{b}$ is the third side of a triangle whose other two sides are $\mathbf{a}$ and $\mathbf{b}$. It therefore seems obvious that

$$|\mathbf{a} + \mathbf{b}| \leqslant |\mathbf{a}| + |\mathbf{b}|,$$

and that equality should hold if the triangle degenerates into a segment with one of $\mathbf{a}$ or $\mathbf{b}$ non-negative multiple of the other. For obvious reasons, this result is called the **triangle inequality**.

8.2e   Theorem. $|\mathbf{a} + \mathbf{b}| \leqslant |\mathbf{a}| + |\mathbf{b}|$, and equality holds if, and only if, one of the vectors is a non-negative multiple of the other.

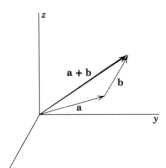

Proof:
$$|\mathbf{a} + \mathbf{b}|^2 = (\mathbf{a} + \mathbf{b}) \cdot (\mathbf{a} + \mathbf{b})$$
$$= |\mathbf{a}|^2 + 2\mathbf{a} \cdot \mathbf{b} + |\mathbf{b}|^2 \leqslant |\mathbf{a}|^2 + 2|\mathbf{a} \cdot \mathbf{b}| + |\mathbf{b}|^2$$
$$\leqslant |\mathbf{a}|^2 + 2|\mathbf{a}|\,|\mathbf{b}| + |\mathbf{b}|^2$$
$$= (|\mathbf{a}| + |\mathbf{b}|)^2.$$ ∎

Explain carefully the inequalities in the proof; in particular, how is the equality case covered? (See Exercise A4.)

It is clear that the length of a vector is not less than any one of its components: $|\mathbf{a}| \geqslant |a_m|$. From the triangle inequality, we can show that its length is not greater than the sum of the absolute values of its components.

8.2f Corollary.

$$|\mathbf{a}| \leqslant |a_1| + |a_2| + |a_3|.$$

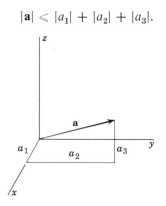

Proof. The proof of this corollary is left as an exercise (B6).   ∎

Another type of vector multiplication is the **vector product** or **cross product**. It is denoted by $\mathbf{a} \times \mathbf{b}$ and is defined by

$$\mathbf{a} \times \mathbf{b} = (a_2b_3 - a_3b_2, \, a_3b_1 - a_1b_3, \, a_1b_2 - a_2b_1).$$

This can be rewritten as

$$\mathbf{a} \times \mathbf{b} = \mathbf{i}(a_2b_3 - a_3b_2) + \mathbf{j}(a_3b_1 - a_1b_3) + \mathbf{k}(a_1b_2 - a_2b_1),$$

$$= \mathbf{i} \begin{vmatrix} a_2 & a_3 \\ b_2 & b_3 \end{vmatrix} - \mathbf{j} \begin{vmatrix} a_1 & a_3 \\ b_1 & b_3 \end{vmatrix} + \mathbf{k} \begin{vmatrix} a_1 & a_2 \\ b_1 & b_2 \end{vmatrix},$$

which is easily seen to be in the form of a determinant:

$$\mathbf{a} \times \mathbf{b} = \begin{vmatrix} \mathbf{i} & \mathbf{j} & \mathbf{k} \\ a_1 & a_2 & a_3 \\ b_1 & b_2 & b_3 \end{vmatrix},$$

in which form it is most easily remembered. Since the elements of one row of this determinant are vectors, we take as its definition the expansion given by the preceding formula. Any of the usual rules for calculating with determinants will have to be rechecked, since these are established for determinants with numerical entries. Actually, this determinant is used largely as a mnemonic device, and we will restrict our calculations to very simple situations in which the expansion makes clear that its use is valid.

We now establish some elementary properties of the vector product.

8.2g Theorem.

(1) $\mathbf{a} \times \mathbf{b} = -\mathbf{b} \times \mathbf{a}$.

(2) $\mathbf{a} \times (\mathbf{b} + \mathbf{c}) = \mathbf{a} \times \mathbf{b} + \mathbf{a} \times \mathbf{c}$.

(3) $\mathbf{a} \times (\alpha\mathbf{b}) = (\alpha\mathbf{a}) \times \mathbf{b} = \alpha(\mathbf{a} \times \mathbf{b})$.

(4) $\mathbf{a} \times \mathbf{a} = \mathbf{O}$.

(4') $\mathbf{i} \times \mathbf{i} = \mathbf{j} \times \mathbf{j} = \mathbf{k} \times \mathbf{k} = \mathbf{O}$.

(5) $\mathbf{i} \times \mathbf{j} = \mathbf{k},\, \mathbf{j} \times \mathbf{k} = \mathbf{i},\, \mathbf{k} \times \mathbf{i} = \mathbf{j}$.

[Note that cyclic permutations of $\mathbf{i}$, $\mathbf{j}$, $\mathbf{k}$ carry any one part of (5) into the other two.]

Proof. (1) Interchanging a's and b's in any one of the expressions for $\mathbf{a} \times \mathbf{b}$ changes its sign.

$$(2) \quad \mathbf{a} \times (\mathbf{b} + \mathbf{c}) = \mathbf{i} \begin{vmatrix} a_2 & a_3 \\ b_2 + c_2 & b_3 + c_3 \end{vmatrix} - \mathbf{j} \begin{vmatrix} a_1 & a_3 \\ b_1 + c_1 & b_3 + c_3 \end{vmatrix}$$
$$+ \mathbf{k} \begin{vmatrix} a_1 & a_2 \\ b_1 + c_1 & b_2 + c_2 \end{vmatrix}.$$

Now

$$\begin{vmatrix} a_2 & a_3 \\ b_2 + c_2 & b_3 + c_3 \end{vmatrix} = \begin{vmatrix} a_2 & a_3 \\ b_2 & b_3 \end{vmatrix} + \begin{vmatrix} a_2 & a_3 \\ c_2 & c_3 \end{vmatrix},$$

and all the other determinants can be similarly decomposed. Thus it is clear that these can be rearranged to form $\mathbf{a} \times \mathbf{b} + \mathbf{a} \times \mathbf{c}$.

(3) The scalar α enters simply as a common factor and can be factored out.

(4) In $\mathbf{a} \times \mathbf{a}$ the coefficients of $\mathbf{i}$, $\mathbf{j}$, $\mathbf{k}$ are easily seen to vanish. (4') follows immediately from (4).

(5) By direct calculation, we get

$$\mathbf{i} \times \mathbf{j} = \begin{vmatrix} \mathbf{i} & \mathbf{j} & \mathbf{k} \\ 1 & 0 & 0 \\ 0 & 1 & 0 \end{vmatrix} = \mathbf{k} \begin{vmatrix} 1 & 0 \\ 0 & 1 \end{vmatrix} = \mathbf{k}.$$

The others are equally simple. ∎

The five parts of this theorem constitute the operational rules for computing with vector products.

8.2h Corollary. **a** ✕ **b** is orthogonal to both **a** and **b**.

Proof. Forming the inner product **a** · (**a** ✕ **b**) gives us

$$\mathbf{a} \cdot (\mathbf{a} \times \mathbf{b}) = \begin{vmatrix} a_1 & a_2 & a_3 \\ a_1 & a_2 & a_3 \\ b_1 & b_2 & b_3 \end{vmatrix} = 0.$$

The determinant is zero, since it has two identical rows. Similarly, **b** · (**a** ✕ **b**) = 0.

8.2i Theorem. $|\mathbf{a} \times \mathbf{b}| = |\mathbf{a}|\,|\mathbf{b}|\sin\theta$, where θ is the angle between **a** and **b**.

Proof:

$$|\mathbf{a} \times \mathbf{b}|^2 = (a_2 b_3 - a_3 b_2)^2 + (a_3 b_1 - a_1 b_3)^2 + (a_1 b_2 - a_2 b_1)^2$$
$$= a_2{}^2 b_3{}^2 - 2a_2 b_3 a_3 b_2 + a_3{}^2 b_2{}^2$$
$$+ a_3{}^2 b_1{}^2 - 2a_3 b_1 a_1 b_3 + a_1{}^2 b_3{}^2$$
$$+ a_1{}^2 b_2{}^2 - 2a_1 b_2 a_2 b_1 + a_2{}^2 b_1{}^2.$$

And $|\mathbf{a}|^2 |\mathbf{b}|^2 \sin^2\theta = |\mathbf{a}|^2|\mathbf{b}|^2(1 - \cos^2\theta) = |\mathbf{a}|^2|\mathbf{b}|^2 - (\mathbf{a} \cdot \mathbf{b})^2$

$$= (a_1{}^2 + a_2{}^2 + a_3{}^2)(b_1{}^2 + b_2{}^2 + b_3{}^2) - (a_1 b_1 + a_2 b_2 + a_3 b_3)^2$$

By expanding this expression, we see that it is the same as the formula we just computed for $|\mathbf{a} \times \mathbf{b}|^2$.   ■

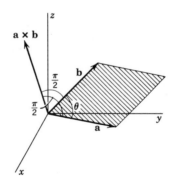

We thus see that **a** ✕ **b** is a vector perpendicular to the plane of **a** and **b**, whose magnitude is the area of the parallelogram with sides **a** and **b**. It also turns out that the direction in which it points can be determined by the so-called **right-hand rule**, which we now describe.

First, we suppose our coordinate system to be a "right-handed" system, as in all our figures. This can be visualized by holding the middle finger, index finger, and thumb of the right hand so that they are mutually perpendicular. If the middle finger points along the x-axis and the thumb along the y-axis, then the index finger points along the z-axis.

In such a coordinate system, the direction of $\mathbf{a} \times \mathbf{b}$ is as follows. Hold your right hand as a loosely closed fist, with your thumb sticking out. If you curl your fingers in the direction of the rotation of $\mathbf{a}$ into $\mathbf{b}$ (through an angle of less than π), your thumb will point in the direction of $\mathbf{a} \times \mathbf{b}$. An equivalent rule is that if the middle finger and thumb of your right hand point in the direction of $\mathbf{a}$ and $\mathbf{b}$ respectively, then your index finger, held perpendicularly to the plane of thumb and middle finger, will point in the direction of $\mathbf{a} \times \mathbf{b}$.

Suppose $\mathbf{a} = a_1\mathbf{i}$ and $\mathbf{b} = b_1\mathbf{i} + b_2\mathbf{j}$. Then, by a simple calculation, $\mathbf{a} \times \mathbf{b} = a_1 b_2 \mathbf{k}$; that is, $\mathbf{a} \times \mathbf{b}$ is in the direction of $\mathbf{k}$ or $-\mathbf{k}$, according as the sign of b_2 is positive or negative. Thus we see that the rules hold if $\mathbf{a}$ is in the direction of $\mathbf{i}$ and $\mathbf{b}$ is in the plane of $\mathbf{i}$ and $\mathbf{j}$. For any other position of $\mathbf{a}$ and $\mathbf{b}$, we argue heuristically as follows: Keeping the angle between $\mathbf{a}$ and $\mathbf{b}$ fixed, and their lengths fixed, rotate the two vectors $\mathbf{a}$ and $\mathbf{b}$ continuously so that $\mathbf{a}$ will point in the direction of $\mathbf{i}$ and $\mathbf{b}$ will be in the plane of $\mathbf{i}$ and $\mathbf{j}$. Then $\mathbf{a} \times \mathbf{b}$, which is clearly a continuous function of $\mathbf{a}$ and $\mathbf{b}$, must move continuously. Since it is always perpendicular to the plane of $\mathbf{a}$ and $\mathbf{b}$, $\mathbf{a} \times \mathbf{b}$ points either as our rules prescribe or in the opposite direction. Furthermore, $\mathbf{a} \times \mathbf{b}$ varies continuously, and our rule describes its direction in the final position. By continuity, then, the direction of $\mathbf{a} \times \mathbf{b}$ must always be given by that rule.

8.3 THE TRIPLE PRODUCTS

The **scalar triple product** of a, b, and c, in that order, is $\mathbf{a} \cdot (\mathbf{b} \times \mathbf{c})$. The parentheses may be removed, since there is only one order in which the multiplications make sense. The important elementary properties of the scalar triple product are proved in the following theorem.

8.3a Theorem.

(i)
$$\mathbf{a} \cdot \mathbf{b} \times \mathbf{c} = \begin{vmatrix} a_1 & a_2 & a_3 \\ b_1 & b_2 & b_3 \\ c_1 & c_2 & c_3 \end{vmatrix}.$$

(ii) Any cyclic permutation of **a**, **b**, and **c** leaves the triple product invariant:

$$\mathbf{a} \cdot \mathbf{b} \times \mathbf{c} = \mathbf{b} \cdot \mathbf{c} \times \mathbf{a} = \mathbf{c} \cdot \mathbf{a} \times \mathbf{b}$$

(iii) Interchange of the inner and vector product leaves the scalar triple-product invariant.

$$\mathbf{a} \cdot (\mathbf{b} \times \mathbf{c}) = \mathbf{a} \times \mathbf{b} \cdot \mathbf{c}$$

Proof:

(i) This proof is clear from the representation of $\mathbf{b} \times \mathbf{c}$ as a determinant.

(ii) This follows from (i), since a cyclic permutation of the rows of a determinant leave the value of the determinant unchanged.

(iii) From (ii), $\mathbf{a} \cdot \mathbf{b} \times \mathbf{c} = \mathbf{c} \cdot \mathbf{a} \times \mathbf{b} = \mathbf{a} \times \mathbf{b} \cdot \mathbf{c}$, the last equality coming from the commutative law for inner products. ∎

The scalar triple product has a very simple geometrical meaning, namely $\mathbf{a} \times \mathbf{b} \cdot \mathbf{c} = \pm$ the volume of the parallelepiped with edges $\mathbf{a}$, $\mathbf{b}$, and $\mathbf{c}$. We can see this in the following manner: $\mathbf{a} \times \mathbf{b}$ is a vector whose

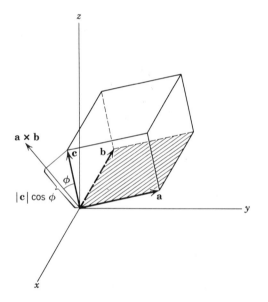

magnitude is the area of the parallelogram determined by $\mathbf{a}$ and $\mathbf{b}$, and which is perpendicular to the plane of that parallelogram. Then $\mathbf{a} \times \mathbf{b} \cdot \mathbf{c}$ is the projection of $\mathbf{c}$ onto $\mathbf{a} \times \mathbf{b}$, times $|\mathbf{a} \times \mathbf{b}|$. Thus if ϕ be the angle between $\mathbf{c}$ and $\mathbf{a} \times \mathbf{b}$ we have $\mathbf{a} \times \mathbf{b} \cdot \mathbf{c} = |\mathbf{a} \times \mathbf{b}| |\mathbf{c}| \cos \phi$. But $|\mathbf{c}| \cos \phi$ is the altitude of the parallelepiped based on the parallelogram determined by $\mathbf{a}$ and $\mathbf{b}$. Thus $\mathbf{a} \times \mathbf{b} \cdot \mathbf{c} = \pm$ volume, the positive sign being taken if $\phi < \pi/2$ and the negative if $\phi > \pi/2$. That is, we choose the positive sign if $\mathbf{c}$ and $\mathbf{a} \times \mathbf{b}$ point to the same side of the plane of $\mathbf{a}$ and $\mathbf{b}$, otherwise we choose the negative sign.

The **vector triple products** of a, b, and c, in that order, are a ✕ (b ✕ c) and (a ✕ b) ✕ c. Here the parentheses are needed. Since this is merely an iterated vector product, its properties are determined by the vector product. However, there is a computationally useful formula which we will derive.

Clearly a ✕ (b ✕ c) is a vector orthogonal to b ✕ c, and hence is a vector in the plane of b and c. It should therefore be expressible as a linear combination (that is, a sum of multiples) of b and c. Similarly, (a ✕ b) ✕ c should be a linear combination of a and b. The following theorem gives the precise formulas.

8.3b   Theorem.

$$a \times (b \times c) = (a \cdot c)b - (a \cdot b)c.$$
$$(a \times b) \times c = (a \cdot c)b - (b \cdot c)a.$$

Proof. We prove this theorem by showing that the components on both sides are the same. The first component of a vector is given by taking the dot product of that vector with i. Thus we will show that

$$i \cdot (\text{right side}) = i \cdot (\text{left side}).$$

Now

$$i \cdot [a \times (b \times c)] = \begin{vmatrix} 1 & 0 & 0 \\ a_1 & a_2 & a_3 \\ \begin{vmatrix} b_2 & b_3 \\ c_2 & c_3 \end{vmatrix} & -\begin{vmatrix} b_1 & b_3 \\ c_1 & c_3 \end{vmatrix} & \begin{vmatrix} b_1 & b_2 \\ c_1 & c_2 \end{vmatrix} \end{vmatrix}$$

$$= a_2(b_1c_2 - b_2c_1) + a_3(b_1c_3 - b_3c_1)$$
$$= b_1(a_1c_1 + a_2c_2 + a_3c_3) - c_1(a_1b_1 + a_2b_2 + a_3b_3)$$
$$= (a \cdot c)b_1 - (a \cdot b)c_1$$
$$= (a \cdot c)(i \cdot b) - (a \cdot b)(i \cdot c)$$
$$= i \cdot [(a \cdot c)b - (a \cdot b)c].$$

The proof for the other components is similar. And the proof of the second equation follows from the first by the skew symmetry of the vector product—that is, since a ✕ b = −b ✕ a.   ∎

We can summarize both formulas verbally by the following device: Denote the vector outside the parentheses as the "outer," the one inside the parentheses and nearest the outer as the "near," and the other as the "far." Then both formulas are expressed by

$$\text{vector triple product} = (\text{outer} \cdot \text{far})\,\text{near} - (\text{outer} \cdot \text{near})\,\text{far}.$$

A EXERCISES

1. Compute $\mathbf{a} + \mathbf{b}$, $\mathbf{a} \cdot \mathbf{b}$, $|\mathbf{a}|$, $|\mathbf{b}|$, and $|\mathbf{a} + \mathbf{b}|$, and verify that $|\mathbf{a} \cdot \mathbf{b}| \leqslant |\mathbf{a}||\mathbf{b}|$ and that $|\mathbf{a} + \mathbf{b}| \leqslant |\mathbf{a}| + |\mathbf{b}|$ for the vectors $\mathbf{a}$ and $\mathbf{b}$ given below.

(*a*) $\mathbf{a} = (2, 3, 4)$; $\mathbf{b} = (1, 2, 3)$ (*b*) $\mathbf{a} = (5, 2, -1)$; $\mathbf{b} = (10, 4, -2)$

(*c*) $\mathbf{a} = (1, -1, 2)$; $\mathbf{b} = (3, -2, 0)$ (*d*) $\mathbf{a} = (1, 4, 2)$; $\mathbf{b} = (-1, 4, -2)$

In each case find $\cos \theta$, where θ is the angle between $\mathbf{a}$ and $\mathbf{b}$.

2. Letting $\mathbf{a} = \mathbf{i} + 2\mathbf{j} + \mathbf{k}$, $\mathbf{b} = \mathbf{i} + \mathbf{j} + \mathbf{k}$, $\mathbf{c} = 2\mathbf{j} + \mathbf{k}$, compute the following:

(*a*) $\mathbf{a} \times \mathbf{b}$ (*b*) $\mathbf{c} \times \mathbf{a}$ (*c*) $\mathbf{a} \times (\mathbf{b} \times \mathbf{c})$

(*d*) $(\mathbf{a} \times \mathbf{b}) \times \mathbf{c}$ (*e*) $(\mathbf{a} \times \mathbf{b}) \times \mathbf{a}$ (*f*) $\mathbf{a} \times \mathbf{a}$

(*g*) $(\mathbf{a} \times \mathbf{b}) \cdot \mathbf{c}$ (*h*) $\mathbf{a} \cdot (\mathbf{b} \times \mathbf{c})$ (*i*) $\mathbf{a} \cdot (\mathbf{a} \times \mathbf{b})$

(*j*) $\mathbf{c} \times 2\mathbf{c}$

3. Under what conditions will $\mathbf{a} \times \mathbf{b} = \mathbf{O}$?

4. Explain in detail the inequalities used to prove Theorem 8.2e.

5. Compute $(\mathbf{a} + \mathbf{b}) \times (\mathbf{a} - \mathbf{b})$.

6. Show that $2\mathbf{i} + 3\mathbf{j} - \mathbf{k}$, $\mathbf{i} + \mathbf{j} + 5\mathbf{k}$, $16\mathbf{i} - 11\mathbf{j} - \mathbf{k}$ form an orthogonal set.

7. Explain geometrically why $(\mathbf{a} \times \mathbf{b}) \times (\mathbf{c} \times \mathbf{d})$ should be expressible as a linear combination (a sum of multiples) of $\mathbf{a}$ and $\mathbf{b}$, and also of $\mathbf{c}$ and $\mathbf{d}$. What can be said about the line along which this vector lies?

8. Let $\mathbf{P}$, $\mathbf{Q}$, $\mathbf{R}$ be three points in space. Interpret the geometrical meaning of $(\mathbf{P} - \mathbf{Q}) \times (\mathbf{P} - \mathbf{R})$.

9. Show that $\mathbf{a} \cdot \mathbf{b} = (|\mathbf{a} + \mathbf{b}|^2 - |\mathbf{a}|^2 - |\mathbf{b}|^2)/2$

and $= (|\mathbf{a} + \mathbf{b}|^2 - |\mathbf{a} - \mathbf{b}|^2)/4$.

10. Do the proof for the $\mathbf{j}$ component in Theorem 8.3b.

11. Show that $\mathbf{a} \times (\mathbf{b} \times \mathbf{c}) + \mathbf{b} \times (\mathbf{c} \times \mathbf{a}) + \mathbf{c} \times (\mathbf{a} \times \mathbf{b}) = \mathbf{O}$.

12. Write out the triangle inequality in terms of components.

B EXERCISES

1. Prove that $(\mathbf{a} \times \mathbf{b}) \cdot (\mathbf{c} \times \mathbf{d}) = \begin{vmatrix} \mathbf{a} \cdot \mathbf{c} & \mathbf{b} \cdot \mathbf{c} \\ \mathbf{a} \cdot \mathbf{d} & \mathbf{b} \cdot \mathbf{d} \end{vmatrix}$.

2. Verify that $\mathbf{a} \times (\mathbf{b} \times \mathbf{a})$ is in the plane of $\mathbf{a}$ and $\mathbf{b}$, and is orthogonal to $\mathbf{a}$.

3. Let $\mathbf{a}$ be a non-zero vector. Show that, for any $\mathbf{b}$

$$\mathbf{b} = \mathbf{a} \times (\mathbf{b} \times \mathbf{a})/|\mathbf{a}|^2 + (\mathbf{a} \cdot \mathbf{b}) \mathbf{a}/|\mathbf{a}|^2.$$

Explain the geometrical meaning of each term.

4. Obtain the two formulas indicated in A7.

5. When is $\mathbf{a} \times (\mathbf{b} \times \mathbf{c}) = (\mathbf{a} \times \mathbf{b}) \times \mathbf{c}$?

6. Prove for finite sums of vectors that

$$|\mathbf{a} + \mathbf{b} + \mathbf{c} + \cdots| \leqslant |\mathbf{a}| + |\mathbf{b}| + |\mathbf{c}| + \cdots,$$

and deduce the proof of Corollary 8.2f.

C EXERCISES

I. Minkowski space M_3 is a three-dimensional vector space with a different definition of vector size. Instead of taking $|\mathbf{a}|$ to be of Euclidean length take

$$|\mathbf{a}| = \max\,[|a_1|,\,|a_2|,\,|a_3|],$$

which we will call the **Minkowski length** of $\mathbf{a}$. Prove that the Minkowski length satisfies the triangle inequality: $|\mathbf{a} + \mathbf{b}| \leqslant |\mathbf{a}| + |\mathbf{b}|$.

2. Letting C_0 be the space of continuous functions on $\{0 \leqslant x \leqslant 1\}$ (see Exercise C1, Section 8.1), define the norm of f by $||f|| = \max\limits_{0 \leqslant x \leqslant 1} |f(x)|$.
Prove the triangle inequality $||f + g|| \leqslant ||f|| + ||g||$.

3. Letting C_1 be the space of continuous functions on $\{0 \leqslant x \leqslant 1\}$, define $||f||$ by

$$||f|| = \int_0^1 |f(x)|\,dx.$$

Prove the triangle inequality $||f + g|| \leqslant ||f|| + ||g||$.

4. Letting C_2 be the space of continuous functions on $\{0 \leqslant x \leqslant 1\}$, and denoting the inner product of f and g by $(f, g) = \int_0^1 f(x)\,g(x)\,dx$, define $||f||$ by

$$||f|| = \sqrt{\int_0^1 |f(x)|^2\,dx} = \sqrt{(f, f)}.$$

Prove the Cauchy-Schwarz inequality for C_2

$$|(f, g)| \leqslant ||f||\,||g||,$$

and from this deduce the triangle inequality

$$||f + g|| \leqslant ||f|| + ||g||.$$

8.4 LINEAR INDEPENDENCE. BASES. ORIENTATION

Suppose we have a finite set of vectors $\mathbf{V}_1, \mathbf{V}_2, \ldots, \mathbf{V}_n$. Then a sum

$$\alpha_1 \mathbf{V}_1 + \alpha_2 \mathbf{V}_2 + \cdots + \alpha_n \mathbf{V}_n,$$

where the α's are scalars, is called a **linear combination** of the $\mathbf{V}$'s. The set of vectors is said to be **linearly independent** if

$$(1) \qquad \alpha_1 \mathbf{V}_1 + \alpha_2 \mathbf{V}_2 + \cdots + \alpha_n \mathbf{V}_n = \mathbf{O}$$

implies that $\alpha_1 = \alpha_2 = \cdots = \alpha_n = 0$—that is, if no linear combination can vanish unless all the coefficients vanish. Otherwise the set is said to be **linearly dependent**. In this case there is a set of α's, not all of which are zero, for which (1) holds.

For a set of two vectors, V_1 and V_2, linear dependence means that there is an α_1 and an α_2, not both zero, for which

$$\alpha_1 V_1 + \alpha_2 V_2 = O.$$

If, for instance $\alpha_1 \neq 0$, then

$$V_1 = -(\alpha_2/\alpha_1)V_2.$$

Here linear dependence means that one vector is a multiple of the other. In this case we also say that the vectors are **collinear**, since they lie on the same line through the origin. Thus collinearity and non-collinearity are equivalent to linear dependence and linear independence.

Similarly, if a set of three vectors is linearly dependent, we can solve for one in terms of the other two, so that the one lies in the plane of the two. In this case we say the vectors are **coplanar**. If they are linearly independent, we say they are **non-coplanar**. It seems geometrically clear that any four vectors must be linearly dependent. Proof of this conclusion is left to the exercises.

8.4a Theorem. The vectors **i**, **j**, **k** form a linearly independent set.

Proof. Suppose there were three scalars α_1, α_2, α_3 so that

$$\alpha_1 \mathbf{i} + \alpha_2 \mathbf{j} + \alpha_3 \mathbf{k} = O.$$

We then compute

$$\alpha_1 \mathbf{i} + \alpha_2 \mathbf{j} + \alpha_3 \mathbf{k} = (\alpha_1, \alpha_2, \alpha_3) = O = (0, 0, 0),$$

and by the definition of vector equality we have

$$\alpha_1 = \alpha_2 = \alpha_3 = 0. \qquad \blacksquare$$

If a set of vectors satisfies these two conditions: (1) it is linearly independent and (2) any vector can be expressed as a linear combination of its vectors, then the set is called a **basis**. This simply means that in some sense the set contains the smallest number of vectors in terms of which all other vectors can be expressed.

8.4b Theorem. The set **i**, **j**, **k** forms a basis in E_3.

Proof. We prove this by Theorems 8.2a and 8.4a. $\qquad \blacksquare$

It seems geometrically clear that any set of three orthogonal vectors would do equally well for a basis in E_3. For simplicity, we take them as unit vectors. A set of unit vectors is said to be **normal**, and an orthogonal set of unit vectors **orthonormal**.

8.4c Theorem. Let $\mathbf{i}'$, $\mathbf{j}'$, $\mathbf{k}'$ be an orthonormal set of three vectors in E_3. They then form a basis.

Proof. First we observe that $\mathbf{i}'$, $\mathbf{j}'$, $\mathbf{k}'$ must be linearly independent (Exercise B7). It remains to show that any vector $\mathbf{a} = a_1\mathbf{i} + a_2\mathbf{j} + a_3\mathbf{k}$

can be expressed in terms of $\mathbf{i}', \mathbf{j}', \mathbf{k}'$. For this, it is sufficient to be able to express the basis vectors $\mathbf{i}, \mathbf{j}, \mathbf{k}$ in terms of $\mathbf{i}', \mathbf{j}', \mathbf{k}'$ (why?). We show how to express $\mathbf{i}$ in this manner.

Since $\mathbf{i}, \mathbf{j}, \mathbf{k}$ do form a basis (Theorem 8.4b), $\mathbf{i}', \mathbf{j}', \mathbf{k}'$ must be expressible in terms of $\mathbf{i}, \mathbf{j}, \mathbf{k}$. Let

$$(1) \qquad \mathbf{i}' = \alpha_{11}\mathbf{i} + \alpha_{12}\mathbf{j} + \alpha_{13}\mathbf{k}$$

$$(2) \qquad \mathbf{j}' = \alpha_{21}\mathbf{i} + \alpha_{22}\mathbf{j} + \alpha_{23}\mathbf{k}$$

$$(3) \qquad \mathbf{k}' = \alpha_{31}\mathbf{i} + \alpha_{32}\mathbf{j} + \alpha_{33}\mathbf{k}.$$

Suppose it were possible to express $\mathbf{i}$ as a linear combination of $\mathbf{i}', \mathbf{j}', \mathbf{k}'$. Then set

$$(4) \qquad \mathbf{i} = \beta_1\mathbf{i}' + \beta_2\mathbf{j}' + \beta_3\mathbf{k}'.$$

Computing $\mathbf{i} \cdot \mathbf{i}'$ from (1), we get

$$\mathbf{i} \cdot \mathbf{i}' = \alpha_{11};$$

and from (4),

$$\mathbf{i} \cdot \mathbf{i}' = \beta_1.$$

Hence

$$\beta_1 = \alpha_{11}.$$

Similarly,

$$\beta_2 = \alpha_{21}, \ \beta_3 = \alpha_{31}.$$

Thus if $\mathbf{i}$ has a representation (4), then (4) must reduce to

$$(5) \qquad \mathbf{i} = \alpha_{11}\mathbf{i}' + \alpha_{21}\mathbf{j}' + \alpha_{31}\mathbf{k}'.$$

We now show that (5) is indeed a correct result. To do this, we substitute for $\mathbf{i}', \mathbf{j}', \mathbf{k}'$ from (1), (2), (3) into (5) to get

$$\begin{aligned}
\alpha_{11}\mathbf{i}' + \alpha_{21}\mathbf{j}' + \alpha_{31}\mathbf{k}' &= \alpha_{11}(\alpha_{11}\mathbf{i} + \alpha_{12}\mathbf{j} + \alpha_{13}\mathbf{k}) \\
&\quad + \alpha_{21}(\alpha_{21}\mathbf{i} + \alpha_{22}\mathbf{j} + \alpha_{23}\mathbf{k}) + \alpha_{31}(\alpha_{31}\mathbf{i} + \alpha_{32}\mathbf{j} + \alpha_{33}\mathbf{k}) \\
&= \mathbf{i}(\alpha_{11}^2 + \alpha_{21}^2 + \alpha_{31}^2) + \mathbf{j}(\alpha_{11}\alpha_{12} + \alpha_{21}\alpha_{22} + \alpha_{31}\alpha_{32}) \\
&\quad + \mathbf{k}(\alpha_{11}\alpha_{13} + \alpha_{21}\alpha_{23} + \alpha_{31}\alpha_{33}) \\
&= \mathbf{i}(\mathbf{i}' \cdot \mathbf{i}') + \mathbf{j}(\mathbf{i}' \cdot \mathbf{j}') + \mathbf{k}(\mathbf{i}' \cdot \mathbf{k}') = \mathbf{i},
\end{aligned}$$

the last equality coming from the orthonormality of $\mathbf{i}', \mathbf{j}', \mathbf{k}'$. ∎

Let $\mathbf{i}', \mathbf{j}', \mathbf{k}'$ be an orthonormal basis in E_3. Then $\mathbf{i}' \times \mathbf{j}'$ can be expressed as linear combination of $\mathbf{i}', \mathbf{j}', \mathbf{k}'$. But since it is orthogonal to both $\mathbf{i}'$ and $\mathbf{j}'$, it must be parallel to $\mathbf{k}'$, that is, a scalar multiple of $\mathbf{k}'$. Now they both have length 1, so that we must have either

$$\mathbf{i}' \times \mathbf{j}' = \mathbf{k}'$$

or

$$\mathbf{i}' \times \mathbf{j}' = -\mathbf{k}'.$$

We say that the basis is **positively** or **negatively oriented** according as $\mathbf{i}' \times \mathbf{j}' = +\mathbf{k}'$ or $-\mathbf{k}'$. This can also be expressed by the scalar triple product: the basis $\mathbf{i}', \mathbf{j}', \mathbf{k}'$ is positively or negatively oriented according as

$$\mathbf{i}' \times \mathbf{j}' \cdot \mathbf{k}' = +1$$

or
$$\mathbf{i}' \times \mathbf{j}' \cdot \mathbf{k}' = -1.$$

We can extend the concept of orientation to arbitrary linearly independent triples of vectors: an ordered triple $\mathbf{a}, \mathbf{b}, \mathbf{c}$ of vectors is **positively** or **negatively oriented** according as

$$\mathbf{a} \times \mathbf{b} \cdot \mathbf{c} > 0$$

or
$$\mathbf{a} \times \mathbf{b} \cdot \mathbf{c} < 0.$$

In particular, we note that $\mathbf{a}, \mathbf{b}, \mathbf{a} \times \mathbf{b}$ form a positive triple, since

$$(\mathbf{a} \times \mathbf{b}) \cdot (\mathbf{a} \times \mathbf{b}) = |\mathbf{a} \times \mathbf{b}|^2.$$

Orientation has a geometric significance. A positive triple is oriented so that $\mathbf{c}$ points to the same side of the plane of $\mathbf{a}$ and $\mathbf{b}$ as $\mathbf{a} \times \mathbf{b}$ itself (why?), and consequently the side of the plane to which $\mathbf{c}$ points can be determined by the right-hand rule described earlier.

8.5 VECTOR ANALYTIC GEOMETRY

Many of the formulas of analytic geometry can be succinctly stated in vector terms. In this section we will indicate briefly and informally how this can be done in a few simple cases dealing with planes and lines.

In analytic geometry, a line is usually specified by giving the equations of two planes which intersect along the line, or it is given in symmetric or parametric form. The parametric equations of a line are in the form

$$x = x_0 + a_1 t$$
$$y = y_0 + a_2 t$$
$$z = z_0 + a_3 t,$$

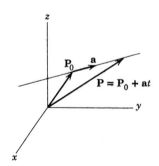

where $P_0 = (x_0, y_0, z_0)$ is a point on the line and a_1, a_2, a_3 are its direction numbers. These are just the component equations of

$$P = P_0 + t\mathbf{a},$$

where $\mathbf{a} = a_1\mathbf{i} + a_2\mathbf{j} + a_3\mathbf{k}$. We will call this equation the **vector equation** of the line. If $|\mathbf{a}| = 1$, then t is the distance of the point P along the line from P_0, measured positively in the direction of $\mathbf{a}$ and negatively in the direction of $-\mathbf{a}$ (why?).

If the equations are given in symmetric form, namely

$$\frac{x - x_0}{a_1} = \frac{y - y_0}{a_2} = \frac{z - z_0}{a_2},$$

we can set the common value of these ratios equal to t and reduce to parametric form.

Finally, if the line is specified by giving two planes through it, there are certain standard ways, familiar to you from analytic geometry, of reducing these to projecting planes and then to symmetric form.

A plane in the form $a_1x + a_2y + a_3z = d$ can clearly be written

$$\mathbf{P} \cdot \mathbf{a} = d.$$

Thus the projection of P on $\mathbf{a}$ is a constant, so that clearly $\mathbf{a}$ is the normal vector to the plane. If $\mathbf{a}$ is normalized to have length one, then $\mathbf{P} \cdot \mathbf{a}$ is the

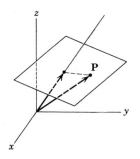

length of the projection of P on $\mathbf{a}$. In this case $d = \pm$ the perpendicular distance from the origin to the plane. Geometrically, what determines the sign of d? [See Exercise A5 (e).]

The plane determined by two vectors,—that is, the set of all vectors of the form $\mathbf{P} = \alpha\mathbf{a} + \beta\mathbf{b}$ where $\mathbf{a}$ and $\mathbf{b}$ are non-collinear can be written as

$$\mathbf{P} \cdot (\mathbf{a} \times \mathbf{b}) = 0$$

(see Exercise C2). Another plane passing through a point $\mathbf{P}_0$ and parallel to the other one can be written

$$\mathbf{P} = \mathbf{P}_0 + \alpha\mathbf{a} + \beta\mathbf{b}.$$

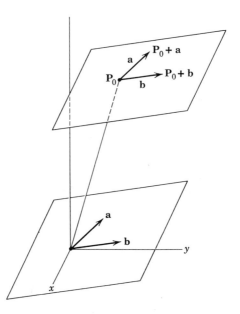

8.6 VECTOR SPACES OF OTHER DIMENSIONS: E_n

The theory of two-dimensional Euclidean vector space E_2 is obtained from the theory for E_3 by simply suppressing the third component. Thus vectors in E_2 are ordered pairs (a_1, a_2) or real numbers. These can be represented in the form $a_1\mathbf{i} + a_2\mathbf{j}$, where $\mathbf{i} = (1, 0)$ and $\mathbf{j} = (0, 1)$. Hence all the vector algebra which does not pertain to cross products carries over immediately.

Higher dimensional spaces are perhaps more difficult to visualize, but the formalism is almost identical to that for E_3. Four-dimensional Euclidean vector space E_4 is the collection of all ordered quadruples of real numbers (a_1, a_2, a_3, a_4). The rules given for E_3 on page 149 can be restated for E_4 by merely adding an extra component in the parentheses, and the length of a vector $\mathbf{a} = (a_1, a_2, a_3, a_4)$ is given by

$$|\mathbf{a}| = \sqrt{a_1{}^2 + a_2{}^2 + a_3{}^2 + a_4{}^2}.$$

In general, n-dimensional Euclidean vector space is the collection of all ordered *n*-tuples of real numbers $(a_1, a_2, \ldots, a_n)$ satisfying our rules and for which the length of a vector $\mathbf{a} = (a_1, a_2, \ldots, a_n)$ is given by

$$|\mathbf{a}| = \sqrt{a_1{}^2 + a_2{}^2 + \cdots + a_n{}^2}.$$

The vectors $\mathbf{e}_1, \mathbf{e}_2, \ldots, \mathbf{e}_n$ given by

$$\mathbf{e}_1 = (1, 0, \ldots, 0), \mathbf{e}_2 = (0, 1, \ldots, 0), \ldots, \mathbf{e}_n = (0, 0, \ldots, 1)$$

form a basis in terms of which all vectors in E_n can be expressed.

The inner product is given by

$$\mathbf{a} \cdot \mathbf{b} = a_1 b_1 + a_2 b_2 + \cdots + a_n b_n = \sum_1^n a_m b_m.$$

The Cauchy-Schwarz inequality, $|\mathbf{a} \cdot \mathbf{b}| \leqslant |\mathbf{a}| \, |\mathbf{b}|$, still holds, for our proof was independent of dimension. In terms of sums, this inequality becomes

$$\left| \sum_1^n a_m b_m \right| \leqslant \sqrt{\sum_1^n a_m{}^2} \sqrt{\sum_1^n b_m{}^2}.$$

The angle θ between $\mathbf{a}$ and $\mathbf{b}$ is defined by $\cos \theta = \mathbf{a} \cdot \mathbf{b}/|\mathbf{a}| \, |\mathbf{b}|$, and the two vectors are orthogonal if $\mathbf{a} \cdot \mathbf{b} = 0$—that is, if $\mathbf{a}$ or $\mathbf{b} = \mathbf{O}$, or if $\theta = \pi/2$. The triangle inequality, $|\mathbf{a} + \mathbf{b}| \leqslant |\mathbf{a}| + |\mathbf{b}|$, again holds, since our proof was a dimension-free argument.

But again the cross product does not carry over. Every other part of vector algebra we will consider as having been proved for E_n, and so will not hesitate to use any or all of our results which do not involve vector products for vector spaces of arbitrary dimension.

A EXERCISES

I. What sets are described by the following?

   (a) $|\mathbf{P} - \mathbf{P}_0| \leqslant c$ (b) $|\mathbf{P} - \mathbf{P}_0| = c$

   (c) $|\mathbf{P} - \mathbf{P}_0| > c$ (d) $|\mathbf{P} - \mathbf{P}_0| + |\mathbf{P} - \mathbf{P}_1| = c$

   (e) $|\mathbf{P} - \mathbf{P}_0| - |\mathbf{P} - \mathbf{P}_1| = c$

2. Write a vector equation for the line through $\mathbf{P}_1$ and $\mathbf{P}_2$.

3. Write a vector equation for the line through $\mathbf{P}_1$ perpendicular to the plane of $\mathbf{P}_1, \mathbf{P}_2, \mathbf{P}_3$.

4. Write the scalar equation of the plane through $\mathbf{P}_0 = (1, 2, -1)$ and perpendicular to the vector $\mathbf{a} = (5, 2, -2)$.

5. Consider a plane given in the form $\mathbf{P} \cdot \mathbf{a} = d$:

   (a) What is the geometrical significance of $d/|\mathbf{a}|$?

   (b) What is the geometrical significance of $\mathbf{P}_0 = d\mathbf{a}/|\mathbf{a}|^2$?

   (c) If $\mathbf{P}$ is a point in the plane what are the vectors $\mathbf{P} - \mathbf{P}_0$?

   (d) If $\mathbf{P}$ is a point in the plane, compute $(\mathbf{P} - \mathbf{P}_0) \cdot \mathbf{a}$.

   (e) Determine conditions under which $\mathbf{P}$ and $\mathbf{Q}$ will be on opposite sides of the plane.

6. Let **a**, **b**, **c**, . . . , **e** be a linearly independent set of vectors in E_n. Show that none of them is zero.

B   EXERCISES

1. Show that any four vectors in E_3 form a linearly dependent set. Show in general that any $n + 1$ vectors in E_n form a linearly dependent set.

2. Given $\mathbf{a} \neq \mathbf{O}$ and **c**, what is the locus of all points **P** for which $\mathbf{a} \times \mathbf{P} = \mathbf{c}$?

3. Can we define a division process complementary to vector multiplication? That is, given $\mathbf{a} \neq \mathbf{O}$, and **c**, can we find a unique **b** such that $\mathbf{a} \times \mathbf{b} = \mathbf{c}$?

4. Show that the vectors $(1, 0, 0)$, $(1, 1, 0)$ $(1, 1, 1)$ form a basis in E_3. Give a formula expressing any vector **a** in terms of these vectors.

5 Let **i,**′ **j,**′ **k,**′ be an orthonormal basis Show that if

$$\mathbf{i}' \times \mathbf{j}' = \mathbf{k}',$$

then

$$\mathbf{j}' \times \mathbf{k}' = \mathbf{i}'$$

$$\mathbf{k}' \times \mathbf{i}' = \mathbf{j}';$$

but if

$$\mathbf{i}' \times \mathbf{j}' = -\mathbf{k}',$$

then

$$\mathbf{j}' \times \mathbf{k}' = -\mathbf{i}'$$

$$\mathbf{k}' \times \mathbf{i}' = -\mathbf{j}'.$$

6. Let $\mathbf{a} = a_1'\mathbf{i}' + a_2'\mathbf{j}' + a_3'\mathbf{k}'$, $\mathbf{b} = b_1'\mathbf{i}' + b_2'\mathbf{j}' + b_3'\mathbf{k}'$. Show that

$$\mathbf{a} \cdot \mathbf{b} = a_1'b_1' + a_2'b_2' + a_3'b_3'$$

and

$$\mathbf{a} \times \mathbf{b} = \pm \begin{vmatrix} \mathbf{i}' & \mathbf{j}' & \mathbf{k}' \\ a_1' & a_2' & a_3' \\ b_1' & b_2' & b_3' \end{vmatrix}$$

where the sign is given by the orientation of **i**′, **j**′, **k**′.

7. Show that any orthogonal set not containing **O** in E_n is linearly independent.

8. Let **i**′, **j**′, **k**′ be an orthonormal basis in E_3 and let them be expressed in terms of **i**, **j**, **k** by equations (1), (2), (3) of Section 8.4. Show that

$$\mathbf{i} = \alpha_{11}\mathbf{i}' + \alpha_{21}\mathbf{j}' + \alpha_{31}\mathbf{k}'$$

$$\mathbf{j} = \alpha_{12}\mathbf{i}' + \alpha_{22}\mathbf{j}' + \alpha_{31}\mathbf{k}'$$

$$\mathbf{k} = \alpha_{13}\mathbf{i}' + \alpha_{23}\mathbf{j}' + \alpha_{33}\mathbf{k}'.$$

9. Show that the determinant of the α's in Exercise B8 is $+1$ or -1 according as **i**′, **j**′, **k**′ is a positively or negatively oriented triple. Show also that

$$\sum_n \alpha^2_{mn} = 1 \qquad \sum_m \alpha_{mn}\alpha_{mp} = 0 \qquad \text{if } n \neq p$$

$$\sum_m \alpha^2_{mn} = 1 \qquad \sum_n \alpha_{mn}\alpha_{pn} = 0 \qquad \text{if } m \neq p.$$

10. Let $\mathbf{a} = a_1\mathbf{i} + a_2\mathbf{j} + a_3\mathbf{k}$ and also $\mathbf{a} = a_1'\mathbf{i}' + a_2'\mathbf{j}' + a_3'\mathbf{k}'$. Show that

$$a_1' = \alpha_{11}a_1 + \alpha_{12}a_2 + \alpha_{13}a_3 \quad \text{and} \quad a_1 = \alpha_{11}a_1' + \alpha_{21}a_2' + \alpha_{31}a_3'$$
$$a_2' = \alpha_{21}a_1 + \alpha_{22}a_2 + \alpha_{23}a_3 \qquad a_2 = \alpha_{12}a_1' + \alpha_{22}a_2' + \alpha_{32}a_3'$$
$$a_3' = \alpha_{31}a_1 + \alpha_{32}a_2 + \alpha_{33}a_3 \qquad a_3 = \alpha_{13}a_1' + \alpha_{23}a_2' + \alpha_{33}a_3'.$$

C EXERCISES

1. Let $\mathbf{a}$, $\mathbf{b}$, $\mathbf{c}$ be three linearly independent vectors in E_n. Define $\mathbf{a}'$, $\mathbf{b}'$, $\mathbf{c}'$ by

$$\mathbf{a}' = \mathbf{a}$$
$$\mathbf{b}' = \mathbf{b} - \frac{\mathbf{b} \cdot \mathbf{a}}{|\mathbf{a}|^2}\,\mathbf{a}$$
$$\mathbf{c}' = \mathbf{c} - \frac{\mathbf{c} \cdot \mathbf{a}'}{|\mathbf{a}|^2}\,\mathbf{a} - \frac{\mathbf{c} \cdot \mathbf{b}'}{|\mathbf{b}'|^2}\,\mathbf{b}',$$

and show that the set $\mathbf{a}'$, $\mathbf{b}'$, $\mathbf{c}'$ is orthogonal. This process of constructing an orthogonal set is called the **Gram-Schmidt orthogonalization process.** Show further that $\mathbf{i}'$, $\mathbf{j}'$, $\mathbf{k}'$ defined by

$$\mathbf{i}' = \mathbf{a}'/|\mathbf{a}'|$$
$$\mathbf{j}' = \mathbf{b}'/|\mathbf{b}'|$$
$$\mathbf{k}' = \mathbf{c}'/|\mathbf{c}'|$$

is an orthonormal set, and hence deduce that any three linearly independent vectors in E_3 forms a basis.

2. Show that a necessary and sufficient condition that $\mathbf{a}$, $\mathbf{b}$, $\mathbf{c}$ be coplanar is that $\mathbf{a} \times \mathbf{b} \cdot \mathbf{c} = 0$. Use C1 above.

8.7 VECTOR FUNCTIONS. CURVES

If to each real number t in some domain—say an interval I: $\{a \leqslant t \leqslant b\}$—we associate a vector $\mathbf{P}$ in E_3 (or E_n for that matter), the set of ordered pairs $(t, \mathbf{P})$, where t is in I and $\mathbf{P}$ is the corresponding vector, is called a **vector function** on I. It is denoted by $\mathbf{F}$ and is given symbolically by

$$(1) \qquad\qquad \mathbf{P} = \mathbf{F}(t) \qquad \{a \leqslant t \leqslant b\}.$$

The point $\mathbf{P}$ corresponding to t is called the **value** of $\mathbf{F}$ at t, and the set of points $\mathbf{P}$ in E_3 which are values of $\mathbf{F}$ for some t in I is called the **range** of $\mathbf{F}$. We will say that $\mathbf{F}$ is continuous at t_0 in I if for each $\epsilon > 0$ there is a $\delta\,(\epsilon, t_0)$ such that $|\mathbf{F}(t) - \mathbf{F}(t_0)| < \epsilon$ for all t in I for which $|t - t_0| < \delta$.

Specifying a vector for each t means specifying three real numbers for each t, namely the components of the vector. Thus equation (1) is equivalent to specifying each component as a function of t

$$(2) \qquad\qquad x = f(t) \qquad y = g(t) \qquad z = h(t).$$

You should convince yourself that asking that $\mathbf{F}$ be continuous at a point t_0 is equivalent to asking that all three of f, g, and h be continuous at t_0. (See Exercise B1. Use Corollary 8.2f.)

If $\mathbf{F}$ is continuous in I, we will call the range of $\mathbf{F}$ a **curve**, t the **curve parameter**, and I the **parameter interval**. You will recognize the equations (2) as the usual parametric form of the equations of a curve.

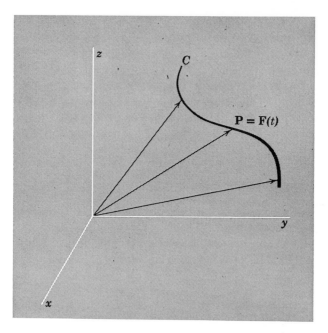

Now a curve can be a very complicated set, in fact, there are curves which will fill out a cube. Such a curve is called a **space-filling curve** or a **Peano curve**. (Yes, the same Peano whose name was associated with the axioms for the natural numbers.)

For reference we now state some definitions.

A **closed curve** is a curve given by (1) with the property that $\mathbf{F}(a) = \mathbf{F}(b)$; that is, the terminal point on the curve coincides with the initial point.

A **simple arc** (or a **simple non-closed curve**) is a curve given by (1) with the property that $\mathbf{F}(t_1) = \mathbf{F}(t_2)$ implies $t_1 = t_2$; that is, the curve does not "cross" itself or even "touch" itself.

A **simple closed curve** or a **Jordan curve** is a closed curve with the property that $\mathbf{F}(t_1) = \mathbf{F}(t_2)$ implies either that (1) $t_1 = t_2$ or (2) $t_1 = a$ and

$t_2 = b$ (or maybe the other way around: $t_2 = a$ and $t_1 = b$). A circle is the simplest example of a Jordan curve:

$$\left.\begin{array}{l} x = a \cos \theta \\ y = b \sin \theta \\ z = 0 \end{array}\right\} \quad \{0 \leqslant \theta \leqslant 2\pi\}.$$

8.8 RECTIFIABLE CURVES AND ARC LENGTH

Let f be a real function defined on an interval $I: \{a \leqslant t \leqslant b\}$ and let Δ be a partition of I:

$$\Delta: a = t_0 < t_1 < \cdots < t_{n-1} < t_n = b.$$

Then if the sums

(1)
$$\sum_{\Delta} |f(t_m) - f(t_{m-1})|$$

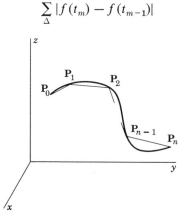

are all bounded we will say that f has **bounded variation** over I. The **variation** of f over I is defined to be the supremum of the values of the sums taken over all partitions of I:

(2)
$$V_f = \sup_{\Delta} \sum |f(t_k) - f(t_{k-1})|.$$

One can make a similar definition in case of a vector function. However in dealing with continuous vector functions (that is, with curves) this has a very important geometrical meaning, as we will now see.

Let C be a curve given by

$$\mathbf{P} = \mathbf{F}(t) \quad \{a \leqslant t \leqslant b\},$$

and let Δ be a partition of the parameter interval:

$$\Delta: a = t_0 < t_1 < \cdots < t_{n-1} < t_n = b.$$

Let the points $\mathbf{P}_0, \mathbf{P}_1, \ldots, \mathbf{P}_n$ be given by

$$\mathbf{P}_m = \mathbf{F}(t_m) \qquad m = 0, 1, \ldots, n.$$

The sum analogous to the sum (1) is

(1') $$L_\Delta = \sum_\Delta |\mathbf{F}(t_m) - \mathbf{F}(t_{m-1})| = \sum_\Delta |\mathbf{P}_m - \mathbf{P}_{m-1}|,$$

and from the latter form we see that this sum is the length of the "broken line" or "polygonal line" inscribed in C leading from one $\mathbf{P}_m$ to the next. This should in some sense approximate the length of the curve. In fact, we are using this approach to define the length of the curve. If the numbers L_Δ as defined by (1') are bounded for all partitions Δ, then we say that the curve C is **rectifiable** and that the **length** of the curve is given by

(2') $$L_C = \sup L_\Delta = \sup \sum_\Delta |\mathbf{P}_m - \mathbf{P}_{m-1}|.$$

If the numbers L_Δ are not bounded, we say the curve is **not rectifiable** or has no arc length.

Now it turns out, not surprisingly, that there is a close connection between rectifiability and bounded variation, as demonstrated in the following theorem.

8.8a   Theorem. Let C be a curve given by

$$\mathbf{P} = \mathbf{F}(t) = f(t)\mathbf{i} + g(t)\mathbf{j} + h(t)\mathbf{k}, \quad I: \{a \leqslant t \leqslant b\}.$$

A necessary and sufficient condition that C be rectifiable is that f, g, and h have bounded variation.

Proof. Necessity. We suppose C to be rectifiable and that L_C as given by (2') exists. Let Δ be any partition of I. Then

$$|f(t_m) - f(t_{m-1})| \leqslant |\mathbf{F}(t_m) - \mathbf{F}(t_{m-1})|,$$

since a vector has greater length than any component. Thus

$$\sum_\Delta |f(t_m) - f(t_{m-1})| \leqslant \sum_\Delta |\mathbf{F}(t_m) - \mathbf{F}(t_{m-1})| \leqslant L_C.$$

Hence f has bounded variation, and so too have g and h by the same argument.

Sufficiency. We suppose that f, g, and h have bounded variation. This means that V_f as defined by (2) exists, and so also do V_g and V_h. Then, by Corollary 8.2f,

$$|\mathbf{F}(t_m) - \mathbf{F}(t_{m-1})| \leqslant |f(t_m) - f(t_{m-1})|$$
$$+ |g(t_m) - g(t_{m-1})| + |h(t_m) - h(t_{m-1})|.$$

Summing over Δ and using (2), we get

$$\sum_\Delta |\mathbf{F}(t_m) - \mathbf{F}(t_{m-1})| \leqslant V_f + V_g + V_h. \qquad \blacksquare$$

Now it is reasonable to expect that if we cut a rectifiable curve at a point, then the two pieces should be rectifiable and the total length should be the sum of the lengths of the two pieces. This is indeed the case.

8.8b   Theorem. Let C be a rectifiable curve given by $\mathbf{P} = \mathbf{F}(t)$, $I: \{a \leqslant t \leqslant b\}$. Let c be an intermediate point in I, and denote by C_1 and C_2 the two curves given respectively by

$$\mathbf{P} = \mathbf{F}(t) \qquad I_1: \{a \leqslant t \leqslant c\}$$
$$\mathbf{P} = \mathbf{F}(t) \qquad I_2: \{c \leqslant t \leqslant b\}.$$

Then both C_1 and C_2 are rectifiable and

$$L_C = L_{C_1} + L_{C_2}.$$

Proof. Let Δ_1 and Δ_2 be partitions of I_1 and I_2 respectively. Together they form a partition Δ of I. Thus

(3) $$L_{\Delta_1} + L_{\Delta_2} = L_\Delta \leqslant L_C,$$

so that

$$L_{\Delta_1} \leqslant L_C - L_{\Delta_2}.$$

If we keep Δ_2 fixed, we see that the set of numbers L_{Δ_1} is bounded so that C_1 is rectifiable. By interchanging Δ_1 and Δ_2, we see by the same argument that C_2 is rectifiable. Then since (3) holds for all partitions Δ_1 and Δ_2, we immediately have

(4) $$L_{C_1} + L_{C_2} \leqslant L_C.$$

To obtain the reverse inequality of (4), let Δ be any partition of I. The intermediate point c will fall in some t interval, say between t_p and t_{p-1}. Then, by introducing c as an additional partition point, we have by the triangle inequality

(5) $$|\mathbf{F}(t_p) - \mathbf{F}(t_{p-1})| \leqslant |\mathbf{F}(t_p) - \mathbf{F}(c)| + |\mathbf{F}(c) - \mathbf{F}(t_{p-1})|.$$

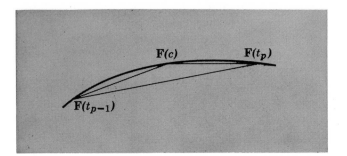

This also creates partitions Δ_1 of I_1 and Δ_2 of I_2, for which we have by (5)

$$L_\Delta \leqslant L_{\Delta_1} + L_{\Delta_2} \leqslant L_{C_1} + L_{C_2}.$$

From this it is clear that

(6) $$L_C \leqslant L_{C_1} + L_{C_2}.$$

Then (4) and (6) together complete the proof.   ∎

8.9 DIFFERENTIABLE CURVES

A great deal could be proved about arc length under no further hypotheses than rectifiability—for example, that arc length is a continuous function of the curve parameter, t, and that a curve can always be re-parameterized so that arc length $s(t)$ (length over the interval from a to t)

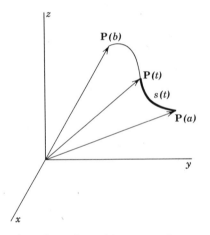

is a strictly increasing function of t. This means that t can be expressed in terms of s, so that the arc length can always be introduced as a curve parameter in a rectifiable curve. Proof of these facts would take a little too long, however, so we turn our attention now to differentiable curves. We will establish these and other properties for such curves.

Let $\mathbf{F}$ be a vector function defined on $I: \{a \leqslant t \leqslant b\}$. We will say that $\mathbf{F}$ is **differentiable** at a point t_0 in I if

$$\lim_{h \to 0} \frac{\mathbf{F}(t_0 + h) - \mathbf{F}(t_0)}{h} = \mathbf{F}'(t_0)$$

exists. The value of this limit, when it exists, will be called the **derivative** of $\mathbf{F}$ at t_0. $\mathbf{F}$ is differentiable in I if it is differentiable at every point in I, the derivatives at the ends being of course one-sided derivatives.

8.9a   Theorem. A necessary and sufficient condition that a vector function $\mathbf{F} = (f, g, h)$ be differentiable is that f, g, and h be differentiable.

Proof. Necessity. Let $\mathbf{F}'(t_0) = \mathbf{a} = a_1\mathbf{i} + a_2\mathbf{j} + a_3\mathbf{k}$. Then

$$\left| \frac{\mathbf{F}(t_0 + h) - \mathbf{F}(t_0)}{h} - \mathbf{a} \right| \geqslant \left| \frac{f(t_0 + h) - f(t_0)}{h} - a_1 \right|.$$

As $h \to 0$, the left side tends to zero. Hence, so must the right, and we conclude that

$$f'(t_0) = a_1.$$

Similarly,

$$g'(t_0) = a_2$$

$$h'(t_0) = a_3.$$

Sufficiency. Suppose $f'(t_0) = a_1$, $g'(t_0) = a_2$, and $h'(t_0) = a_3$. Define $\mathbf{a} = a_1\mathbf{i} + a_2\mathbf{j} + a_3\mathbf{k}$ and estimate

$$\left| \frac{\mathbf{F}(t_0 + h) - \mathbf{F}(t_0)}{h} - \mathbf{a} \right|.$$

By Corollary 8.2f, we see that $\mathbf{F}$ is differentiable at t_0 and that

$$\mathbf{F}'(t_0) = \mathbf{a}. \qquad \blacksquare$$

The analogy between our discussions of arc length and integration should be clear. We can now show that if C is given by

$$\mathbf{P} = \mathbf{F}(t) \qquad I : \{a \leqslant t \leqslant b\}$$

where $\mathbf{F}$ is continuously differentiable in I, then its arc length is given by an integral.

8.9b   Theorem. Let C be given by

$$\mathbf{P} = \mathbf{F}(t) \qquad I : \{a \leqslant t \leqslant b\},$$

where $\mathbf{F}$ is differentiable in I and $\mathbf{F}'$ is continuous in I. Then

$$L_C = \int_a^b |\mathbf{F}'(t)| \, dt.$$

Proof. Let $s(t_0)$ represent the arc length over that part of C defined by

$\mathbf{P} = \mathbf{F}(t)$, $\{a \leqslant t \leqslant t_0\}$. Then, by the additivity of arc length (Theorem 8.8b),

$$s(t_0 + h) - s(t_0) = L(t_0, t_0 + h)$$

where $L(t_0, t_0 + h)$ is the length of the segment of C between t_0 and $t_0 + h$.

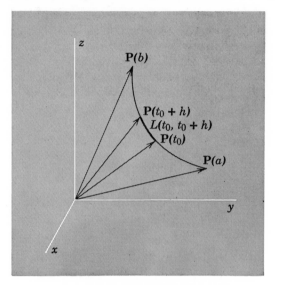

We proceed to estimate this length from above and below. First the easy side:

$$L(t_0, t_0 + h) \geqslant |\mathbf{F}(t_0 + h) - \mathbf{F}(t_0)| = h|[\mathbf{F}(t_0 + h) - \mathbf{F}(t_0)]/h|.$$

Hence, since $L(t_0, t_0 + h) = s(t_0 + h) - s(t_0)$,

$$(7) \qquad \frac{s(t_0 + h) - s(t_0)}{h} \geqslant |[\mathbf{F}(t_0 + h) - \mathbf{F}(t_0)]/h|.$$

To estimate from above, let Δ be a partition of the interval from t_0 to $t_0 + h$. Then

$$\sum_{\Delta} |\mathbf{F}(t_m) - \mathbf{F}(t_{m-1})|$$
$$= \sum_{\Delta} \sqrt{[f(t_m) - f(t_{m-1})]^2 + [g(t_m) - g(t_{m-1})]^2 + [h(t_m) - h(t_{m-1})]^2}$$

By the mean-value theorem, this can be written in the form

$$\sum_{\Delta} \sqrt{f'^2(\xi_m) + g'^2(\eta_m) + h'^2(\zeta_m)} \qquad (t_m - t_{m-1}),$$

where ξ_m, η_m, ζ_m all lie in $\{t_{m-1} \leqslant t \leqslant t_m\}$.

Now f', g', h' are continuous; hence there is a point ξ between t_0 and $t_0 + h$ at which f'^2 achieves its maximum for that interval, a point η at which g'^2 achieves its maximum, and a point ζ at which h'^2 achieves its maximum. Then, estimating our last expression, we get

$$\sum_\Delta |F(t_m) - F(t_{m-1})| \leq \sqrt{f'^2(\xi) + g'^2(\eta) + h'^2(\zeta)} \quad \sum_\Delta (t_m - t_{m-1})$$

$$= \sqrt{f'^2(\xi) + g'^2(\eta) + h'^2(\zeta)}\, h$$

Now the sum on the left is an approximating sum for $L(t_0, t_0 + h)$; hence the right-hand side forms an upper bound for all such sums. We get therefore

$$(8) \quad s(t_0 + h) - s(t) = L(t_0, t_0 + h) \leq \sqrt{f'^2(\xi) + g'^2(\eta) + h'^2(\zeta)}\, h.$$

From (7) and (8) we get

$$|[F(t_0 + h) - F(t_0)]/h| \leq [s(t_0 + h) - s(t_0)]/h$$
$$\leq \sqrt{f'^2(\xi) + g'^2(\eta) + h'^2(\zeta)}.$$

As $h \to 0$, we have ξ, η, ζ each tending to t_0. Thus both ends of this inequality become $|F'(t_0)|$, so that we see finally that

$$s'(t_0) = |F'(t_0)| = \sqrt{f'^2(t_0) + g'^2(t_0) + h'^2(t_0)}$$

for every t_0 in I: $\{a \leq t \leq b\}$. But by hypothesis, $|F'(t)|$ is a continuous function, and therefore an integrable function on I. Then by Theorem 4.5b,

$$s(b) - s(a) = L_C = \int_a^b |F'(t)|\, dt = \int_a^b \sqrt{f'^2(t) + g'^2(t) + h'^2(t)}\, dt. \quad \blacksquare$$

In passing, let us comment on another approach to this last theorem We could have defined L_C by $L_C = \lim_{\|\Delta\| \to 0} L_\Delta$. In fact, it can be proved that this definition is equivalent to the one we gave, but to do so would be nearly as difficult, involving much the same type of argument, as to prove that an integral is the limit of a Riemann sum.

Defining arc length this way, one observes that the approximants L are very nearly in the form of Riemann sums. They are so close that they can be juggled into that form with an error which tends to zero as $\|\Delta\| \to 0$.

It would now be convenient to have arc length as a curve parameter. Thus we begin by giving conditions under which this will be done. As indicated earlier, this is always possible for rectifiable curves, but to give the proof on the hypothesis of rectifiability alone is a little beyond the scope of this book.

8.9c   Theorem. Let C be a curve described by

$$\mathbf{P} = \mathbf{F}(t) = f(t)\mathbf{i} + g(t)\mathbf{j} + h(t)\mathbf{k} \qquad I: \{a \leqslant t \leqslant b\},$$

where $\mathbf{F}'(t)$ is continuous and never vanishes. Then arc length can be introduced as a curve parameter and $|d\mathbf{F}/ds| = 1$.

Proof. By Theorem 8.9b, we have $s'(t) = |\mathbf{F}'(t)| > 0$. Thus $s(t)$ is strictly monotone-increasing and continuous. It therefore has a unique inverse function $t(s)$ where $t'(s)$ exists and is positive on $\{0 \leqslant s \leqslant L_C\}$. Thus C is given by

$$\mathbf{P} = \mathbf{F}[t(s)] = f[t(s)]\mathbf{i} + g[t(s)]\mathbf{j} + h[t(s)]\mathbf{k} \qquad \{0 \leqslant s \leqslant L_C\},$$

and by the chain rule we have

$$\frac{d\mathbf{F}}{ds} = [f'(t)\mathbf{i} + g'(t)\mathbf{j} + h'(t)\mathbf{k}]\frac{dt}{ds} = \mathbf{F}'(t)/s'(t).$$

Thus
$$\left|\frac{d\mathbf{F}}{ds}\right| = \frac{|\mathbf{F}'(t)|}{s'(t)} = 1. \qquad \blacksquare$$

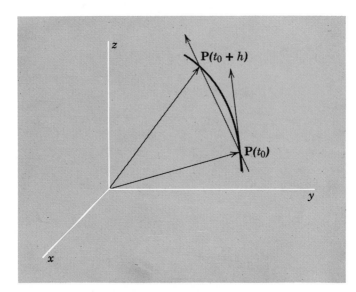

Geometrically, the difference quotient

$$[\mathbf{F}(t_0 + h) - \mathbf{F}(t_0)]/h$$

can be interpreted as a vector with its initial point at $\mathbf{P}(t_0) = \mathbf{F}(t_0)$ and pointing from there in the direction through $\mathbf{P}(t_0 + h) = \mathbf{F}(t_0 + h)$. It therefore represents a secant vector of the curve at $\mathbf{P}(t_0)$. As $h \to 0$, the point $\mathbf{P}(t_0 + h) = \mathbf{F}(t_0 + h)$ slides down the curve and in the limit coincides with $\mathbf{P}(t_0)$. The limiting position of the vector is called a **tangent vector**. It is given by $\mathbf{F}'(t_0)$. In particular, the vector

$$\mathbf{T} = \frac{d\mathbf{F}}{ds} = \frac{dx}{ds}\mathbf{i} + \frac{dy}{ds}\mathbf{j} + \frac{dz}{ds}\mathbf{k}$$

is called the **unit tangent vector,** because its length is one by Theorem 8.9c. It can be computed by the formula

$$\mathbf{T} = \mathbf{F}'(t)/s'(t) = \mathbf{F}'(t)/|\mathbf{F}'(t)|.$$

Let us suppose now that $\mathbf{F}$ has higher derivatives. We observe that

$$\mathbf{T} \cdot \mathbf{T} = 1.$$

So [see Exercise A1(b)]

$$\mathbf{T} \cdot \frac{d\mathbf{T}}{ds} = 0,$$

or, in coordinate form,

$$\frac{dx}{ds}\frac{d^2x}{ds^2} + \frac{dy}{ds}\frac{d^2y}{ds^2} + \frac{dz}{ds}\frac{d^2z}{ds^2} = 0.$$

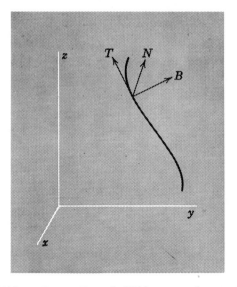

Thus either $d\mathbf{T}/ds = \mathbf{O}$, or $\mathbf{T}$ and $d\mathbf{T}/ds$ are orthogonal. At all points where $d\mathbf{T}/ds \neq \mathbf{O}$, we define the unit vector $\mathbf{N}$ in the direction of $d\mathbf{T}/ds$ as

$$\mathbf{N} = \frac{d\mathbf{T}}{ds} \bigg/ \left|\frac{d\mathbf{T}}{ds}\right|$$

Thus
$$\frac{d\mathbf{T}}{ds} = \kappa \mathbf{N},$$

where κ is a scalar function of s (or t) along C, called **curvature**. The vector $\mathbf{N}$ is called the **principal normal** of C at the point where it is evaluated. The vector $\mathbf{B}$ defined by $\mathbf{B} = \mathbf{T} \times \mathbf{N}$ is called the **binormal**. The triple $\mathbf{T}$, $\mathbf{N}$, $\mathbf{B}$ form a positively oriented triple of vectors.

If $\mathbf{P} = \mathbf{F}(t)$ describes the motion of a particle moving along C, where t represents time then the vectors $\mathbf{V} \equiv d\mathbf{P}/dt$ and $\mathbf{a} \equiv d^2\mathbf{P}/dt^2$ are called the **velocity** and **acceleration** of the particle, respectively.

We conclude this chapter with a few remarks about vector integration. Let $\mathbf{F} = f\mathbf{i} + g\mathbf{j} + h\mathbf{k}$ be a vector-valued function defined on I: $\{a \leqslant t \leqslant b\}$, and let

$$\Delta: a = t_0 < t_1 < \cdots < t_n = b$$

be a partition of I. In each partition interval I_k: $\{t_{k-1} \leqslant t \leqslant t_k\}$ we choose a point τ_k and form the sum

$$\mathbf{S}_\Delta(\mathbf{F}, \tau) = \sum_\Delta \mathbf{F}(\tau_k) \Delta_k t.$$

If $\mathbf{J} = \lim_{||\Delta|| \to 0} \mathbf{S}_\Delta$ exists, we say that $\mathbf{J}$ is the integral of $\mathbf{F}$ over I and denote it by

$$\mathbf{J} = \int_a^b \mathbf{F}(t)\, dt$$

It should be clear that a necessary and sufficient condition that $\mathbf{F}$ be integrable is that f, g, and h each be integrable. In this case

$$\int_a^b \mathbf{F}(t)\, dt = \mathbf{i} \int_a^b f(t)\, dt + \mathbf{j} \int_a^b g(t)\, dt + \mathbf{k} \int_a^b h(t)\, dt.$$

A EXERCISES

1. Let $\mathbf{F}$ and $\mathbf{G}$ be differentiable vector functions, and α a differentiable scalar function. Prove that:

(a) $\dfrac{d}{dt}(\alpha \mathbf{F}) = \alpha \dfrac{d\mathbf{F}}{dt} + \dfrac{d\alpha}{dt} \mathbf{F}$

(b) $\dfrac{d}{dt}(\mathbf{F} \cdot \mathbf{G}) = \mathbf{F} \cdot \dfrac{d\mathbf{G}}{dt} + \mathbf{G} \cdot \dfrac{d\mathbf{F}}{dt}$

(c) $\dfrac{d}{dt}(\mathbf{F} \times \mathbf{G}) = \mathbf{F} \times \dfrac{d\mathbf{G}}{dt} + \dfrac{d\mathbf{F}}{dt} \times \mathbf{G}$

2. Show that if f is a monotone function on I: $\{a \leqslant t \leqslant b\}$, then f has bounded variation there and $V_f = |f(b) - f(a)|$.

3. Find **T**, **N**, and **B** for each of the following curves:

(a) $\mathbf{P} = \sin t\mathbf{i} + \cos t\mathbf{j} + ct\mathbf{k}$
(b) $\mathbf{P} = \sin at\mathbf{i} + \cos bt\mathbf{j} + ct\mathbf{k}$

4. Sketch the curve in 3(a) above showing **T**, **N**, and **B** at the point where $t = \pi/2$.

5. Letting t represent time in Exercise A3, compute the velocity and acceleration in terms of **T**, **N**, and **B**.

6. Let C be a curve given by $\mathbf{P} = t^3\mathbf{i} + t^2\mathbf{j} + 3t\mathbf{k}$. Compute $s(t)$ as an integral where s is measured from the origin.

B EXERCISES

1. Show that, for a vector function $\mathbf{F} = f\mathbf{i} + g\mathbf{j} + h\mathbf{k}$ to be continuous, it is necessary and sufficient that f, g, and h be continuous.

2. Prove that the acceleration vector **a** is always in the plane of **T** and **N**, and in fact that the component of **a** in the direction **N** is non-negative. Explain the geometrical meaning of this.

3. Show that:

(a) If f has a bounded derivative on $I: \{a \leqslant t \leqslant b\}$, then f has bounded variation there.

(b) If f' is continuous on I, then

$$V_f = \int_a^b |f'(t)|\, dt.$$

C EXERCISES

1. Let C be given by

$$\mathbf{P} = t^\alpha \sin \frac{1}{t}\mathbf{i} + t\mathbf{j} \qquad 0 < t \leqslant 1$$

$$\mathbf{P} = \mathbf{O} \qquad\qquad t = 0$$

Show that C is rectifiable if, and only if, $\alpha > 1$.

2. Let C be given by $\mathbf{P} = \mathbf{F}(t)$, where **F** is three times continuously differentiable. Show that $d\mathbf{B}/ds$ is in the direction of **N**, so that there is a scalar τ (called the torsion) such that

$$\frac{d\mathbf{B}}{ds} = -\tau\mathbf{N}.$$

Prove Frenet's formulas

$$\frac{d\mathbf{T}}{ds} = \kappa\mathbf{N}$$

$$\frac{d\mathbf{N}}{ds} = -\kappa\mathbf{T} + \tau\mathbf{B}$$

$$\frac{d\mathbf{B}}{ds} = -\tau\mathbf{N}.$$

9

Functions of Several Variables. Limits and Continuity

9.1 A LITTLE TOPOLOGY: OPEN AND CLOSED SETS

It will now be necessary to extend to higher dimensions some of the concepts of point sets which were found useful in one dimension. We will frame our statements (definitions, and theorems, etc.) so that they apply equally well to two, three, and higher dimensions. Most of our examples and illustrations will be two-dimensional. We will use vector notation quite freely, and such vectors are to be thought of as 2, 3, or higher dimensional according to the dimension of the space under consideration. Since cross products do not occur here, we will have no difficulty in performing any of the necessary vector operations.

The large number of definitions given in this section will be difficult to assimilate all at once. You should therefore constantly refer back to them when necessary until you are familiar with the technical terms defined here.

By a **neighborhood** of a point $\mathbf{P}_0$ we mean the set of all points $\mathbf{P}$ lying within some fixed distance, say δ, of $\mathbf{P}_0$; that is, all points $\mathbf{P}$ such that $|\mathbf{P} - \mathbf{P}_0| < \delta$. This means that

$$\sqrt{(x - x_0)^2 + (y - y_0)^2} < \delta,$$

in two dimensions. In three, it becomes

$$\sqrt{(x - x_0)^2 + (y - y_0)^2 + (z - z_0)^2} < \delta,$$

and in higher dimensions analogous formulas describe the condition. Thus a neighborhood of $\mathbf{P}_0$ is the inside of a circle or sphere centered at $\mathbf{P}_0$.

A **deleted neighborhood** of a point $\mathbf{P}_0$ is a neighborhood of $\mathbf{P}_0$ with $\mathbf{P}_0$ itself removed.

A point $\mathbf{P}_0$ is said to be an **interior point** of a set S if there is a neighborhood of $\mathbf{P}_0$ which lies entirely in S.

A set S is an **open set** if it consists entirely of interior points.

EXAMPLE. Show that the set S of points $\mathbf{P}$ for which $|\mathbf{P} - \mathbf{P}_0| < a$ is an open set.

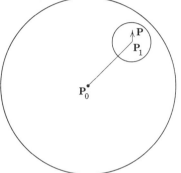

Solution. Geometrically, this seems clear enough; but we want to give a non-geometrical argument.

To show that the set is open, we must show that every point is an interior point; that is, we must show that every point in S has a neighborhood which also belongs to the set. So let $\mathbf{P}_1$ be any point of the set. Then

$$|\mathbf{P}_1 - \mathbf{P}_0| < a.$$

Now choose δ so that

$$|\mathbf{P}_1 - \mathbf{P}_0| + \delta < a.$$

That is, choose δ so that

$$\delta < a - |\mathbf{P}_1 - \mathbf{P}_0|.$$

Now let $\mathbf{P}$ be any point in the δ-neighborhood of $\mathbf{P}_1$. We want to conclude that $\mathbf{P}$ belongs to S. To say that $\mathbf{P}$ is in the δ-neighborhood of $\mathbf{P}_1$ means that $|\mathbf{P} - \mathbf{P}_1| < \delta$. Hence

$$|\mathbf{P} - \mathbf{P}_0| = |(\mathbf{P} - \mathbf{P}_1) + (\mathbf{P}_1 - \mathbf{P}_0)|$$
$$\leqslant |\mathbf{P} - \mathbf{P}_1| + |\mathbf{P}_1 - \mathbf{P}_0| < \delta + (a - \delta) = a.$$

We have thus shown that $|\mathbf{P} - \mathbf{P}_0| < a$, which means that $\mathbf{P}$ belongs to S. This, in turn, means that we have found a neighborhood of $\mathbf{P}_1$ which is entirely in S.

The **complement** CS of a set S is the set of all points which do not belong to S.

EXAMPLE. If S is a neighborhood $\{|\mathbf{P} - \mathbf{P}_0| < \delta\}$, then CS is described by

$$\{|\mathbf{P} - \mathbf{P}_0| \geqslant \delta\}.$$

A set is **closed** if its complement is open.

A point $\mathbf{Q}$ is a **boundary point** of a set S (whether or not $\mathbf{Q}$ is itself a point of S) if *every* neighborhood of $\mathbf{Q}$ contains both (1) points of S and (2) points of CS. The set of boundary points of a set S is called its **boundary**.

EXAMPLE. Again let S be a neighborhood $|\mathbf{P} - \mathbf{P}_0| < \delta$. Then the boundary of S is the set of points $\mathbf{Q}$ for which

$$|\mathbf{Q} - \mathbf{P}_0| = \delta.$$

This is geometrically clear. Can you prove it?

9.1a   Theorem. For any set S, the boundary of S and of CS are identical.

Proof. Immediate from the definition, since the complement of CS is S itself,

$$CCS = S. \qquad \blacksquare$$

9.1b   Theorem. If S is open then S contains none of its boundary points.

Proof. Clearly, no boundary point of a set S can be an interior point of S (check the definitions). Since S consists entirely of interior points, it can contain no boundary points. $\qquad \blacksquare$

9.1c   Theorem. If S is closed, it contains all of its boundary points.

Proof. Let CS be the complement of S. Then CS is open by the definition of a closed set. By Theorem 9.1a, S and CS have the same boundary. And by Theorem 9.1b, CS contains no points of the boundary, so S must contain the whole boundary. $\qquad \blacksquare$

A **line segment** connecting points $\mathbf{P}_1$ and $\mathbf{P}_2$ is the set of points $\mathbf{P}$ given by

$$\mathbf{P} = (1 - t)\mathbf{P}_1 + t\mathbf{P}_2 \qquad \{0 \leqslant t \leqslant 1\}.$$

$\mathbf{P}_1$ is called the **initial point**, and $\mathbf{P}_2$ the **terminal point**.

A **broken line** or **polygonal line** is a finite number of segments connected end to end.

A **region** R is an open set any two of whose points can be connected by a polygonal line lying entirely in R.

EXAMPLE. A neighborhood is a region, but two disjoint neighborhoods (that is, with no points in common) form an open set which is not a region.

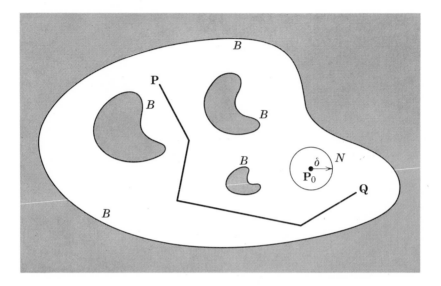

A region, showing connectedness, the boundary B and a neighborhood N.

A **closed region** is a region together with its boundary. A **partially closed region** is one which includes part but not all of its boundary.

A word of warning: since we have emphasized open and closed sets, do not be misled into thinking that a set must be one or the other. This is not the case. Make up some examples of sets which are neither open nor closed.

Another concept which we will find occasionally useful is that of a diameter of a bounded set. In the first place, a set S is **bounded** if there exists a number M such that

$$|\mathbf{P}| < M \qquad \text{for all } \mathbf{P} \text{ in } S.$$

In this case we say that sup $|\mathbf{P} - \mathbf{Q}|$, where the supremum is computed over all points $\mathbf{P}$ and $\mathbf{Q}$ in S, is the **diameter** of S.

There is a famous theorem, known as the **Jordan curve theorem**, which relates the concepts of region and curve in E_2—that is, in the plane. It states that every Jordan curve (simple closed curve; see Section 8.7) separates the plane into two disjoint regions, one bounded and one unbounded and having the curve as their common boundary. The bounded one is called the **interior** of the curve and the unbounded one the **exterior**.

Though geometrically obvious, this theorem is surprisingly difficult to prove.

Another point which is perhaps difficult to appreciate is that the boundary of a region in E_2 need not be a curve. It can be much more complicated. In fact, there exist regions no part of the boundary of which is a curve. Our considerations will, however, not be concerned with the pathology of plane sets. We will restrict ourselves to relatively simple situations where such strange phenomena are either not considered or are of no importance.

9.2 A LITTLE MORE TOPOLOGY: SEQUENCES, CLUSTER VALUES, ACCUMULATION POINTS, CAUCHY CRITERION

Let $\mathbf{F}$ be a vector function whose domain—that is, the set of t's for which $\mathbf{F}(t)$ is defined—is the set of all integers greater than or equal to some n_0. Such a function will be called a **sequence** of vectors and will be denoted by $\{\mathbf{P}_n\}$ where the vectors $\mathbf{P}_n$ are given by

$$\mathbf{P}_n = \mathbf{F}(n) \qquad n \geqslant n_0.$$

The number n_0 will be indicated explicitly or implicitly.

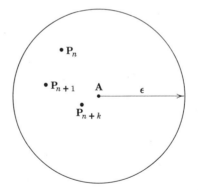

We will say the sequence $\{\mathbf{P}_n\}$ has a limit $\mathbf{A}$ if for each $\epsilon > 0$ there is an $N(\epsilon)$ such that

$$|\mathbf{P}_n - \mathbf{A}| < \epsilon \qquad \text{whenever } n > N.$$

The standard limit notations are taken over:

$$\lim \mathbf{P}_n = \mathbf{A}$$

or

$$\mathbf{P}_n \to \mathbf{A}.$$

As in the case of sequences of real numbers, we find it convenient to define the concept of a **cluster value** or **cluster point** of a sequence $\mathbf{P}_n$. A point $\mathbf{A}$ will be called a cluster value or cluster point of a sequence $\{\mathbf{P}_n\}$ if there is a sub-sequence $\{\mathbf{P}_{n_k}\}$ converging to $\mathbf{A}$.

The analogous concept for sets is the following: a point $\mathbf{A}$ is called a **point of accumulation** of a set S if every deleted neighborhood of $\mathbf{A}$ contains points of S. An equivalent definition (see Exercise B8) is that there is a sequence $\{\mathbf{P}_n\}$ with $\mathbf{P}_n$ in S for each n, and $\mathbf{P}_n \neq \mathbf{P}_m$ if $n \neq m$, such that $\mathbf{P}_n \to \mathbf{A}$.

We formulate the definition in terms of a deleted neighborhood, so that we will exclude isolated points of S from being points of accumulation, where by an **isolated point** of S we mean a point $\mathbf{P}$ of S such that there is a neighborhood N of $\mathbf{P}$ in which no other points of S lie.

9.2a **Theorem.** Let R be a region. Then any boundary point of R is also an accumulation point of R.

Proof. Suppose R is an open region. Let $\mathbf{Q}$ be a boundary point and $\epsilon > 0$ be given. Then, by the definition of a boundary point, there is a point $\mathbf{P}$ in R for which $|\mathbf{P} - \mathbf{Q}| < \epsilon$. But $\mathbf{P} \neq \mathbf{Q}$, so that $\mathbf{P}$ is in the deleted ϵ-neighborhood of $\mathbf{Q}$. Thus the theorem is proved for open regions. The proof for closed or partially closed regions is left as an exercise (B9). ∎

An important property of closed sets is given by the following theorem. It provides a characterization of closed sets which we will use again and again.

9.2b **Theorem.** If S is a closed set, then it contains all its accumulation points.

Proof. Let $\mathbf{Q}$ be an accumulation point of S, and suppose (for contradiction) that $\mathbf{Q}$ is not in S. Then $\mathbf{Q}$ is in CS which is open. As a consequence of the openness of CS, there is a neighborhood of $\mathbf{Q}$ which lies in CS and which therefore can contain no points of S itself. This is a contradiction, since every neighborhood of an accumulation point of S contains points of S. ∎

The Cauchy criterion is as useful in its higher dimensional setting as in one dimension, and it follows quite easily from the one-dimensional case.

9.2c **Theorem.** In order that $\{\mathbf{P}_n\}$ have a limit, it is necessary and sufficient that for each $\epsilon > 0$ there exists an $N(\epsilon)$ for which

$$|\mathbf{P}_n - \mathbf{P}_m| < \epsilon \qquad \text{whenever } n > N, \, m > N.$$

Proof. Necessity. Suppose $\mathbf{P}_n \to \mathbf{P}$. This means that for each ϵ there is an $N(\epsilon)$ such that

$$|\mathbf{P}_n - \mathbf{P}| < \frac{\epsilon}{2} \qquad \text{if } n > N(\epsilon).$$

Then $|\mathbf{P}_n - \mathbf{P}_m| \leqslant |\mathbf{P}_n - \mathbf{P}| + |\mathbf{P}_m - \mathbf{P}| < \dfrac{\epsilon}{2} + \dfrac{\epsilon}{2} = \epsilon \qquad \text{if } n, m > N.$

Sufficiency. (For E_3.) Let $\{\mathbf{P}_n\}$ satisfy the ϵ-condition of the Cauchy criterion. Then clearly [here we take $\mathbf{P}_n = (x_n, y_n, z_n)$]

$$|x_n - x_m| \leqslant |\mathbf{P}_n - \mathbf{P}_m| < \epsilon \qquad \text{if } n, m > N,$$

so that $\{x_n\}$ is a sequence of real numbers which satisfy the Cauchy criterion. Consequently $\{x_n\}$ has a limit, which we may denote by x. Similarly, there are numbers y and z such that $y_n \to y$ and $z_n \to z$. We now define $\mathbf{P}$ by $\mathbf{P} = (x, y, z)$ and consider

$$|\mathbf{P}_n - \mathbf{P}| \leqslant |x_n - x| + |y_n - y| + |z_n - z|. \qquad \text{(How?)}$$

Clearly, then,

$$|\mathbf{P}_n - \mathbf{P}| \to 0 \qquad \text{when } n \to \infty. \qquad \blacksquare$$

Our next theorem generalizes the principle of nested intervals.

9.2d   Theorem. Let S_n be a sequence of non-empty closed sets, each contained in the preceding one, and such that the diameter of S_n tends to zero as $n \to \infty$. Then there is exactly one point $\mathbf{P}$ with the property that $\mathbf{P}$ is in S_n for every n.

Proof. Choose a sequence of points in the following manner: Let $\mathbf{P}_1$ be in S_1, $\mathbf{P}_2$ in $S_2, \ldots, \mathbf{P}_n$ in $S_n, \ldots$. Then given $\epsilon > 0$, choose N so large that the diameter of S_N is $< \epsilon$. Then for $m \geqslant n > N$ we have $\mathbf{P}_n$ and $\mathbf{P}_m$, both in S_N (why?). Thus

$$|\mathbf{P}_m - \mathbf{P}_n| < \epsilon,$$

and, by the Cauchy criterion, $\{\mathbf{P}_n\}$ has a limit which we may denote by $\mathbf{Q}$. To see that $\mathbf{Q}$ is in S_n, we note that $\mathbf{P}_m$ is in S_n for all $m \geqslant n$. Thus $\mathbf{Q}$ is the limit of a sequence of points of S_n; that is, $\mathbf{Q}$ is an accumulation point of S_n. But since S_n is closed, $\mathbf{Q}$ must be in S_n.

It remains only to show that there is no other point $\mathbf{Q}'$, say, which is in every S_n. But suppose there were. Then let $|\mathbf{Q} - \mathbf{Q}'| = \delta > 0$. Choose n so large that the diameter of S_n is less than $\delta/2$. But then

$$\delta = |\mathbf{Q} - \mathbf{Q}'| \leqslant \text{diameter of } S_n < \delta/2.$$

This contradiction completes the proof. $\blacksquare$

The **Bolzano-Weierstrass theorem** for higher dimensions can be stated in the same form as in one dimension.

9.2e   Theorem. A bounded infinite set has at least one accumulation point, and a bounded sequence at least one cluster point.

Proof. (See Theorem 6.1a.) We write out the proof for sets in E_2. Let the set be denoted by D. Since it is bounded, there is a big square S_0: $\{-a \leqslant x \leqslant a, -a \leqslant y \leqslant a\}$ which contains D. Now divide S_0 into four (in E_n it would be 2^n) squares by bisecting each dimension:

$$\begin{pmatrix} -a \leqslant x \leqslant 0 \\ -a \leqslant y \leqslant 0 \end{pmatrix}, \quad \begin{pmatrix} -a \leqslant x \leqslant 0 \\ 0 \leqslant y \leqslant a \end{pmatrix}, \quad \begin{pmatrix} 0 \leqslant x \leqslant a \\ -a \leqslant y \leqslant 0 \end{pmatrix}, \quad \begin{pmatrix} 0 \leqslant x \leqslant a \\ 0 \leqslant y \leqslant a \end{pmatrix}$$

In at least one of these there must lie infinitely many points of D (why?). Choose such a square and denote it by S_1, and choose a point of D in S_1

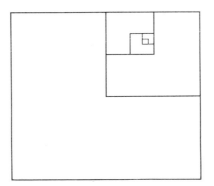

and denote it by $\mathbf{P}_1$. Again divide S_1 into four squares by bisecting each of its sides. At least one of the four resulting squares must contain infinitely many points of D. Denote such a square by S_2 and choose in it a point $\mathbf{P}_2$ of D, making sure that $\mathbf{P}_2 \neq \mathbf{P}_1$. Iterate this procedure: This constructs a sequence of squares S_n of diameter $\sqrt{2}a/2^{n-1}$, with points $\mathbf{P}_n$ in S_n. Thus by the preceding theorem the sequence $\{\mathbf{P}_n\}$ has a limit $\mathbf{P}$.

To see that $\mathbf{P}$ is a point of accumulation of D, let N be any neighborhood of $\mathbf{P}$. By the definition of convergence, there is an n_0 such that $\mathbf{P}_n$ are all in N if $n \geqslant n_0$. But at most one $\mathbf{P}_n$ can equal $\mathbf{P}$ (why?). Hence there are points of D in the deleted neighborhood of $\mathbf{P}$ formed by deleting $\mathbf{P}$ from N.

A EXERCISES

I. Without detailed proofs, tell why:

   (a) The square $\{0 < x < 1, 0 < y < 1\}$ is open in E_2.

   (b) The square $\{0 \leqslant x \leqslant 1, 0 \leqslant y \leqslant 1\}$ is closed in E_2.

2. Write down without proof the accumulation points of

$$(1/n, 1/m), \qquad m, n = 1, 2, 3, \ldots.$$

3. Describe the set of points **P** for which

$$|\mathbf{P} - \mathbf{Q}_1| + |\mathbf{P} - \mathbf{Q}_2| < c,$$

where $\mathbf{Q}_1$, $\mathbf{Q}_2$, and c are given.

4. Let S be the set of points $\mathbf{P} = (x, y)$ for which both

$$\{x^2 + y^2 \leqslant 1\} \quad \text{and} \quad \{x^2 + (y - 1)^2 > 1\}.$$

What is the boundary of S? Is S open or closed? Why?

5. Give an example of a set in E_3 which has no interior points.

B EXERCISES

1. Prove the statements in A1 above.

2. Show that each of the following sets is open in E_2:
   (a) $\{x^2 + 4y^2 < 4\}$ (b) $\{y^2 < 4x\}$.

3. Show that the set in E_2 described by $\{x^2 + y^2 = 1\}$ is closed.

4. Prove your answer to Exercise A2.

5. Let $\{\mathbf{P}_n\}$ be a sequence of points. Show that either (1) $|\mathbf{P}_n| \to \infty$ or (2) $\{\mathbf{P}_n\}$ has a finite cluster value.

6. What is the boundary of the set S in E_2 described by $\{x^2 + y^2 = 1\}$?

7. Show that the set of accumulation points of a set S consist of its boundary together with its interior.

8. Prove the equivalence of the two definitions of accumulation point. (See the last part of the proof of Theorem 9.2e.)

9. Complete the proof of Theorem 9.2a.

C EXERCISES

1. Let S be any set. Show that the boundary of S is closed.

2. Let S be any set and P any point in S. Show that P is either an interior point or a boundary point.

3. Show that, if S contains no boundary points, it is open.

4. Show that, if a set S contains all its boundary points, it is closed.

9.3 LIMITS

In Chapter 2 we discussed what is meant by a function of a single real variable. We now want to extend this idea to define a function of several real variables, or, what comes to the same thing, a function of a point in Euclidean vector space of several dimensions. Our main concern will be with two- and three-dimensional spaces, and our examples will be in these spaces.

Let S_1 be a set of real numbers and S_2 a set in a Euclidean vector space. Suppose that for each $\mathbf{P}$ in S_2 there corresponds a w in S_1. The set of all pairs $(\mathbf{P}, w)$, where $\mathbf{P}$ is in S_2 and w is the corresponding value in S_1, is called a **function** and is denoted by f, as in Section 2.1. The functional **values** are denoted by

$$w = f(\mathbf{P})$$

or equivalently

$$w = f(x, y), \quad w = f(x, y, z), \ldots,$$

according to the dimension of the space.

The language for discussing functions is brought over from the one-dimensional case without change. In particular, we mention that the set of $\mathbf{P}$'s for which f is defined is called the **domain** of the function and will be denoted by D. The set of **values** of the function—that is, the set of w's which correspond to some $\mathbf{P}$ in D—is called the **range** of f and is denoted by R.

Next, we turn our attention to limits of functions. Most of the theorems are stated and proved for functions defined on sets with few restrictions. However, you may find it simpler to visualize the domain of any of the functions as a region—open, closed, or partially closed—and you will not be misled by this visual simplification.

Let f be defined on a domain D and let $\mathbf{P}_0$ be an accumulation point of D. We then say that f has a **limit** A as $\mathbf{P} \to \mathbf{P}_0$, if for each $\epsilon > 0$ there is a $\delta(\epsilon, \mathbf{P}_0)$ for which

$$|f(\mathbf{P}) - A| < \epsilon \quad \text{whenever} \quad |\mathbf{P} - \mathbf{P}_0| < \delta \text{ and } \mathbf{P} \text{ is in } D.$$

We express this symbolically as

$$\lim_{\mathbf{P} \to \mathbf{P}_0} f(\mathbf{P}) = A \quad \text{or} \quad f(\mathbf{P}) \to A \quad \text{as} \quad \mathbf{P} \to \mathbf{P}_0.$$

Geometrically, the ϵ-, δ-condition can be stated thus: for each $\epsilon > 0$ there is a neighborhood N of $\mathbf{P}_0$ such that $|f(\mathbf{P}) - A| < \epsilon$, if $\mathbf{P}$ is in the common part of D and N. The figure illustrates the situation for $\mathbf{P}_0$ an interior point and for $\mathbf{P}_0$ boundary points.

EXAMPLE 1. Let $f(\mathbf{P}) = f(x, y) = x^2 y^2/(x^2 + y^2)$.

Solution. The domain of this function is the whole plane (E_2) except the origin. We take $\mathbf{P}_0 = (0, 0)$ and investigate the limit of $f(\mathbf{P})$ as $\mathbf{P} \to \mathbf{P}_0$. Let $\epsilon > 0$ be given. Then we want to show that there is a δ such that

(1) $\qquad |f(\mathbf{P})| < \epsilon \quad \text{whenever} \quad |\mathbf{P}| = \sqrt{x^2 + y^2} < \delta.$

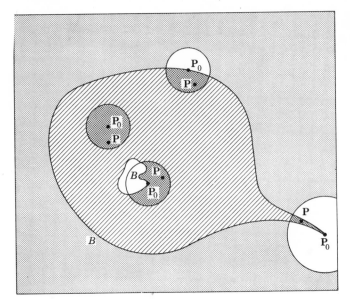

Now clearly

$$x^2 \leqslant x^2 + y^2$$

and

$$y^2 \leqslant x^2 + y^2,$$

so that

$$|f(\mathbf{P})| = \frac{x^2 y^2}{x^2 + y^2} \leqslant \frac{(x^2 + y^2)^2}{x^2 + y^2} = (x^2 + y^2) < \epsilon$$

if $|\mathbf{P}| = \sqrt{x^2 + y^2} < \sqrt{\epsilon}.$

Thus we have satisfied (1) with $\delta = \sqrt{\epsilon}$ and see that

$$\lim_{\mathbf{P} \to \mathbf{O}} f(\mathbf{P}) = 0$$

EXAMPLE 2. Let $f(\mathbf{P}) = xy/(x^2 + y^2)$.

Solution. Again the domain of f is E_2 punctured at the origin, and again we examine the values of f near the puncture—that is, near $\mathbf{P}_0 = (0, 0)$.

If we introduce polar coordinates $x = \rho \cos \theta$, $y = \rho \sin \theta$, then f takes the form

$$xy/(x^2 + y^2) = \rho \cos \theta \, \rho \sin \theta / \rho^2 = \sin \theta \cos \theta = \tfrac{1}{2} \sin 2\theta$$

Here, of course,

$$\rho = |\mathbf{P}| = \sqrt{x^2 + y^2}.$$

From this formula, it is clear that f is constant on each straight line through the origin and that in general, the constant is different on different lines. Clearly, then, the values of f cannot be made close to any one constant A by simply restricting ρ. Thus $\lim\limits_{P \to P_0} f(P)$ does not exist in this case.

An alternative method is to substitute $y = ax$. Then we have

$$f(x, ax) = \frac{a}{1 + a^2}.$$

Again we see that f has different constant values on lines through the origin, so the limit cannot exist.

A word of warning is perhaps in order here. One frequently sees or hears the statement that, for a limit of a function of several variables to exist at a point, it must be independent of the manner of approach. This may be misleading if "manner" is too narrowly interpreted. It is definitely misleading if "manner" is replaced by "direction." There are functions for which the limit will exist for approach along each straight line leading into a point P_0, for which all these limits are equal, and yet for which the limit in the two-dimensional sense does not exist. This means that in thinking about limits in the two-dimensional and higher spaces you should think in terms of the "approaching" point P being close to P_0, rather than in terms of approach along various directions.

EXAMPLE 3. Define f over the whole plane (E_2) by

$$f(P) = f(x, y) = \begin{cases} (|x|/y^2)e^{-|x|/y^2} & y \neq 0 \\ 0 & y = 0. \end{cases}$$

Solution. On the line $x = 0$, we have $f(0, y) = 0$, and the limit is zero as $P \to P_0 = O = (0, 0)$ along this line. On any other line $x = ay$ through the origin we have

$$f(ay, y) = (|ay|/y^2)e^{-|ay|/y^2} = (|a/y|)e^{-|a/y|},$$

and the limit of this expression as $y \to 0$ is easily seen to be 0, by l'Hospital's rule, for example.

Thus as $P \to O$ along any straight line leading into O, we have $f(P)$ tending to zero. But along the parabola $x = y^2$ we have

$$f(y^2, y) = y^2/y^2 e^{-y^2/y^2} = e^{-1}.$$

Hence f is identically e^{-1} along a curve passing through the origin, and clearly then $\lim\limits_{P \to O} f(P)$ cannot be zero.

9.4 VECTOR FUNCTIONS OF A VECTOR

Once again, for the last time, we extend the concept of a function. Let S_1 be a set in a Euclidean vector space of, say, m dimensions, and S_2 be a set in a Euclidean vector space of n dimensions. Suppose for each point $\mathbf{P}$ in S_2 there corresponds a point $\mathbf{Q}$ in S_1. The set of all ordered pairs $(\mathbf{P}, \mathbf{Q})$ will be called a **vector function** of $\mathbf{P}$ on S_2 to S_1, and is symbolized by $\mathbf{F}$. The **values** of $\mathbf{F}$ are vectors $\mathbf{Q}$ in S_1 and are denoted by

$$(1) \qquad\qquad \mathbf{Q} = \mathbf{F(P)}.$$

The point $\mathbf{Q}$ which corresponds to a particular $\mathbf{P}$ in S_2 is called a **value** of $\mathbf{F}$. The set S_2 where $\mathbf{F}$ is defined is its **domain**, and the set of points $\mathbf{Q}$ in S_1 which are values of $\mathbf{F}$ is called the **range** of $\mathbf{F}$.

A vector function is sometimes called a **mapping** of S_2 into or onto (see Section 2.1) S_1 and denoted thus:

$$\mathbf{F}: S_2 \to S_1.$$

You should realize that the definition of the vector function $\mathbf{F}$ requires the definition of m real functions of n real variables. Let us denote $\mathbf{P}$ by the n-tuple $(x_1, x_2, \ldots, x_n)$ and $\mathbf{Q}$ by the m-tuple $(y_1, y_2, \ldots, y_m)$. Since the values of $\mathbf{F}$ lie in E_m, it must have m components, each of which depends on $\mathbf{P}$. Thus (1) could be expressed as

$$(2) \qquad (y_1, y_2, \ldots, y_m) = [\,f_1(\mathbf{P}), f_2(\mathbf{P}), \ldots, f_m(\mathbf{P})\,].$$

which in turn can be written out as

$$
\begin{aligned}
y_1 &= f_1(x_1, x_2, \ldots, x_n) \\
y_2 &= f_2(x_1, x_2, \ldots, x_n) \\
&\;\;\vdots \\
&\;\;\vdots \\
y_m &= f_m(x_1, x_2, \ldots, x_n).
\end{aligned}
$$

(3)

Consequently the system (3) is equivalent to (1).

Limits of vector functions can be defined in terms of $\mathbf{F}$ or of the component functions $f_j, j = 1, \ldots, m$. As you might guess, the statement is much simpler to write down in vector form. That the two are equivalent will be left to the exercises. The formal definition of a limit follows.

Let $\mathbf{F}$ be a vector function defined on a domain D in E_n and having values in E_m, and let $\mathbf{P}_0$ be an accumulation point of D. Then we say that $\mathbf{F(P)}$ has a **limit** $\mathbf{A}$ as $\mathbf{P} \to \mathbf{P}_0$ if for each $\epsilon > 0$ there is a $\delta(\epsilon, \mathbf{P}_0)$ for which

$$|\mathbf{F(P)} - \mathbf{A}| < \epsilon \qquad \text{whenever} \qquad |\mathbf{P} - \mathbf{P}_0| < \delta \qquad \text{and} \qquad \mathbf{P} \text{ is in } D.$$

In this case we write

$$F(P) \to A \quad \text{as} \quad P \to P_0$$

or
$$\lim_{P \to P_0} F(P) = A.$$

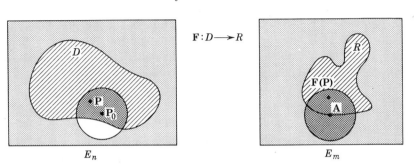

Continuity of a vector function

Geometrically, the ϵ-, δ-condition can be stated thus: for each neighborhood N_1 of A in E_m there is a neighborhood N_2 of P_0 in E_n such that, whenever P is in the common part of D and N_2, $F(P)$ is in N_1.

A EXERCISES

1. Describe the domain and range of each of the following real-valued functions:

   (a) $\sin 1/(x^2 + y^2)$ (b) $\text{Arc} \sin (x^2 + y^2)$

   (c) $\sin (x^2 + y^2)$ (d) $\sqrt{1 - x^2 - y^2}$

   (e) $\sqrt{1 - x^2 + y^2}$ (f) $\log (1 + xy)$

2. Describe the domain and range of each of the following vector-valued functions:

   (a) $5xy\mathbf{i} + 2x^2\mathbf{j} + z^2\mathbf{k}$ (b) $\sin (x + y)\mathbf{i} + \cos (x + y)\mathbf{j} + z\mathbf{k}$

   (c) $\sqrt{1 - x^2 - y^2}\mathbf{i} + \sqrt{x^2 + y^2 - 1}\mathbf{j} + (x^2 + y^2)\mathbf{k}$

   (d) $[x^2 + w^2, y^2 + z^2 - 1, w^2 + x^2 + y^2 + z^2, x - w]$

3. For each of the following functions, either compute the limit as $(x, y) \to (0, 0)$ or show that it doesn't exist:

   (a) $\dfrac{x - y}{x + y}$ (b) $\dfrac{x^2 - y^2}{x^2 + y^2}$ (c) $\dfrac{1}{x} \sin (x^2 + |xy|)$

   (d) $\begin{cases} x^2 + y^2 & x \text{ or } y \text{ irrational} \\ 0 & \text{otherwise} \end{cases}$

   (e) $\dfrac{5x^2y + 6x^7 + 3x^4y^3 + x^8(y^4 - x)}{(x^2 + y^2)^3}$ (f) $\dfrac{x \sin xy}{x^2 + y^2}$

   (g) $\dfrac{\sin xy}{\sin x \sin y}$ (h) $\dfrac{\tan x}{\sin^2 x + \sin^2 y}$ (i) $\dfrac{x \tan xy}{2 - \cos x - \cos y}$

4. Let f be continuous in a neighborhood of $\mathbf{P}_0 = (x_0, y_0)$ in E_2. Show that $f(x, y_0)$ defines a continuous function of x near x_0.

B   EXERCISES

1. In each case in Exercise A3 where the limit A exists, compute a $\delta(\epsilon)$ such that $|f(\mathbf{P}) - A| < \epsilon$ if $|\mathbf{P}| < \delta$.

2. Find the range of following vector functions.
   (a) $\sin x^2 \mathbf{i} + \sin (x^2 + y^2)\mathbf{j} + \sin (x^2 + y^2 + z^2)\mathbf{k}$,
   (b) $\sin x \cos y \mathbf{i} + \sin x \sin y \mathbf{j} + \cos x \mathbf{k}$.

3. Examine $x^4 y^4 / (x^4 + y^2)^3$ on each straight line through the origin. Does this function have a limit at $(0, 0)$?

4. Consider the function $(x^2 - y^2)/(x^2 + y^2)$ on the set $D:\{|y| < x^2\}$. Show that on D this function has a limit at the origin.

5. We might say that a vector-valued function $\mathbf{F}$ has a limit at $\mathbf{P}_0$ if each of its components does. Show that this is equivalent to the definition given in the text.

6. Compute $\displaystyle\lim_{(x,y)\to(0,0)} \frac{\sqrt{(1 + 4x)(1 + 6y)} - 1}{2x + 3y}$.

9.5   OPERATIONS WITH LIMITS

For completeness, we state here the theorems on operations with limits for functions of vectors which are analogous to the operational theorems of Section 2.5. Most of the proofs are missing, since they differ from the proofs of Section 2.5 only in the meaning of the absolute value signs: $|\ |$. Furthermore, while they are stated for real-valued functions, certain of them (these will be indicated) carry over to vector-valued functions.

9.5a   Theorem. Suppose f is defined on a domain D, $\mathbf{P}_0$ is an accumulation point of D, and $\displaystyle\lim_{\mathbf{P}\to\mathbf{P}_0} f(\mathbf{P}) = A$. Let $\{\mathbf{P}_n\}$ be a sequence of points in D such that $\mathbf{P}_n \to \mathbf{P}_0$, and define $z_n = f(\mathbf{P}_n)$.

Then $$z_n \to A.$$

Proof. Let $\epsilon > 0$ be given. There is then a δ for which $|f(\mathbf{P}) - A| < \epsilon$ if $|\mathbf{P} - \mathbf{P}_0| < \delta$, $\mathbf{P}$ in D.

With δ so determined, there is an $N[\delta(\epsilon)]$ for which $|\mathbf{P}_n - \mathbf{P}_0| < \delta$ if $n > N$. Thus for $n > N$ we have

$$|z_n - A| = |f(\mathbf{P}_n) - A| < \epsilon,$$

since $|\mathbf{P}_n - \mathbf{P}_0| < \delta$.   ∎

Again, although we will not prove this theorem, it is correct to say that if for every sequence $\{\mathbf{P}_n\}$ tending to $\mathbf{P}_0$ we have $f(\mathbf{P}_n) \to A$, then

$$\lim_{\mathbf{P} \to \mathbf{P}_0} f(\mathbf{P}) = A.$$

In the theorems that follow, f and g are assumed to be real-valued functions defined on a domain D and $\mathbf{P}_0$ is an accumulation point of D. The limits of f and g are meant to be limits as $\mathbf{P} \to \mathbf{P}_0$ and are assumed to exist. The existence of the other limits is then implied.

9.5b   **Theorem.** If $\lim f(\mathbf{P}) = A$ exists, then there is a deleted neighborhood of $\mathbf{P}_0$ such that f is bounded in the common part of D and the neighborhood.

9.5c   **Theorem.** $\lim [f(\mathbf{P}) \pm g(\mathbf{P})] = \lim f(\mathbf{P}) \pm \lim g(\mathbf{P})$.

9.5d   **Theorem.** $\lim f(\mathbf{P})g(\mathbf{P}) = (\lim f(\mathbf{P}))(\lim g(\mathbf{P}))$.

9.5e   **Theorem.** $\lim f(\mathbf{P})/g(\mathbf{P}) = \lim f(\mathbf{P})/\lim g(\mathbf{P})$ if $\lim g(\mathbf{P}) \neq 0$.

9.5f   **Theorem.** $\lim |f(\mathbf{P})| = |\lim f(\mathbf{P})|$.

9.5g   **Theorem.** If $f(\mathbf{P}) \geqslant 0$, then $\lim f(\mathbf{P}) \geqslant 0$.

9.5h   **Theorem.** If $f(\mathbf{P}) \geqslant g(\mathbf{P})$, then $\lim f(\mathbf{P}) \geqslant \lim g(\mathbf{P})$.

9.5i   **Theorem.** If $f(\mathbf{P}) \geqslant 0$, then $\lim \sqrt{f(\mathbf{P})} = \sqrt{\lim f(\mathbf{P})}$.

9.5j   **Theorem.** If f and g are replaced by vector-valued functions $\mathbf{F}$ and $\mathbf{G}$, then Theorems 9.5a, b, c, f remain valid. Theorem 9.5d holds if multiplication is either inner or vector multiplication, and Theorem 9.5e is valid if f is replaced by $\mathbf{F}$.

9.6   CONTINUITY

We now turn to the concept of continuity of a function of several variables—that is, of a function of a vector. Again the formalism is much the same as for a real function of a real variable.

A function f defined in a domain D is **continuous** there if

$$\lim_{\mathbf{P} \to \mathbf{P}_0} f(\mathbf{P}) = f(\mathbf{P}_0)$$

for every point $\mathbf{P}_0$ in D. In ϵ, δ terms this becomes: f is continuous in D if for each $\epsilon > 0$ and each $\mathbf{P}_0$ in D there is a $\delta(\epsilon, \mathbf{P}_0)$ for which $|f(\mathbf{P}) - f(\mathbf{P}_0)| < \epsilon$ whenever $|\mathbf{P} - \mathbf{P}_0| < \delta$ and $\mathbf{P}$ is in D.

The concept of uniform continuity carries over immediately: If in the preceding definition we can find a $\delta(\epsilon, D)$ such that $|f(\mathbf{P}) - f(\mathbf{P}_0)| < \epsilon$ for every $\mathbf{P}$ and $\mathbf{P}_0$ in D for which $|\mathbf{P} - \mathbf{P}_0| < \delta$, we say that f is **uniformly continuous** in D.

Precisely the same definitions hold for vector-valued functions $\mathbf{F}$.

9.6a   Theorem. Let f and g be continuous functions. Then:

(i) $f + g, f - g$, and fg are continuous.

(ii) $|f|$ is continuous.

(iii) f/g is continuous if $g \neq 0$.

(iv) $\sqrt{f}$ is continuous if $f \geqslant 0$. ·

Proof. The proofs are almost identical with those of the theorems in Section 9.5.   ∎

It should also be clear that if $\mathbf{F}$ and $\mathbf{G}$ are vector-valued continuous functions, then (i) holds if the multiplication is either an inner or vector product; (ii) holds; and (iii) holds for $\mathbf{F}/g$ where g is a scalar-valued continuous non-zero function.

Next we come to the deeper properties of continuous functions, which are the analogues of the theorems of Section 6.4.

9.6b   Theorem. If f (or $\mathbf{F}$) is a continuous function on a closed bounded set D, it is bounded there.

Proof. We write out the proof of f; it is exactly the same for $\mathbf{F}$. Suppose f were not bounded. Then there is a

$$\mathbf{P}_1 \text{ in } D \text{ for which } |f(\mathbf{P}_1)| \geqslant 1$$

$$\mathbf{P}_2 \text{ in } D \text{ for which } |f(\mathbf{P}_2)| \geqslant 2$$

$$\vdots$$

$$\mathbf{P}_n \text{ in } D \text{ for which } |f(\mathbf{P}_n)| \geqslant n.$$

$$\vdots$$

We have therefore constructed a sequence $\{\mathbf{P}_n\}$ for which $|f(\mathbf{P}_n)| \to \infty$. But $\{\mathbf{P}_n\}$ is a bounded sequence and therefore has a cluster point $\mathbf{P}_0$ (why?), and $\mathbf{P}_0$ is in D since D is closed. There is then a sub-sequence $\{\mathbf{P}_{n_k}\}$ converging to $\mathbf{P}_0$. For this sub-sequence we have, by continuity, that

$$|f(\mathbf{P}_{n_k})| \to |f(\mathbf{P}_0)|,$$

and simultaneously that

$$|f(\mathbf{P}_{n_k})| \to \infty.$$

This contradiction completes the proof.   ∎

The next theorem is restricted to real-valued functions.

9.6c **Theorem.** Let f be continuous on a closed bounded set D. Then there is a point $\mathbf{P}_0$ in D and a point $\mathbf{P}_1$ in D for which

$$f(\mathbf{P}_0) \leqslant f(\mathbf{P}) \leqslant f(\mathbf{P}_1) \qquad \text{for all} \qquad \mathbf{P} \text{ in } D.$$

Proof. By Theorem 9.6b, f is bounded, so that $\sup_D f$ and $\inf_D f$ are finite. We will show that there is a point $\mathbf{P}_0$ for which $f(\mathbf{P}_0) = \inf_D f$. The proof that the supremum is assumed is similar.

Let $m = \inf_D f$, and suppose (for contradiction) that there were no point $\mathbf{P}_0$ for which $f(\mathbf{P}_0) = m$. Then $f(\mathbf{P}) - m$ is a positive continuous function; hence so is $1/(f(\mathbf{P}) - m)$ [Theorem 9.6a (iii)]. This latter function is therefore bounded, say by B:

$$1/[f(\mathbf{P}) - m] \leqslant B \qquad \text{in } D.$$

Thus $f(\mathbf{P}) \geqslant m + 1/B > m$ which contradicts the fact that $m = \inf_D f$. ∎

The final theorem in this section is concerned with the most important property of continuous functions which we will establish.

9.6d **Theorem.** A function f (or a vector-valued function $\mathbf{F}$) which is continuous in a closed bounded set D is uniformly continuous there.

Proof. We must show that for each $\epsilon > 0$ there is a $\delta(\epsilon, D)$ such that for all $\mathbf{P}, \mathbf{Q}$ in D

$$|f(\mathbf{P}) - f(\mathbf{Q})| < \epsilon \qquad \text{whenever} \qquad |\mathbf{P} - \mathbf{Q}| < \delta.$$

The proof is again by contradiction: suppose the theorem were not true. This would mean that there is an exceptional $\epsilon > 0$, say ϵ_0, such that for every $\delta > 0$ there are a pair of points $\mathbf{P}, \mathbf{Q}$, in D with $|\mathbf{P} - \mathbf{Q}| < \delta$ for which $|f(\mathbf{P}) - f(\mathbf{Q})| \geqslant \epsilon_0$. With δ successively equal to $1, \frac{1}{2}, \frac{1}{3}, \ldots,$ $1/n, \ldots,$ there are

$$\mathbf{P}_1, \mathbf{Q}_1 \text{ with } |\mathbf{P}_1 - \mathbf{Q}_1| < 1 \quad \text{for which } |f(\mathbf{P}_1) - f(\mathbf{Q}_1)| \geqslant \epsilon_0$$

$$\mathbf{P}_2, \mathbf{Q}_2 \text{ with } |\mathbf{P}_2 - \mathbf{Q}_2| \leqslant \tfrac{1}{2} \quad \text{for which } |f(\mathbf{P}_2) - f(\mathbf{Q}_2)| \geqslant \epsilon_0$$

$$\vdots$$

$$\mathbf{P}_n, \mathbf{Q}_n \text{ with } |\mathbf{P}_n - \mathbf{Q}_n| < 1/n \text{ for which } |f(\mathbf{P}_n) - f(\mathbf{Q}_n)| \geqslant \epsilon_0.$$

$$\vdots$$

As in the proof of Theorem 9.6b, the sequence $\{\mathbf{P}_n\}$ is bounded and has therefore a convergent sub-sequence $\{\mathbf{P}_{n_k}\}$ whose limit $\mathbf{P}_0$ is in D, since D is closed. Now $\mathbf{Q}_{n_k} \to \mathbf{P}_0$ also, since

$$|\mathbf{Q}_{n_k} - \mathbf{P}_0| \leqslant |\mathbf{Q}_{n_k} - \mathbf{P}_{n_k}| + |\mathbf{P}_{n_k} - \mathbf{P}_0| \to 0 \qquad \text{as } k \to \infty.$$

By continuity, then, we have

$$|f(\mathbf{P}_{n_k}) - f(\mathbf{Q}_{n_k})| \to |f(\mathbf{P}_0) - f(\mathbf{P}_0)| = 0,$$

which contradicts the construction that

$$|f(\mathbf{P}_{n_k}) - f(\mathbf{Q}_{n_k})| \geqslant \epsilon_0. \qquad \blacksquare$$

9.7 GEOMETRICAL PICTURE OF A FUNCTION

To say that a real function is defined in its domain D, which we may picture as a region or as a closed region, is to say that to each point $\mathbf{P}$ in this region we associate a number. This can be represented, in the case of a function defined in a two-dimensional domain, as a height above (or below if the value is negative) the plane domain. That is, the graphical realization of the function is a set of points (x, y, z) in three-dimensional space characterized by the fact that they are related through the equation $z = f(x, y)$—in other words, a **surface**.

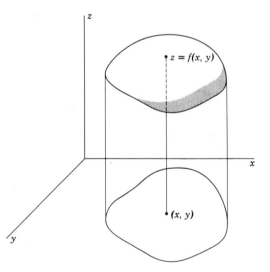

For higher dimensions, the formal relationship remains: to each point $\mathbf{P}$ in a three-dimensional domain we attach a number, the value of our function at that point. But the plotting of this value parallel to an additional coordinate axis is beyond our powers. However, there is one device which is useful, especially for continuous functions of three and more variables. Let us think now of a function defined in some three-dimensional domain—that is, in some volume in space. We now pass among these points and put a dab of paint on all points **P** for which $f(\mathbf{P}) = 5$, say. That is, we fix our attention on a sub-set of the points where f is defined, namely those at which its value is 5. This gives then a set of points characterized by

$$f(x, y, z) = 5.$$

If we think of this relation now being solved for z, we see that this again defines a surface. This is called a **level surface** of the function. Setting

$$f(x, y, z) = C$$

gives a new level surface for each value of C. An examination of these level surfaces gives us some understanding of the behavior of the function.

This idea is also useful in two dimensions. Here the geometry is perhaps a little clearer. Let us plot

$$z = f(x, y)$$

as a surface above a domain in the x, y plane, just as a relief map of a mountainous area is plotted above a base plane at sea level. If we visualize a plane parallel to the base plane slicing through this surface at a height C, the curve in which it is cut is given by

$$f(x, y) = C.$$

This can be plotted as a curve in the xy plane. For different C's we get different curves, each one a level curve. This is precisely what a cartographer does when drawing a contour map. The contour lines are the level curves of the landscape being plotted on the map.

A EXERCISES

1. How must $f(0, 0)$ be defined so as to make f continuous at the origin?

(a) $x^3/(x^2 + y^2)$
(b) $|x|^{1+\epsilon}y/\sqrt{x^2 + y^2}\ \sqrt{\sin^2 x + \sin^2 y}$

(c) $|y|^{1+\epsilon}x/(\sin^2 x + \sin^2 y)$
(d) $(1 - \cos\sqrt{x^2 + y^2})/(x^2 + y^2)$

2. Draw the level curves for each of the following functions:

(a) $\log(x^2 + y^2)$
(b) $e^{x^2+y^2}$

(c) $e^{x^2} \cdot e^y$
(d) $e^{-1/|x-y|}$

(e) $x + y - [x + y]$ (brackets indicate the greatest integer function)

(f) $(2x + 2y)/(x^2 + y^2)$
(h) $\sqrt{1 - x^2 + y}$

(i) If you know the level lines of a function, do you know the function [see (a) and (b) above]? What else do you need to know?

3. Where are $x + y - [x + y]$ and $[x + y] + [-x - y]$ discontinuous?

4. If f is continuous in a region D and is positive at a point $\mathbf{P}_0$ in D, show that there is a neighborhood of $\mathbf{P}_0$ in which f is positive.

5. Under what conditions will $|f(\mathbf{P}) - f(\mathbf{Q})|$ be less than 10^{-10}?

(a) $\sqrt{1 + x^2 + y^2}$

(b) $x^2 + xy + y^2$ in the circle $|x^2 + y^2| \leqslant 100$.

B EXERCISES

1. Suppose f is continuous in a region and is not zero. Show that it has one sign in this region.

2. Let f be defined by

$$f(x, y) = \begin{cases} \sqrt{1 - x^2 - y^2} & x^2 + y^2 \leqslant 1 \\ \exp\{-(x^2 + y^2 - 1)^{-1}\} & x^2 + y^2 > 1. \end{cases}$$

(a) Is f uniformly continuous in every circle?

(b) Is f uniformly continuous in E_2?

3. Let f be defined by

$$f(x, y) = (1 - \cos \sqrt{xy})/y \qquad y \neq 0.$$

Is it possible to define f when $y = 0$ so as to be continuous?

4. Let f be a function of a single real variable which has a continuous derivative on $\{a \leqslant x \leqslant b\}$. Define g on the square $\{a \leqslant x \leqslant b, a \leqslant y \leqslant b\}$ except when $x = y$ by

$$g(x, y) = \frac{f(x) - f(y)}{x - y}.$$

Can g be defined for $x = y$ so as to be continuous in the square?

5. Let f be defined by $f(x, y) = (\sin x - \sin y)/(\tan x - \tan y)$ in the square $\{0 \leqslant x \leqslant \pi/4, 0 \leqslant y \leqslant \pi/4\}$ except when $x = y$. Can f be defined for $x = y$ so as to be continuous in the square?

C EXERCISES

1. Let f be a bounded continuous real-valued function defined in a region D. If $M = \sup_D f$, $m = \inf_D f$, and $m < \mu < M$, then there is a point $\mathbf{P}$ in D for which $f(\mathbf{P}) = \mu$. (*Hint:* Check the definition of a region.)

2. Let f be uniformly continuous in the sphere $\{|\mathbf{P}| < 1\}$ in a Euclidean vector space. Thus there is a uniform δ such that $|f(\mathbf{P}) - f(\mathbf{Q})| < \epsilon$ whenever $|\mathbf{P} - \mathbf{Q}| < \delta$, if $\mathbf{P}$ and $\mathbf{Q}$ are in the sphere. Show that f can be defined on the boundary $\{|\mathbf{P}| = 1\}$ so as to be uniformly continuous in the closed sphere $\{|\mathbf{P}| \leqslant 1\}$, and in fact that we then have $|f(\mathbf{P}) - f(\mathbf{Q})| \leqslant \epsilon$ whenever $|\mathbf{P} - \mathbf{Q}| < \delta$ (the same δ) if $\mathbf{P}$ and $\mathbf{Q}$ are in the closed sphere.

3. Let $\mathbf{F}$ be a continuous vector-valued function whose domain is a closed region D, and let $\mathbf{G}$ be a vector-valued function whose range is contained in D. Then, if $\lim\limits_{P \to P_0} \mathbf{G}(P) = \mathbf{A}$, show that

(a) $\mathbf{A}$ is in D 　　　　　　　　　　(b) $\lim\limits_{P \to P_0} \mathbf{F}[\mathbf{G}(P)] = \mathbf{F}(\mathbf{A})$

4. Let f be a real-valued function defined on a region D. If there is a number α, $0 < \alpha \leqslant 1$ and a number M such that $|f(\mathbf{P}) - f(\mathbf{Q})| \leqslant M|\mathbf{P} - \mathbf{Q}|^{\alpha}$, we say that f satisfies a **Hölder condition** with exponent α. Show that if f and g both satisfy a Hölder condition on D, then so doing the following:

(a) $f \pm g$ 　　　　　(b) fg 　　　　　　　(c) f/g

if g is bounded away from zero in D.

10

Differentiable Functions

10.1 PARTIAL DERIVATIVES

Let f be a function of two variables defined in a neighborhood of a point $\mathbf{P}_0 = (a, b)$. If we set $y = b$, then f becomes a function of a single variable x in a neighborhood of $x = a$. We can ask if this function of one variable has a derivative at a. This means, of course, that we are asking about the existence of

$$\lim_{x \to a} \frac{f(x, b) - f(a, b)}{x - a}.$$

If this limit exists, we call it the **partial derivative** of f with respect to x at (a, b), and we denote its value by

$$\frac{\partial f}{\partial x}(a, b) \qquad f_x(a, b) \qquad f_1(a, b)$$

or

$$\frac{\partial f}{\partial x}(\mathbf{P}_0) \qquad f_x(\mathbf{P}_0) \qquad f_1(\mathbf{P}_0).$$

On the set of points $\mathbf{P}$ where $f_1(\mathbf{P})$ exists, these values define a function which will be called the **partial derivative** of f with respect to x and will be denoted by

$$\frac{\partial f}{\partial x}, \qquad f_x, \qquad \text{or } f_1.$$

Similarly, if

$$\lim_{y \to b} \frac{f(a, y) - f(a, b)}{y - b}$$

exists, it is denoted by $f_2(a, b)$, $f_2(\mathbf{P}_0)$, and so on. The function defined by the partial with respect to y is denoted by $f_y, f_2,$ or $\dfrac{\partial f}{\partial y}$.

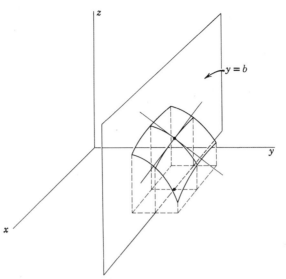

Partial derivatives inherit their geometrical meaning from that of ordinary derivatives. The derivative of a function of one variable, F, at a point a is the slope of the tangent line to the curve described by $z = F(x)$ at $x = a$. Thus $f_1(a, b)$ is the slope of the tangent line to the curve described by $z = f(x, b)$ in the plane described by $y = b$,—that is, the curve of intersection of the surface $z = f(x, y)$ and the plane $y = b$.

Second derivatives are defined as derivatives of first derivatives, and third derivatives as derivatives of second derivatives. The order of a derivative is the total number of differentiations performed to compute the derivative in question. The notations of the derivatives are as follows.

First derivatives
$$\begin{cases} \dfrac{\partial f}{\partial x} = f_x = f_1 \\[2mm] \dfrac{\partial f}{\partial y} = f_y = f_2 \end{cases}$$

Second derivatives
$$\begin{cases} \dfrac{\partial}{\partial x}\left(\dfrac{\partial f}{\partial x}\right) = \dfrac{\partial^2 f}{\partial x^2} = f_{xx} = f_{11} \\[2mm] \dfrac{\partial}{\partial x}\left(\dfrac{\partial f}{\partial y}\right) = \dfrac{\partial^2 f}{\partial x\,\partial y} = f_{yx} = f_{21} \\[2mm] \dfrac{\partial}{\partial y}\left(\dfrac{\partial f}{\partial x}\right) = \dfrac{\partial^2 f}{\partial y\,\partial x} = f_{xy} = f_{12} \\[2mm] \dfrac{\partial}{\partial y}\left(\dfrac{\partial f}{\partial y}\right) = \dfrac{\partial^2 f}{\partial y^2} = f_{yy} = f_{22} \end{cases}$$

$$\text{Third derivatives} \begin{cases} \dfrac{\partial}{\partial x}\left(\dfrac{\partial^2 f}{\partial x^2}\right) = \dfrac{\partial^3 f}{\partial x^3} = f_{xxx} = f_{111} \\ \vdots \end{cases}$$

EXAMPLE 1. Compute the partial derivatives of the function f given by

$$f(x, y) = x^3 y^2 + x^4 \sin y + \cos xy.$$

Solution:

$$f_1(x, y) = 3x^2 y^2 + 4x^3 \sin y - y \sin xy$$

$$f_2(x, y) = 2x^3 y + x^4 \cos y - x \sin xy$$

$$f_{11}(x, y) = 6xy^2 + 12x^2 \sin y - y^2 \cos xy$$

$$f_{12}(x, y) = 6x^2 y + 4x^3 \cos y - \sin xy - xy \cos xy$$

$$f_{21}(x, y) = 6x^2 y + 4x^3 \cos y - \sin xy - xy \cos xy$$

$$f_{22}(x, y) = 2x^3 - x^4 \sin y - x^2 \cos xy$$

$$f_{111}(x, y) = 6y^2 + 24x \sin y + y^3 \sin xy$$

$$\vdots$$

EXAMPLE 2. Suppose there is a function z which satisfies the equation

$$x^3 - xy^2 + yz^2 - z^3 = 5$$

and that the partial derivatives of z exist. Compute z_1 and z_2.

Solution. Differentiating with respect to x, we get

$$3x^2 - y^2 + 2yzz_1 - 3z^2 z_1 = 0,$$

from which we get

$$z_1 = \frac{\partial z}{\partial x} = \frac{y^2 - 3x^2}{2yz - 3z^2} \qquad \text{if } 2yz \neq 3z^2.$$

Similarly,

$$z_2 = \frac{\partial z}{\partial y} = \frac{2xy - z^2}{2yz - 3z^2} \qquad \text{if } 2yz \neq 3z^2.$$

EXAMPLE 3. Suppose u and v are two given functions of x and y which satisfy the equations

$$u^2 - v^2 = x$$

$$2uv = y.$$

Compute u_1, u_2, v_1, and v_2, assuming that they exist.

Solution. Differentiating with respect to x, we get

$$2uu_1 - 2vv_1 = 1$$

$$vu_1 + uv_1 = 0.$$

Solving for u_1 and v_1 by Cramer's rule, we get

$$u_1 = \begin{vmatrix} 1 & -2v \\ 0 & u \end{vmatrix} \bigg/ \begin{vmatrix} 2u & -2v \\ v & u \end{vmatrix} = \frac{u}{2(u^2 + v^2)},$$

and

$$v_1 = \begin{vmatrix} 2u & 1 \\ v & 0 \end{vmatrix} \bigg/ \begin{vmatrix} 2u & -2v \\ v & u \end{vmatrix} = \frac{-v}{2(u^2 + v^2)}.$$

Differentiating the original system with respect to y, we can solve for u_2 and v_2 to get

$$u_2 = \frac{v}{2(u^2 + v^2)}$$

and

$$v_2 = \frac{u}{2(u^2 + v^2)}.$$

Before proceeding further, it should be noted that although our discussion and examples have involved only functions of two independent variables, still the ideas extend immediately to functions in higher dimensions. For instance, if f is defined in a three-dimensional neighborhood of a point $P_0 = (a, b, c)$, then

$$f_1(P_0) = f_x(P_0) = \frac{\partial f}{\partial x}(P_0) = f_1(a, b, c) = f_x(a, b, c) = \frac{\partial f}{\partial x}(a, b, c)$$

each means the derivatives of f with respect to x at $x = a$, with y and z being held fixed at the values b and c respectively. Similarly defined are $f_2(P_0)$ and $f_3(P_0)$, along with the other notational symbols for the same values. These remarks of course, as you will readily recognize, apply equally well to functions in four or higher dimensional spaces.

In the case of a function of a single variable, you will recall (Theorem 3.5a) that the existence of a derivative at a point a implies the continuity of the function at a. However, a function of several variables may have a partial derivative at a point; indeed it may have all its first partials existing at a point P and may still not be continuous there. The reason is the following: The existence of the derivative f_1 at a point P has something to say about the behavior of the function f only on a single line through P, namely the line through P parallel to the x-axis. Similarly the existence of f_2 says that f must be nicely behaved, in particular continuous, along the line parallel to the y-axis. Elsewhere, between these lines the function may be very badly behaved. The next example illustrates this.

EXAMPLE 4. Let f be given by

$$f(x, y) = \begin{cases} \dfrac{xy}{x^2 + y^2} & (x, y) \neq (0, 0) \\[2mm] 0 & (x, y) = (0, 0) \end{cases}$$

Solution. Now f is clearly not continuous at the origin, as we saw in the last chapter (Example 2, Section 9.3). But

$$f_1(0, 0) = \lim_{x \to 0} \frac{f(x, 0) - f(0, 0)}{x} = \lim_{x \to 0} \frac{0 - 0}{x} = \lim_{x \to 0} 0 = 0$$

and $\quad f_2(0, 0) = \lim_{y \to 0} \frac{f(0, y) - f(0, 0)}{y} = \lim_{y \to 0} \frac{0 - 0}{y} = \lim_{y \to 0} 0 = 0.$

As we have seen in Example 1, $f_{12} = f_{21}$. We now demonstrate that this is not always the case.

EXAMPLE 5. Define f in the whole plane by

$$f(x, y) = \begin{cases} \dfrac{xy(x^2 - y^2)}{x^2 + y^2} & (x, y) \neq (0, 0) \\[2mm] 0 & (x, y) = (0, 0). \end{cases}$$

Solution. For $(x, y) \neq (0, 0)$, we compute that

$$f_1(x, y) = y\left[\frac{x^2 - y^2}{x^2 + y^2} + \frac{4x^2 y^2}{(x^2 + y^2)^2}\right]$$

$$f_2(x, y) = x\left[\frac{x^2 - y^2}{x^2 + y^2} - \frac{4x^2 y^2}{(x^2 + y^2)^2}\right].$$

In particular, $\qquad f_1(0, y) = -y, f_2(x, 0) = x$

Furthermore, $\qquad f_1(0, 0) = \lim_{x \to 0} \frac{f(x, 0) - f(0, 0)}{x} = 0$

and $\qquad f_2(0, 0) = \lim_{y \to 0} \frac{f(0, y) - f(0, 0)}{y} = 0.$

Thus $\qquad f_{12}(0, 0) = \lim_{y \to 0} \frac{f_1(0, y) - f_1(0, 0)}{y} = \lim_{y \to 0} \frac{-y}{y} = -1$

and $\qquad f_{21}(0, 0) = \lim_{x \to 0} \frac{f_2(x, 0) - f_2(0, 0)}{x} = \lim_{x \to 0} \frac{x}{x} = 1.$

However, this is a pathological situation which does not often arise. The following theorem shows that, under reasonably mild restrictions, the two derivatives are equal.

10.1a   Theorem. Let f, f_1, f_2, and f_{12} exist and be continuous in a neighborhood of a point $\mathbf{P}_0 = (x_0, y_0)$. Then $f_{21}(\mathbf{P}_0)$ exists and $f_{12}(\mathbf{P}_0) = f_{21}(\mathbf{P}_0)$.

Proof. Let $\phi(x) = f(x, y_0 + k) - f(x, y_0)$, where k and y are held fixed. Then for x sufficiently near x_0 and k small, ϕ is a function of the single variable x near x_0. To this function we apply the mean-value theorem for functions of one variable between x_0 and $x_0 + h$:

$$\phi(x_0 + h) - \phi(x_0) = h\phi'(x_0 + \theta_1 h),$$

where the prime (') denotes differentiation with respect to x and where $0 < \theta_1 < 1$. Thus

$$\phi(x_0 + h) - \phi(x_0) = h[f_1(x_0 + \theta_1 h, y_0 + k) - f_1(x_0 + \theta_1 h, y_0)].$$

Now for each h we apply the mean-value theorem again to the second variable:

$$\phi(x_0 + h) - \phi(x_0) = hk[f_{12}(x_0 + \theta_1 h, y_0 + \theta_2 k)]$$
$$= hk[f_{12}(x_0, y_0) + \eta],$$

where $\eta \to 0$ as $h \to 0$ and $k \to 0$ in any manner whatever, since f_{12} is continuous.

Recalling the meaning of ϕ, we can rewrite this as

$$[f(x_0 + h, y_0 + k) - f(x_0 + h, y_0)] - [f(x_0, y_0 + k) - f(x_0, y_0)]$$
$$= hk[f_{12}(x_0, y_0) + \eta]$$

Dividing by k and letting $k \to 0$, we get

$$f_2(x_0 + h, y_0) - f_2(x_0, y_0) = h[f_{12}(x_0, y_0) + \eta].$$

Then dividing by h, as $h \to 0$,

$$f_{21}(x_0, y_0) = f_{12}(x_0, y_0). \qquad \blacksquare$$

It should be clear that this suffices for the interchange of orders of differentiation for mixed derivatives of all orders. For example, to show that $f_{212} = f_{221}$, we apply the theorem to f_2. In general, one can show by induction that if all partials up to order n are continuous, then all the mixed partials up to order n are independent of the order of differentiation.

A EXERCISES

1. Compute the partial derivatives through order 2 of the following functions:

(a) $\log (x^2 + y^2 + z^2 + w^2)$

(b) $e^{z^2+w^2} \log (x^2 + y^2)$

(c) $x^3 + 7x^2y - y^3$

(d) $\dfrac{e^x}{e^y - e^z}$

(e) $\arcsin \dfrac{x^2}{y^2}$

(f) $e^{-x} \sin y$

(g) $\dfrac{x - y}{x + y}$

(h) x^y

2. (a) Set $u = \log 1/\sqrt{x^2 + y^2}$ and show that $u_{11} + u_{22} = 0$.

(b) Set $u = 1/\sqrt{x^2 + y^2 + z^2}$ and show that $u_{11} + u_{22} + u_{33} = 0$.

(c) Set $u = x^2y + y^2z + z^2x$ and show that $u_1 + u_2 + u_3 = (x + y + z)^2$.

3. Suppose there is a function z satisfying the equation below. Find its first-order partials.

(a) $x^3 + y^3 + z^3 + \sin xz + \cos yz = 15$

(b) $e^z + x^2 \log z + y = 0$

4. Suppose there are functions u, v satisfying the following equations. Compute their first-order partials.

(a) $\begin{cases} u \cos v = x + 1 \\ u \sin v = x + y \end{cases}$

(b) $\begin{cases} x^2 - y \cos uv + z^2 = 5 \\ x^2 + y^2 - \sin uv = 8 - 2z^2 \\ xy - \sin u \cos v + z = 0. \end{cases}$

5. In Exercise 4a, consider x and y as functions of u and v. Compute their first-order partials.

B EXERCISES

1. Define the function f by

$$f(x, y) = \begin{cases} x^2 \arctan y/x - y^2 \arctan x/y & xy \neq 0 \\ 0 & xy = 0 \end{cases}$$

Show that $f_{12}(0, 0) \neq f_{21}(0, 0)$.

2. If $x = r \cos \theta$ and $y = r \sin \theta$, consider r and θ as functions of x and y, and show that

$$\frac{\partial^2 \theta}{\partial x \, \partial y} = - \frac{\cos 2\theta}{r^2}.$$

10.2 DIFFERENTIABILITY. TOTAL DIFFERENTIALS

In this section we explore the difficulty indicated by Example 4 of Section 10.1. Since continuity of f at a point requires that all near-by points give rise to near-by function values, and the existence of the partials does not involve all near-by points, we turn to a tool which does involve all near-by points, namely the differential.

In the case of one variable, the differential gives an approximation of the change in the value of a function due to a change in the independent variable. That is, if f is differentiable at x_0, then

$$dy = f'(x_0)\, dx$$

is approximately equal to

$$\Delta y = f(x_0 + dx) - f(x_0).$$

In fact,

$$\Delta y = f'(x_0)\, dx + \epsilon\, dx,$$

where $\epsilon \to 0$ as $dx \to 0$. (Recall that dx and dy were new variables introduced with the origin at the point $[x_0, f(x_0)]$.)

As seen in the last example, f need not be continuous for f_1 and f_2 to exist at a point. Hence, in order to extend the idea of a differential, we will have to demand more of our function than that it merely possess first order partials. With the idea of defining a differential as our ultimate goal, we first define a differentiable function of two (or more) variables. (In this discussion you will recognize that $h = dx$ and $k = dy$.)

Suppose f is defined in a neighborhood of a point $\mathbf{P}_0 = (a, b)$ and there are numbers A and B so that

$$f(a + h, b + k) = f(a, b) + Ah + Bk + \eta \sqrt{h^2 + k^2},$$

where $\eta \to 0$ as $\sqrt{h^2 + k^2} \to 0$. We then say that f is **differentiable** at $\mathbf{P}_0$. Furthermore, we say that f is **differentiable** in a region if it is differentiable at each point of the region. Here of course A and B will in general depend on $\mathbf{P}_0$, but they must be independent of h and k. If A and B depend continuously on $\mathbf{P}_0$ on a set D, we say that f is **continuously differentiable** on D.

Differentiability is a stronger condition than the existence of partial derivatives; for if a function is differentiable at a point, it is easy to see that it is continuous and that both partial derivatives exist. This is the content of the following two theorems.

10.2a   Theorem. If f is differentiable at $\mathbf{P}_0 = (a, b)$, then f is continuous at $\mathbf{P}_0$.

Proof. For $\mathbf{P} = (x, y)$ in a neighborhood of $\mathbf{P}_0 = (a, b)$, we have by the definition of differentiability

$$f(\mathbf{P}) - f(\mathbf{P}_0) = A(x - a) + B(y - b) + \eta \sqrt{(x - a)^2 + (y - b)^2}$$

Now

$$|x - a| \leqslant \sqrt{(x - a)^2 + (y - b)^2} = |\mathbf{P} - \mathbf{P}_0|$$

and

$$|y - b| \leqslant |\mathbf{P} - \mathbf{P}_0|.$$

So

$$|f(\mathbf{P}) - f(\mathbf{P}_0)| \leqslant \{|A| + |B| + |\eta|\}\, |\mathbf{P} - \mathbf{P}_0|.$$

10.2b   Theorem. If f is differentiable at $P_0 = (a, b)$, then the first-order partials exist at P_0 and

$$f_1(P_0) = A$$
$$f_2(P_0) = B.$$

Proof. From the difference quotient,

$$\frac{f(a + h, b) - f(a, b)}{h} = \frac{Ah + \eta\sqrt{h^2}}{h} = A + \eta \frac{|h|}{h}.$$

Thus

$$\left| \frac{f(a + h, b) - f(a, b)}{h} - A \right| = |\eta| \to 0 \text{ as } h \to 0.$$

Thus $f_1(P_0)$ exists and equals A. Similarly,

$$f_2(P_0) = B. \qquad \blacksquare$$

If f is a differentiable function of two variables (x, y) at a point P_0, then the expression

$$df = dz = \frac{\partial f}{\partial x}(P_0)\, dx + \frac{\partial f}{\partial y}(P_0)\, dy$$

is called the **total differential**, or more simply the **differential**, of f at P_0. The symbol dz is inspired by the common notation $z = f(x, y) = f(P)$.

The total differential gives, for a differentiable function, an approximation to the change Δz in z, owing to changes dx in x and dy in y. The sense in which it approximates the change in the function f—that is, in z—is made precise by the definition of a differentiable function.

Frequently we write simply

$$(1) \qquad dz = \frac{\partial f}{\partial x}\, dx + \frac{\partial f}{\partial y}\, dy,$$

it being understood that the partial derivatives are to be evaluated at some point P_0, the formula then giving the differential of f at P_0.

As in the case of functions of one variable, we introduce new coordinates, with origin at the point (a, b, c) where $c = f(P_0) = f(a, b)$. These new coordinates, namely x-a, y-b, z-c, we denote by dx, dy, dz respectively. Thus (1) becomes the equation of a plane passing through the origin (that is, in the dx, dy, dz space). Its equation in the old coordinates is then

$$(2) \qquad z - c = \frac{\partial f}{\partial x}(x - a) + \frac{\partial f}{\partial y}(y - b).$$

This plane is called the **tangent plane** to the surface S given by $z = f(x, y)$ at point P_0.

It follows (see Section 8.5) that the direction numbers of the normal to S at $\mathbf{P}_0$ are $\left(\dfrac{\partial f}{\partial x}, \dfrac{\partial f}{\partial y}, -1\right)$.

It is clear that in order to write down the formal expression (1), which is called the differential, it is only necessary to be able to compute the two partial derivatives involved. Why then should we confine ourselves by the additional restriction that the function f be differentiable in the technical sense in which differentiability was defined? The reason is that it is the property of differentiability in which we are really interested and that for such functions the differential is a useful expression, basically because it gives a good approximation to Δz.

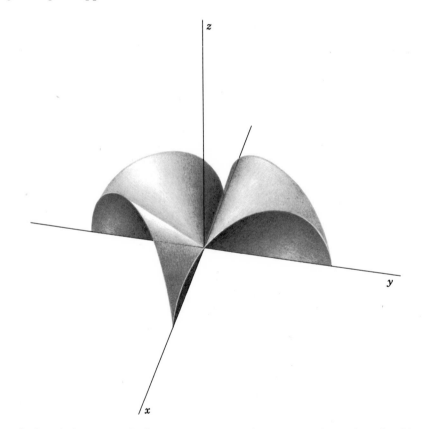

In heuristic geometrical terms, we expect the tangent plane given by (2) (which is after all a geometrical realization of the differential) to fit closely the surface described by $z = f(x, y)$ in the sense that the angle between the tangent plane and the surface should be zero. A glance at the graph of

$\sqrt{|xy|}$ shows the behavior of this function near the origin. It has $f_x(0, 0) = f_y(0, 0) = 0$, so that formally $dz = 0$; that is, the "tangent plane" is the xy plane given by $z = 0$. However, along the lines $y = \pm x$, the height of the surface above the xy plane is given by $z = |x|$. Thus along these lines the surface makes an angle arc tan $1/\sqrt{2}$ with the xy plane. In such a situation the plane determined by the formal differential is not called the tangent plane. In case a function is differentiable at a point, one can show that in a precise sense the angle between the tangent plane and the surface is zero at the point of tangency (see Exercise C1).

We should like to emphasize the fact that the phrase "f has a differential" is reserved for differentiable functions and that we do not admit the expression (1) as a differential unless f is differentiable.

We turn now to a criterion for determining when a function is differentiable.

10.2c   Theorem. Suppose f has continuous first partial derivatives in a region D. Then f is differentiable at each point of D.

Proof. Let $\mathbf{P_0} = (a, b)$ be a point of D. There is a neighborhood N of $\mathbf{P_0}$ which is in D. Then for h and k sufficiently small $\mathbf{P} = (a + h, y + k)$ is in N.

Let $\qquad \Delta f = f(\mathbf{P}) - f(\mathbf{P_0}) = f(a + h, b + k) - f(a, b).$

Then $\Delta f = [f(a + h, b + k) - f(a + h, b)] + [f(a + h, b) - f(a, b)]$

Using the mean-value theorem for functions of one variable on each of the differences on the right, we get

$$\Delta f = kf_2(a + h, y_1) + hf_1(x_1, b).$$

By hypothesis, f_1 and f_2 are continuous at $\mathbf{P_0}$, so that

$$f_2(a + h, y_1) = f_2(a, b) + \eta_2$$

and $\qquad\qquad f_1(x_1, b) = f_1(a, b) + \eta_1,$

where both η_1 and η_2 tend to zero as $\sqrt{h^2 + k^2} \to 0$. Thus

$$\Delta f = hf_1(a, b) + kf_2(a, b) + \eta_1 h + \eta_2 k.$$

By the definition of differentiability, we have only to show that

$$\frac{(\eta_1 h + \eta_2 k)}{\sqrt{h^2 + k^2}} \to 0.$$

But $\qquad \left| \frac{(\eta_1 h + \eta_2 k)}{\sqrt{h^2 + k^2}} \right| \leqslant |\eta_1| + |\eta_2| \to 0 \quad$ as $\sqrt{h^2 + k^2} \to 0.$ ∎

All the ideas of this section extend immediately to higher dimensions. Thus f is differentiable near a point $\mathbf{P}_0 = (a_1, a_2, \ldots, a_n)$ in n-space if there is a neighborhood of $\mathbf{P}_0$ in which

$$f(\mathbf{P}) = f(\mathbf{P}_0) + A_1 h_1 + A_2 h_2 + \cdots + A_n h_n + \eta \sqrt{h_1^2 + h_2^2 + \cdots + h_n^2},$$

such that $\eta \to 0$ as

$$|\mathbf{P} - \mathbf{P}_0| = \sqrt{h_1^2 + \cdots + h_n^2} \to 0,$$

where
$$\mathbf{P} = (a_1 + h_1, \ldots, a_n + h_n).$$

In this case, its first-order partials exist at $\mathbf{P}_0$, and

$$f_1(\mathbf{P}_0) = A_1, \ldots, f_n(\mathbf{P}_0) = A_n.$$

The total differential at $\mathbf{P}_0$ is

$$df = \frac{\partial f}{\partial x_1} dx_1 + \frac{\partial f}{\partial x_2} dx_2 + \cdots + \frac{\partial f}{\partial x_n} dx_n,$$

where the derivatives are evaluated at $\mathbf{P}_0$. The tangent hyperplane to the hypersurface $z = f(\mathbf{P})$ at $\mathbf{P}_0$ is

$$z - z_0 = \frac{\partial f}{\partial x_1} (x_1 - a_1) + \cdots + \frac{\partial f}{\partial x_n} (x_n - a_n),$$

where $z_0 = f(\mathbf{P}_0)$. Finally, a function is differentiable in a region if all its first-order partials are continuous there. (See Exercise B4.)

A EXERCISES

1. Compute the differentials of the functions given by each of the following expressions:

(a) $f(x, y) = x/y$

(b) $f(x, y) = \arctan y/x$

(c) $f(x, y) = \log 1/\sqrt{x^2 + y^2}$

(d) $f(x, y) = 2xy + y^2$

(e) $f(x, y, z) = 1/\sqrt{x^2 + y^2 + z^2}.$

2. Find the equation of the tangent plane to the surface given by $z = f(x, y)$ at the point $(1, 1)$ for each function in Exercise 1(a), (b), (c), and (d) above. In 1(e), write the equation of the tangent hyperplane at $(1, 1, 1, 1/\sqrt{3})$.

3. Compare df with Δf in 1(a) and (d) above.

4. The period of a pendulum is given by $T = 2\pi \sqrt{l/g}$. Approximate the error made in computing the period if the length l is known to be $8 \pm .01$ ft and the value of g is taken to be 32 ft/sec^2 rather than the correct (sic!) value of 31.8

B EXERCISES

1. Complete the discussion of the function given by $\sqrt{|xy|}$ begun in the text. Show that the function is continuous but not differentiable at $(0, 0)$.

2. Show that the function f defined by $f(x) = \begin{cases} xy/\sqrt{x^2 + y^2} & x \neq 0 \\ 0 & x = 0 \end{cases}$

is continuous but not differentiable at $(0, 0)$, although it has both partial derivatives existing there.

3. Let f be defined by

$$f(x, y) = \begin{cases} (x^2 + y^2) \sin 1/\sqrt{x^2 + y^2} & (x, y) \neq (0, 0) \\ 0 & (x, y) = (0, 0). \end{cases}$$

Show that f is differentiable everywhere and that the partial derivatives are bounded, but are discontinuous at $(0, 0)$.

4. Let f be defined by

$$f(x, y) = \begin{cases} (x^2 + y^2) \sin 1/(x^2 + y^2) & (x, y) \neq (0, 0) \\ 0 & (x, y) = (0, 0). \end{cases}$$

Show that f is differentiable everywhere, but has unbounded partial derivatives.

5. Determine the values of α for which f is differentiable at $(0, 0)$ when

$$f(x, y) = \begin{cases} (x^2 + y^2)^\alpha \sin 1/(x^2 + y^2) & (x, y) \neq (0, 0) \\ 0 & (x, y) = (0, 0), \end{cases}$$

6. Define f by

$$f(x, y) = \begin{cases} x^2 + y^2 & x, y \text{ both rational} \\ 0 & \text{otherwise} \end{cases}$$

Show that f is continuous at only one point and is differentiable there.

7. Let f be a differentiable function of one variable x, in an interval $I: \{a < x < b\}$. Define the function g in the strip $S: \{a < x < b, \ -\infty < y < \infty\}$ by $g(x, y) = f(x)$, and show that g is differentiable in S.

C EXERCISES

1. Let f be differentiable at (x_0, y_0). Let $\mathbf{P}_0 = (x_0, y_0, z_0)$, where $z_0 = f(x_0, y_0)$. If $\mathbf{P}$ is another point on the surface S described by $z = f(x, y)$ and α is the angle between the vector $\mathbf{P} - \mathbf{P}_0$ and the tangent plane to S at $\mathbf{P}_0$, show that

$$\alpha \to 0 \quad \text{as} \quad \mathbf{P} \to \mathbf{P}_0.$$

Conversely, show that if $\alpha \to 0$, then f is differentiable at $\mathbf{P}_0$.

10.3 THE GRADIENT VECTOR. THE DEL OPERATOR. DIRECTIONAL DERIVATIVES

In this section we will do our computations in three dimensions, although it will be clear as we proceed that all the results hold for spaces of any finite number of dimensions.

Let f be differentiable at a point $\mathbf{P} = (x, y, z)$. Then the **gradient vector** of f at $\mathbf{P}$ is denoted by $\nabla f(\mathbf{P})$ and defined by the formula

$$\nabla f = \frac{\partial f}{\partial x}\mathbf{i} + \frac{\partial f}{\partial y}\mathbf{j} + \frac{\partial f}{\partial z}\mathbf{k},$$

where each of the partials is evaluated at $\mathbf{P}$. We read the symbol ∇f as gradient f or del f. Sometimes ∇f is also denoted by **grad** f. For many purposes, it is convenient to think of ∇f as a formal product of the scalar f and the "vector" del, defined by

$$\nabla = \frac{\partial}{\partial x}\mathbf{i} + \frac{\partial}{\partial y}\mathbf{j} + \frac{\partial}{\partial z}\mathbf{k}.$$

Then ∇f can be written as

$$\nabla f = \left(\frac{\partial}{\partial x}\mathbf{i} + \frac{\partial}{\partial y}\mathbf{j} + \frac{\partial}{\partial z}\mathbf{k}\right) f$$

$$= \frac{\partial f}{\partial x}\mathbf{i} + \frac{\partial f}{\partial y}\mathbf{j} + \frac{\partial f}{\partial z}\mathbf{k}.$$

If $\mathbf{P} = x\mathbf{i} + y\mathbf{j} + z\mathbf{k}$ is the vector representation of a point $\mathbf{P}$, we can let

$$d\mathbf{P} = dx\mathbf{i} + dy\mathbf{j} + dz\mathbf{k}$$

and represent near-by points in the form $\mathbf{P} + d\mathbf{P}$, this being of course given by

$$\mathbf{P} + d\mathbf{P} = (x + dx)\mathbf{i} + (y + dy)\mathbf{j} + (z + dz)\mathbf{k}.$$

In terms of this notation, we can put the results of the last section in very compact form, reminiscent of the formulas for functions of one dimension. In particular, differentiability can be defined as follows: A function f is differentiable at $\mathbf{P}$ if

$$\Delta f = f(\mathbf{P} + d\mathbf{P}) - f(\mathbf{P}) = \nabla f \cdot d\mathbf{P} + \eta|d\mathbf{P}|,$$

where $\eta \to 0$ as $|d\mathbf{P}| \to 0$. The differential can be expressed as

$$df = \nabla f \cdot d\mathbf{P}.$$

The new notation is also well adapted to the investigation of a new concept, the idea of a directional derivative. Let $\boldsymbol{\alpha}$ be a unit vector:

$$\boldsymbol{\alpha} = \alpha_1\mathbf{i} + \alpha_2\mathbf{j} + \alpha_3\mathbf{k}, \quad |\boldsymbol{\alpha}| = 1.$$

(A unit vector will frequently be called a **direction**.) Then, by the **directional derivative** of f at $\mathbf{P}$ in the direction $\boldsymbol{\alpha}$, we mean

$$\lim_{h \to 0}\frac{f(\mathbf{P} + h\boldsymbol{\alpha}) - f(\mathbf{P})}{h} = \lim_{h \to 0}\frac{\Delta f}{h},$$

if the limit exists. The directional derivative, when it exists, will be denoted variously by $\mathbf{\nabla}_{\alpha} f$ or $\dfrac{\partial f}{\partial \alpha}$ or $\left(\dfrac{df}{ds}\right)_{\alpha}$—usually the first.

10.3a   Theorem. If f is differentiable at a point $\mathbf{P}$, then $\mathbf{\nabla}_{\alpha} f$ exists for all unit vectors α, and

$$\mathbf{\nabla}_{\alpha} f = (\alpha \cdot \mathbf{\nabla}) f \equiv \alpha_1 f_1 + \alpha_2 f_2 + \alpha_3 f_3$$

Proof. By the definition of differentiability and Theorem 10.2b,

$$\Delta f = f(\mathbf{P} + h\alpha) - f(\mathbf{P}) = \alpha_1 \frac{\partial f}{\partial x} h + \alpha_2 \frac{\partial f}{\partial y} h + \alpha_3 \frac{\partial f}{\partial z} h + \eta |h|,$$

where $\eta \to 0$ as $h \to 0$. Dividing by h and taking limits gives us the result. ∎

This gives us a tool for investigating the geometrical meaning of the gradient vector. Let θ be the angle between $\mathbf{\nabla} f$ at a point $\mathbf{P}$ and the direction given by α. We then have

$$\mathbf{\nabla}_{\alpha} f = \alpha \cdot \mathbf{\nabla} f = |\mathbf{\nabla} f| \cos \theta.$$

This will be the greatest (at a given fixed point $\mathbf{P}$, of course) if $\cos \theta = 1$— that is, if α is in the direction of $\mathbf{\nabla} f$ itself. Since a derivative represents a rate of change, we see that this rate is the greatest when the derivative is taken in the direction of $\mathbf{\nabla} f$.

On another tack, we can see that, for any direction α orthogonal to $\mathbf{\nabla} f$,

$$\mathbf{\nabla}_{\alpha} f = \mathbf{\nabla} f \cdot \alpha = 0$$

That is, the rate of change in this direction is zero. The totality of the vectors $\mathbf{P}_0 + t\alpha$ where α is normal to $\mathbf{\nabla} f$ then gives the tangent plane to the surface $f = c$, which implies that $\mathbf{\nabla} f$ is normal to the surface $f = c$, since it is orthogonal to the tangent plane. These ideas will be discussed more carefully when we consider implicit functions.

For each fixed α, the directional derivative $\mathbf{\nabla}_{\alpha} f$ defines a new function of which one can take a directional derivative. Generally we will be concerned with computing these higher directional derivatives in the same direction α. For example,

$$\mathbf{\nabla}_{\alpha}^{2} f, \qquad \frac{\partial^2 f}{\partial \alpha^2}, \quad \text{or} \quad \left(\frac{\partial^2 f}{\partial s^2}\right)_{\alpha}$$

will be used to denote the second directional derivative in the direction α.

10.3b   Theorem. Let f have continuous second partials in a neighborhood of a point $\mathbf{P}$. Then at $\mathbf{P}$,

$$\mathbf{\nabla}_{\alpha}^{2} f = (\alpha \cdot \mathbf{\nabla})^2 f.$$

Proof. At each point of the neighborhood

$$\mathbf{V}_\alpha f = (\boldsymbol{\alpha} \cdot \mathbf{V})f = \alpha_1 f_1 + \alpha_2 f_2 + \alpha_3 f_3.$$

Under the hypotheses of the theorem, f_1, f_2, and f_3 are all differentiable. Hence the directional derivative of $\mathbf{V}_\alpha f$ is given by

$$\begin{aligned}
\mathbf{V}_\alpha^2 f &= \alpha_1(\mathbf{V}_\alpha f_1) + \alpha_2(\mathbf{V}_\alpha f_2) + \alpha_3(\mathbf{V}_\alpha f_3) \\
&= \alpha_1^2 f_{11} + \alpha_1\alpha_2 f_{12} + \alpha_1\alpha_3 f_{13} \\
&\quad + \alpha_1\alpha_2 f_{21} + \alpha_2^2 f_{22} + \alpha_2\alpha_3 f_{23} \\
&\quad + \alpha_1\alpha_3 f_{31} + \alpha_2\alpha_3 f_{32} + \alpha_3^2 f_{33}.
\end{aligned}$$

Since $f_{12} = f_{21}$, this becomes

$$\alpha_1^2 \frac{\partial^2 f}{\partial x^2} + \alpha_2^2 \frac{\partial^2 f}{\partial y^2} + \alpha_3^2 \frac{\partial^2 f}{\partial z^2} + 2\alpha_1\alpha_2 \frac{\partial^2 f}{\partial x\,\partial y} + 2\alpha_1\alpha_3 \frac{\partial^2 f}{\partial x\,\partial z} + 2\alpha_2\alpha_3 \frac{\partial^2 f}{\partial y\,\partial z}$$

$$= \left(\alpha_1 \frac{\partial}{\partial x} + \alpha_2 \frac{\partial}{\partial y} + \alpha_3 \frac{\partial}{\partial z}\right)^2 f = (\boldsymbol{\alpha} \cdot \mathbf{V})^2 f. \qquad \blacksquare$$

10.3c Corollary. Let f have continuous n^{th}-order derivatives near **P**. Then at **P** the nth-order directional derivative for each direction $\boldsymbol{\alpha}$ exists and

$$\mathbf{V}_\alpha^n f = (\boldsymbol{\alpha} \cdot \mathbf{V})^n f.$$

Proof. Prove by induction, from Theorem 10.3b. $\qquad\blacksquare$

EXAMPLE. Find the directional derivative of $x^4 + x^3 y + 2x^2 z + y^8 \sin z + z^3$ at $(1, 2, 5)$ toward the point $(5, 0, 7)$.

Solution. The direction numbers of the direction we are concerned with are $(4, -2, 2)$; hence the unit vector is that direction is

$$\frac{2}{\sqrt 6}\mathbf{i} - \frac{1}{\sqrt 6}\mathbf{j} + \frac{1}{\sqrt 6}\mathbf{k}.$$

And $\quad \mathbf{V}f = (4x^3 + 3x^2 y + 4xz)\mathbf{i}$
$$+ (x^3 + 8y^7 \sin z)\mathbf{j} + (2x^2 + y^8 \cos z + 3z^2)\mathbf{k}.$$

When evaluated at $(1, 2, 5)$, we get

$$\mathbf{V}f = 30\mathbf{i} + (1 + 1024 \sin 5)\mathbf{j} + (77 + 256 \cos 5)\mathbf{k}.$$

Then $\quad \mathbf{V}_\alpha f = \boldsymbol{\alpha} \cdot \mathbf{V}f = \dfrac{60}{\sqrt 6} - \dfrac{(1 + 1024 \sin 5)}{\sqrt 6} + \dfrac{77 + 256 \cos 5}{\sqrt 6}$

$$= \frac{136 - 1024 \sin 5 + 256 \cos 5}{\sqrt 6}.$$

10.4 COMPOSITE FUNCTIONS. THE CHAIN RULE

If **F** is a vector-valued function defined on a region D of a Euclidean vector space, we can ask about the existence of the partial derivatives, of the directional derivatives, and of differentials. It is clear that the results of the previous sections extend immediately, and that a necessary and sufficient condition for any of these to exist for a vector-valued function **F** is that it exist for each of the components. Thus if

$$\boldsymbol{\Phi} = \phi\mathbf{i} + \psi\mathbf{j} + \chi\mathbf{k},$$

where ϕ, ψ, and χ are functions, for example, of $\mathbf{Q} = (t, u, v, w)$, then $\partial\boldsymbol{\Phi}/\partial t$ means that

$$\lim_{\Delta t \to 0} \frac{\boldsymbol{\Phi}(t + \Delta t, u, v, w) - \boldsymbol{\Phi}(t, u, v, w)}{\Delta t}$$

if this limit exists; and a necessary and sufficient condition for this limit to exist is that $\partial\phi/\partial t$, $\partial\psi/\partial t$, and $\partial\chi/\partial t$ all exist.

Our main aim in this section is to consider what form the chain rule (see Section 3.5) takes when we are dealing with functions of vectors—that is, functions of several real variables. For example, if f is a function of (x, y, z) and each of these in turn is a function of (t, u, v, w), then f becomes a function of (t, u, v, w) and we want to inquire into the methods of computing the partials of f with respect to t, u, v, and w. In vector terminology, if f is a function of **P** on a region R, and $\boldsymbol{\Phi}$ is a vector function in D with values in R, then it makes sense to discuss the function g defined on D by $g(\mathbf{Q}) = f[\boldsymbol{\Phi}(\mathbf{Q})]$ and to ask for the partials of g with respect to the components of **Q**.

We could frame our discussion in quite general terms, by considering $\boldsymbol{\Phi}$ to be a mapping from E_m to E_n and f a function defined on E_n. However, to fix ideas, and to keep the calculations simple, we will take m to be 4 and n to be 3. Thus we follow the pattern laid down in the preceding paragraph where $\mathbf{P} = (x, y, z)$ and $\mathbf{Q} = (t, u, v, w)$. The extensions to all other cases should be apparent from this discussion.

A word about notation: Under the substitution $\mathbf{P} = \boldsymbol{\Phi}(\mathbf{Q})$, we have

$$\frac{\partial \mathbf{P}}{\partial t} = \frac{\partial \boldsymbol{\Phi}}{\partial t} = \frac{\partial \phi}{\partial t}\mathbf{i} + \frac{\partial \psi}{\partial t}\mathbf{j} + \frac{\partial \chi}{\partial t}\mathbf{k}.$$

Since $\mathbf{P} = \boldsymbol{\Phi}(\mathbf{Q})$ implies that $x = \phi(\mathbf{Q})$, $y = \psi(\mathbf{Q})$, and $z = \chi(\mathbf{Q})$, we interchange $\dfrac{\partial x}{\partial t}$ and $\dfrac{\partial \phi}{\partial t}$, and so forth, so that

$$\frac{\partial \mathbf{P}}{\partial t} = \frac{\partial x}{\partial t}\mathbf{i} + \frac{\partial y}{\partial t}\mathbf{j} + \frac{\partial z}{\partial t}\mathbf{k}.$$

The other partials of **P** (that is, of **Φ**) are similarly expressed. Also, we write the differential $d\mathbf{P}$ in the form

$$d\mathbf{P} = \frac{\partial \mathbf{P}}{\partial t}\, dt + \frac{\partial \mathbf{P}}{\partial u}\, du + \frac{\partial \mathbf{P}}{\partial v}\, dv + \frac{\partial \mathbf{P}}{\partial w}\, dw.$$

10.4a   Theorem. Let f and g be related by $g(\mathbf{Q}) = f(\mathbf{Φ}(\mathbf{Q}))$ as described above, where f and **Φ** are differentiable. Then

$$\frac{\partial g}{\partial t} = \nabla f \cdot \frac{\partial \mathbf{P}}{\partial t}, \quad \frac{\partial g}{\partial u} = \nabla f \cdot \frac{\partial \mathbf{P}}{\partial u}, \dots,$$

that is,

$$\frac{\partial g}{\partial t} = \frac{\partial f}{\partial x}\frac{\partial x}{\partial t} + \frac{\partial f}{\partial y}\frac{\partial y}{\partial t} + \frac{\partial f}{\partial z}\frac{\partial z}{\partial t}, \dots.$$

Proof. Let $\mathbf{Q} = (t, u, v, w)$, and let $\mathbf{Q} + \Delta\mathbf{Q} = (t + \Delta t, u, v, w)$ be a near-by point in D. Then Δg is defined by

$$\Delta g = g(\mathbf{Q} + \Delta\mathbf{Q}) - g(\mathbf{Q})$$

and

$$\Delta x = \phi(\mathbf{Q} + \Delta\mathbf{Q}) - \phi(\mathbf{Q})$$
$$\Delta y = \psi(\mathbf{Q} + \Delta\mathbf{Q}) - \psi(\mathbf{Q})$$
$$\Delta z = \chi(\mathbf{Q} + \Delta\mathbf{Q}) - \chi(\mathbf{Q}).$$

So

$$\Delta g = f(\phi(\mathbf{Q} + \Delta\mathbf{Q}), \psi(\mathbf{Q} + \Delta\mathbf{Q}), \chi(\mathbf{Q} + \Delta\mathbf{Q})) - f(\phi(\mathbf{Q}), \psi(\mathbf{Q}), \chi(\mathbf{Q}))$$
$$= f_x \Delta x + f_y \Delta y + f_z \Delta z + \eta |\Delta\mathbf{P}|,$$

where $\eta \to 0$ as $|\Delta\mathbf{P}| \to 0$, since f is differentiable. Then

$$\frac{\Delta g}{\Delta t} = f_x \frac{\Delta x}{\Delta t} + f_y \frac{\Delta y}{\Delta t} + f_z \frac{\Delta z}{\Delta t} + \eta \frac{|\Delta\mathbf{P}|}{\Delta t}.$$

Now as $\Delta t \to 0$,

$$\frac{\Delta x}{\Delta t} \to \frac{\partial x}{\partial t}, \dots, \frac{\Delta\mathbf{P}}{\Delta t} \to \frac{\partial \mathbf{P}}{\partial t},$$

and $\eta \to 0$. Thus, passing to the limit, we get

$$\frac{\partial g}{\partial t} = f_x \frac{\partial x}{\partial t} + f_y \frac{\partial y}{\partial t} + f_z \frac{\partial z}{\partial t}. \quad\blacksquare$$

Let us note that the same formula,

$$\frac{\partial g}{\partial t} = \nabla f \cdot \frac{\partial \mathbf{P}}{\partial t},$$

holds no matter what the dimensions of **P** or of **Q**. In particular, if **Q** is just one-dimensional—that is, if $\mathbf{Q} = t$—the formula becomes

$$g' = \frac{dg}{dt} = \frac{d}{dt} f[x(t), y(t), z(t)] = \nabla f \cdot \frac{d\mathbf{P}}{dt} .$$

It is sometimes convenient, and notationally perhaps a little simpler, if we do not introduce a new symbol g for the function f when the new variables are introduced. Thus, we think of f as being a function of x, y, z. Then, when x, y, z are expressed in terms of t, u, v, w, we think of f as a function of t, u, v, w. From the one master formula for the differential

$$df = \nabla f \cdot d\mathbf{P}$$

we can read off all partials of f with respect to whatever variables are involved. Thus

$$\frac{\partial f}{\partial t} = \nabla f \cdot \frac{\partial \mathbf{P}}{\partial t} \cdots .$$

10.4b   **Remark.** In particular, when f is expressed as a function of $t, u, v,$ w, the differential formula

$$df = \nabla f \cdot d\mathbf{P}$$

is the correct expression for df in terms of the differentials $dt, du,$ dv, dw, if $d\mathbf{P}$ in turn is expressed in terms of these. For by definition, if f is expressed in terms of $t, u, v, w,$

$$df = \frac{\partial f}{\partial t} dt + \frac{\partial f}{\partial u} du + \frac{\partial f}{\partial v} dv + \frac{\partial f}{\partial w} dw.$$

Then, by the previous theorem,

$$df = \left(\nabla f \cdot \frac{\partial \mathbf{P}}{\partial t}\right) dt + \left(\nabla f \cdot \frac{\partial \mathbf{P}}{\partial u}\right) du + \left(\nabla f \cdot \frac{\partial \mathbf{P}}{\partial v}\right) dv$$

$$+ \left(\nabla f \cdot \frac{\partial \mathbf{P}}{\partial w}\right) dw$$

$$= \nabla f \cdot \left(\frac{\partial \mathbf{P}}{\partial t} dt + \frac{\partial \mathbf{P}}{\partial u} du + \frac{\partial \mathbf{P}}{\partial v} dv + \frac{\partial \mathbf{P}}{\partial w} dw\right)$$

$$= \nabla f \cdot d\mathbf{P}.$$

EXAMPLE. Let $F(x, y)$ be a differentiable function of (x, y) in the rectangle $R: \{a < x < b, c < y < d\}$, and suppose there is a function y in $\{a < x < b\}$ with range in $\{c < y < d\}$ for which $F(x, y) = 0$. Compute $y' = dy/dx$ in $\{a < x < b\}$.

Solution. We observe that

$$dF = F_y \, dy + F_x \, dx = 0.$$

Thus

$$F_y \frac{dy}{dx} + F_x = 0.$$

Hence

$$y' = \frac{dy}{dx} = -F_x/F_y,$$

provided $F_y \neq 0$. This condition, $F_y \neq 0$, is sufficient to guarantee that such a function y exists (see Section 11.6). Then the formula for y' is valid.

EXAMPLE. Let $F(u, v, x, y, z)$ and $G(u, v, x \ y, z)$ represent differentiable functions of the five variables in a region R of five-space. Suppose further that u, v are two functions of (x, y, z) in three-space which satisfy the equations

$$F(u, v, x, y, z) = 0$$
$$G(u, v, x, y, z) = 0.$$

Compute the partials of u, v with respect to x.

Solution. Note that

$$dF = F_u \, du + F_v \, dv + F_x \, dx + F_y \, dy + F_z \, dz = 0,$$

since y and z are held fixed $dy = dz = 0$. Thus

$$F_u \frac{\partial u}{\partial x} + F_v \frac{\partial v}{\partial x} + F_x = 0,$$

Similarly,

$$G_u \frac{\partial u}{\partial x} + G_v \frac{\partial v}{\partial x} + G_x = 0.$$

Or

$$F_u u_x + F_v v_x = -F_x$$
$$G_u u_x + G_v v_x = -G_x$$

These form a pair of linear equations for the determination of u_x and v_x. Hence, by Cramer's rule,

$$u_x = -\frac{\begin{vmatrix} F_x & F_v \\ G_x & G_v \end{vmatrix}}{\begin{vmatrix} F_u & F_v \\ G_u & G_v \end{vmatrix}}, \qquad v_x = -\frac{\begin{vmatrix} F_u & F_x \\ G_u & G_x \end{vmatrix}}{\begin{vmatrix} F_u & F_v \\ G_u & G_v \end{vmatrix}},$$

provided the determinant in the denominator does not vanish. Hence the formulas are valid at each point (x, y, z) at which this determinant is different from zero. Such a determinant is called a **Jacobian determinant** and is denoted by

$$J\left(\frac{F, G}{u, v}\right) \quad \text{or} \quad \frac{\partial(F, G)}{\partial(u, v)} .$$

With this notation, we can write the formulas for u_x and v_x as

$$u_x = - \frac{\partial(F, G)}{\partial(x, v)} \bigg/ \frac{\partial(F, G)}{\partial(u, v)} , \qquad v_x = - \frac{\partial(F, G)}{\partial(u, x)} \bigg/ \frac{\partial(F, G)}{\partial(u, v)}$$

Similarly,

$$u_y = - \frac{\partial(F, G)}{\partial(y, v)} \bigg/ \frac{\partial(F, G)}{\partial(u, v)} , \ldots .$$

As we will see (Section 11.6), the non-vanishing of the Jacobian determinant in the denominator is sufficient to guarantee that there are functions u, v which satisfy the equations $F = 0$, $G = 0$, and the formulas for their partial derivatives are then given as above.

In general, if $F, G, \ldots, K$ are n functions depending on the n variables $u, v, \ldots, z$ (and perhaps other variables as well),

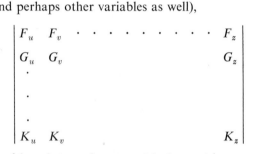

is called a **Jacobian determinant** and is denoted by

$$J\left(\frac{F, G, \ldots, K}{u, v, \ldots, z}\right) \quad \text{or} \quad \frac{\partial(F, G, \ldots, K)}{\partial(u, v, \ldots, z)} .$$

A   EXERCISES

I. Compute the directional derivatives of the following functions in the direction indicated:

(a) $2x^2 - z^2 - y^2$ at $(1, 2, 2)$ toward $(4, 5, 0)$.

(b) $x^2 + y^2 + z^2 + xyz$ at $(1, 0, 1)$ toward $(2, 1, 2)$.

(c) $x^2 + 2xy + y^2$ at $(1, 1, 1)$ in the toward $(1, 5, 2)$.

(d) $x^2 + 3xy + 4y^2$ (as a function of two variables) in the directions making a 60° angle with the positive x-axis.

(e) $x^2 + 4y^2 + e^x \cos y$ at $(0, 0)$ in the directions making a 30° angle with the positive x-axis.

(f) $x^2 + y^2 - 3xy$ at $(1, 2)$ in the direction of the tangent of the curve described by $y = x^3$.

(g) $x^3 + 4xy + z^2 - 2yz$ at $(1, 2, 1)$ in the direction of the tangent of the curve described by $x = t$, $y = 2t^2$, $z = t^3$.

(h) $x^2 - 8xy + z^2$ in the direction of the outer normal of the surface $x^2 + y^2 + z = 17$ at the point $(4, 4, 1)$.

2. Let $\boldsymbol{\beta}$ be any vector, and let $\mathbf{P}(t) = \mathbf{P_0} + \boldsymbol{\beta} \, t$. Compute $\dfrac{d}{dt} f [\mathbf{P}(t)]$, assuming that f is differentiable.

3. Let f be a differentiable function of (u, v), and let g be a function of x, y defined by $g(x, y) = f(x^2 - y^2, 2xy)$. Compute g_x and g_y in terms of f_u and f_v.

4. Let f be a differentiable function of (u, v, w), and let g be a function of (x, y) defined by $g(x, y) = f(x - y, x + y, 2x)$. Compute g_x and g_y in terms of $f_u, f_v,$ and f_w.

5. Let f be a differentiable function of (x, y), and let g be a function of (u, v, w) defined by

$$g(u, v, w) = f(a_{11}u + a_{12}v + a_{13}w, a_{21}u + a_{22}v + a_{23}w).$$

Compute $g_u, g_v,$ and g_w in terms of f_x and f_y.

6. Show that if $\mathbf{F}$, $\mathbf{G}$, and $\mathbf{H}$ are differentiable vector functions, then

(a) $\dfrac{\partial}{\partial x} (\mathbf{F} \cdot \mathbf{G}) = \dfrac{\partial \mathbf{F}}{\partial x} \cdot \mathbf{G} + \mathbf{F} \cdot \dfrac{\partial \mathbf{G}}{\partial x}$

(b) $\dfrac{\partial}{\partial x} (\mathbf{F} \times \mathbf{G}) = \dfrac{\partial \mathbf{F}}{\partial x} \times \mathbf{G} + \mathbf{F} \times \dfrac{\partial \mathbf{G}}{\partial x}$

(c) $\dfrac{\partial}{\partial x} (\mathbf{F} \cdot \mathbf{G} \times \mathbf{H}) = \dfrac{\partial \mathbf{F}}{\partial x} \cdot \mathbf{G} \times \mathbf{H} + \mathbf{F} \cdot \dfrac{\partial \mathbf{G}}{\partial x} \times \mathbf{H} + \mathbf{F} \cdot \mathbf{G} \times \dfrac{\partial \mathbf{H}}{\partial x}$

7. Compute the formula for $\dfrac{\partial^2}{\partial x \, \partial y} \mathbf{F} \cdot \mathbf{G}$.

B   EXERCISES

1. Suppose there are functions u, v, w of x, y which satisfy $F(u, v, w, x, y) = 0$, $G(u, v, w, x, y) = 0$, and $H(u, v, w, x, y) = 0$ in some region of (x, y) space where F, G, and H are differentiable functions in an appropriate region in (u, v, w, x, y) space. Compute the partials of u, v, w with respect to x and y.

2. Let $F, G, \ldots, K$ be n differentiable functions of the $n + m$ variables $(u_1, u_2, \ldots, u_n, v_1, v_2, \ldots, v_m)$, and suppose that $u_1, u_2, \ldots, u_n$ are functions of $(v_1, v_2 \cdots v_m)$ which satisfy the equations $F = 0, G = 0, \ldots, K = 0$. Show formally that

$$\frac{\partial u_j}{\partial v_k} = - \frac{\partial(F, G, \ldots, K)}{\partial(u_1, \ldots, u_{j-1}, v_k, u_{j+1}, \ldots u_n)} \Bigg/ \frac{\partial(F, G, \ldots, K)}{\partial(u_1, u_2, \ldots, u_n)}.$$

3. Let F be a differentiable function of (x, y, z) in a region R. Let C, described by

$$\mathbf{P}(t) = f(t)\mathbf{i} + g(t)\mathbf{j} + h(t)\mathbf{k},$$

be a differentiable curve through R with unit tangent $\mathbf{T}$ at a point $\mathbf{P_0} = \mathbf{P}(t_0)$. Let s represent arc length along the curve. Show that

$$\frac{d}{ds} F[\mathbf{P}(t_0)] = (\mathbf{T} \cdot \nabla) F(\mathbf{P_0}) = \nabla_{\mathbf{T}} F.$$

4. Let u and v be two differentiable functions of (x, y) in a region R which satisfy the Cauchy-Riemann equations $u_x = v_y$, $u_y = -v_x$ at each point in R. Let $\nabla_\alpha f$ be the directional derivative in the direction making an angle α with the positive x-axis. Show

$$\nabla_\alpha u = \nabla_{\alpha + \pi/2}\, v$$

for each point in R and every angle α.

5. Let f be a differentiable function of r, and let $r = \sqrt{x^2 + y^2 + z^2}$. Show that

$$|\nabla f| = \left| \frac{df}{dr} \right|.$$

Explain the geometrical meaning of this.

6. Let f be a differentiable function of (x, y), and let $x = s \cos \alpha - t \sin \alpha$, $y = s \sin \alpha + t \cos \alpha$, where α is a constant. Calculate

$$\left(\frac{\partial f}{\partial s} \right)^2 + \left(\frac{\partial f}{\partial t} \right)^2.$$

7. Let f have continuous second derivatives in a region R and let it assume a maximum at a point $\mathbf{P_0}$ in R. Show that, for every direction α, $(\alpha \cdot \nabla) f = 0$ and $(\alpha \cdot \nabla)^2 f \leqslant 0$ at $\mathbf{P_0}$.

8. Let f and g be differentiable functions. Show that $\nabla(fg) = f\nabla g + g\nabla f$,

$$\nabla \frac{f}{g} = \frac{g\,\nabla f - f\,\nabla g}{g^2}, \text{ if } g \text{ does not vanish.}$$

9. Let f be a differentiable function of one variable. Define g by $g = f(x^2 + y^2 + z^2)$. Compute $\nabla g \cdot \nabla g$.

10. Let f and g be two functions of one variable for which f'' and g'' both exist. Compute all first and second partials of h, defined by $h(x, y) = f[xg(y)]$.

11. Let f be a differentiable function of (x, y, z), and let y, z be differentiable functions of x. Distinguish between $\partial f / \partial x = f_1$ and df/dx.

C EXERCISES

1. We say that $f(\mathbf{P})$ is a **homogeneous function** of degree k if $f(t\mathbf{P}) = t^k f(\mathbf{P})$. In terms of coordinates in three dimensions, this becomes

$$f(tx, ty, tz) = t^k f(x, y, z).$$

Show that if f is a differentiable homogeneous function, then

$$(\mathbf{P} \cdot \nabla) f(\mathbf{P}) = kf(\mathbf{P}) \quad \text{and} \quad (\mathbf{P} \cdot \nabla)^2 f = k(k - 1) f(\mathbf{P}).$$

2. Show that a necessary and sufficient condition that f be a solution of $f_x = f_y$ in a region is that it be a function of the combination $x + y$. That is, there exists a differentiable function g of one variable for which $f(x, y) = g(x + y)$. (*Hint*: Set $u = x + y, v = x - y$.)

3. Show that a necessary and sufficient condition that f be a solution of $f_{xx} = f_{yy}$ in a region is that it be the sum of a function of $x + y$ and a function of $x - y$. That is, there are two functions g and h of a single variable, each having two derivatives, for which $f(x, y) = g(x + y) + h(x - y)$.

4. Show by an example that a function can have directional derivatives in every direction at a point $\mathbf{P}$ yet not be differentiable at $\mathbf{P}$.

5. Let f be continuous in a closed region R. Let f assume a maximum at a point $\mathbf{P}$ on the boundary. Show that $\nabla_{\mathbf{n}} f(\mathbf{P}) \leqslant 0$, where $\mathbf{n}$ is the inner normal if this one-sided derivative exists.

10.5 THE MEAN-VALUE THEOREM AND TAYLOR'S THEOREM FOR SEVERAL VARIABLES

The mean-value theorem for functions of one variable has an analogue for functions of several variables, and consequently there is a form of Taylor's theorem for several variables, since that theorem comes as a consequence of the mean-value theorem. The mean-value theorem follows.

10.5a Theorem. Let f be differentiable in a neighborhood N. Then for any two points $\mathbf{P}$ and $\mathbf{Q}$ in N there is a point $\mathbf{P}_0$ on the segment connecting them for which

$$f(\mathbf{P}) - f(\mathbf{Q}) = \nabla f(\mathbf{P}_0) \cdot (\mathbf{P} - \mathbf{Q}).$$

Proof. Letting $\boldsymbol{\beta} = \mathbf{P} - \mathbf{Q}$ and $\mathbf{P}(t) = \mathbf{Q} + t\boldsymbol{\beta}$, define F as a function of the one variable t by

$$F(t) = f[\mathbf{P}(t)] = f(\mathbf{Q} + t\boldsymbol{\beta}).$$

Clearly F is differentiable, and by the mean-value theorem for one variable we get

$$\frac{F(1) - F(0)}{1 - 0} = F'(t_0) \quad \text{where } 0 < t_0 < 1.$$

But this is just precisely

$$f(\mathbf{P}) - f(\mathbf{Q}) = \nabla f(\mathbf{P}_0) \cdot \boldsymbol{\beta} = \nabla f(\mathbf{P}_0) \cdot (\mathbf{P} - \mathbf{Q}),$$

where $\quad \mathbf{P}_0 = \mathbf{Q} + t_0\boldsymbol{\beta} = \mathbf{Q} + t_0(\mathbf{P} - \mathbf{Q}) = (1 - t_0)\mathbf{Q} + t_0\mathbf{P}.$ ∎

In terms of components in three dimensions, the result of this theorem can be stated thus:

$$f(x, y, z) - f(a, b, c) = f_1(x_0, y_0, z_0)(x - a)$$
$$+ f_2(x_0, y_0, z_0)(y - b) + f_3(x_0, y_0, z_0)(z - c),$$

where (x_0, y_0, z_0) lies somewhere on the segment connecting (a, b, c) and (x, y, z). This means that

$$\frac{x - x_0}{x - a} = \frac{y - y_0}{y - b} = \frac{z - z_0}{z - c},$$

and the common value of these quotients is between 0 and 1.

We get the higher dimensional Taylor theorem as a consequence of Taylor's theorem for functions of one variable.

10.5b   Theorem. Let f and all its partial derivatives up through order n be continuous in a neighborhood N of $\mathbf{Q}$. Then, for $\mathbf{P}$ in N,

$$f(\mathbf{P}) = f(\mathbf{Q}) + ((\mathbf{P} - \mathbf{Q}) \cdot \nabla)f(\mathbf{Q}) + \frac{1}{2!}((\mathbf{P} - \mathbf{Q}) \cdot \nabla)^2 f(\mathbf{Q})$$

$$+ \cdots + \frac{1}{(n-1)!}((\mathbf{P} - \mathbf{Q}) \cdot \nabla)^{n-1}f(\mathbf{Q}) + \frac{1}{n!}((\mathbf{P} - \mathbf{Q}) \cdot \nabla)^n f(\mathbf{P}_0),$$

where $\mathbf{P}_0$ is a point on the segment connecting $\mathbf{P}$ to $\mathbf{Q}$.

Proof. Let $\boldsymbol{\beta} = \mathbf{P} - \mathbf{Q}$, $\mathbf{P}(t) = \mathbf{Q} + t\boldsymbol{\beta}$. We apply the Taylor theorem for functions of one variable to F where F is defined by $F(t) = f[\mathbf{P}(t)]$. This yields

$$F(t) = F(0) + F'(0)t + \frac{1}{2!}F''(0)t^2 + \cdots$$

$$+ \frac{1}{(n-1)!}F^{(n-1)}(0)t^{n-1} + \frac{1}{n!}F^{(n)}(t_0)t^n.$$

Setting $t = 1$, we get exactly the Taylor formula of the theorem. ∎

In order to fully understand the meaning of the formula, write it out for different cases. For example, in two dimensions, if we set $\mathbf{Q} = (a, b)$ and $\mathbf{P} = (x, y)$, we get

$$f(x, y) = f(a, b) + \left((x - a)\frac{\partial}{\partial x} + (y - b)\frac{\partial}{\partial y}\right)f(a, b)$$

$$+ \frac{1}{2!}\left((x - a)\frac{\partial}{\partial x} + (y - b)\frac{\partial}{\partial y}\right)^2 f(a, b)$$

$$+ \frac{1}{3!}\left((x - a)\frac{\partial}{\partial x} + (y - b)\frac{\partial}{\partial y}\right)^3 f(a, b)$$

$$+ \cdots + \frac{1}{n!}\left((x - a)\frac{\partial}{\partial x} + (y - b)\frac{\partial}{\partial y}\right)^n f(x_0, y_0) + \cdots$$

Expanding, we get

$$f(x, y) = f(a, b) + (x - a)\frac{\partial f}{\partial x}(a, b) + (y - b)\frac{\partial f}{\partial y}(a, b)$$

$$+ \frac{1}{2!}\left[(x - a)^2 \frac{\partial^2 f(a, b)}{\partial x^2} + 2(x - a)(y - b)\frac{\partial^2 f(a, b)}{\partial x\,\partial y}\right.$$

$$\left. + (y - b)^2 \frac{\partial^2 f(a, b)}{\partial y^2}\right]$$

$$+ \frac{1}{3!}\left[(x - a)^3 \frac{\partial^3 f(a, b)}{\partial x^3} + 3(x - a)^2(y - b)\frac{\partial^3 f(a, b)}{\partial x^2\,\partial y}\right.$$

$$\left. + 3(x - a)(y - b)^2 \frac{\partial^3 f(a, b)}{\partial x\,\partial y^2} + (y - b)^3 \frac{\partial^3 f(a, b)}{\partial y^3}\right]$$

$$+ \frac{1}{4!}\left[\cdot \quad \cdot \quad \cdot \quad \cdot \quad \cdot \quad \cdot \quad \cdot \quad \cdot \quad \cdot \quad \cdot \quad \cdot \quad \cdot \quad \cdot\right]$$

$$+ \cdot \quad \cdot \quad \cdot \quad \cdot \quad \cdot \quad \cdot \quad \cdot \quad \cdot \quad \cdot \quad \cdot \quad \cdot \quad \cdot \quad \cdot \quad \cdot \quad \cdot \quad \cdot\,.$$

Write out the first few terms of the expansion for the case of three and four variables. For simplicity, take $\mathbf{Q} = \mathbf{O}$.

10.6 THE DIVERGENCE AND CURL OF A VECTOR FIELD

Let f, g, h be three functions defined on a domain D in three-dimensional space. At any point $\mathbf{P}$ in D, the three numbers $f(\mathbf{P})$, $g(\mathbf{P})$, $h(\mathbf{P})$ can be taken as the components of a vector. If we denote this vector by $\mathbf{Q}$, we have then

$$\mathbf{Q} = \mathbf{F}(\mathbf{P}) = f(\mathbf{P})\mathbf{i} + g(\mathbf{P})\mathbf{j} + h(\mathbf{P})\mathbf{k},$$

a vector function on D. A vector function is frequently called a **vector field**. Geometrically, we usually visualize it as a vector $\mathbf{Q}$ with its base at the point $\mathbf{P}$.

EXAMPLE 1. Newton's law of gravitation asserts that two particles attract each other with a force which is proportional to the product of their masses and inversely proportional to the square of the distance between them. We want to express this relationship in the form of a vector function.

Solution. First, let us note that implicitly the word "attract" means that the force on particle B due to the gravitation of A is along the segment connecting A and B, and that it points from B to A.

Now let us take one of the point masses, say A as origin, and write the force acting on B as a function of the position $\mathbf{P}$ of B. The magnitude of the force must be

$$|\mathbf{F}| = k \frac{mM}{|\mathbf{P}|^2},$$

where k is a constant of proportionality. All that remains is to point it in the right direction—that is, to multiply it by a unit vector in the right direction. The unit vector should point in the opposite direction from $\mathbf{P}$. This would then be $-\mathbf{P}/|\mathbf{P}|$, so we get

$$\mathbf{F} = -\frac{kmM\mathbf{P}}{|\mathbf{P}|^3}.$$

We now want to introduce two new concepts, namely the divergence and curl of differentiable vector fields. If $\mathbf{F} = f\mathbf{i} + g\mathbf{j} + h\mathbf{k}$ is a differentiable vector field, the scalar function

$$\frac{\partial f}{\partial x} + \frac{\partial g}{\partial y} + \frac{\partial h}{\partial z}$$

is called the **divergence** of $\mathbf{F}$. It is denoted by div $\mathbf{F}$. Clearly, it can be expressed in terms of the operator $\boldsymbol{\nabla}$: div $\mathbf{F} = \boldsymbol{\nabla} \cdot \mathbf{F}$. We can see this as follows:

$$\boldsymbol{\nabla} \cdot \mathbf{F} = \left(\frac{\partial}{\partial x}\mathbf{i} + \frac{\partial}{\partial y}\mathbf{j} + \frac{\partial}{\partial z}\mathbf{k} \right) \cdot (f\mathbf{i} + g\mathbf{j} + h\mathbf{k})$$

$$= \left(\frac{\partial}{\partial x}\right)f + \left(\frac{\partial}{\partial y}\right)g + \left(\frac{\partial}{\partial z}\right)h = \frac{\partial f}{\partial x} + \frac{\partial g}{\partial y} + \frac{\partial h}{\partial z}$$

$$= \text{div } \mathbf{F}.$$

EXAMPLE 2. Compute the divergence of the gradient of a scalar function with two continuous derivatives.

Solution:

$$\mathbf{grad} \, f = \boldsymbol{\nabla} f = \frac{\partial f}{\partial x}\mathbf{i} + \frac{\partial f}{\partial y}\mathbf{j} + \frac{\partial f}{\partial z}\mathbf{k}$$

$$\text{div } \mathbf{grad} \, f = \boldsymbol{\nabla} \cdot \boldsymbol{\nabla} f = \frac{\partial^2 f}{\partial x^2} + \frac{\partial^2 f}{\partial y^2} + \frac{\partial^2 f}{\partial z^2}.$$

In many applications, one deals with so-called **solenoidal** vector fields. These are fields for which the divergence is zero.

EXAMPLE 3. Show that the force field

$$\mathbf{F} = -k\frac{Mm\mathbf{P}}{|\mathbf{P}|^3}$$

constructed in Example 1 is solenoidal.

Solution. Denote $|\mathbf{P}|$ by $r = \sqrt{x^2 + y^2 + z^2}$. Then

$$\mathbf{F} = -kMm\left[\frac{x}{r^3}\mathbf{i} + \frac{y}{r^3}\mathbf{j} + \frac{z}{r^3}\mathbf{k}\right]$$

$$\boldsymbol{\nabla} \cdot \mathbf{F} = -kMm\left[\frac{\partial}{\partial x}\left(\frac{x}{r^3}\right) + \frac{\partial}{\partial y}\left(\frac{y}{r^3}\right) + \frac{\partial}{\partial z}\left(\frac{z}{r^3}\right)\right].$$

Now

$$\frac{\partial}{\partial x}\left(\frac{x}{r^3}\right) = \frac{1}{r^3} - \frac{3x}{r^4}\frac{\partial r}{\partial x}$$

But

$$r^2 = x^2 + y^2 + z^2$$

so

$$2r\frac{\partial r}{\partial x} = 2x$$

or

$$\frac{\partial r}{\partial x} = \frac{x}{r}$$

Then

$$\frac{\partial}{\partial x}\left(\frac{x}{r^3}\right) = \frac{1}{r^3} - \frac{3x^2}{r^5}$$

By symmetry,

$$\frac{\partial}{\partial y}\left(\frac{y}{r^3}\right) = \frac{1}{r^3} - \frac{3y^2}{r^5}$$

and

$$\frac{\partial}{\partial z}\left(\frac{z}{r^3}\right) = \frac{1}{r^3} - \frac{3z^2}{r^5}$$

Adding, we get

$$\boldsymbol{\nabla} \cdot \mathbf{F} = -kMm\left[\frac{3}{r^3} - \frac{3(x^2 + y^2 + z^2)}{r^5}\right]$$

$$= -kMm\left[\frac{3}{r^3} - \frac{3r^2}{r^5}\right] = 0.$$

The divergence is expressed in terms of the formal inner product of the operator $\boldsymbol{\nabla}$ with $\mathbf{F}$. This suggests that we might also consider the formal cross product of $\boldsymbol{\nabla}$ and $\mathbf{F}$. The result of this is called the **curl** of $\mathbf{F}$.

$$\text{curl } \mathbf{F} = \boldsymbol{\nabla} \times \mathbf{F} = \begin{vmatrix} \mathbf{i} & \mathbf{j} & \mathbf{k} \\ \dfrac{\partial}{\partial x} & \dfrac{\partial}{\partial y} & \dfrac{\partial}{\partial z} \\ f & g & h \end{vmatrix}$$

$$= \mathbf{i}\left(\frac{\partial h}{\partial y} - \frac{\partial g}{\partial z}\right) + \mathbf{j}\left(\frac{\partial f}{\partial z} - \frac{\partial h}{\partial x}\right) + \mathbf{k}\left(\frac{\partial g}{\partial x} - \frac{\partial f}{\partial y}\right).$$

This last line can be taken as the correct definition of **curl F**, and the other expressions may be taken as being themselves defined by the last line.

EXAMPLE 4. Compute **curl F** when

$$\mathbf{F} = (x^2 + y^2)\mathbf{i} + (3xz - 5z^2y)\mathbf{j} + (x^2 - 2z)\mathbf{k}.$$

Solution:

$$\nabla \times \mathbf{F} = \begin{vmatrix} \mathbf{i} & \mathbf{j} & \mathbf{k} \\ \dfrac{\partial}{\partial x} & \dfrac{\partial}{\partial y} & \dfrac{\partial}{\partial z} \\ x^2 + y^2 & 3xz - 5z^2y & x^2 - 2z \end{vmatrix}$$

$$= \mathbf{i}(-3x + 10zy) + \mathbf{j}(-2x) + \mathbf{k}(3z - 2y)$$

$$= (10zy - 3x)\mathbf{i} - 2x\mathbf{j} + (3z - 2y)\mathbf{k}.$$

10.6a   Theorem. Suppose f is a function with continuous second derivatives in a region R. Then

$$\text{curl grad } f = \mathbf{O} \qquad \text{in } R.$$

Proof. $\text{grad } f = \nabla f = \mathbf{i}f_x + \mathbf{j}f_y + \mathbf{k}f_z,$

and $\text{curl grad } f = \nabla \times \nabla f$

$$= \begin{vmatrix} \mathbf{i} & \mathbf{j} & \mathbf{k} \\ \dfrac{\partial}{\partial x} & \dfrac{\partial}{\partial y} & \dfrac{\partial}{\partial z} \\ f_x & f_y & f_z \end{vmatrix}$$

$$= \mathbf{i}(f_{zy} - f_{yz}) + \mathbf{j}(f_{xz} - f_{zx}) + \mathbf{k}(f_{yx} - f_{xy}) = \mathbf{O}.$$

It is reasonable now to inquire if this theorem represents the only circumstance under which the curl of a vector can vanish. The answer is effectively "yes", and the details will be given in the appropriate place.

These two vector differentiation operations of div and **curl**, represented symbolically by $\nabla \cdot$ and $\nabla \times$, have important physical interpretations and equally important applications in the theory of multiple integrals, as we shall see.

A EXERCISES

1. Write out Taylor's formula for the following functions, as indicated:

    (a) $\sin x \sin y$ about $(0, 0)$ to 3 terms
    (b) $\sin x \sin y$ about $(\pi, 0)$ to 3 terms
    (c) $x^2 + x^3y + xy + x^2y^2$ about $(1, 2)$ to 17 terms
    (d) $e^{x \cos y}$ about $(1, 0)$ to 4 terms

(e) $\cos(e^x + y^2 + \log z)$ about $(0, 0, 1)$ to 2 terms
(f) $\log(x \cos y)$ about $(1, 0)$ to 3 terms
(g) $1/xy$ about $(1, 1)$ to 4 terms
(h) $1/(1 - x - y)$ about $(0, 0)$ to 15 terms
(i) $1/(x + y + z)$ about $(1, 0, 0)$ to 13 terms

2. Compute div $\mathbf{F}$ and **curl** $\mathbf{F}$ for each of the following vector fields. Which are solenoidal?

(a) $\mathbf{F} = \mathbf{P} = x\mathbf{i} + y\mathbf{j} + z\mathbf{k}$ (b) $\mathbf{F} = \mathbf{P}/|\mathbf{P}|^2$
(c) $\mathbf{F} = f(x)\mathbf{i} + g(y)\mathbf{j} + h(z)\mathbf{k}$ (d) $\mathbf{F} = 3xz\mathbf{i} + 5y^2x^3\mathbf{j} + (7z^4 + 5y^2)\mathbf{k}$

3. Compute formulas for the following:

(a) $\nabla \cdot \nabla(fg)$ (b) $\nabla \cdot (f\mathbf{F})$ (c) $\nabla \cdot (\mathbf{F} + \mathbf{G})$
(d) $\nabla \times (\mathbf{F} \times \mathbf{G})$ (e) $\nabla \times (f\mathbf{F})$ (f) $\nabla \times \mathbf{P}$
(g) $\nabla \times (\nabla \times \mathbf{F})$

4. Let f, g, h be differentiable functions of x, y, z. Show that

$$\frac{\partial(f, g, h)}{\partial(x, y, z)} = \nabla f \cdot \nabla g \times \nabla h.$$

What does this suggest about the geometrical significance of the Jacobian?

B EXERCISES

1. Let $\mathbf{F} = (6xy + 3x^2y^2z)\mathbf{i} + (3x^2 + 2x^3yz + 2z^4y)\mathbf{j} + (x^3y^2 + 4z^3y^2)\mathbf{k}$. Verify that **curl** $\mathbf{F} = \mathbf{O}$. Find all functions f such that $\mathbf{F} = \mathbf{grad}\, f$.

2. Let f be a differentiable function in a neighborhood N, and suppose that all first derivatives of f are identically zero in N. Show that f is constant in N.

3. Suppose in Exercise B2 that N is replaced by a general region R. Show that f is constant in R.

C EXERCISES

1. Let f be a twice continuously differentiable function in a region R. Suppose there is a point $\mathbf{P}_0$ in R for which $(\boldsymbol{\alpha} \cdot \nabla) f(\mathbf{P}_0) = 0$ and $(\boldsymbol{\alpha} \cdot \nabla)^2 f(\mathbf{P}_0) < 0$ for every direction $\boldsymbol{\alpha}$. Show then that f achieves a local maximum at $\mathbf{P}_0$—that is, there is a neighborhood N of $\mathbf{P}_0$ in which $f(\mathbf{P}) < f(\mathbf{P}_0)$ for all $\mathbf{P} \neq \mathbf{P}_0$ in the neighborhood N.

11

Transformations and Implicit Functions. Extreme Values

II.I   TRANSFORMATIONS.   INVERSE TRANSFORMATIONS

Let $\mathbf{F}$ be a vector-valued function defined on a domain D in a Euclidean vector space of n dimensions with range R in a Euclidean vector space of m dimensions.   Such a function is called a **mapping** or **transformation**, which maps or transforms D into R.   This means that for each $\mathbf{Q}$ in D there is a unique $\mathbf{P}$ in R for which

$$\mathbf{P} = \mathbf{F(Q)}.$$

Let $\mathbf{G}$ be a function whose domain is R and whose range is D.   This means that for each $\mathbf{P}$ in R there is a $\mathbf{Q}$ in D such that

$$\mathbf{Q} = \mathbf{G(P)}.$$

Suppose that $\mathbf{G}$ is related to $\mathbf{F}$ in such a way that, whenever $\mathbf{F}$ maps $\mathbf{Q_0}$

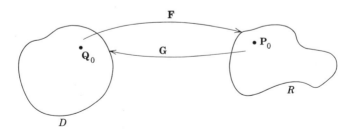

into P_0, G maps P_0 back into Q_0. Then G is called the **inverse mapping** or **inverse transformation** of F.

11.1a Theorem. A necessary and sufficient condition that a transformation F have an inverse is that no two points in D have the same image in R under the transformation F. That is, $F(Q_0) = P_0$ and $F(Q_1) = P_0$ implies that $Q_0 = Q_1$.

Proof. For each P in R, define $G(P)$ to be that point Q in D for which $P = F(Q)$. ∎

In terms of components, if $Q = (q_1, q_2, \ldots, q_n)$ and $P = (p_1, p_2, \ldots, p_m)$, then $P = F(Q)$ becomes

$$p_1 = f_1(q_1, q_2, \ldots, q_n)$$
$$p_2 = f_2(q_1, q_2, \ldots, q_n)$$
$$\cdot$$
$$\cdot$$
$$\cdot$$
$$p_m = f_m(q_1, q_2, \ldots, q_n).$$

To seek an inverse transformation means that, given any $P = (p_1, p_2, \ldots, p_m)$ in R, we seek to solve the above equations uniquely for the q's:

$$q_1 = g_1(p_1, p_2, \ldots, p_m)$$
$$q_2 = g_2(p_1, p_2, \ldots, p_m)$$
$$\cdot$$
$$\cdot$$
$$\cdot$$
$$q_n = g_n(p_1, p_2, \ldots, p_m).$$

11.2 LINEAR TRANSFORMATIONS

A **linear transformation** L is one which is given by a set of linear equations:

(1)
$$\left\{ \begin{array}{l} p_1 = a_{11}q_1 + a_{12}q_2 + \cdots + a_{1n}q_n \\ p_2 = a_{21}q_1 + a_{22}q_2 + \cdots + a_{2n}q_n \\ \cdot \\ \cdot \\ \cdot \\ p_m = a_{m1}q_1 + a_{m2}q_2 + \cdots + a_{mn}q_n. \end{array} \right.$$

In fact this describes a linear transformation from E_n, where the point $\mathbf{Q}$ has been denoted by $(q_1, q_2, \ldots, q_n)$ to E_m, where $\mathbf{P}$ has been denoted by $(p_1, p_2, \ldots, p_m)$.

11.2a   Theorem. If $\mathbf{L}$ is a linear transformation, then

$$\mathbf{L}(\mathbf{Q} + \mathbf{Q'}) = \mathbf{L}(\mathbf{Q}) + \mathbf{L}(\mathbf{Q'})$$
$$\mathbf{L}(a\mathbf{Q}) = a\mathbf{L}(\mathbf{Q}).$$

Proof. To prove the second equation, simply note that if in (1) each q is replaced by aq, the a factors out of the right-hand side of each equation.

To prove the first, observe that replacing each q by $q + q'$ enables us to separate the right side of each equation in (1) into the sum of two parts, namely the right side evaluated for the q's plus the right side evaluated for the q''s. ∎

An $m \times n$ **matrix** is a rectangular array of numbers having m rows and n columns:

$$\begin{pmatrix} a_{11} & a_{12} & \cdots & a_{1n} \\ a_{21} & a_{22} & \cdots & a_{2n} \\ \cdot & & & \\ \cdot & & & \\ \cdot & & & \\ a_{m1} & a_{m2} & \cdots & a_{mn} \end{pmatrix},$$

It is sometimes convenient to think of each row as being composed of the components of an n-vector, called a **row vector**, and each column as being composed of the components of an m-vector, called a **column vector**.

We see immediately that there is an intimate connection between matrices and linear transformations, since the jth-row vector is composed of the coefficients of the q's in the expression for p_j in (1). In fact this expression for p_j is precisely the scalar product of this row vector with $\mathbf{Q}$. To express this in standard matrix notation, we write $\mathbf{Q}$ as a column vector just to the right of the matrix:

(2)

$$\begin{pmatrix} a_{11} & a_{12} & \cdots & a_{1n} \\ a_{21} & a_{22} & \cdots & a_{2n} \\ \cdot & & & \\ \cdot & & & \\ \cdot & & & \\ a_{m1} & a_{m2} & \cdots & a_{mn} \end{pmatrix} \begin{pmatrix} q_1 \\ q_2 \\ \cdot \\ \cdot \\ \cdot \\ q_n \end{pmatrix}$$

Now we say that an $m \times n$ matrix acting on a column n-vector, symbolized by (2), produces a column m-vector according to the formula

$$\begin{pmatrix} a_{11} & a_{12} & \cdots & a_{1n} \\ a_{21} & a_{22} & \cdots & a_{2n} \\ \vdots & & & \\ a_{m1} & a_{m2} & \cdots & a_{mn} \end{pmatrix} \begin{pmatrix} q_1 \\ q_2 \\ \vdots \\ q_n \end{pmatrix} = \begin{pmatrix} a_{11}q_1 + a_{12}q_2 + \cdots + a_{1n}q_n \\ a_{21}q_1 + a_{22}q_2 + \cdots + a_{2n}q_n \\ \vdots \\ a_{m1}q_1 + a_{m2}q_2 + \cdots + a_{mn}q_n \end{pmatrix},$$

where the jth element of the resulting vector is the dot product of the jth-row vector with $\mathbf{Q}$. Thus the equations (1) in terms of components can be written in matrix notation as

$$\begin{pmatrix} p_1 \\ p_2 \\ \vdots \\ p_m \end{pmatrix} = \begin{pmatrix} a_{11} & a_{12} & \cdots & a_{1n} \\ a_{21} & a_{22} & \cdots & a_{2n} \\ \vdots & & & \\ a_{m1} & a_{m2} & \cdots & a_{mn} \end{pmatrix} \begin{pmatrix} q_1 \\ q_2 \\ \vdots \\ q_n \end{pmatrix}.$$

For example, the equations

$$y_1 = a_{11}x_1 + a_{12}x_2$$
$$y_2 = a_{21}x_1 + a_{22}x_2$$
$$y_3 = a_{31}x_1 + a_{31}x_2$$

become, in matrix notation,

$$\begin{pmatrix} y_1 \\ y_2 \\ y_3 \end{pmatrix} = \begin{pmatrix} a_{11} & a_{12} \\ a_{21} & a_{22} \\ a_{31} & a_{32} \end{pmatrix} \begin{pmatrix} x_1 \\ x_2 \end{pmatrix}.$$

Clearly, any linear transformation gives rise to a matrix, namely its coefficient matrix, and conversely any matrix may serve as the coefficient matrix of a linear transformation. This gives a natural one-to-one correspondence between linear transformations and matrices. Thus we may speak of a linear transformation being given by a matrix, or we say that a matrix is a linear transformation.

From now on we will restrict ourselves to linear transformations from E_n to E_n, or, in matrix terminology, to $n \times n$ matrices. When we use the term "matrix" it will mean an $n \times n$ matrix, and all linear transformations without further qualification will be from E_n to E_n.

It is clear that any linear transformation has all of E_n for its domain, since the right side of (1) makes sense for all $\mathbf{Q}$. We want now to inquire about the range.

11.2b   Theorem. A necessary and sufficient condition that the linear transformation $\mathbf{L}$ (from E_n to E_n) have an inverse defined over all E_n is that the determinant of the coefficients be not zero. In this case the inverse is also a linear transformation, and the determinant of its coefficients is the reciprocal of the determinant of $\mathbf{L}$.

We will not prove this theorem, which we assume you know from algebra (although perhaps in different terms), but instead will make a few comments about it: In coordinate terms in three dimensions, it says that to be able to solve uniquely

$$u = a_{11}x + a_{12}y + a_{13}z$$
$$v = a_{21}x + a_{22}y + a_{23}z$$
$$w = a_{31}x + a_{32}y + a_{33}z,$$

no matter what u, v, and w are, it is necessary and sufficient that the determinant of the a's should not be zero. The solution is then given by Cramer's rule

$$x = \begin{vmatrix} u & a_{12} & a_{13} \\ v & a_{22} & a_{23} \\ w & a_{32} & a_{33} \end{vmatrix} \bigg/ \begin{vmatrix} a_{11} & a_{12} & a_{13} \\ a_{21} & a_{22} & a_{23} \\ a_{31} & a_{32} & a_{33} \end{vmatrix}$$

$$y = \text{etc.,}$$

from which it is clear that the inverse is again a linear transformation. From this, it is not a difficult calculation to show that the determinants are reciprocals.

A linear transformation, or its matrix, is said to be **singular** if its determinant vanishes. Otherwise it is **non-singular**. Theorem 11.2a states that the range of a non-singular linear transformation is E_n. Although we will not pursue the matter, one can show that the range of a singular linear transformation is a linear sub-space which can be interpreted as a plane, or hyperplane, or a line.

11.2c   Corollary. If $\mathbf{L}$ is a non-singular linear transformation, it maps no non-zero vector $\mathbf{Q}$ into $\mathbf{O}$.

Proof. If it did map a non-zero vector $\mathbf{Q}$ into $\mathbf{O}$, we would have both

$$\mathbf{L(Q)} = \mathbf{O}$$

and

$$\mathbf{L(O)} = \mathbf{O}.$$

Then, by Theorem 11.1a,

$$\mathbf{Q} = \mathbf{O}.$$ ∎

11.2d Corollary. If **L** is a non-singular linear transformation and **P** is any non-zero vector, then there is a unit vector α such that $\mathbf{L}(\alpha)$ is a positive scalar multiple of **P**.

Proof. Let **Q** be the solution of $\mathbf{P} = \mathbf{L}(\mathbf{Q})$. Setting $\alpha = \mathbf{Q}/|\mathbf{Q}|$, we compute

$$\mathbf{L}(\alpha) = \mathbf{L}(\mathbf{Q}/|\mathbf{Q}|) = (1/|\mathbf{Q}|)\mathbf{L}(\mathbf{Q}) = (1/|\mathbf{Q}|)\mathbf{P}. \qquad \blacksquare$$

11.2e Theorem. Let **L** be a non-singular linear transformation. Then there are points $\mathbf{Q}_0$ and $\mathbf{Q}_1$ on $\{|\mathbf{Q}| = 1\}$ such that

$$0 < |\mathbf{L}(\mathbf{Q}_0)| \leqslant |\mathbf{L}(\mathbf{Q})| \leqslant |\mathbf{L}(\mathbf{Q}_1)| \qquad \text{for all } \mathbf{Q} \text{ on } \{|\mathbf{Q}| = 1\}.$$

Proof. $|\mathbf{L}(\mathbf{Q})|$ is a continuous positive function on a closed bounded set. The positivity follows immediately from Corollary 11.2d. The continuity we leave as an exercise (B1). Thus $|\mathbf{L}(\mathbf{Q})|$ assumes its supremum and infimum on $\{|\mathbf{Q}| = 1\}$. $\qquad \blacksquare$

The numbers $|\mathbf{L}(\mathbf{Q}_0)|$ and $|\mathbf{L}(\mathbf{Q}_1)|$ will be denoted by m and M respectively, with a subscript **L** when necessary. Geometrically, these numbers represent the lengths of the shortest and longest (respectively) vectors which arise as images of vectors on $\{|\mathbf{Q}| = 1\}$ under the transformation **L**.

11.2f Corollary. For any non-singular linear transformation **L**, we have for every **Q** in E_n,

$$m|\mathbf{Q}| \leqslant |\mathbf{L}(\mathbf{Q})| \leqslant M|\mathbf{Q}|.$$

Proof. Letting $\alpha = \mathbf{Q}/|\mathbf{Q}|$, apply Theorem 11.2e and multiply by $|\mathbf{Q}|$. $\qquad \blacksquare$

If each element a_{ij} of a matrix is a function of a parameter, then the linear transformation defined by that matrix depends on the parameter. If each a_{ij} is a continuous function of the parameter, we would expect the transformation to depend continuously in some sense on the parameter. In the form in which we need this result, the parameter is itself a point in a Euclidean vector space. If **T** is the parameter, we will denote the transformation by $\mathbf{L}(\mathbf{T}, \mathbf{Q})$, where **Q** is the vector being transformed.

11.2g Theorem. Let $\mathbf{L}(\mathbf{T}, \mathbf{Q})$ be a linear transformation whose coefficients depend continuously on **T** in a neighborhood of $\mathbf{T}_0$, and let $\mathbf{L}(\mathbf{T}_0, \mathbf{Q})$ be non-singular. Then there is an $\epsilon > 0$ such that

$$|\mathbf{L}(\mathbf{T}, \mathbf{Q}) - \mathbf{L}(\mathbf{T}_0, \mathbf{Q})| \leqslant \tfrac{1}{2}|\mathbf{L}(\mathbf{T}_0, \mathbf{Q})|$$

for every **Q**, and for $|\mathbf{T} - \mathbf{T}_0| < \epsilon$.

Proof. (For two dimensions.) Let **L** be given by

$$\mathbf{U} = \mathbf{L}(\mathbf{T}, \mathbf{Q}) \qquad \text{where } \mathbf{U} = (u, v), \, \mathbf{Q} = (x, y).$$

Then **L** is given in coordinates by

$$u(\mathbf{T}) = a_{11}(\mathbf{T})x + a_{12}(\mathbf{T})y$$
$$v(\mathbf{T}) = a_{21}(\mathbf{T})x + a_{22}(\mathbf{T})y.$$

Then $|\mathbf{L}(\mathbf{T}, \mathbf{Q}) - \mathbf{L}(\mathbf{T}_0, \mathbf{Q})| = \sqrt{[u(\mathbf{T}) - u(\mathbf{T}_0)]^2 + [v(\mathbf{T}) - v(\mathbf{T}_0)]^2}.$

Now let $\qquad m = \min_{|\mathbf{Q}| = 1} |\mathbf{L}(\mathbf{T}_0, \mathbf{Q})| > 0.$

We then have

$$|u(\mathbf{T}) - u(\mathbf{T}_0)| \leqslant |a_{11}(\mathbf{T}) - a_{11}(\mathbf{T}_0)|\,|x| + |a_{12}(\mathbf{T}) - a_{12}(\mathbf{T}_0)|\,|y|.$$

Since the a's are continuous in **T**, there is an ϵ_1 such that $|\mathbf{T} - \mathbf{T}_0| < \epsilon_1$ insures that

$$|a_{11}(\mathbf{T}) - a_{11}(\mathbf{T}_0)| < \frac{m}{4\sqrt{2}}$$

and $\qquad\qquad |a_{12}(\mathbf{T}) - a_{12}(\mathbf{T}_0)| < \frac{m}{4\sqrt{2}}\,.$

Then, since $|x| \leqslant |\mathbf{Q}|$ and $|y| \leqslant |\mathbf{Q}|$,

$$|u(\mathbf{T}) - u(\mathbf{T}_0)| < m|\mathbf{Q}|/2\sqrt{2}.$$

Similarly, there is an ϵ_2 such that $|\mathbf{T} - \mathbf{T}_0| < \epsilon_2$ insures that

$$|v(\mathbf{T}) - v(\mathbf{T}_0)| < m|\mathbf{Q}|/2\sqrt{2}.$$

Thus if $\epsilon = \min(\epsilon_1, \epsilon_2)$ and $|\mathbf{T} - \mathbf{T}_0| < \epsilon$,

$$|\mathbf{L}(\mathbf{T}, \mathbf{Q}) - \mathbf{L}(\mathbf{T}_0, \mathbf{Q})| \leqslant \sqrt{(m|\mathbf{Q}|/2\sqrt{2})^2 + (m|\mathbf{Q}|/2\sqrt{2})^2}$$
$$= m|\mathbf{Q}|/2 \leqslant \tfrac{1}{2}|\mathbf{L}(\mathbf{T}_0, \mathbf{Q})|. \qquad\blacksquare$$

A   EXERCISES

I. Let a linear transformation **L** be given by the matrix

$$\begin{pmatrix} 1 & 2 & 1 \\ 3 & 5 & 1 \\ 4 & 2 & -1 \end{pmatrix}.$$

Find the result of applying **L** to:

(a) $(1, 0, 0)$ $\qquad\qquad$ (b) $(0, 1, 0)$ $\qquad\qquad$ (c) $(0, 0, 1)$

2. Let **L** be the transformation given in $A1$. Show that any plane is carried into a plane, and any line is carried into a line.

3. How do you know that **L** in $A1$ does not map E_3 into a plane?

B EXERCISES

1. Let **L** be a linear transformation. Show that $|\mathbf{L(Q)}|$ is a continuous function of **Q**, and thus complete the proof of Theorem 11.2e.

2. Apply Theorem 11.2f and conclude that $\mathbf{L(Q)}$ is uniformly continuous over all of E_n.

3. Find a linear transformation from E_3 to E_3 with $\mathbf{L(i)} = 5\mathbf{i} + 2\mathbf{j}$, $\mathbf{L(j)} = 2\mathbf{i} + 3\mathbf{j} - 4\mathbf{k}$, and $\mathbf{L(k)} = 3\mathbf{j} + 4\mathbf{k}$. Is there another one?

4. Describe geometrically the transformation given by the matrix

$$\begin{pmatrix} \frac{1}{2}\sqrt{3} & \frac{1}{2} \\ -\frac{1}{2} & \frac{1}{2}\sqrt{3} \end{pmatrix}.$$

5. Let **L** be a linear transformation from E_n to E_m, and **M** be a linear transformation from E_m to E_s; and let **T** be the transformation from E_n to E_s defined by $\mathbf{T(Q)} = \mathbf{M[L(Q)]}$, where **Q** is in E_n. Show that **T** is linear, and compute its matrix elements c_{ij} from those of **L** and **M**, denoted by a_{ij} and b_{ij} respectively. The matrix of c's defines the **product** of the matrices of **L** and **M**.

6. Show that the orientation of a triple of vectors is preserved or reversed by a non-singular linear transformation according as the sign of its determinant is $+$ or $-$, and the volume of the rectangular parallelpiped determined by the triple is multiplied by the magnitude of the determinant.

7. Let **L** be a linear transformation which maps E_2 into E_3. Show that the image of E_2 is in general a plane in E_3, but may be a line or a point.

8. Let **L** be a non-singular linear transformation mapping E_n into E_n, and let $(\mathbf{e}_1, \mathbf{e}_2, \ldots, \mathbf{e}_n)$ be any basis. Show that $\mathbf{L(e_1)}, \mathbf{L(e_2)}, \ldots, \mathbf{L(e_n)}$ is also a basis.

C EXERCISES

1. Let $f(\mathbf{Q})$ be a real-valued function of **Q** on E_n with the properties
(a) $f(\mathbf{Q}_1 + \mathbf{Q'}) = f(\mathbf{Q}_1) + f(\mathbf{Q'})$ and   (b) $f(a\mathbf{Q}) = af(\mathbf{Q})$.
Show that there is a fixed vector **A** such that $f(\mathbf{Q}) = \mathbf{A \cdot Q}$. (*Hint:* Express **Q** in terms of basis vectors $\mathbf{Q} = q_1\mathbf{e}_1 + q_2\mathbf{e}_2 + \cdots + q_n\mathbf{e}_n$.)

2. Use Exercise 1 to show that if a transformation **T** satisfies $\mathbf{T(Q + Q')} = \mathbf{T(Q)} + \mathbf{T(Q')}$ and $\mathbf{T}(a\mathbf{Q}) = a\mathbf{T(Q)}$, it is a linear transformation.

3. Let **L** be a linear transformation from E_n to E_m. Show that there is an M such that $|\mathbf{L(Q)}| \leq M|\mathbf{Q}|$, and further that $M \leq \sqrt{\sum_{i,j} a_{ij}^2}$ where the a_{ij} are the elements of the coefficient matrix of **L**.

4. Let **L** be a linear transformation of E_3 into E_3 having **rank** 2. This means that determinant of **L** is 0, but one of the 2×2 subdeterminants formed by removing a row and a column (that is one of the 2×2 minors) is not zero. Show that **L** maps E_3 onto a plane.

5. Show that if all 2×2 minors are zero (that is, if $\mathbf{L}$ has rank 1), but not all entries are zero, then $\mathbf{L}$ maps E_3 onto a line.

11.3   THE INVERSION THEOREM

Let $\mathbf{F}$ be a differentiable transformation from a domain D in E_n to a range R in E_n. For example, if $n = 3$, the components of $\mathbf{F}$ would be given by

(1)
$$\begin{cases} u = f(x, y, z) \\ v = g(x, y, z) \\ w = h(x, y, z). \end{cases}$$

Suppose further that there is a point $\mathbf{Q} = (a, b, c)$ at which $A = f(a, b, c)$, $B = g(a, b, c)$, and $C = h(a, b, c)$. We want to inquire into the existence of an inverse transformation in a neighborhood of $\mathbf{P} = (A, B, C)$ in the space of (u, v, w).

Let $\mathbf{P} + d\mathbf{P} = (A + du, B + dv, C + dw)$ be a near-by point. Then, if there is an inverse function defined in a neighborhood of $\mathbf{P}$, there must be a unique $d\mathbf{Q} = (dx, dy, dz)$ such that $\mathbf{P} + d\mathbf{P} = \mathbf{F}(\mathbf{Q} + d\mathbf{Q})$; that is,

(2)
$$\begin{cases} A + du = f(a + dx, b + dy, c + dz) \\ B + dv = g(a + dx, b + dy, c + dz) \\ C + dw = h(a + dx, b + dy, c + dz). \end{cases}$$

By the methods of the last chapter, we see that approximately

(3)
$$\begin{cases} du = f_1(\mathbf{Q})\, dx + f_2(\mathbf{Q})\, dy + f_3(\mathbf{Q})\, dz \\ dv = g_1(\mathbf{Q})\, dx + g_2(\mathbf{Q})\, dy + g_3(\mathbf{Q})\, dz \\ dw = h_1(\mathbf{Q})\, dx + h_2(\mathbf{Q})\, dy + h_3(\mathbf{Q})\, dz. \end{cases}$$

In matrix notation, this becomes

$$d\mathbf{P} = \begin{pmatrix} du \\ dv \\ dw \end{pmatrix} = \begin{pmatrix} f_1(\mathbf{Q}) & f_2(\mathbf{Q}) & f_3(\mathbf{Q}) \\ g_1(\mathbf{Q}) & g_2(\mathbf{Q}) & g_3(\mathbf{Q}) \\ h_1(\mathbf{Q}) & h_2(\mathbf{Q}) & h_3(\mathbf{Q}) \end{pmatrix} \begin{pmatrix} dx \\ dy \\ dz \end{pmatrix} \equiv \mathbf{J}(\mathbf{Q}, d\mathbf{Q}).$$

The matrix of the above linear transformation is called the **Jacobian matrix**, because its determinant is the Jacobian determinant.

One bit of information which we can read off this last equation is that the transformation carrying $d\mathbf{Q}$ at $\mathbf{Q}$ into $d\mathbf{P}$ at $\mathbf{P}$ is a linear transformation.

In other words, the change in **F** from **Q** to **Q** + d**Q** is very nearly a linear one. Now this linear transformation will have a unique inverse if the determinant $J(\mathbf{Q})$ is not zero. That is, given d**P**, we can find d**Q** if $J(\mathbf{Q}) \neq 0$. Having found d**Q**, we have then found an approximate solution of the inverse problem, for (2) will hold approximately.

We now proceed to show rigorously that a transformation can be inverted locally near a point **Q** if $J(\mathbf{Q}) \neq 0$. We build up to this through a series of lemmas. Beginning with a short discussion of the differentiability of vector functions, we say that a vector function **F** is differentiable at a point **Q** if it is defined in a neighborhood of **Q** and if

$$\mathbf{F}(\mathbf{Q} + \mathbf{h}) - \mathbf{F}(\mathbf{Q}) = \mathbf{J}(\mathbf{Q}, \mathbf{h}) + \mathbf{u}(\mathbf{Q}, \mathbf{h})|\mathbf{h}|,$$

where $\mathbf{u} \to \mathbf{O}$ as $\mathbf{h} \to \mathbf{O}$. From this it follows (Exercise B6) that a necessary and sufficient condition that **F** be differentiable is that each component of **F** be differentiable. If $\mathbf{J}(\mathbf{Q}, \mathbf{h})$ is a continuous function of **Q**, we say that **F** is continuously differentiable.

11.3a   Lemma. Let **F** be a differentiable vector function defined in a neighborhood N, and let **Q** and **Q** + $\boldsymbol{\alpha}$ be two points in N. Then

$$\frac{d}{dt} \mathbf{F}(\mathbf{Q} + t\boldsymbol{\alpha}) = \mathbf{J}(\mathbf{Q} + t\boldsymbol{\alpha}, \boldsymbol{\alpha}).$$

Proof. We leave it as an exercise that **Q** + $t\boldsymbol{\alpha}$ is in N for $\{0 \leqslant t \leqslant 1\}$. Let the jth component of **F** be f. Then, by Theorem 10.4a,

$$\frac{d}{dt} f(\mathbf{Q} + t\boldsymbol{\alpha}) = f_1(\mathbf{Q} + t\boldsymbol{\alpha})\alpha_1 + f_2(\mathbf{Q} + t\boldsymbol{\alpha})\alpha_2 + \cdots + f_n(\mathbf{Q} + t\boldsymbol{\alpha})\alpha_n$$

But this is exactly the jth component of $\mathbf{J}(\mathbf{Q} + t\boldsymbol{\alpha}, \boldsymbol{\alpha})$.   ∎

11.3b   Lemma. Let **F** be a vector-valued function defined in a region R and having continuous derivatives there, and let $\mathbf{Q}_0$ be a point in R at which the Jacobian is not zero. Then there is an $\epsilon > 0$ such that whenever $\mathbf{Q}_1$ and $\mathbf{Q}_2$ are in N_ϵ: $\{|\mathbf{Q} - \mathbf{Q}_0| < \epsilon\}$,

$$\tfrac{1}{2}m|\mathbf{Q}_2 - \mathbf{Q}_1| \leqslant |\mathbf{F}(\mathbf{Q}_2) - \mathbf{F}(\mathbf{Q}_1)| \leqslant \tfrac{3}{2}M|\mathbf{Q}_2 - \mathbf{Q}_1|,$$

where

$$M = \sup_{|\alpha|=1} |\mathbf{J}(\mathbf{Q}_0, \boldsymbol{\alpha})|$$

and

$$m = \inf_{|\alpha|=1} |\mathbf{J}(\mathbf{Q}_0, \boldsymbol{\alpha})|.$$

Proof. Choose ϵ so that, by Theorem 11.2g,

(1) $$|\mathbf{J}(\mathbf{Q}, \boldsymbol{\alpha}) - \mathbf{J}(\mathbf{Q}_0, \boldsymbol{\alpha})| \leqslant \tfrac{1}{2}|\mathbf{J}(\mathbf{Q}_0, \boldsymbol{\alpha})|$$

for every vector α if Q is in N_ϵ. Set $\alpha = Q_2 - Q_1$; then the segment connecting Q_1 to Q_2 is described by $Q(t) = Q_1 + t\alpha$. Then

$$\text{(2)} \quad |F(Q_2) - F(Q_1)| = \left| \int_0^1 \frac{dF}{dt} [Q(t)] \, dt \right| = \left| \int_0^1 J[Q(t), \alpha] \, dt \right|$$

$$= \left| \int_0^1 [J(Q_0, \alpha) + J(Q(t), \alpha) - J(Q_0, \alpha)] \, dt \right|$$

$$\geqslant \left| \int_0^1 J(Q_0, \alpha) \, dt \right| - \left| \int_0^1 (J(Q(t), \alpha) - J(Q_0, \alpha)) \, dt \right|$$

$$\geqslant |J(Q_0, \alpha)| - \tfrac{1}{2}|J(Q_0, \alpha)| = \tfrac{1}{2}|J(Q_0, \alpha)|$$

$$\geqslant \tfrac{1}{2}m|\alpha| = \tfrac{1}{2}m|Q_2 - Q_1|.$$

If we estimate from above we get the other side of the inequality. ∎

11.3c Lemma. Under the conditions of Lemma 11.3b, $F(Q)$ does not take the same value more than once in N_ϵ; that is, if $F(Q_1) = F(Q_2)$,

$$Q_1 = Q_2.$$

Proof. The proof is immediate from

$$|F(Q_2) - F(Q_1)| \geqslant \tfrac{1}{2}m|Q_2 - Q_1|.$$ ∎

In spaces of one dimension, a differentiable function which takes no value more than once is a monotone function. The lemma we have just proved is an analogous result for higher dimensions. In one dimension, the main tool for studying such problems was the mean-value theorem. Unfortunately the mean-value theorem does not extend to transformations (see Exercise B2). However, the integral formula (2) with which we started the proof is an integral analogue of the mean-value theorem and can be bent to our purposes, although the calculations are necessarily more complicated.

11.3d Lemma. Let F be a vector-valued function defined in a region D and having continuous derivatives there. Let Q_0 be a point in D at which the Jacobian is not zero, and denote $F(Q_0)$ by P_0. Then there is a $\delta > 0$ and an $\epsilon > 0$ such that, for each P in $\mathcal{N}_\delta$: $\{|P - P_0| < \delta\}$, there is a Q in N_ϵ: $\{|Q - Q_0| < \epsilon\}$ such that $P = F(Q)$.

Proof. Determine ϵ as in Lemma 11.3b, and define $\delta = m\epsilon/9$, where $m = \min_{|\alpha|=1} |J(Q_0, \alpha)|$ (see Corollary 11.2g).

Let P_1 be any point in $\mathcal{N}_\delta$. We want to show that there is a Q_1 in N_ϵ such that $F(Q_1) = P_1$. We will in fact show that Q_1 exists and is in $N_{\epsilon/2}$.

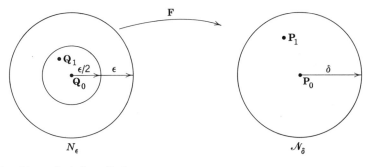

To this end, define $\mathbf{Q}_1$ by

$$|\mathbf{F}(\mathbf{Q}_1) - \mathbf{P}_1| = \min_{|\mathbf{Q} - \mathbf{Q}_0| \leqslant \epsilon/2} |\mathbf{F}(\mathbf{Q}) - \mathbf{P}_1|.$$

Such a $\mathbf{Q}_1$ exists, since a continuous function on a closed bounded set attains its infimum. We first show that $|\mathbf{Q}_1 - \mathbf{Q}_0| < \epsilon/2$. For if $|\mathbf{Q}_1 - \mathbf{Q}_0| = \epsilon/2$, we could apply Lemma 11.3b to get

$$|\mathbf{F}(\mathbf{Q}_1) - \mathbf{P}_0| = |\mathbf{F}(\mathbf{Q}_1) - \mathbf{F}(\mathbf{Q}_0)| \geqslant \tfrac{1}{2}m|\mathbf{Q}_1 - \mathbf{Q}_0| = m\epsilon/4 > 2\delta.$$

From this we get

$$|\mathbf{F}(\mathbf{Q}_1) - \mathbf{P}_1| \geqslant |\mathbf{F}(\mathbf{Q}_1) - \mathbf{P}_0| - |\mathbf{P}_0 - \mathbf{P}_1| \geqslant 2\delta - \delta$$
$$= \delta > |\mathbf{P}_0 - \mathbf{P}_1| = |\mathbf{F}(\mathbf{Q}_0) - \mathbf{P}_1| \geqslant |\mathbf{F}(\mathbf{Q}_1) - \mathbf{P}_1|.$$

The last inequality is true by the choice of $\mathbf{Q}_1$. This contradiction shows that $|\mathbf{Q}_1 - \mathbf{Q}_0| < \epsilon/2$.

We now want to show that $\mathbf{F}(\mathbf{Q}_1) = \mathbf{P}_1$. To do this we will show that, if $\mathbf{F}(\mathbf{Q}_1) \neq \mathbf{P}_1$, we can find a $\mathbf{Q}_2$ with $|\mathbf{Q}_2 - \mathbf{Q}_0| < \epsilon/2$ for which

$$(5) \qquad\qquad |\mathbf{F}(\mathbf{Q}_2) - \mathbf{P}_1| < |\mathbf{F}(\mathbf{Q}_1) - \mathbf{P}_1|.$$

But this will contradict the definition of $\mathbf{Q}_1$ and hence complete the proof. To find such a $\mathbf{Q}_2$, we look at all points of the form $\mathbf{Q}_2 = \mathbf{Q}_1 + \eta\boldsymbol{\alpha}$, where $\boldsymbol{\alpha}$ is a unit vector and η is a positive constant so small that $|\mathbf{Q}_2 - \mathbf{Q}_1| < \epsilon/2$. (How is it possible to choose η so small?) Then we want to choose $\boldsymbol{\alpha}$ so that (5) holds. To make it possible to choose such an $\boldsymbol{\alpha}$, we note first that

$$\mathbf{F}(\mathbf{Q}_2) - \mathbf{F}(\mathbf{Q}_1) - \eta\mathbf{J}(\mathbf{Q}_0, \boldsymbol{\alpha}) = \mathbf{F}(\mathbf{Q}_1 + \eta\boldsymbol{\alpha}) - \mathbf{F}(\mathbf{Q}_1) - \eta\mathbf{J}(\mathbf{Q}_0, \boldsymbol{\alpha})$$

$$= \eta \int_0^1 \{\mathbf{J}[\mathbf{Q}(t), \boldsymbol{\alpha}] - \mathbf{J}(\mathbf{Q}_0, \boldsymbol{\alpha})\} \, dt.$$

Hence

$$(6) \qquad\qquad |\mathbf{F}(\mathbf{Q}_2) - \mathbf{F}(\mathbf{Q}_1) - \eta\mathbf{J}(\mathbf{Q}_0, \boldsymbol{\alpha})| \leqslant \tfrac{1}{2}\eta|\mathbf{J}(\mathbf{Q}_0, \boldsymbol{\alpha})|.$$

We then have

$$|F(Q_2) - P_1| = |[F(Q_1) - P_1 + \eta J(Q_0, \alpha)]$$
$$+ [F(Q_2) - F(Q_1) - \eta J(Q_0, \alpha)]|$$
$$\leqslant |F(Q_1) - P_1 + \eta J(Q_0, \alpha)|$$
$$+ |F(Q_2) - F(Q_1) - \eta J(Q_0, \alpha)|.$$

By Corollary 11.2d, we can choose α so that $J(Q_0, \alpha) = -k[F(Q_1) - P_1]$, where $k > 0$. Applying (6) to the second term in the last inequality gives us

$$|F(Q_2) - P_1| \leqslant |1 - \eta k| \, |F(Q_1) - P_1| + \tfrac{1}{2}\eta k |F(Q_1) - P_1|.$$

By taking η still smaller (if necessary), so that $\eta k < 1$, we get

$$|F(Q_2) - P_1| \leqslant (1 - \tfrac{1}{2}\eta k)|F(Q_1) - P_1| < |F(Q_1) - P_1|.$$

This completes the proof of the fact that $F(Q_1) = P_1$. ∎

We now have the main inversion theorem.

11.3e **Theorem.** Let F be a vector-valued continuously differentiable transformation from a region D in E_n to a set R in E_n, and let Q_0 be a point in D at which the Jacobian is not zero. If we denote $F(Q_0)$ by P_0, there is an $\epsilon > 0$ and a $\delta > 0$ such that an inverse function G is defined in $\mathcal{N}_\delta$: $\{|P - P_0| < \delta\}$, taking values in N_ϵ: $\{|Q - Q_0| < \epsilon\}$. Furthermore, G is continuously differentiable in a neighborhood of P_0 and the Jacobian of G at P_0 is the reciprocal of the Jacobian of F at Q_0.

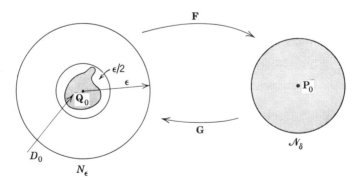

Proof. Choosing ϵ and δ as in the previous lemmas, we see that the set of points D_0 in N_ϵ which maps onto $\mathcal{N}_\delta$ satisfies the conditions of Theorem 11.1a, so that an inverse function G exists on $\mathcal{N}_\delta$ and takes values in N_ϵ.

In fact, by definition it maps $\mathcal{N}_\delta$ back onto D_0. To show that **G** is differentiable in $\mathcal{N}_\delta$, let **P** and **P** + **h** be vectors in $\mathcal{N}_\delta$, and let

$$\mathbf{Q} = \mathbf{G(P)} \quad \text{and} \quad \mathbf{Q} + \mathbf{k} = \mathbf{G(P + h)}.$$

Thus $\mathbf{P} = \mathbf{F(Q)} \quad \text{and} \quad \mathbf{P} + \mathbf{h} = \mathbf{F(Q + k)}$

so that $\mathbf{h} = \mathbf{F(Q + k)} - \mathbf{F(Q)} \quad \text{and} \quad \mathbf{k} = \mathbf{G(P + h)} - \mathbf{G(P)}.$

Since **F** is differentiable at **Q**,

$$(6) \qquad \mathbf{h} = \mathbf{F(Q + k)} - \mathbf{F(Q)} = \mathbf{J(Q, k)} + \mathbf{u(Q, k)}|\mathbf{k}|,$$

where $\mathbf{u} \to \mathbf{O}$ as $\mathbf{k} \to \mathbf{O}$.

Now since the determinant $J(\mathbf{Q})$ is not zero, there exists a linear transformation $\mathbf{J_1(P, h)}$ inverse to $\mathbf{J(Q, k)}$. Hence, from (6), we get

$$\mathbf{k} = \mathbf{J_1(P, h)} + \mathbf{J_1[P, u(Q, k)]}|\mathbf{k}|$$

or $\mathbf{G(P + h)} - \mathbf{G(P)} = \mathbf{J_1(P, h)} + \mathbf{v(P, h)}|\mathbf{h}|,$

where $\mathbf{v(P, h)} \equiv |\mathbf{k}|\mathbf{J_1[P, u(Q, k)]}/|\mathbf{h}|.$

It remains to be shown that $\mathbf{v} \to \mathbf{O}$ as $\mathbf{h} \to \mathbf{O}$.

By Lemma 11.3b, we have

$$|\mathbf{k}| = |\mathbf{G(P + h)} - \mathbf{G(P)}| \leqslant (2/m)|\mathbf{h}|,$$

so that $|\mathbf{k}| \to 0$ as $|\mathbf{h}| \to 0$, and, in fact, $|\mathbf{k}|/|\mathbf{h}| \leqslant 2/m$.

Thus $|\mathbf{v}| \leqslant (2/m)|\mathbf{J_1}| \to 0 \qquad \text{as } |\mathbf{h}| \to 0.$

Furthermore we see that **G** is continuously differentiable since $\mathbf{J_1}$ is continuous, and $\mathbf{J_1}$ is continuous since **J** is continuous and not zero. If $\mathbf{Q} = (x_1, x_2, \ldots, x_n)$ and $\mathbf{P} = (y_1, y_2, \ldots, y_n)$, it follows from the fact that **J** and $\mathbf{J_1}$ are inverses that

$$\frac{\partial x_i}{\partial y_j} = \frac{(-1)^{j+i}}{J(\mathbf{Q})} \frac{\partial(y_1, \ldots, y_{j-1}, y_{j+1}, \ldots, y_n)}{\partial(x_1, \ldots, x_{i-1}, x_{i+1}, \ldots, x_n)},$$

where J is the Jacobian determinant of **F**, namely

$$J(\mathbf{Q}) = \frac{\partial(y_1, y_2, \ldots, y_n)}{\partial(x_1, x_2, \ldots, x_n)}.$$

(See Exercise C1.)

A EXERCISES

1. Compute the Jacobian of each of the following transformations and discuss local behavior:

(a) $u = \dfrac{1}{\sqrt{2}} (x - y)$

$\quad v = \dfrac{1}{\sqrt{2}} (x + y)$

(b) $u = x + x^2 + y$

$\quad v = x^2 + y^2$

(c) $x = e^r \cos \theta$

$\quad y = e^r \sin \theta$

(d) $u = x + y$

$\quad v = y^{1/n} \qquad n > 0$

(e) $u = \dfrac{x}{x^2 + y^2}$

$\quad v = \dfrac{y}{x^2 + y^2}$

(f) $x = r \sin \phi \cos \theta$

$\quad y = r \sin \phi \sin \theta$

$\quad z = r \cos \phi$

2. Describe the image of the square $\{0 < x < 1, \, 0 < y < 1\}$ in 1(a), (b), (d) above.

3. Find inverse transformations for 1(a), (c), (d), (e) and (f). Describe the sets on which the inverses are defined.

4. Compute the Jacobians of the inverse transformation obtained in Exercise 3 and verify directly that the product of the Jacobians of the direct and inverse transformations is 1 in each instance.

5. Let $u = x + y + z$, $v = x^2 + y^2 + z^2$, and $w = x^3 + y^3 + z^3$. Compute $\partial x/\partial u$, $\partial x/\partial v$, and $\partial x/\partial w$.

6. Let f be a function of (x, y). In a change of coordinates to polar coordinates, write out formulas for $\partial f/\partial x$ and $\partial f/\partial y$.

7. Express $\partial^2 f / \partial x^2$ in polar coordinates.

8. Let $u = f(x, y)$. Express $\Delta u = u_{xx} + u_{yy}$ in polar coordinates

9. Let $u = f(x, y, z)$. Express $\Delta u = u_{xx} + u_{yy} + u_{zz}$ in (a) cylindrical coordinates; (b) spherical coordinates.

10. Let $u = f(x, y)$. Compute $\Delta u = u_{xx} + u_{yy}$ under the change of variables given in Exercise A1(c) above.

11. Let $x = f(u, v)$, $y = g(u, v)$ give a change of variables for which $f_1 = g_2$ and $f_2 = -g_1$.
Letting $w = h(x, y)$, show that

$$w_{uu} + w_{vv} = (w_{xx} + w_{yy})[(\partial x/\partial u)^2 + (\partial y/\partial u)^2].$$

12. Express $(\partial u/\partial x)^2 + (\partial u/\partial y)^2$ in polar coordinates.

13. Let N be a neighborhood in E_n, and let Q and $Q + \alpha$ be in N. Show that $Q(t) = Q + t\alpha$ is in N for $\{0 \leqslant t \leqslant 1\}$.

B EXERCISES

1. Express $\Delta^2 u = u_{xxxx} + 2u_{xxyy} + u_{yyyy}$ in polar coordinates. Use Exercise A8 above.

2. Show that the mean-value theorem can be extended to transformations in the following form: Let $\mathbf{F}$ be a continuously differentiable transformation, and let $\mathbf{Q}$, $\mathbf{Q}'$, and the segment connecting them lie in the domain of $\mathbf{F}$. Then $\mathbf{F}(\mathbf{Q}) - \mathbf{F}(\mathbf{Q}') = \mathbf{J}^* (\mathbf{Q}_1, \mathbf{Q}_2, \ldots, \mathbf{Q}_n; \mathbf{Q} - \mathbf{Q}')$, where $\mathbf{J}^*$ is a modified Jacobian acting on $\mathbf{Q} - \mathbf{Q}'$. $\mathbf{J}^*$ has the form of a Jacobian with the jth row having its elements evaluated at a point $\mathbf{Q}_j$ on the segment from $\mathbf{Q}$ to $\mathbf{Q}'$.

3. Show that the transformation $\mathbf{F}$ given by $u = x^2 - y^2$, $v = 2xy$ is **conformal** at every point except the origin. That is, if $\mathbf{Q}_0$ is mapped into $\mathbf{P}_0$, any two differentiable curves through $\mathbf{Q}_0$ map into two differentiable curves through $\mathbf{P}_0$, so that the angle between them is preserved. What happens to angles at the origin?

4. Suppose $x = f(u, v)$, $y = g(u, v)$, $z = h(u, v)$ are so related in a region D_1 of the (u, v) plane that there is a region D_2 of the (x, y) plane such that $z = \phi(x, y)$ in D_2, where f, g and h, ϕ are continuously differentiable in their respective domains. Evaluate $\partial z / \partial x$ and $\partial z / \partial y$ in terms of f, g, and h.

5. If u and v are differentiable functions of (x, y, z), which in turn are differentiable functions of (r, s) show that

$$\frac{\partial(u, v)}{\partial(r, s)} = \frac{\partial(u, v)}{\partial(x, y)} \frac{\partial(x, y)}{\partial(r, s)} + \frac{\partial(u, v)}{\partial(y, z)} \frac{\partial(y, z)}{\partial(r, s)} + \frac{\partial(u, v)}{\partial(z, x)} \frac{\partial(z, x)}{\partial(r, s)}.$$

6. Show that a necessary and sufficient condition that $\mathbf{F}$ be differentiable is that each component of $\mathbf{F}$ be differentiable.

C EXERCISES

1. Establish the formula for $\partial x_i / \partial y_j$ given on page 249.

2. Use the modified mean-value theorem of Exercise B2 to prove Lemma 11.3b and equation (6) of Theorem 11.3d, and hence construct a proof of the inversion theorem independent of the integral argument used in the text.

11.4 GLOBAL INVERSES

The theorem we have just proved shows that the non-vanishing of the Jacobian at a point $\mathbf{Q}_0$ is sufficient to guarantee the existence of an inverse function of a differentiable transformation $\mathbf{F}$ in a sufficiently small neighborhood of $\mathbf{Q}_0$. Under these conditions, we say that a **local inverse** transformation exists. We now want to inquire about the existence of a **global inverse**—that is, an inverse function defined over the whole of the range R of the function **F**. As we have seen, a necessary and sufficient condition that such an inverse exists is that the map produced by **F** is a one-to-one map (Theorem 11.1a).

Let us note first that a local inverse can exist at each point of a region without a global inverse existing. We can see this geometrically in the figure. Let a mapping be given physically by bending the straight strip so as to overlap the ends. Then points $\mathbf{Q_0}$ and $\mathbf{Q_1}$ both map into the single

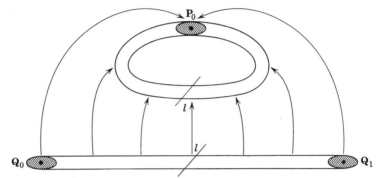

point $\mathbf{P_0}$, so that no global inverse can exist. However, if we cut the strip in two by the slant line l, the mapping of each end is one to one, so that an inverse of each of these maps exists. Although the argument given here is purely geometrical, it is not difficult to give explicit formulas where such a phenomenon occurs (see Exercise A6).

These examples indicate that a condition which guarantees a local inverse will not necessarily guarantee a global one. In particular, the fact that **F** is differentiable in a region R and has a positive Jacobian at each point of R is no guarantee that a global inverse will exist. However, the following theorem, which we state without proof, gives a set of sufficient conditions.

11.4a   Theorem. Let **F** be a continuously differentiable mapping defined in a region D in E_2, and let its Jacobian never be zero in D. Suppose further that C is a simple closed curve which, together with its interior (recall the Jordan curve theorem), lies in D, and that **F** takes no value twice on C—that is, $\mathbf{F(Q_1)} = \mathbf{F(Q_2)}$ implies $\mathbf{Q_1} = \mathbf{Q_2}$ for $\mathbf{Q_1}$ and $\mathbf{Q_2}$ on C. Then the image Γ of C is a simple closed curve which, together with its interior, lies in R. Furthermore, **F** takes no value twice in the closed region consisting of C and its interior, so that an inverse function can be defined in the closed region consisting of Γ and its interior.

A similar theorem holds also for higher dimensions.

A transformation which is one to one and continuous and has a continuous inverse is called a **topological transformation**. A topological transformation may badly distort the size and shape of a region, but certain properties are preserved. For example, the number of "holes" is preserved under such a mapping. A property which is not changed is called a **topological invariant**. The study of such properties forms a large part of the subject of topology, but we pursue them no further here.

11.5 CURVILINEAR COORDINATES

Let $u = f(x, y)$, $v = g(x, y)$ describe a one-to-one and continuous transformation from a region D to a region R, and let the inverse be described by

(1)
$$x = \phi(u, v)$$
$$y = \psi(u, v).$$

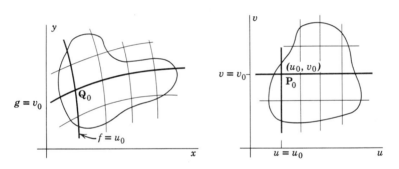

Each point Q_0 is given by its coordinates (x, y). It can also be expressed as the image of a unique point P_0 in R by means of the equations (1) above. In order to understand the geometrical meaning of this fact, let us consider all points P of the form $P = (u_0, v)$ where v is arbitrary—that is, all those points on the vertical line through P_0. The image of this line will be a curve in the (x, y) plane given parametrically by

$$x = \phi(u_0, v)$$
$$y = \psi(u_0, v),$$

and will also be given as a level curve of the function f:

$$f(x, y) = u_0$$

Similarly, the horizontal line $v = v_0$ maps into the curve $g(x, y) = v_0$.

These two curves intersect in only one point (why?), namely $\mathbf{Q}_0$. Likewise, for any other point $\mathbf{P}_1 = (u_1, v_1)$, the two level curves given by $f(x, y) = u_1$ and $g(x, y) = v_1$ determine the inverse image of (u_1, v_1) in D; and conversely any $\mathbf{Q}$ in D is at the intersection of exactly one level curve of f with one of g. No two curves $f = a_1$ and $f = a_2$ can intersect in D; nor can two level curves of g meet in D.

Thus the curves given by $f(x, y) = a$ and $g(x, y) = b$ cover D with a grid of curves whose intersections determine uniquely the points of D. Such a set of curves we will call a **curvilinear coordinate system.** This, then, gives another geometrical interpretation of a topological transformation: it can be interpreted as a curvilinear coordinate system.

The most familiar system of curvilinear coordinates in E_2 is, of course, polar coordinates described by $x = \rho \cos \theta$, $y = \rho \sin \theta$, with the local inverse given by $\rho = \sqrt{x^2 + y^2}$, $\theta = \arctan y/x$.

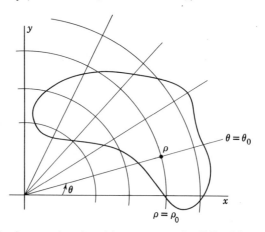

Because the inverse is a local inverse certain difficulties arise. The first but not very serious difficulty arises from the fact that θ is not single-valued over the whole plane. Thus in any region which encircles the origin—as, for example, an annular region between two circles centered at the origin— no global inverse exists. However, as you have undoubtedly already done many times, it is possible to carve such a region up into pieces in each of which a global inverse exists. The second troublesome aspect of polar coordinates arises from the fact that θ is not defined at the origin, and, as we shall see, the Jacobian causes trouble there too. This will cause some worry when we come to discuss the change of variables in a double integral. However, you will find that most of these difficulties can be overcome by one means or another.

Let us compute the Jacobian,

$$\frac{\partial(\rho, \theta)}{\partial(x, y)} = \begin{vmatrix} \dfrac{\partial \rho}{\partial x} & \dfrac{\partial \rho}{\partial y} \\[2ex] \dfrac{\partial \theta}{\partial x} & \dfrac{\partial \theta}{\partial y} \end{vmatrix} = \begin{vmatrix} \dfrac{x}{\sqrt{x^2 + y^2}} & \dfrac{y}{\sqrt{x^2 + y^2}} \\[2ex] \dfrac{-y}{x^2 + y^2} & \dfrac{x}{x^2 + y^2} \end{vmatrix}$$

$$= \frac{x^2}{\rho^3} + \frac{y^2}{\rho^3} = \frac{1}{\rho}$$

By Theorem 11.3e,

$$\frac{\partial(x, y)}{\partial(\rho, \theta)} = \rho.$$

In three-space, the most familiar systems of curvilinear coordinates are spherical and cylindrical. Some of their properties, as well as those of some less familiar systems, are explored in the exercises.

In terms of curvilinear coordinates, we can give a geometrical meaning to the Jacobian, which is most easily appreciated in three-space.

Let a one-to-one and continuously differentiable transformation, mapping a region D onto a region R, be given by $u = f(x, y, z)$, $v = g(x, y, z)$, and $w = h(x, y, z)$. Let $\mathbf{P}_0$ be a point in R and $\mathbf{P}_1$ a near-by point defined by $\mathbf{P}_1 - \mathbf{P}_0 = (du, 0, 0)$, and let $\mathbf{P}_2$ and $\mathbf{P}_3$ be defined by $(0, dv, 0)$ and $(0, 0, dw)$ respectively. These points determine a small rectangular box of

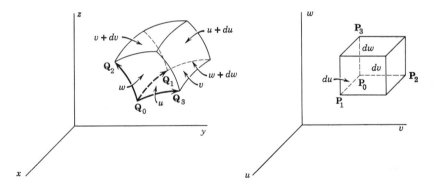

volume $du\ dv\ dw$. By the inverse mapping, this box is mapped onto a "curvilinear parallelepiped," having corners at $\mathbf{Q}_0, \mathbf{Q}_1, \mathbf{Q}_2, \mathbf{Q}_3$, the images of $\mathbf{P}_0, \mathbf{P}_1, \mathbf{P}_2, \mathbf{P}_3$ respectively. The edge $\mathbf{Q}_1 - \mathbf{Q}_0$ is approximately the vector $dx\mathbf{i} + dy\mathbf{j} + dz\mathbf{k}$ due to displacement du. Thus it is $\left(\dfrac{\partial x}{\partial u}\mathbf{i} + \dfrac{\partial y}{\partial u}\mathbf{j} + \dfrac{\partial z}{\partial u}\mathbf{k} \right) du$.

Similarly, the other vectors are approximately given by

$$\mathbf{Q}_2 - \mathbf{Q}_0 = \left(\frac{\partial x}{\partial v}\mathbf{i} + \frac{\partial y}{\partial v}\mathbf{j} + \frac{\partial z}{\partial v}\mathbf{k}\right) dv$$

and

$$\mathbf{Q}_3 - \mathbf{Q}_0 = \left(\frac{\partial x}{\partial w}\mathbf{i} + \frac{\partial y}{\partial w}\mathbf{j} + \frac{\partial z}{\partial w}\mathbf{k}\right) dw.$$

Then the triple scalar product of these is

$$\begin{vmatrix} \dfrac{\partial x}{\partial u} & \dfrac{\partial y}{\partial u} & \dfrac{\partial z}{\partial u} \\[2mm] \dfrac{\partial x}{\partial v} & \dfrac{\partial y}{\partial v} & \dfrac{\partial z}{\partial v} \\[2mm] \dfrac{\partial x}{\partial w} & \dfrac{\partial y}{\partial w} & \dfrac{\partial z}{\partial w} \end{vmatrix} du\, dv\, dw = \frac{\partial(x, y, z)}{\partial(u, v, w)} du\, dv\, dw$$

$= \pm$ volume (approximately) of the "parallelepiped" $= V_{xyz}$, where the sign is $+$ or $-$ according as the orientation of the triple $(\mathbf{P}_1 - \mathbf{P}_0, \mathbf{P}_2 - \mathbf{P}_0, \mathbf{P}_3 - \mathbf{P}_0)$ is left unchanged or is changed when it is mapped into $(\mathbf{Q}_1 - \mathbf{Q}_0, \mathbf{Q}_2 - \mathbf{Q}_0, \mathbf{Q}_3 - \mathbf{Q}_0)$. And

$$V_{xyz} = \left|\frac{\partial(x, y, z)}{\partial(u, v, w)}\right| V_{uvw}.$$

Thus the absolute value of the Jacobian is approximately the ratio, in the small, of corresponding volumes in the coordinate transformation. We will see this in a more rigorous form later.

A system of curvilinear coordinates is said to be an **orthogonal system** if the curves defined by them intersect at right angles. Suppose, as before, that u, v, w form a system of curvilinear coordinates in a region D of (x, y, z) space. If v and w are held fixed, then $\mathbf{Q} = (x, y, z)$ traces out a curve along which u alone varies. (In our previous discussion, $\mathbf{Q}_0$ and $\mathbf{Q}_1$ were neighboring points on such a curve.) Thus a tangent vector (not necessarily the unit tangent) of this curve in the direction of increasing u is

$$\mathbf{T}_1 = \frac{\partial x}{\partial u}\mathbf{i} + \frac{\partial y}{\partial u}\mathbf{j} + \frac{\partial z}{\partial u}\mathbf{k}.$$

Similarly, tangent vectors to the v and w curves are

$$\mathbf{T}_2 = \frac{\partial x}{\partial v}\mathbf{i} + \frac{\partial y}{\partial v}\mathbf{j} + \frac{\partial z}{\partial v}\mathbf{k}$$

and

$$\mathbf{T}_3 = \frac{\partial x}{\partial w}\mathbf{i} + \frac{\partial y}{\partial w}\mathbf{j} + \frac{\partial z}{\partial w}\mathbf{k}.$$

Clearly the condition that the system be orthogonal is that

$$\mathbf{T}_1 \cdot \mathbf{T}_2 = \mathbf{T}_2 \cdot \mathbf{T}_3 = \mathbf{T}_3 \cdot \mathbf{T}_1 = 0$$

or that

$$\frac{\partial x}{\partial u}\frac{\partial x}{\partial v} + \frac{\partial y}{\partial u}\frac{\partial y}{\partial v} + \frac{\partial z}{\partial u}\frac{\partial z}{\partial v} = 0$$

$$\frac{\partial x}{\partial v}\frac{\partial x}{\partial w} + \frac{\partial y}{\partial v}\frac{\partial y}{\partial w} + \frac{\partial z}{\partial v}\frac{\partial z}{\partial w} = 0$$

$$\frac{\partial x}{\partial w}\frac{\partial x}{\partial u} + \frac{\partial y}{\partial w}\frac{\partial y}{\partial u} + \frac{\partial z}{\partial w}\frac{\partial z}{\partial u} = 0.$$

11.6 IMPLICIT FUNCTIONS

In one of the first examples of the computation of partial derivatives, we were asked to compute the first partials of a function z, depending on x and y, which satisfied the equation

$$x^3 - xy^2 + yz^2 - z^3 = 5.$$

Assuming that such a function exists and that the derivatives exist, we were able to obtain formulas for the derivatives. We consider now the question of the existence and differentiability of such implicitly defined functions.

11.6a   Theorem. Let f be a continuously differentiable real-valued function of $\mathbf{Q} = (x, y, z)$ in a neighborhood of a point $\mathbf{Q}_0 = (a, b, c)$ and suppose $f(\mathbf{Q}_0) = C$, $f_3(\mathbf{Q}_0) \neq 0$. There then exists a unique continuously differentiable function z, defined in a neighborhood of (a, b), for which $z(a, b) = c$ and $f[x, y, z(x, y)] = C$.

Proof. Consider the transformation $\mathbf{F}$ given by $u = x$, $v = y$, $w = f(x, y, z)$. Now $\mathbf{F}$ maps (a, b, c) into (a, b, C) and

$$\frac{\partial(u, v, w)}{\partial(x, y, z)} = \begin{vmatrix} 1 & 0 & f_1 \\ 0 & 1 & f_2 \\ 0 & 0 & f_3 \end{vmatrix} = f_3 \neq 0.$$

Hence, by Theorem 11.3e, $\mathbf{F}$ has a unique differentiable inverse $\mathbf{G}$ in a neighborhood $\mathcal{N}_\delta$ of (a, b, C): $\{(u - a)^2 + (v - b)^2 + (w - C)^2 < \delta^2\}$. Now $\mathbf{G}$ expresses (x, y, z) in terms of (u, v, w), and clearly $x = u$, $y = v$, so that in terms of coordinates $\mathbf{G}$ has the form

$$x = u, \qquad y = v, \qquad z = \zeta(u, v, w),$$

where ζ is a differentiable function defined in $\mathcal{N}_\delta$, and where

$$\zeta(a, b, C) = c,$$

and where $w = f[u, v, \zeta(u, v, w)]$ in $\mathcal{N}_\delta$.

Thus setting $w = C$ gives

$$z = \zeta(u, v, C) \qquad \text{in } \{(u - a)^2 + (v - b)^2 < \delta^2\}.$$

But $u = x$, $v = y$, so that

$$z = \zeta(x, y, C) \qquad \text{in } \{(x - a)^2 + (y - b)^2 < \delta^2\},$$

and $C = f[x, y, \zeta(x, y, C)]$ in $\{(x - a)^2 + (y - b)^2 < \delta^2\}$.   ∎

Observe that there is in this theorem nothing essential about the fact that the third coordinate is singled out. Thus, if instead of $f_3(\mathbf{Q}_0) \neq 0$ we had assumed that $f_2(\mathbf{Q}_0) \neq 0$, we could conclude that the equation $f(x, y, z) = C$ could be solved for y in terms of x and z in a neighborhood of (a, c) in the (x, z) plane. Hence, if at $\mathbf{Q}_0$ we have $\nabla f \neq \mathbf{0}$, the equation $f(x, y, z) = C$ can be solved for one of the three variables in terms of the other two.

We would like to determine the tangent plane to the surface $f(x, y, z) = C$ at $\mathbf{Q}_0$. Now

$$f_1 + f_3 \frac{\partial z}{\partial x} = 0$$

and

$$f_2 + f_3 \frac{\partial z}{\partial y} = 0.$$

Thus

$$\frac{\partial z}{\partial x} = -\frac{f_1}{f_3}$$

and

$$\frac{\partial z}{\partial y} = -\frac{f_2}{f_3}.$$

Then the tangent plane at $\mathbf{Q}_0$ is given by

$$(z - c) = \frac{\partial z}{\partial x}\Big|_{\mathbf{Q}_0}(x - a) + \frac{\partial z}{\partial y}\Big|_{\mathbf{Q}_0}(y - b)$$

or $(z - c) = -(f_1/f_3)(x - a) - (f_2/f_3)(y - b),$

or finally $f_1(\mathbf{Q}_0)(x - a) + f_2(\mathbf{Q}_0)(y - b) + f_3(\mathbf{Q}_0)(z - c) = 0.$

This proves the following corollary and justifies the heuristic remarks in Section 10.3.

11.6b   Corollary. Under the conditions of Theorem 11.6a, the tangent plane of $f(x, y, z) = C$ at $\mathbf{Q}_0$ is given by

$$f_1(\mathbf{Q}_0)(x - a) + f_2(\mathbf{Q}_0)(y - b) + f_3(\mathbf{Q}_0)(z - c) = 0,$$

from which it is clear that the normal to the surface is in the direction of the gradient

$$f_1(\mathbf{Q}_0)\mathbf{i} + f_2(\mathbf{Q}_0)\mathbf{j} + f_3(\mathbf{Q}_0)\mathbf{k}.$$

The same technique can be applied to solving $f(\mathbf{Q}) = C$ for one of the components of $\mathbf{Q}$ in terms of the others, and to solving simultaneous equations. We state one theorem below concerning simultaneous equations.

11.6c   Theorem. Let f and g be continuously differentiable functions in a five-dimensional neighborhood of a point $(x_0, y_0, z_0, u_0, v_0)$. Suppose that $f(x_0, y_0, z_0, u_0, v_0) = 0$ and $g(x_0, y_0, z_0, u_0, v_0) = 0$, but that $\partial(f, g)/\partial(u, v) \neq 0$ at $(x_0, y_0, z_0, u_0, v_0)$. There is then a three-dimensional neighborhood in which u and v are continuously differentiable functions of x, y, and z which satisfy $f(x, y, z, u, v) = 0$ and $g(x, y, z, u, v) = 0$.

Proof. (Outline). Set up the transformation into the space of w's by $w_1 = x$, $w_2 = y$, $w_3 = z$, $w_4 = f$, $w_5 = g$. Then observe that

$$\frac{\partial(w_1, w_2, w_3, w_4, w_5)}{\partial(x, y, z, u, v)} = \frac{\partial(f, g)}{\partial(u, v)} \neq 0,$$

and argue as before.   ∎

A   EXERCISES

1. Let z be given implicitly by

$$z^3 + z^2 y - 7x^2 y^2 z + 2 = 0,$$

near $(\hat{1}, 1, 2)$. Give an approximate solution for z near $(x, y) = (0, 0)$.

2. Does there exist a function f defined and continuous in a neighborhood of $(0, 0)$ which satisfies each of the following equation? In each case state how many functions are so determined and the value of the function at the origin:

(a) $x^2 + y^2 + [f(x, y)]^2 = 25$ (b) $x^2 + 2x + y^2 + f^2(x, y) = 0$.

3. Show that the following systems of curvilinear coordinates are orthogonal systems:

(a) Polar coordinates in the plane.
(b) Spherical coordinates in three-space.
(c) Cylindrical coordinates in three-space.

4. For what values of x and y can the equation

$$f(x, y, z) = e^{x^2 + y^2 + z^2} - \cos(x^2 + y^2 + z^2) = 0$$

be solved for z?

5. Suppose $f(u, v, x, y) = 0$, $g(u, v, x, y) = 0$ can be solved for either two variables in terms of the other two. If all the derivatives involved exist, how many meanings could $\partial u / \partial x$ have? If none of the Jacobians involved vanish, give a formula for each meaning. Can one expect that $\dfrac{\partial u}{\partial x} \dfrac{\partial x}{\partial u} = 1$?

6. Let $u = x \cos y, v = x \sin y$. Show in the rectangle R: $\{1 < x < 2, 0 < y < 7\}$ that $\partial(u, v)/\partial(x, y) > 0$, so that the map produced of R in the (u, v) plane is locally one to one. By sketching the image of R in the (u, v) plane, show that it is not globally one to one. Interpret (x, y) as curvilinear coordinates in the (u, v) plane, and so give a geometrical explanation of this mapping.

B EXERCISES

1. State and prove the two-dimensional analogue of Theorem 11.6a.

2. Complete the proof of Theorem 11.6c.

3. If $f(x, y, z) = 0$ can be solved for x, y, or z, and all the derivatives in question exist, show that in general $\dfrac{\partial z}{\partial x} \cdot \dfrac{\partial x}{\partial y} \cdot \dfrac{\partial y}{\partial z} = -1$.

4. If $F(Q, P)$ is an n-vector function of the n-vector P and the m-vector Q, under what conditions can we be expected to solve $F(Q, P) = 0$ for P in terms of Q?

5. Show that $z^3 + p(x, y)z = 15$ has a unique positive solution $z = f(x, y)$ defined for all (x, y) if p is a positive continuously differentiable function of (x, y).

6. Show that the conclusion of Exercise B5 holds under merely the hypothesis that p is non-negative.

7. What is the geometrical meaning of the Jacobian in two dimensions?

8. Parabolic coordinates are given by $x = uv, y = \frac{1}{2}(u^2 - v^2)$:
(a) Sketch the curves $u = c$ and $v = c$.
(b) Sketch the area bounded by $u = 1$, $u = 2$, $v = 1$, $v = 2$.
(c) Compute $\Delta f = f_{xx} + f_{yy}$ in these coordinates.
(d) Show that this is an orthogonal system.

9. Let $x = u \cos v, y = 2u \sin v$, and examine as in Exercise B8.

10. Suppose $f(x, y, z) = 0$ and $g(x, y, z) = 0$ define two surfaces which intersect in a curve. Show under sufficiently heavy restrictions that the tangent vector to the curve is

$$\frac{\partial(f, g)}{\partial(y, z)} \mathbf{i} + \frac{\partial(f, g)}{\partial(z, x)} \mathbf{j} + \frac{\partial(f, g)}{\partial(x, y)} \mathbf{k}.$$

C EXERCISES

1. Let (u, v, w) be an orthogonal system of curvilinear coordinates in a region D of (x, y, z) space. At each point $Q = (x, y, z)$, let $e_1(Q)$, $e_2(Q)$, $e_3(Q)$ be unit vectors in the directions of $\mathbf{T}_1$, $\mathbf{T}_2$, $\mathbf{T}_3$ respectively (see Section 11.5). Let $(\partial/\partial s_j)$ be the directional derivative in the direction $\mathbf{e}_j$. Then:

(*a*) Show for differentiable f in D that

$$\nabla f = \frac{\partial f}{\partial s_1} \mathbf{e}_1 + \frac{\partial f}{\partial s_2} \mathbf{e}_2 + \frac{\partial f}{\partial s_3} \mathbf{e}_3.$$

(*b*) For differentiable vector functions $\mathbf{F}$ in D, define

$$F_1 = \mathbf{F} \cdot \mathbf{e}_1, \; F_2 = \mathbf{F} \cdot \mathbf{e}_2, \; F_3 = \mathbf{F} \cdot \mathbf{e}_3,$$

and show that

$$\nabla \cdot \mathbf{F} = \frac{\partial F_1}{\partial s_1} + \frac{\partial F_2}{\partial s_2} + \frac{\partial F_3}{\partial s_3}$$

and
$$\nabla \times \mathbf{F} = \begin{vmatrix} \mathbf{e}_1 & \mathbf{e}_2 & \mathbf{e}_3 \\ \dfrac{\partial}{\partial s_1} & \dfrac{\partial}{\partial s_2} & \dfrac{\partial}{\partial s_3} \\ F_1 & F_2 & F_3 \end{vmatrix}$$

2. In particular for spherical coordinates show that

$$\nabla f = \frac{\partial f}{\partial r} \mathbf{e}_r + \frac{1}{r \sin \phi} \frac{\partial f}{\partial \theta} \mathbf{e}_\theta - \frac{1}{r} \frac{\partial f}{\partial \phi} \mathbf{e}_\phi.$$

11.7 EXTREME VALUES

A point $\mathbf{P}_0$ is a **local maximum point** of a function f if there is a neighborhood of $\mathbf{P}_0$ in which $f(\mathbf{P}) \leqslant f(\mathbf{P}_0)$, and a **local minimum** if the reverse inequality holds. It is an **absolute maximum** or **minimum** if the appropriate inequality holds for all points in the domain of definition of the function. We also distinguish **weak** and **strict** maximum points according as $f(\mathbf{P}) \leqslant f(\mathbf{P}_0)$ or $f(\mathbf{P}) < f(\mathbf{P}_0)$ for $\mathbf{P} \neq \mathbf{P}_0$. The generic term which covers both maximum and minimum points is **extreme** points. The corresponding values of the function are **extreme values**, local or absolute as the case may be.

The test we are going to describe in this section is for local interior extreme points. Of course we have no guarantee that an extreme value will be attained; and even when we know that an extreme value is attained, as in the case of a continuous function defined on a closed bounded set, it may be attained at many points, some or all of which may occur on the boundary. Thus any complete examination of a function requires that the values on the boundary be taken into account.

In order that a differentiable function have an extreme value at some point $\mathbf{P}_0$ interior to its domain of definition, it must attain this extreme value on any straight line passing through $\mathbf{P}_0$. Therefore it is necessary that the directional derivative of f at $\mathbf{P}_0$ vanish for every direction through $\mathbf{P}_0$, and consequently the gradient must vanish at $\mathbf{P}_0$:

$$\nabla f(\mathbf{P}_0) = \mathbf{O}.$$

This is equivalent to a system of scalar equations $f_1(\mathbf{P}_0) = 0$, $f_2(\mathbf{P}_0) = 0$, and in three dimensions $f_3(\mathbf{P}_0) = 0$, for the determination of the coordinates of $\mathbf{P}_0$. Clearly, in any Euclidean vector space, the number of equations is equal to the number of unknowns. A solution of this system—that is, a point $\mathbf{P}_0$ for which $\nabla f(\mathbf{P}_0) = \mathbf{O}$—is called a **critical point**.

Geometrically, critical points are those at which the surface $z = f(\mathbf{P})$ has a horizontal tangent plane. They include both kinds of extreme points and others which are in some ways analogous to inflection points. These will be called **saddle points**, because the shape of the surface near the simplest of these somewhat resembles a saddle.

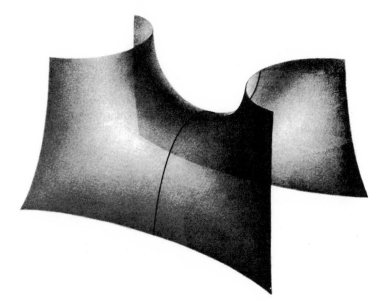

We now give a criterion for distinguishing between maxima, minima, and saddle points. To establish such a criterion, we examine the higher directional derivatives. The simplest such test follows.

11.7a   Theorem. Let f have all its second derivatives continuous in a region D, and let $\mathbf{Q}$ be a critical point of f. Then at $\mathbf{Q}$ the function f has

  (i) a minimum if $(\boldsymbol{\alpha} \cdot \nabla)^2 f(\mathbf{Q}) > 0$ for every unit vector $\boldsymbol{\alpha}$
  (ii) a maximum if $(\boldsymbol{\alpha} \cdot \nabla)^2 f(\mathbf{Q}) < 0$ for every unit vector $\boldsymbol{\alpha}$

(iii) a saddle point if the sign of $(\boldsymbol{\alpha} \cdot \nabla)^2 f(\mathbf{Q})$ can change sign.

In two dimensions, we can rewrite the conditions:

(i) $f_{11} > 0, f_{11}f_{22} - (f_{12})^2 > 0$ (minimum)

(ii) $f_{11} < 0, f_{11}f_{22} - (f_{12})^2 > 0$ (maximum)

(iii) $f_{11}f_{22} - (f_{12})^2 < 0$ (saddle point).

For those of you familiar with algebra, the conclusion can be succinctly stated as follows: If the quadratic form $\Sigma f_{ij}\alpha_i\alpha_j$ is definite, an extreme value is attained. This value is a minimum if the form is positive and a maximum if it is negative. If the form is indefinite, then f has a saddle point at $\mathbf{Q}$. If, however, $\Sigma f_{ij}\alpha_i\alpha_j$ is merely semi-definite, the test fails, as we can see by example (see Exercise A7).

Proof. (For a minimum.) By Taylor's theorem, we have for $\mathbf{P}$ near $\mathbf{Q}$

$$f(\mathbf{P}) = f(\mathbf{Q}) + (\mathbf{P} - \mathbf{Q}) \cdot \nabla f(\mathbf{Q}) + \tfrac{1}{2}[(\mathbf{P} - \mathbf{Q}) \cdot \nabla]^2 f(\mathbf{P}_0),$$

where $\mathbf{P}_0$ is on the segment between $\mathbf{P}$ and $\mathbf{Q}$. Thus

$$f(\mathbf{P}) - f(\mathbf{Q}) = \tfrac{1}{2}((\mathbf{P} - \mathbf{Q}) \cdot \nabla)^2 f(\mathbf{P}_0).$$

If we introduce the unit vector $\boldsymbol{\alpha}$ in the direction of $\mathbf{P} - \mathbf{Q}$, we can express this last formula as

$$f(\mathbf{P}) - f(\mathbf{Q}) = \tfrac{1}{2}|\mathbf{P} - \mathbf{Q}|^2 \, \nabla_\alpha^2 f(\mathbf{P}_0).$$

Since the second derivatives of f are continuous at $\mathbf{Q}$ and $|\boldsymbol{\alpha}| = 1$, we have

(1) $$\nabla_\alpha^2 f(\mathbf{P}_0) = \nabla_\alpha^2 f(\mathbf{Q}) + \eta,$$

where $\eta \to 0$, and the limit is attained uniformly with respect to $\boldsymbol{\alpha}$.

Now the quantity $\nabla_\alpha^2 f(\mathbf{Q})$ is a function of $\boldsymbol{\alpha}$ alone, since $\mathbf{Q}$ is fixed. In fact, it is a homogeneous polynomial $(\Sigma f_{ij}\alpha_i\alpha_j)$ of the second degree in $\boldsymbol{\alpha}$, defined on the closed bounded set $|\boldsymbol{\alpha}| = 1$. It therefore attains a minimum value m for some $\boldsymbol{\alpha}_0$; and this minimum value must be positive, since $\nabla_\alpha^2 f(\mathbf{Q})$ is positive for every $\boldsymbol{\alpha}$. Now take $\mathbf{P}$ so close to $\mathbf{Q}$ that $|\eta| < m/2$. Then

$$f(\mathbf{P}) - f(\mathbf{Q}) \geqslant \tfrac{1}{2}|\mathbf{P} - \mathbf{Q}|^2\{m - |\eta|\} \geqslant \tfrac{1}{2}|\mathbf{P} - \mathbf{Q}|^2\left(m - \frac{m}{2}\right)$$
$$= m|\mathbf{P} - \mathbf{Q}|^2/4 > 0.$$

Hence f attains a minimum as asserted. The proof for a maximum is similar.

When $\nabla_\alpha^2 f(\mathbf{Q})$ can change sign, it is clear from (1) that $f(\mathbf{P}) - f(\mathbf{Q})$ can also change sign in every neighborhood of $\mathbf{Q}$, so that this indicates a saddle point.

It only remains to establish the special formulas for two dimensions.

Here we have

(2) $$\nabla_\alpha^2 f(\mathbf{Q}) = f_{11}\alpha_1^2 + 2f_{12}\alpha_1\alpha_2 + f_{22}\alpha_2^2.$$

By completing the square, we can write this in the form

(3) $$f_{11}[\alpha_1 + \alpha_2 f_{12}/f_{11}]^2 + \alpha_2^2(f_{11}f_{22} - f_{12}^2)/f_{11}.$$

Clearly, then, if $f_{11}f_{22} - f_{12}^2 > 0$, the sign of this is either the sign of f_{11} or it is zero. If it vanishes, $\alpha_2 = \alpha_1 = 0$, which is not possible. This shows the equivalence of $f_{11} > 0$ with $\nabla_\alpha^2 f(\mathbf{Q}) > 0$ and $f_{11} < 0$ with $\nabla_\alpha^2 f(\mathbf{Q}) < 0$.

If $f_{11}f_{22} - f_{12}^2 < 0$ and $f_{11} \neq 0$, then the two terms in (3) have opposite signs. Choosing $\boldsymbol{\alpha} = (1, 0)$, we see that

$$\nabla_\alpha^2 f(\mathbf{Q}) = f_{11},$$

and choosing $\boldsymbol{\alpha}$ so that $f_{11}\alpha_1 = -f_{12}\alpha_2$, we see that

$$\nabla_\alpha^2 f(\mathbf{Q}) = \alpha_2^2(f_{11}f_{22} - f_{12}^2)/f_{11},$$

and these two values have opposite signs.

If $f_{12}f_{22} - f_{12}^2 < 0$ and $f_{22} \neq 0$, then (2) can be written as

$$f_{22}[\alpha_2 + \alpha_1 f_{12}/f_{22}] + \alpha_1^2(f_{11}f_{22} - f_{12}^2)/f_{22},$$

and the same type of argument again shows that $\nabla_\alpha^2 f(\mathbf{Q})$ can change sign.

If both $f_{11} = 0$ and $f_{22} = 0$, then $f_{12} \neq 0$, for

$$f_{11}f_{22} - f_{12}^2 = -f_{12}^2 < 0.$$

Then $$\nabla_\alpha^2 f(\mathbf{Q}) = 2f_{12}\alpha_1\alpha_2,$$

which clearly changes sign. ∎

It is clear that the conditions of the theorem are sufficient but not necessary, for certainly $f(x, y) = x^2 + y^4$ attains a minimum at the origin, yet it does not meet these conditions. We will not pursue this matter further, although it is clear that an examination of the higher derivatives would yield more esoteric theorems about the existence of extrema. It should also be clear that the problem is by no means as simple when there are several variables as when there is only one.

11.8   EXTREME VALUES UNDER CONSTRAINTS

A new type of problem arises in discussing the extreme values of functions of several variables which does not come up in the case of functions of a single variable. This occurs when we ask for an extremum of one function, say f, under the condition (called a **constraint** or a **side condition**) that another function shall vanish.

If we want to maximize $f(x, y)$ under the condition that $g(x, y) = 0$, we might try solving the equation $g(x, y) = 0$ for y in terms of x, substitute into $f(x, y)$, and minimize the resulting function of x. In many cases this is difficult or even impossible, so we need another approach.

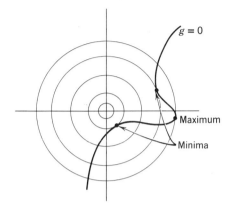

For example, suppose we want the smallest or largest value of the function f given by

$$f(x, y) = \sqrt{x^2 + y^2}$$

under the constraint $g(x, y) = 0$. It is easy to see that the problem is to maximize or minimize the distance from the origin to a point on the curve described by $g(x, y) = 0$. The level lines of the function f are circles centered at the origin. As a point traverses the curve, it will be crossing the level lines either going inward or outward. We would therefore expect extreme values at the points where the direction of crossing changes.

In general, the situation is much the same when we are seeking to maximize a function f on a curve given by $g = 0$. A point tracing out the

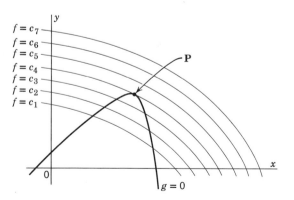

curve $g = 0$ will cross the curves $f = c$ in the direction of increasing or decreasing c's. When the direction of the crossing changes, we expect an extreme point. In the figure, the function f will attain a maximum on $g = 0$ at **P** if the direction of increasing c is up; otherwise it will attain a minimum there.

If all functions are smooth—that is, if they have continuous derivatives—we would expect the curve $g = 0$ to be tangent to the curve $f = c$ at **P**. That is, we would expect their tangent lines (or planes in higher dimensions) to coincide. Thus if (a, b) is the extreme point,

$$(x - a)f_1(a, b) + (y - b)f_2(a, b) = 0$$

and
$$(x - a)g_1(a, b) + (y - b)g_2(a, b) = 0$$

should represent the same line. This means, of course, that their coefficients should be proportional. In other words, there should be a λ such that

$$f_1(a, b) + \lambda g_1(a, b) = 0$$
$$f_2(a, b) + \lambda g_2(a, b) = 0,$$

and of course

$$g(a, b) = 0.$$

Thus we have three equations for the three unknowns a, b, and λ.

The method we have outlined for the location of critical points is known as **Lagrange's method,** and λ is called a **multiplier.** Since the multiplier method yields only critical points, it is still necessary to distinguish by some means the maximum, minimum, and inflection-type points. We now offer proof that the method just described yields a necessary condition for the existence of an extreme value.

II.8a   Theorem.   Let f and g be defined and differentiable in a region D. In order that f attain an extreme value under the condition that $g(\mathbf{P}) = 0$ at a point $\mathbf{P_0}$ in D, where $\nabla g \neq \mathbf{O}$, it is necessary that there be a number λ such that

$$\nabla f(\mathbf{P_0}) + \lambda \nabla g(\mathbf{P_0}) = \mathbf{O}$$

and
$$g(\mathbf{P_0}) = 0.$$

Proof. (For three dimensions.) The assumption that $\nabla g(\mathbf{P_0}) \neq \mathbf{O}$ means that not all of g_1, g_2, and g_3 vanish at $\mathbf{P_0} = (a, b, c)$. Suppose, to fix ideas, that $g_3(\mathbf{P_0}) \neq 0$. We can now solve $g(x, y, z) = 0$ for z to get $z = \phi(x, y)$ near (a, b), $\phi(a, b) = c$. Then $f[x, y, \phi(x, y)]$ must attain an extreme value at a, so that

$$f_1[a, b, \phi(a, b)] + f_3[a, b, \phi(a, b)]\phi_1(a, b) = 0,$$

and
$$f_2[a, b, \phi(a, b)] + f_3[a, b, \phi(a, b)]\phi_2(a, b) = 0.$$

But since $\phi(a, b) = c$, these equations become:

(1) $f_1(a, b, c) + f_3(a, b, c)\phi_1(a, b) = 0$

(2) $f_2(a, b, c) + f_3(a, b, c)\phi_2(a, b) = 0$

Now $g[x, y, \phi(x, y)] \equiv 0$ near (a, b). Hence g also satisfies

(3) $g_1(a, b, c) + g_3(a, b, c)\phi_1(a, b) = 0$

(4) $g_2(a, b, c) + g_3(a, b, c)\phi_2(a, b) = 0.$

We define λ by

(5) $\lambda = -f_3(a, b, c)/g_3(a, b, c)$

and use (5) to eliminate ϕ_1 and ϕ_2 from (1), (2), (3), and (4). This gives rise to

$$f_1(a, b, c) + \lambda g_1(a, b, c) = 0$$
$$f_2(a, b, c) + \lambda g_2(a, b, c) = 0$$

and (5) is equivalent to

$$f_3(a, b, c) + \lambda g_3(a, b, c) = 0.$$

These last three equations are merely the components of

$$\nabla f(\mathbf{P}_0) + \lambda \nabla g(\mathbf{P}_0) = \mathbf{O}. \qquad \blacksquare$$

Where there are several constraining conditions, the rule is basically the same: A necessary condition that f attain an extreme value under the constraints $g = 0$, $h = 0$, $\ldots$, $p = 0$ at a point $\mathbf{P}_0$ is that there exist multipliers $\lambda_1, \lambda_2, \ldots, \lambda_k$ such that

$$\nabla f(\mathbf{P}_0) + \lambda_1 \nabla g(\mathbf{P}_0) + \lambda_2 \nabla h(\mathbf{P}_0) + \cdots + \lambda_k \nabla p(\mathbf{P}_0) = \mathbf{O}.$$

No proof will be given for this. You should convince yourself (heuristically) that normally we would have $k \leqslant n - 1$, where n is the dimension of the space.

A EXERCISES

1. Find and test the critical points of the following functions:

(a) $x^3 + xy + y^2 - 3x - 9y$

(d) $\dfrac{xy}{8} + \dfrac{1}{x} - \dfrac{1}{y}$

(b) $x^3 + 12xy + y^3 + 5$

(e) $x^2 + xy + y^2 + \dfrac{24}{x} + \dfrac{24}{y}$

(c) $x^3 - y^3 + 3axy$

(f) $(x + y) e^{-x^2 - y^2}$

2. Find the absolute extreme values of the following functions:

(a) $x^2 + y^2 - 2y$ on $\{x^2 + 2x + y^2 \leqslant 3\}$

(b) $x^2 + 12xy + y^2$ on $\{x^2 + y^2 = 4\}$

(c) $\cos x \cos y \cos (x + y)$ $\qquad$ on $\{0 \leqslant x \leqslant \pi, 0 \leqslant y \leqslant \pi\}$

(d) $\sqrt{(6 - x)(6 - y)(x + y - 6)}$ $\qquad$ on the triangle bounded by $x = 6$, $y = 6$, $x + y = 6$.

3. Let P_1, P_2, be given points in three-space. Find P so that $|P_1 - P| + |P_2 - P|$ is the least.

4. Find the dimensions of the largest rectangular parallelepiped with three faces in the coordinate planes and a vertex on $x + 3y + 2z = 6$ if x, y, z are positive.

5. A long strip of sheet metal 15 inches wide is made into a trough by bending up a strip of width x along each edge so as to form equal angles θ with the base. Find x and θ so that the trough will have the largest volume.

6. Find the point P nearest the origin on the line of intersection of the two planes $2x + 3y + z = 6$ and $x + 2y + 2z = 4$. Verify that the segment from O to P is orthogonal to the line.

7. Verify that f, given by $f(x, y) = x^2 + y^4$, has a minimum at the origin, but does not satisfy the conditions of Theorem 11.7a.

B   EXERCISES

1. Prove the theorem outlined at the end of Section 11.6.

2. Show that the function f defined by $f(x, y) = (y - x^3)(y - 8x^3)$ has a saddle point at the origin. Show that, on every straight line through the origin, f attains a minimum at the origin.

3. Find the largest value of $\sin x/2 \sin y/2 \sin z/2$ if x, y, and z are positive and $x + y + z = \pi$.

4. Find and test the critical points of:

(a) $x^4 + y^4 + 4xy - 2y^2$ $\qquad\qquad$ (b) $y^4 + x^2 - 2xy$

5. Find x and y such that $\int_0^1 (\sqrt{t} - x - yt)^2 \, dt$ is the least.

C   EXERCISES

1. Suppose f is a continuously differentiable function in three-space, and P_0 is the point on the surface S described by $f(x, y, z) = 0$ at which S comes closest to a point Q_0, not itself on S. If $\nabla f(P_0) \neq O$, show first by a geometrical argument, then rigorously, that $Q_0 - P_0$ is normal to S at P_0.

2. (a) Show that the maximum value of $x^2y^2z^2$ on the sphere $x^2 + y^2 + z^2 = \rho^2$ is $(\rho^2/3)^3$.

(b) Show the minimum of $x^2 + y^2 + z^2$ on $x^2y^2z^2 = (\rho^2/3)^3$ is ρ^2.

(c) Generalize (a) or (b) and so deduce that, for positive a's $(a_1 a_2 \cdots a_n)^{1/n} \leqslant (a_1 + a_2 + \cdots + a_n)/n$, that is, the geometric mean is less than or equal to the arithmetic mean.

12

Multiple Integrals

12.1 INTEGRALS OVER RECTANGLES

We now study integrals of functions of several variables. The motivations and heuristics connected with multiple integrals are much the same as with simple integrals (as we will now call the integrals of a function of a real variable). For this reason, you should reread the introduction to Chapter 4.

First we consider integrals over rectangular regions given in two dimensions by

$$R: \begin{cases} a_1 \leqslant x \leqslant b_1 \\ a_2 \leqslant y \leqslant b_2 \end{cases}$$

and in three dimensions by

$$R: \begin{cases} a_1 \leqslant x \leqslant b_1 \\ a_2 \leqslant y \leqslant b_2 \\ a_3 \leqslant z \leqslant b_3 \end{cases}$$

Our discussion will concern itself largely with integrals in two and three dimensions, with only occasional remarks about the higher dimensions but a careful reading of the proofs should make it clear that no essential changes are required to handle integrals in higher dimensions. In n dimensions, the rectangle would be described by

$$R: \{a_i \leqslant x_i \leqslant b_i \qquad i = 1, 2, 3, \ldots, n\}.$$

We proceed to set up notation in a manner analogous to that used in Chapter 4.

Form a partition of each dimension of R:

$$a_1 = x_0 < x_1 < \cdots < x_n = b_1$$
$$a_2 = y_0 < y_1 < \cdots < y_p = b_2,$$

and if in three dimensions,

$$a_3 = z_0 < z_1 < \cdots < z_r = b_3.$$

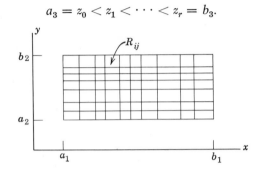

These form a partition Δ of R into smaller rectangles:

$$R_{ij}: \begin{cases} x_{i-1} \leqslant x \leqslant x_i \\ y_{j-1} \leqslant y \leqslant y_j \end{cases} \quad \text{or} \quad R_{ijk}: \begin{cases} x_{i-1} \leqslant x \leqslant x_i \\ y_{j-1} \leqslant y \leqslant y_j \\ z_{k-1} \leqslant z \leqslant z_k \end{cases}.$$

The **norm** of the partition Δ, written $\|\Delta\|$, we take to be the maximum diameter of the sub-rectangles—that is, in two dimensions

$$\|\Delta\| = \max_{\Delta} \sqrt{(x_{i-1} - x_i)^2 + (y_{j-1} - y_j)^2},$$

where max means that the maximum is to be taken of all the diameters Δ (in this case diagonals) of all the sub-rectangles which make up Δ.

Further, we set $A_{ij} = (x_i - x_{i-1})(y_j - y_{j-1})$ and $V_{ijk} = (x_i - x_{i-1})(y_j - y_{j-1})(z_k - z_{k-1})$. These, of course, are the area and volume of R_{ij} and R_{ijk}, respectively.

We assume our function to be defined and bounded on R. We will use the following notation consistently:

$$M = \sup_{R} f \qquad m = \inf_{R} f$$

$$M_{ij} = \sup_{R_{ij}} f \qquad m_{ij} = \inf_{R_{ij}} f,$$

and in three dimensions,

$$M_{ijk} = \sup_{R_{ijk}} f \qquad m_{ijk} = \inf_{R_{ijk}} f.$$

By an upper sum $\bar{S}_\Delta(f, R)$—or more briefly $\bar{S}_\Delta$, since f and R will remain unchanged—we mean

$$\sum_\Delta M_{ij}A_{ij} \quad \text{or} \quad \sum_\Delta M_{ijk}V_{ijk},$$

according to the dimension. Of course $\sum_\Delta$ means that, for each R_{ij}, the product $M_{ij}A_{ij}$ is computed, and the sum is taken over all R_{ij} in Δ. A similar remark applies to the three-dimensional case.

By a lower sum $\underline{S}_\Delta(f, R)$, or more briefly $\underline{S}_\Delta$, we mean

$$\sum_\Delta m_{ij}A_{ij} \quad \text{or} \quad \sum_\Delta m_{ijk}V_{ijk}.$$

We come now to a series of lemmas similar to those of Chapter 4.

12.1a Lemma. $\bar{S}_\Delta \geqslant \underline{S}_\Delta$

Proof. Immediate since $M_{ij} \geqslant m_{ij}$. ∎

We will say that a partition Δ' is a refinement of a partition Δ if the partition of the x interval for Δ' is a refinement of the partition of the x interval for Δ, and if the same is true for the y and z intervals.

12.1b Lemma. If Δ' is a refinement of Δ, then

$$\bar{S}_{\Delta'} \leqslant \bar{S}_\Delta \quad \text{and} \quad \underline{S}_{\Delta'} \geqslant \underline{S}_\Delta.$$

Proof. (For two dimensions.) Let R_{ij} be a sub-rectangle in the partition Δ. Then either it occurs unchanged in Δ', or it will be cut up into a finite number of sub-rectangles R'_{qr} belonging to Δ'. The contribution

$$R_{ij}$$

R'_{qr}	R'_{qr}
R'_{qr}	R'_{qr}
R'_{qr}	R'_{qr}

to $\bar{S}_{\Delta'}$ arising from R_{ij} is (1) the same, if R_{ij} is not subdivided; or (2) is $\sum_{R_{ij}} M'_{qr} A'_{qr}$, where the sum is taken over those rectangles into which R_{ij} is subdivided. But there $M'_{qr} \leqslant M_{ij}$, so that

$$\sum_{R_{ij}} M'_{qr}A'_{qr} \leqslant \sum_{R_{ij}} M_{ij}A'_{qr} = M_{ij}\sum_{R_{ij}} A'_{qr} = M_{ij}A_{ij}.$$

Thus in either case the contribution to $\bar{S}_{\Delta'}$ arising from R_{ij} is less than or equal to the contribution to $\bar{S}_\Delta$ arising from the same R_{ij}. Then, by summing over all R_{ij} in Δ, we get the desired result. Clearly the inequality for lower sums goes the other way, and equally clearly the same argument works in any number of dimensions. ∎

12.1c Lemma. If Δ_1 and Δ_2 are any two partitions of R, then

$$\bar{S}_{\Delta_1} \geqslant \underline{S}_{\Delta_2}.$$

Proof. Let Δ' be a common refinement of Δ_1 and Δ_2. (How can one be formed?) Then, by Lemmas 12.1a and b,

$$\bar{S}_{\Delta_1} \geqslant \bar{S}_{\Delta'} \geqslant \underline{S}_{\Delta'} \geqslant \underline{S}_{\Delta_2}. \qquad \blacksquare$$

Thus we can now assert that, for a given bounded function f defined on a rectangle R, the class of numbers formed by the upper sums has any lower sum as a lower bound; and conversely the class of numbers formed by the lower sums has any upper sum as an upper bound. Hence

$$\inf \bar{S}_\Delta \geqslant \underline{S}_{\Delta'}$$

for any partition Δ'. Forming the supremum of the right hand side, we then get

$$\inf \bar{S}_\Delta \geqslant \sup \underline{S}_\Delta.$$

These extreme bounds are called the **upper** and **lower Riemann-Darboux integrals**, respectively, and are denoted by

$$\inf \bar{S}_\Delta = \overline{\iint_R} f(\mathbf{P}) \, dA \quad \text{or} \quad \overline{\iiint_R} f(\mathbf{P}) \, dV$$

and

$$\sup \underline{S}_\Delta = \underline{\iint_R} f(\mathbf{P}) \, dA \quad \text{or} \quad \underline{\iiint_R} f(\mathbf{P}) \, dV.$$

We have thus proved

12.1d Lemma.

$$\overline{\iint_R} f(\mathbf{P}) \, dA \geqslant \underline{\iint_R} f(\mathbf{P}) \, dA$$

and

$$\overline{\iiint_R} f(\mathbf{P}) \, dV \geqslant \underline{\iiint_R} f(\mathbf{P}) \, dV.$$

We can now define the Riemann integral of a function f on a rectangle R. Let f be a bounded function defined on R. If

$$\overline{\iint_R} f(\mathbf{P}) \, dA = \underline{\iint_R} f(\mathbf{P}) \, dA,$$

we say that f is **Riemann integrable** on R. The common value we call the **Riemann integral** of f over R and denote it by

$$\iint_R f(\mathbf{P}) \, dA \quad \text{or} \quad \iint_R f(\mathbf{P}) \, dx \, dy.$$

The volume or triple Riemann integral is analogously defined. It will be denoted by

$$\iiint_R f(\mathbf{P})\, dV \quad \text{or} \quad \iiint_R f(\mathbf{P})\, dx\, dy\, dz$$

An immediate consequence of Lemma 12.1c is the following criterion for integrability.

12.1e Theorem. Let f be a bounded function defined on a rectangle R. A necessary and sufficient condition that f be integrable on R is that for each $\epsilon > 0$ there exists a partition Δ of R such that

$$\bar{S}_\Delta - \underline{S}_\Delta < \epsilon.$$

Proof. See Exercise B4.

We now want to explore the idea of the integral as a limit of a Riemann sum. For this purpose we need the following lemma.

12.1f Lemma. If f is a bounded function on a rectangle R, then for each $\epsilon > 0$ there is a $\delta(\epsilon)$ such that

$$\bar{S}_\Delta < \overline{\iint_R} f(\mathbf{P})\, dA + \epsilon$$

and

$$\underline{S}_\Delta > \underline{\iint_R} f(\mathbf{P})\, dA - \epsilon$$

for all partitions Δ for which $\|\Delta\| < \delta(\epsilon)$. The same result holds for triple integrals, of course.

We prove the first inequality. The second is similar. For simplicity, our proof is only for the case of double integrals, but you will see as it develops that the argument is not essentially different in three (or more) dimensions.

Proof. By the definition of an upper integral, there is a partition Δ' for which

$$\overline{\iint_R} f(\mathbf{P})\, dA \leqslant \bar{S}_{\Delta'} \leqslant \overline{\iint_R} f(\mathbf{P})\, dA + \epsilon/2.$$

This partition will be so chosen and will remain fixed throughout the following argument. Let the partition points of Δ' be given by

$$a_1 = x_0' < x_1' < \cdots < x_{n'}' = b_1$$
$$a_2 = y_0' < y_1' < \cdots < y_{m'}' = b_2.$$

We now choose
$$\delta = \sqrt{\epsilon/2(M - m)(n' + m')},$$
where M, m are $\sup_{D} f$ and $\inf_{D} f$. We will show that any D with $\|\Delta\| < \delta$ satisfies the conclusion of the theorem.

Let Δ be any such partition, and Δ'' be the common refinement of Δ and Δ' with corresponding sub-rectangles R''_{pq}. Suppose R_{ij} is a sub-rectangle of Δ which is subdivided by the refinement into certain R''_{pq}'s. Then any one term of $\bar{S}_{\Delta}$ can be written as
$$M_{ij}A_{ij} = M_{ij} \sum_{R_{ij}} A''_{pq},$$
where $M_{ij} = \sup_{R_{ij}} f$, and so forth, and where the sum is extended over all R''_{pq} contained in R_{ij}. For each such R''_{pq}, define $\mathscr{M}''_{pq} = M_{ij}$. Then
$$M_{ij}A_{ij} = \sum_{R_{ij}} \mathscr{M}''_{pq} A''_{pq}.$$
Summing over all R_{ij}'s in Δ, we get
$$\bar{S}_{\Delta} = \Sigma \, \mathscr{M}''_{pq} A''_{pq}.$$
And by definition,
$$\bar{S}_{\Delta''} = \Sigma \, M''_{pq} A''_{pq}.$$

We want to estimate the difference between these two sums. For this purpose we separate the rectangles R_{ij} of Δ into two classes: (I) those which remain unchanged by the refinement to and which therefore occur as R''_{pr}'s, and (II) those which are subdivided by the refinement and hence form two or more R''_{pq}'s. Clearly the contribution to $\bar{S}_{\Delta}$ and $\bar{S}_{\Delta''}$ from rectangles of the first class is the same, and therefore these contributions cancel out when we compute the difference.

The rectangles of class II may be cut by a vertical line $x = x_i'$ or a horizontal one $y = y_j'$. Since $\|\Delta\| < \delta$, certainly any one dimension of any rectangle in Δ is $< \delta$. Consequently the area of any one such rectangle is less than δ^2, and there are at most n' of them, so that the total area of all such rectangles is at most $n'\delta^2$. Similarly, the total area of all rectangles cut by lines of the form $y = y'$ is at most $m'\delta^2$. Thus
$$0 \leqslant \bar{S}_{\Delta} - \bar{S}_{\Delta''} = \sum_{\Delta} \sum_{R_{ij}} (\mathscr{M}''_{pq} - M''_{pq}) A''_{pq}$$
$$\leqslant \sum_{(\mathrm{II})} \sum_{R_{ij}} (M - m) A''_{pq} = \sum_{(\mathrm{II})} (M - m) A_{ij} = (M - m)\delta^2(n' + m'),$$
where $\sum_{(\mathrm{II})}$ means that the sum is taken over all rectangles of class II.

Substituting for δ,

$$0 \leqslant \bar{S}_\Delta - \bar{S}_{\Delta''} < \epsilon/2.$$

Now $\bar{S}_{\Delta''} \leqslant \bar{S}_{\Delta'}$, since Δ'' is a refinement of Δ'. Thus we finally get

$$0 \leqslant \bar{S}_\Delta - \overline{\iint_R} f(\mathbf{P})\, dA < \bar{S}_\Delta - \bar{S}_{\Delta'} + \epsilon/2 \leqslant \bar{S}_\Delta - \bar{S}_{\Delta''} + \epsilon/2 < \epsilon. \quad \blacksquare$$

Let f be a bounded function on R and Δ a partition of R. In each sub-rectangle R_{ij} of Δ, we can choose a point $\mathbf{P}_{ij}$ (or $\mathbf{P}_{ijk}$ in three dimensions) and form the sum

$$S_\Delta(f, R, \mathbf{P}) = \sum_\Delta f(\mathbf{P}_{ij}) A_{ij}$$

or

$$S_\Delta(f, R, \mathbf{P}) = \sum_\Delta f(\mathbf{P}_{ijk}) V_{ijk},$$

which we will sometimes abbreviate to $S_\Delta(\mathbf{P})$. Such a sum is called a **Riemann sum.**

We will say that $\lim_{\|\Delta\| \to 0} S_\Delta(\mathbf{P}) = J$ if for each $\epsilon > 0$ there is a δ such that

$$|S_\Delta(\mathbf{P}) - J| < \epsilon \qquad \text{if } \|\Delta\| < \delta$$

for all choices of the $\mathbf{P}$'s. Then, as in the one-dimensional case, we have the following theorem.

12.1g   Theorem. Let f be a bounded function on R. A necessary and sufficient condition that $\iint_R f(\mathbf{P})\, dA$ or $\iiint_R f(\mathbf{P})\, dV$ exists and equals J is that $\quad \lim_{\|\Delta\| \to 0} S_\Delta(\mathbf{P}) = J.$

Proof. See Exercise B4.

12.2   PROPERTIES OF THE INTEGRAL. CLASSES OF INTEGRABLE FUNCTIONS

We now want to lay out some of the elementary properties of integrals on rectangles which are useful in calculations. The proofs are so similar to those of the one-dimensional case that they are usually omitted. However, it would serve as a good review to write out the proofs of these theorems for yourself. (See Exercise C5.)

12.2a   Theorem. If f is integrable on a rectangle R, it is integrable on any sub-rectangle of R.

12.2b **Theorem.** If f is integrable on a rectangle R, and if R_1 and R_2 are formed from R by cutting it with a line (or plane) parallel with one of the coordinate axes (or planes), then

$$\iint_{R_1} f(\mathbf{P})\, dA + \iint_{R_2} f(\mathbf{P})\, dA = \iint_{R} f(\mathbf{P})\, dA$$

or

$$\iiint_{R_1} f(\mathbf{P})\, dV + \iiint_{R_2} f(\mathbf{P})\, dV = \iint_{R} \int f(\mathbf{P})\, dV.$$

12.2c **Theorem.** If f and g are integrable on R, and if $f(\mathbf{P}) \geqslant g(\mathbf{P})$ on R, then

$$\iint_{R} f(\mathbf{P})\, dA \geqslant \iint_{R} g(\mathbf{P})\, dA$$

or

$$\iiint_{R} f(\mathbf{P})\, dV \geqslant \iiint_{R} g(\mathbf{P})\, dV.$$

12.2d **Theorem.** If f is integrable on R, then so are f^+, f^- and $|f|$. (For the definition of f^+ and f^-, see Section 4.4).

12.2e **Theorem.** If f and g are integrable on R, so are $f \pm g$ and $f \cdot g$; and, if there is a constant $c > 0$ such that $|g| \geqslant c$, so is f/g.

12.2f **Theorem.** If f is a continuous function on R, it is integrable on R.
Proof. By Theorem 9.6d, f is uniformly continuous on R, since R is a closed bounded set. Thus, corresponding to each $\epsilon > 0$, there is a uniform δ such that $|f(\mathbf{P}) - f(\mathbf{Q})| < \epsilon$ for every pair of points $\mathbf{P}, \mathbf{Q}$ in R for which $|\mathbf{P} - \mathbf{Q}| < \delta$.

Choose Δ so that $\|\Delta\| < \epsilon$. Then in each R_{ij} of Δ, we have $0 \leqslant M_{ij} - m_{ij} \leqslant \epsilon$, since there are points $\mathbf{P}_{ij}$ and $\mathbf{Q}_{ij}$ at which $f(\mathbf{P}_{ij}) = M_{ij}$ and $f(\mathbf{Q}_{ij}) = m_{ij}$. We compare the upper and lower sums:

$$\bar{S}_\Delta - \underline{S}_\Delta = \sum_\Delta (M_{ij} - m_{ij})A_{ij} < \epsilon \sum_\Delta A_{ij} = \epsilon A,$$

where A is the area of R. Similarly, in three dimensions $\bar{S}_\Delta - \underline{S}_\Delta < \epsilon V$. Thus, by Theorem 12.1d, the function f is integrable ∎

The mean-value theorem carries over into multiple integrals.

12.2g **Theorem.** If f and g are integrable on R, and g is non-negative there, then there is a number μ, $\inf_R f \leqslant \mu \leqslant \sup_R f$ such that

$$\iint_{R} f(\mathbf{P})g(\mathbf{P})\, dA = \mu \iint_{R} g(\mathbf{P})\, dA,$$

and if f is continuous there is a point $\mathbf{P}_0$ in R at which $\mu = f(\mathbf{P}_0)$. (See Exercise C1 of Section 9.7.)

12.3   ITERATED INTEGRALS

If f is defined on a rectangle $R:\{a_1 \leqslant x \leqslant b_1, a_2 \leqslant y \leqslant b_2\}$, and if for each fixed x it is an integrable function of y, then this integral defines a function g on $\{a_1 \leqslant x \leqslant b_1\}$:

$$g(x) = \int_{a_2}^{b_2} f(x, y)\, dy.$$

If in turn g is an integrable function of x, the result

$$\int_{a_1}^{b_1}\left(\int_{a_2}^{b_2}(x, y)\, dy \right) dx$$

is called an **iterated integral** and will be denoted here by

$$\int_{a_1}^{b_1} dx \int_{a_2}^{b_2} f(x, y)\, dy.$$

A Riemann sum for a double integral

$$S_\Delta = \sum_\Delta f(\mathbf{P}_{ij}) A_{ij}$$

can be arranged as an iterated sum:

$$S = \sum_\Delta f(x_i, y_j)(x_i - x_{i-1})(y_j - y_{j-1})$$

$$= \sum_i (x_i - x_{i-1})\sum_j f(x_i y_j)(y_j - y_{j-1}).$$

The form of this sum seems to suggest that its limit might be an iterated integral. Therefore we would expect, under sufficient restrictions, to be able to show that

(1)
$$\iint_R f(\mathbf{P})\, dA = \int_{a_1}^{b_1} dx \int_{a_2}^{b_2} f(x, y)\, dy.$$

That this is indeed the case is proved in the following theorem.

12.3a   Theorem. Suppose f is integrable in $R: \{a_1 \leqslant x \leqslant b_1, a_2 \leqslant y \leqslant b_2\}$, and suppose that for each fixed x it is an integrable function of y in $\{a_2 \leqslant y \leqslant b_2\}$. Then the function g, defined by

$$g(x) = \int_{a_2}^{b_2} f(x, y)\, dy,$$

is an integrable function of x on $\{a_1 \leqslant x \leqslant b_1\}$ and (1) holds.

Proof. Let Δ be a partition on R, and for each i let ξ_i be an arbitrarily chosen number in $\{x_{i-1} \leqslant x \leqslant x_i\}$. Then, by the mean-value theorem for simple integrals, there is a μ_{ij} such that

$$\int_{y_{j-1}}^{y_j} f(\xi_i, y) \, dy = \mu_{ij} \, \Delta_j y,$$

where $m_{ij} \leqslant \mu_{ij} \leqslant M_{ij}$. Therefore

$$\underline{S}_\Delta \leqslant \sum \mu_{ij} A_{ij} \leqslant \bar{S}_\Delta.$$

Since f is integrable on R, it follows that the sum in the previous expression tends to

(2) $$\iint_R f(\mathbf{P}) \, dA \qquad \text{as } \|\Delta\| \to 0.$$

This sum can also be written as

$$\sum_\Delta \mu_{ij} A_{ij} = \sum_{i,j} \Delta_i x \int_{y_{j-1}}^{y_i} f(\xi_i, y) \, dy$$

$$= \sum_i \int_{a_2}^{b_2} f(\xi_i, y) \, dy \, \Delta_i x = \sum_i g(\xi_i) \, \Delta_i x.$$

By what we have shown, this last sum has a limit as the norm of the x-partition tends to zero. But this is the meaning of the integrability of g. Furthermore the value of this limit, namely (2), is the integral of g. ∎

It is clear from the symmetry of the argument that the roles of x and y can be interchanged, provided, of course, that the hypotheses are correspondingly interchanged. Thus if f is integrable in x for each y and integrable in y for each x, then the two iterated integrals are equal to each other, since they are both equal to the double integral. Thus we have the following corollary.

12.3b   Corollary. If f is integrable as a double integral on $R_1\{a_1 \leqslant x \leqslant b_1, a_2 \leqslant y \leqslant b_2\}$, and if it is integrable in x for each y and integrable in y for each x, then

$$\int_{a_1}^{b_1} dx \int_{a_2}^{b_2} f(x, y) \, dy = \int_{a_2}^{b_2} dy \int_{a_1}^{b_1} f(x, y) \, dx.$$

It would be nice to have a converse of Theorem 12.3a which would say something like this: If f is integrable in y for each x, and if the result is integrable in x, then the double integral also exists and is equal to the iterated integral. However, the situation is not quite that simple (see Exercise B1 for a counter-example); some additional condition is needed to guarantee the existence of the double integral. And of course once such a condition is presupposed it could replace the hypothesis that the double integral exists.

Theorem 12.3a extends to triple integrals in the following manner.

12.3c   Theorem. Let f be an integrable function on the rectangle $R: \{a_1 \leqslant x \leqslant b_1, a_2 \leqslant y \leqslant b_2, a_3 \leqslant z \leqslant b_3\}$, and suppose that for each fixed x it is an integrable function over the rectangle $R_{yz}: \{a_2 \leqslant y \leqslant b_2, a_3 \leqslant z \leqslant b_3\}$. This integral is then an integrable function of x and

$$\iiint_R f(\mathbf{P}) \, dV = \int_{a_1}^{b_1} dx \iint_{R_{yz}} f(x, y, z) \, dy \, dz$$

12.3d   Theorem. Let f be an integrable function on the rectangle $R: \{a_1 \leqslant x \leqslant b_1, a_2 \leqslant y \leqslant b_2, a_3 \leqslant z \leqslant b_3\}$, and suppose that for each fixed (y, z) it is an integrable function of x. This integral is then an integrable function of (y, z) over R_{yz} and

$$\iiint_R f(\mathbf{P}) \, dV = \iint_{R_{yz}} dy \, dz \int_{a_1}^{b_1} f(x, y, z) \, dx.$$

The proofs of these two theorems are similar to the proof of Theorem 12.3a and so are left as exercises.

If the hypotheses of Theorem 12.3a are satisfied, we can apply it to the double integral which occurs in 12.3c or d to express the triple integral as a triple iterated integral. For example,

$$\iiint_R f(\mathbf{P}) \, dV = \int_{a_1}^{b_1} dx \int_{a_2}^{b_2} dy \int_{a_3}^{b_3} f(x, y, z) \, dz.$$

In particular we may note that, if f is continuous, then all the integrals in question exist, so that the integral of a continuous function defined on a rectangle can be evaluated by iterated integrals where iteration can be taken in any order.

A EXERCISES

1. Evaluate the following integrals:

(a) $\displaystyle\iint_R (x + y) \, e^{x+y} \, dx \, dy$ $\qquad\qquad R: \{0 \leqslant x \leqslant 2, 1 \leqslant y \leqslant 4\}$

(b) $\displaystyle\iint_R |x + y| \, dx \, dy$ $\qquad\qquad R: \{|x| \leqslant 1, |y| \leqslant 1\}$

(c) $\displaystyle\iint\limits_{R} \frac{x}{y}\, dx\, dy$ $R: \{|x| \leqslant 1,\, 1 \leqslant y \leqslant 2\}$

(d) $\displaystyle\iiint\limits_{R} \cos (x + 2y + 3z)\, dx\, dy\, dz$ $R: \{0 \leqslant x \leqslant 2,\, 1 \leqslant y \leqslant 3,\, |z| \leqslant 1\}$

2. Show that if f is integrable over R, and c is a constant, then

$$\iint\limits_{R} cf(\mathbf{P})\, dA = c \iint\limits_{R} f(\mathbf{P})\, dA$$

3. Suppose f and g are integrable over R, $g \geqslant 0$, and $\displaystyle\iint\limits_{R} g(\mathbf{P})\, dA = 0$. Show that $\displaystyle\iint\limits_{R} f(\mathbf{P})\, g(\mathbf{P})\, dA = 0$.

B EXERCISES

1. Let f be defined over $R: \{0 \leqslant x \leqslant 1,\, 0 \leqslant y \leqslant 1\}$ by

$$f(x, y) = \begin{cases} 1 & \text{if } x \text{ is irrational} \\ 3y^2 & \text{if } x \text{ is rational.} \end{cases}$$

Show that:

(a) f is not integrable over R.

(b) the iterated integral $\displaystyle\int_{0}^{1} dx \int_{0}^{1} f(x, y)\, dy$ exists.

(c) the other iterated integral does not exist.

2. Let f be defined on $R: \{a_1 \leqslant x \leqslant b_1,\, a_2 \leqslant y \leqslant b_2\}$, be monotone in x for each y, and be monotone in y for each x.

(a) Show that f is integrable over R.

(b) If f is increasing in y, show that

$$(b_2 - a_2) \int_{a_1}^{b_1} f(x, a_2)\, dx \leqslant \iint\limits_{R} f\, dA \leqslant (b_2 - a_2) \int_{a_1}^{b_1} f(x, b_2)\, dx.$$

3. Let f be continuous on $R: \{a_1 \leqslant x \leqslant b_1,\, a_2 \leqslant y \leqslant b_2\}$. For (α, β) in R, denote $\{a_1 \leqslant x \leqslant \alpha,\, a_2 \leqslant y \leqslant \beta\}$ by $R_{\alpha\beta}$. Show that $\displaystyle\frac{\partial^2}{\partial \alpha\, \partial \beta} \iint\limits_{R_{\alpha\beta}} f(x, y)\, dA = f(\alpha, \beta)$.

4. Prove Theorems 12.1d and 12.1f.

C EXERCISES

1. Let $f = \begin{cases} x^2 y + y^3 & \text{in } \{0 \leqslant x \leqslant 1,\, 0 \leqslant y \leqslant 1\} \\ x^3 y + x & \text{in } \{1 < x \leqslant 2,\, 0 \leqslant y \leqslant 1\}. \end{cases}$

Show that f is integrable over $\{0 \leqslant x \leqslant 2,\, 0 \leqslant y \leqslant 1\}$.

2. Let f be an integrable function of x in $\{a_1 \leqslant x \leqslant b_1\}$ and g integrable in $\{a_2 \leqslant y \leqslant b_2\}$. Show that $f(x)g(y)$ defines an integrable function in $\{a_1 \leqslant x \leqslant b_1, a_2 \leqslant y \leqslant b_2\}$.

3. Let f and g be integrable on $\{a \leqslant x \leqslant b\}$. Denote $\{a \leqslant x \leqslant b, a \leqslant y \leqslant b\}$ by S and, using Exercise 2 above, show that

$$\frac{1}{2}\int\!\!\int_S [f(x)\,g(y) - f(y)\,g(x)]^2 \, dx\, dy$$

$$= \left(\int_a^b f^2(x)\, dx\right)\left(\int_a^b g^2(x)\, dx\right) - \left(\int_a^b f(x)\,g(x)\, dx\right)^2$$

4. If f and g are integrable on $\{a \leqslant x \leqslant b\}$, then

$$\frac{1}{2}\int\!\!\int_S [f(x) - f(y)][g(x) - g(y)]\, dx\, dy$$

$$= (b - a)\int_a^b f(x)\,g(x)\, dx - \left(\int_a^b f(x)\, dx\right)\left(\int_a^b g(x)\, dx\right)$$

and if f and g are monotone, both in the same sense, then

$$\frac{1}{b - a}\int_a^b f(x)\,g(x)\, dx \geqslant \left(\frac{1}{b - a}\int_a^b f(x)\, dx\right)\left(\frac{1}{b - a}\int_a^b g(x)\, dx\right).$$

5. Prove Theorems 12.2a, b, c, d, and e.

12.4 INTEGRATION OVER REGIONS. AREA AND VOLUME

Now we come to the problem of integration over more general sets. In getting down to particulars, we will restrict our considerations to regions (open, closed, or partially closed) whose boundaries are not too complicated. The description of the conditions permitted will be given later. First we deal with the general situation.

We say that a set S of points is a **null set** or has **Jordan content zero** (or more simply, **content zero**) if for each $\epsilon > 0$ there are a finite number of rectangles $R_1, R_2, \ldots, R_n$ such that each point of S is in at least one of these rectangles, and such that the sum of the areas (or volumes) of the rectangles is $< \epsilon$. In the case of one dimension, the rectangles are replaced by intervals having a total length $< \epsilon$.

Clearly such a set must be in some sense small. The point which concerns us about such sets is that they are negligible so far as integration is concerned, in ways which will be made precise by the following discussion. We begin with a fundamental result.

12.4a   Theorem. Let f be a bounded function defined on a rectangle (or an interval) R. If the set S of points where it is discontinuous has content zero, then f is integrable on R.

Proof. The proof will be given for two dimensions. However, it is also valid for all dimensions. You should check to see that in particular it holds for single (that is, one-dimensional) integrals.

Let $\epsilon > 0$ be given, and let $R_1, R_2, \ldots, R_n$ be the covering set of rectangles with total area $< \epsilon$. If we place over each rectangle R_j another rectangle R_j', having the same center and twice the measurements of R_j, the new set of rectangles will have a total area $< 4\epsilon$. Furthermore, among the rectangles R_j there will be a shortest side. Denote its length by $2r$.

Let R' denote the remainder of R after the interiors of the R_j's are removed. On this closed set R', our function f is continuous, and is therefore uniformly continuous. Thus there is a uniform $\delta(\epsilon)$ such that $|f(\mathbf{P}) - f(\mathbf{Q})| < \epsilon$ if $|\mathbf{P} - \mathbf{Q}| < \delta$ for any two points $\mathbf{P}$ and $\mathbf{Q}$ in R'.

Let Δ be a partition of R with norm less than δ and less than r. We want to estimate

$$\bar{S}_\Delta - \underline{S}_\Delta = \Sigma(M_{ij} - m_{ij})A_{ij}.$$

For this purpose we divide the sub-rectangles R_{ij} into two classes: (I) all R_{ij} which have a point in common with one of the original R_j's, and (II) all others. We divide the sum into two sums according to the class in which R_{ij} falls:

$$\sum_\Delta (M_{ij} - m_{ij})A_{ij} = \sum_{\mathrm{I}}(M_{ij} - m_{ij})A_{ij} + \sum_{\mathrm{II}}(M_{ij} - m_{ij})A_{ij}.$$

Now all the rectangles in class I touch an R_j. Any such rectangle has its maximum dimension $< r =$ half the smallest dimension of an R_j, and is therefore contained in an R_j'. Since the R_{ij}'s are non-overlapping, the total area of all such rectangles is less than the total of the R_j''s, and is therefore $< 4\epsilon$. Consequently

(1) $$\sum_{\mathrm{I}}(M_{ij} - m_{ij})A_{ij} \leqslant 2M\sum_{\mathrm{I}}A_{ij} \leqslant 2M4\epsilon = 8M\epsilon,$$

where $M = \sup_R f$.

In the other sum, $M_{ij} - m_{ij} < \epsilon$ by uniform continuity. Thus

(2) $$\sum_{\mathrm{II}}(M_{ij} - m_{ij})A_{ij} \leqslant \epsilon\sum_{\mathrm{II}}A_{ij} \leqslant A\epsilon,$$

where A is the area of R.

Combining (1) and (2), we get

$$\bar{S}_\Delta - \underline{S}_\Delta \leqslant (8M + A)\epsilon.$$

By Theorem 12.1e, we conclude the integrability of f.   ∎

This theorem holds also for simple (that is, one-dimensional) integrals. The proof is left as an exercise (B7).

We are now in a position to consider integrals of continuous functions over more general sets. Let D be a bounded set and f a bounded function defined on D. Choose a rectangle R so large that D is contained in the interior of R, and define g in R by

$$g(\mathbf{P}) = \begin{cases} f(\mathbf{P}) & \text{if } \mathbf{P} \text{ is in } D \\ 0 & \text{otherwise.} \end{cases}$$

If g is integrable over R, then we say that f is integrable over D and that

$$\iint_D f(\mathbf{P})\, dA = \iint_R g(\mathbf{P})\, dA.$$

If g is not integrable over R, we say that f is not integrable over D.

We want to point out that for our definition to make sense we must know that the definition of the integral over D is independent of the rectangle R enclosing D. That this is indeed so is covered by Exercise B5.

Where D is a region (open, closed, or partially closed) and f is continuous on D, we see that it is sufficient to determine conditions under which the boundary of D has content zero, since g is clearly continuous in R except on the boundary of D. We therefore study the geometry of curves and surfaces a little.

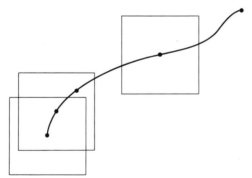

12.4b   Theorem. If C is a rectifiable curve, it has content zero.

Proof. (Two dimensions.) Let s be the length of the curve and n be an arbitrary integer. Choose points $\mathbf{P}_1, \ldots, \mathbf{P}_n$ whose distances from the initial point of C are $s/n, 2s/n, 3s/n, \ldots, (n-1)s/n, s$, respectively. At each $\mathbf{P}_j$ construct the square centered at $\mathbf{P}_j$, with sides parallel to the axes with the length of each side equal to $4s/n$. Then any point on C is at a distance less than s/n from one of the $\mathbf{P}_j$'s, and hence is in at least one such square. The area of each square is $16s^2/n^2$, and the number of squares is n, so that the total area is $16s^2/n$. Clearly, for each $\epsilon > 0$, we can choose n so large that $16s^2/n < \epsilon$. ∎

The following theorem is an immediate consequence of the two previous theorems.

12.4c   Theorem. Let R be a region in E_2 whose boundary consists of a finite number of rectifiable curves. If f is continuous on R, then f is integrable on R.

Proof. For clearly any finite number of sets of content zero will be a set which has content zero. ∎

In order to discuss the situation in three dimensions, we need to consider when a surface will be of content zero. The only type of surface we deal with are those representable in the form $z = f(x, y)$, where f is a continuous function. Our discussion here will be restricted to such surfaces. The same type of discussion will apply to curves of the form $y = f(x)$, whether they be rectifiable or not, thus giving an extension of Theorem 12.4b.

12.4d   Theorem. Let f be a continuous function defined on a closed bounded region D in E_2. The surface given by S: $z = f(x, y)$ is a set of three-dimensional content zero.

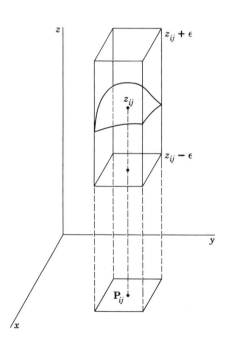

Proof. Since f is continuous on D, it is uniformly continuous there; that is, for each $\epsilon > 0$ there is a $\delta(\epsilon)$ such that $|f(\mathbf{P}) - f(\mathbf{Q})| < \epsilon$ if $\mathbf{P}$ and $\mathbf{Q}$ are in D and $|\mathbf{P} - \mathbf{Q}| < \delta$. Enclose D in a big rectangle R, and form a partition Δ of R so that $\|\Delta\| < \delta$. In each sub-rectangle R_{ij} of Δ which touches D, choose a $\mathbf{P}_{ij}$ in the common part of R_{ij} and D. This determines a height $z_{ij} = f(\mathbf{P}_{ij})$ of a point on S.

Let $\mathcal{R}_{ij}$ be the three-dimensional rectangle above R_{ij} which consists of all points (x, y, z) for which (x, y) is in R_{ij} and $z_{ij} - \epsilon \leqslant z \leqslant z_{ij} + \epsilon$. Then that part of S above R_{ij} is in $\mathcal{R}_{ij}$, and consequently S is covered completely by the totality of the $\mathcal{R}_{ij}$. The volume of each $\mathcal{R}_{ij}$ is $2\epsilon A_{ij}$, so the total volume of all the $\mathcal{R}_{ij}$ is $2\epsilon A$, where A is the area of R. ∎

12.4e Theorem. Let f be a continuous function defined on a closed bounded interval I. The curve given by $C: y = f(x)$ is a set of two-dimensional content zero.

Proof. The proof is similar to that of Theorem 12.4d.

We will say that a surface is **projectable** onto the (x, y) plane if there is a closed bounded region D in the x, y plane in which the equation $z = f(x, y)$ describes the surface. Similarly, a surface may be projectable onto the (y, z) or the (x, z) plane.

12.4f Theorem. Let D be a bounded region (open, closed, or partially closed) whose boundary is composed of a finite number of projectable surfaces. If f is continuous on D, then it is integrable on D.

Proof. The proof is clear.

The situation now is this: if D is region whose boundary is a null set (that is, has content zero), then we can integrate continuous functions over D. Theorems 12.4b, d, and e give sufficient conditions under which certain types of boundaries will be null.

Do not, however, make the mistake of thinking that all regions have null boundaries. In fact, under a somewhat sophisticated definition of area (Lebesgue measure), one can show that there are regions (in two dimensions, for example) with area arbitrarily small which have boundaries whose area (sic!) is arbitrarily large.

12.4g Theorem. Suppose D is a bounded region (open, closed or partially closed) with a null boundary. Let S be a curve (or surface) which divides D into two sub-regions D_1 and D_2, and which has content zero. If f is continuous on D, then f is integrable over D_1 and D_2, and

$$\iint\limits_{D_1} f(\mathbf{P})\, dA + \iint\limits_{D_2} f(\mathbf{P})\, dA = \iint\limits_{D} f(\mathbf{P})\, dA.$$

If D is three-dimensional, the integrals will of course be volume integrals.

Proof. (Outline.) Choose a big rectangle R enclosing D and set

$$g(\mathbf{P}) = \begin{cases} f(\mathbf{P}) & \text{in } D \\ 0 & \text{otherwise}; \end{cases}$$

$$g_1(\mathbf{P}) = \begin{cases} f(\mathbf{P}) & \text{in } D_1, \\ 0 & \text{otherwise}; \end{cases}$$

$$g_2(\mathbf{P}) = \begin{cases} f(\mathbf{P}) & \text{in } D_2, \\ 0 & \text{otherwise}. \end{cases}$$

Apply Theorem 12.2d and the definition of integration over D, D_1, and D_2. ∎

This theorem easily extends to any decomposition into a finite number of sub-regions by dividing D by null surfaces or curves. In this case we have

$$\int\int_D f(\mathbf{P}) \, dA = \sum_k \int\int_{D_k} f(\mathbf{P}) \, dA.$$

We can now extend our definition of area. If D is any bounded set, we define the area of D by the formula

$$A_D = \int\int_D 1 \, dA$$

whenever the integral exists. We leave it as an exercise (B3) to show that this definition is consistent with that of Chapter 4.

Similarly, the volume of a set in three dimensions is defined by

$$V_D = \int\int\int_D dV.$$

Whenever the area (or volume) of D exists, we say that D is **quadrable.**

From Theorem 12.4g we see that if a quadrable region is divided up into a finite number of sub-regions by null surfaces (or curves), the sum of the areas of the sub-regions is the area of the original region:

$$A_D = \sum_k A_{D_k}.$$

Let D be a bounded region with a null boundary. Suppose it is sub-divided into smaller regions, D_k, $k = 1, 2, \ldots, n$, by null curves (or surfaces). Such a decomposition will be called a **curvilinear partition** Δ of D. The norm of Δ, again denoted by $\|\Delta\|$, is defined as the maximum of the diameters of the D_k's. (Recall that the diameter of a set is sup $|\mathbf{P} - \mathbf{Q}|$ where $\mathbf{P}$ and $\mathbf{Q}$ are in the set.) The area (or volume) of D_k will be denoted by A_k (or V_k).

12.4h **Theorem.** Let D be a bounded region with a null boundary and $f(\mathbf{P})$ a bounded function continuous on D. Let Δ be a curvilinear partition of D. In each D_k, choose a $\mathbf{P}_k$ arbitrarily. Then

$$\lim_{\|\Delta\| \to 0} \sum_{\Delta} f(\mathbf{P}_k) A_k = \int\int_D f(\mathbf{P})\, dA$$

or, in three dimensions,

$$\lim_{\|\Delta\| \to 0} \sum_{\Delta} f(\mathbf{P}_k) V_k = \int\int\int_D f(\mathbf{P})\, dV.$$

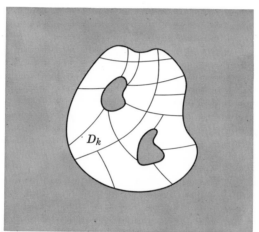

Proof. We will give the proof for D closed. If D is open or only partially closed, a more careful analysis is called for, as in the proofs of Theorems 12.4b and d. We write A, A_k, etc., but the argument is independent of the dimension.

If D is closed, we have f uniformly continuous. Hence for each $\epsilon > 0$, there is a $\delta(\epsilon)$ such that $|f(\mathbf{P}) - f(\mathbf{Q})| < \epsilon$ for all $\mathbf{P}$ and $\mathbf{Q}$ in D such that $|\mathbf{P} - \mathbf{Q}| < \delta$. Now choose Δ so that $\|\Delta\| < \delta$. Set

$$S_\Delta = \sum_{\Delta} f(\mathbf{P}_k) A_k = \sum_{\Delta} \int\int_{D_k} f(\mathbf{P}_k)\, dA$$

and

$$I_D = \int\int_D f(\mathbf{P})\, dA = \sum_{\Delta} \int\int_{D_k} f(\mathbf{P})\, dA.$$

Then
$$|S_\Delta - I_D| \leqslant \sum_\Delta \int\int_{D_k} |f(\mathbf{P}_k) - f(\mathbf{P})|\, dA$$

$$\sum_\Delta \int\int_{D_k} \epsilon\, dA = \sum_\Delta \epsilon A_k = \epsilon A_D. \quad\blacksquare$$

The possibility of expressing a multiple integral over a region as an iterated integral is assured by the theorems in Section 12.3. Any nontrivial theorems beyond those of Section 12.3 are awkward to state and difficult to prove. Individual problems can be handled usually by those theorems.

A EXERCISES

I. Show that each integral exists and evaluate:

(a) $\displaystyle\int\int_R (x + y)\, \mathrm{sgn}\,(x - y)\, dx\, dy$ $\quad R: \{0 \leqslant x \leqslant 1, 0 \leqslant y \leqslant 1\}$

(b) $\displaystyle\int\int\int_R (x + y + z)\, \mathrm{sgn}\,(x - y)\, dx\, dy\, dz$ $\quad R: \{0 \leqslant x \leqslant 1, 0 \leqslant y \leqslant 1,$
$0 \leqslant z \leqslant 1\}$

2. If f is continuous, show that:

$$\int_0^a dx \int_0^x f(x, y)\, dy = \int_0^a dy \int_y^a f(x, y)\, dx$$

3. Find the smaller of the areas enclosed by:

(a) $x^2 + y^2 = 4$ and $x + y = 2$ (b) $x^{1/2} + y^{1/2} = a^{1/2}$ and $x + y = a$

4. Evaluate and describe the region of integration in the xy plane:

(a) $\displaystyle\int_0^a dy \int_{a-y}^{\sqrt{a^2-y^2}} x\, dx$ (b) $\displaystyle\int_0^1 dx \int_x^1 e^{x/y}\, dy$

5. Reverse the order of integration:

(a) $\displaystyle\int_0^a dx \int_0^{\sqrt{a^2-x^2}} f(x, y)\, dy$ (b) $\displaystyle\int_1^1 dy \int_y^{y^{2/3}} f(x, y)\, dx$

(c) $\displaystyle\int_0^{\sqrt5} dy \int_y^{\sqrt{10-y^2}} f(x, y)\, dx$ (d) $\displaystyle\int_a^b dx \int_c^x f(x, y)\, dy$ (three cases)

B EXERCISES

I. Find the volume common to the sphere $\{x^2 + y^2 + z^2 \leqslant a^2\}$ and the cylinder $\{x^2 + y^2 \leqslant ax\}$.

2. Compute the area bounded by the four curves $y^3 = ax^2$, $y^3 = bx^2$, $x^4 = cy^3$, $x^4 = dy^3$. (Assume $b > a > 0$, $d > c > 0$).

3. Show that the definition of area given in this section is compatible with the definition of Chapter 4.

4. Prove Theorem 12.4e.

5. Show that the definition of an integral over an arbitrary closed set D is independent of the enclosing rectangle R.

6. Show that a set of content zero is a bounded set.

7. Verify Theorem 12.4a for simple integrals.

C EXERCISES

1. Let f be an integrable function on a quadrable region D_0, and suppose it is continuous at a point $\mathbf{P}_0$ in D_0. Show that $\dfrac{1}{A_D} \displaystyle\iint_D f(\mathbf{P})\, dA \to f(\mathbf{P}_0)$ as the diameter of $D \to 0$, where D represents a quadrable subset of D_0 containing $\mathbf{P}_0$.

2. Let D be the region bounded by $x = \pm 1$ on the right and left, by $y = -2$ below and above by $y = \sin 1/x$, for $x \neq 0$, and by the segment $\{x = 0, -1 \leqslant y \leqslant 1\}$. Show that D is quadrable.

13

Line and Surface
Integrals

13.1 LINE INTEGRALS. POTENTIALS

Let us re-emphasize that all our vector operations which do not involve vector products carry over immediately to Euclidean spaces of arbitrary dimension. In particular, in the present section we need only suppress the **k** component in order that the proofs be correct for two dimensions.

If C is a curve given by

$$\mathbf{P} = \mathbf{P}(t) = x(t)\mathbf{i} + y(t)\mathbf{j} + z(t)\mathbf{k} \qquad I: \{a \leqslant t \leqslant b\},$$

where $\mathbf{P}'(t)$ is continuous and not zero in I, then we will say that C is a **smooth curve.** We will also discuss piecewise smooth curves. A curve is **piecewise smooth** if the parameter interval I can be partitioned so that C is smooth in each sub-interval. More precisely, suppose there is a partition Δ of I

$$\Delta: a = t_0 < t_1 < \cdots < t_n = b$$

such that $\mathbf{P}'(t)$ exists in each open interval $\{t_{m-1} < t < t_m\}$ of Δ. If both one-sided derivatives $\mathbf{P}'(t_m - 0)$ and $\mathbf{P}'(t_m + 0)$ exist at each partition point, and $\mathbf{P}'(t)$ is continuous in each open interval $\{t_{m-1} < t < t_m\}$, we say that C is piecewise smooth.

Let f be a function defined on a piecewise smooth curve C. We want to define what we mean by the **line integral** of f over C. Let Δ be a partition of I: $\Delta: a = t_0 < t_1 < \cdots < t_n = b$. This induces a partition of C:

$$\mathbf{P}_0 = \mathbf{P}(t_0), \mathbf{P}_1 = \mathbf{P}(t_1), \ldots, \mathbf{P}_n = \mathbf{P}(t_n),$$

with of course x_m, y_m, and z_m defined by

$$\mathbf{P}_m = x_m\mathbf{i} + y_m\mathbf{j} + z_m\mathbf{k} \qquad m = 0, 1, \ldots, n.$$

In each sub-interval $\{t_{m-1} \leqslant t \leqslant t_m\}$. Choose a τ_m and define $\mathbf{Q}_k = \mathbf{P}(\tau_k)$, and form the sum

$$\sigma_\Delta = \sum_\Delta f(\mathbf{Q}_k) \, \Delta_k x,$$

where $\Delta_k x = x_k - x_{k-1}$. This is an **approximate sum**. If $\lim\limits_{\|\Delta\| \to 0} \sigma_\Delta$ exists we will denote its value by $\int_C f(\mathbf{P}) \, dx$ or $\int_C f(x, y, z) \, dx$. There are similar definitions for $\int_C f(\mathbf{P}) \, dy$ and $\int_C f(\mathbf{P}) \, dz$.

13.1a   Theorem. If C is a piecewise smooth curve, and if f is continuous on C, then $\int_C f(\mathbf{P}) \, dx$ exists and equals $\int_a^b f[x(t), y(t), z(t)] \, x'(t) \, dt$.

Proof. Suppose, first, that C is smooth. Then the second integral exists. Furthermore, for any partition,

$$\sigma_\Delta = \sum_\Delta f(\mathbf{Q}_k) \, \Delta_k x$$

$$= \sum_\Delta f(\mathbf{Q}_k) \frac{x(t_k) - x(t_{k-1})}{t_k - t_{k-1}} \Delta_k t$$

$$= \sum f[\mathbf{P}(\tau_k)] x'(\xi_k) \, \Delta_k t$$

by the mean-value theorem, where ξ_k is in $\{t_{k-1} \leqslant t \leqslant t_k\}$. Let S_Δ be an approximating sum to the second integral formed over Δ with τ_k as the intermediate point. Then

$$\sigma_\Delta - S_\Delta = \sum_\Delta f[\mathbf{P}(\tau_k)](x'(\xi_k) - x'(\tau_k)) \, \Delta_k t$$

Now f is bounded, say by M, and x' is uniformly continuous on $I : \{a \leqslant t \leqslant b\}$. Then, given $\epsilon > 0$, choose $\|\Delta\|$ so small that $|x'(t) - x'(\tau)| < \epsilon$ whenever t and τ are in the same sub-interval. On this basis we can estimate the difference $\sigma_\Delta - S_\Delta$ as follows

$$|\sigma_\Delta - S_\Delta| \leqslant M\epsilon \sum_\Delta \Delta_k t = M\epsilon(b - a).$$

Then if
$$J = \int_a^b f[\mathbf{P}(t)] x'(t) \, dt,$$

$$|\sigma_\Delta - J| \leqslant |\sigma_\Delta - S_\Delta| + |S_\Delta - J| \to 0 \quad \text{as} \quad \|\Delta\| \to 0.$$

This proves the theorem for smooth curves. By the additivity of the integral, the proof extends immediately to piecewise smooth curves. The details of this extension are left as an exercise. ∎

The parameterization given in describing a curve defines an orientation of the curve; that is, it induces a direction on the curve. If we think of $\mathbf{P}(t)$ as a moving point occupying the position $\mathbf{P}(t)$ at time t, the parameterization introduces an order relationship among the points of the curve. If the curve is simple (and this will be the case in most of the examples with which we are concerned) this ordering will be uniquely determined by specifying the initial and terminal points.

EXAMPLE. Evaluate $\int_C x^2 y \, dx + (x^2 - y^2) \, dy$, where C is the arc of $y = 3x^2$ from $(0, 0)$ to $(1, 3)$.

Solution. No parameterization of the curve is given, but we can take x as a parameter:

$$C: \quad x = t, \quad y = 3t^2 \quad \{0 \leqslant t \leqslant 1\}.$$

The integral then becomes

$$\int_0^1 [t^2(3t^2) \, dt + (t^2 - 9t^4)6t \, dt] = \int_0^1 (3t^4 + 6t^3 - 9t^5) \, dt,$$

which is easily evaluated by elementary means.

Now consider a line integral of the form

$$I = \int_C L \, dx + M \, dy + N \, dz,$$

where L, M, N are continuous functions defined on a smooth or piecewise smooth curve C. This can be written

$$I = \int_C \mathbf{F} \cdot d\mathbf{P}$$

if $\mathbf{F}$ is the vector function $\mathbf{F} = L\mathbf{i} + M\mathbf{j} + N\mathbf{k}$. On introducing the arc length as a parameter, this becomes

$$I = \int_C \mathbf{F} \cdot \mathbf{T} \, ds,$$

where $\mathbf{T}$ is as usual the unit tangent vector $d\mathbf{P}/ds$.

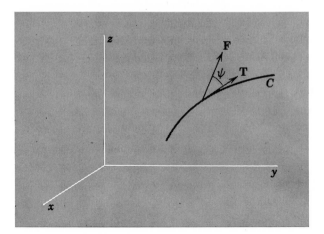

Now $\mathbf{F} \cdot \mathbf{T} = |\mathbf{F}| \cos \psi$, where ψ is the angle between $\mathbf{F}$ and $\mathbf{T}$. Thus

$$I = \int_C |\mathbf{F}| \cos \psi \, ds.$$

If $\mathbf{F}$ is a force field, then this integral is just exactly the definition of the **work** done by the force field on a particle of unit mass moving from the initial point to the terminal point along C.

It turns out that certain force fields important in physics arise from a potential. If there is a function ϕ defined in a region R, and if a force field $\mathbf{F}$ has the property that

$$\mathbf{F} = \nabla \phi = \mathbf{grad}\ \phi,$$

then ϕ is said to be a **potential** of $\mathbf{F}$. Clearly if ϕ is a potential of $\mathbf{F}$, so then is $\phi + C$ for every constant C. It is also easy to see that any two potentials of the same force field can differ only by a constant (Exercise B2). In physical applications, the choice of C is usually made so as to normalize some convenient physical quantity.

We borrow our nomenclature from physics. A continuous vector field which arises as the gradient field of a scalar function will be called a **gradient field**, and a function ϕ from which it arises the (or a) **potential function**.

13.1b Theorem. Let $\mathbf{F}$ be a gradient field with potential ϕ defined in a region R, and let $\mathbf{Q}_0$ and $\mathbf{Q}_1$ be any two points in R. Then

$$\int_C \mathbf{F} \cdot d\mathbf{P} = \phi(\mathbf{Q}_1) - \phi(\mathbf{Q}_0),$$

where C is a piecewise smooth curve in R going from $\mathbf{Q}_0$ to $\mathbf{Q}_1$.

Proof. Let C be given by

$$\mathbf{P} = \mathbf{P}(t) \qquad \{a \leqslant t \leqslant b\},$$

and let us first assume that C is smooth. Then

$$\int_C \mathbf{F} \cdot d\mathbf{P} = \int_C \frac{\partial \phi}{\partial x} \, dx + \frac{\partial \phi}{\partial y} \, dy + \frac{\partial \phi}{\partial z} \, dz$$

$$= \int_a^b \left(\frac{\partial \phi}{\partial x} \frac{\partial x}{\partial t} + \frac{\partial \phi}{\partial y} \frac{\partial y}{\partial t} + \frac{\partial \phi}{\partial z} \frac{\partial z}{\partial t} \right) dt$$

$$= \int_a^b \frac{d\phi}{dt} \left[\mathbf{P}(t) \right] dt$$

$$= \phi[\mathbf{P}(t)] \Big|_a^b$$

$$= \phi[\mathbf{P}(b)] - \phi[\mathbf{P}(a)]$$

$$= \phi(\mathbf{Q}_1) - \phi(\mathbf{Q}_0).$$

If C is only piecewise smooth, this calculation applies to each smooth piece. When we add the results of integrating over each smooth piece to get the integral over the whole curve, the contributions arising from the intermediate points cancel leaving the desired result.   ∎

When the value of an integral $\int \mathbf{F} \cdot d\mathbf{P}$ over a piecewise smooth path connecting two points in a region R depends only on the end points, we say that the integral is **independent of the path**. Theorem 13.1b immediately implies the following.

13.1c   Theorem. If $\mathbf{F}$ is a gradient field in a region R, then $\int \mathbf{F} \cdot d\mathbf{P}$ is independent of the path.

It is not difficult to see that also the converse of this theorem is true.

13.1d   Theorem. If $\mathbf{F} = L\mathbf{i} + M\mathbf{j} + N\mathbf{k}$ is a continuous vector field in a region R, and if $\int \mathbf{F} \cdot d\mathbf{P}$ is independent of the path, then $\mathbf{F}$ is a gradient field.

Proof. Since the integral is independent of the path, choose a fixed $\mathbf{P}_0$ in R and define ϕ in R by

$$(1) \qquad \phi(\mathbf{P}) = \int_{\mathbf{P}_0}^{\mathbf{P}} \mathbf{F} \cdot d\mathbf{P},$$

where the integral is computed over any piecewise smooth curve in R.

To show that $\phi_1(\mathbf{P}) = L(\mathbf{P})$, we let $\mathbf{P} + \Delta\mathbf{P} = (x + h, y, z)$ if $\mathbf{P} = (x, y, z)$. Then the difference quotient $\Delta\phi/\Delta x$ takes the form

$$\frac{\Delta\phi}{\Delta x} = \frac{1}{h} \int_{\mathbf{P}}^{\mathbf{P}+\Delta\mathbf{P}} \mathbf{F} \cdot d\mathbf{P}. \quad \text{(Why?)}$$

Since R is a region, there is a neighborhood about $\mathbf{P}$ which lies in R. We can therefore take h so small that $\mathbf{P} + \Delta\mathbf{P}$ lies in this neighborhood. Consequently we can take the path of integration to be the line segment from $\mathbf{P}$ to $\mathbf{P} + \Delta\mathbf{P}$, and we can parameterize this by

$$\mathbf{P}(t) = \mathbf{P} + t\mathbf{i} \qquad \{0 \leqslant t \leqslant h\}.$$

Thus $\qquad\qquad \dfrac{\Delta\phi}{\Delta x} = \dfrac{1}{h} \int_0^h L(x + t, y, z)\, dt.$

By the mean-value theorem, this becomes

$$\frac{\Delta\phi}{\Delta x} = L(x + t', y, z),$$

where t' lies between 0 and h. Then, as $h \to 0$, we get the desired result. Similarly $\phi_2 = M$ and $\phi_3 = N$.   ∎

This sequence of theorems says that, in order for $\int \mathbf{F} \cdot d\mathbf{P}$ to be independent of the path in a region R, it is necessary and sufficient that $\mathbf{F}$

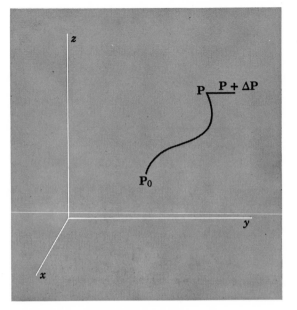

be a gradient field; in other words, that there be a scalar function ϕ, the potential, so that $\mathbf{F} = \boldsymbol{\nabla}\phi$. In this case

$$\mathbf{F} \cdot d\mathbf{P} = \boldsymbol{\nabla}\phi \cdot d\mathbf{P} = d\phi,$$

the total differential of ϕ. For that reason the differential form

$$\mathbf{F} \cdot d\mathbf{P} = L\,dx + M\,dy + N\,dz$$

is called an **exact differential**, as opposed to the case where it is not the total differential of some scalar function.

If a force field has the property that the work done on a moving particle as it moves from one point to another is independent of the path, it is called a **conservative field**. The results of the previous theorems can be restated as follows: a necessary and sufficient condition for a force field to be conservative is that it be a gradient field.

Since it may be difficult to compute all line integrals between all pairs of points in a given region, it would be desirable to have a simple criterion for determining when a given field is a gradient field. Of course in simple cases we may be able to compute a function ϕ by means of (1), which we can verify is a potential. If this is not feasible, there is a test which we can apply to differentiable vector fields. For the two-dimensional case, this test will be given in the next section as corollary of Green's theorem.

We close this section as we began it, by emphasizing that the results apply equally well in all Euclidean vector spaces of finite dimension.

A EXERCISES

I. Compute the following line integrals:

(a) $\int_C x^2 y \, dx + (x^2 - y^2) \, dy$ from $(0, 0)$ to $(1, 2)$ along $y = 2x^2$.

(b) $\int_C x^2 \, dx + y^2 \, dy$ from $(0, 0)$ to (a, b) along the straight line between them.

(c) $\int_C y \sin x \, dx - x \cos y \, dy$ from $(0, 0)$ to $(1, 1)$ along $x = y$.

(d) $\int_C (y - x^2) \, dx + x \, dy$ from $(1, 0)$ to $(-1, 0)$ around the upper half of $x^2 + y^2 = 1$.

(e) Evaluate the integral in (d) along the polygonal line connecting $(1, 0)$ to $(1, 1)$ to $(-1, 1)$ to $(-1, 0)$.

(f) Evaluate the integral in (d) along the x-axis from $(1, 0)$ to $(-1, 0)$.

(g) $\int_C \mathbf{P} \cdot d\mathbf{P}$, where C is one turn of the helix $\mathbf{P} = (\cos t, \sin t, t)$ from $(1, 0, 0)$ to $(1, 0, 2\pi)$.

2. Evaluate each of the following integrals around the circle $x^2 + y^2 = 1$ in the counterclockwise direction:

(a) $\int_C \dfrac{x \, dy - y \, dx}{x^2 + y^2}$ (b) $\int_C x^2 y \, dx$ (c) $\int_C x^2 \, ds$

3. Evaluate $\int_C x \, dy - y \, dx$ around $x^2 + y^2 = 1$ in the counterclockwise direction.

4. Evaluate $\int_C ds$, where C is $y = x^2$ from $(0, 0)$ to $(2, 4)$.

5. Near the earth's surface, the earth's gravitational field is approximately given by $-g\mathbf{k}$, where $\mathbf{k}$ points vertically upwards. Show that if a particle moves from a height h_1 to a height h_2, along a smooth curve, that the work done on it by this field is $mg(h_1 - h_2)$. Find a potential function.

6. Let $\mathbf{F}$ be a continuous vector field defined in a region R. Show that $\int_C \mathbf{F} \cdot d\mathbf{P}$ is independent of the path if, and only if, $\int_C \mathbf{F} \cdot d\mathbf{P} = 0$ over every closed piecewise smooth curve in R.

7. Show that the following vector fields are gradient fields by finding a potential:

(a) $x\mathbf{i} + y\mathbf{j}$ in E_2 (b) $3x^2 y\mathbf{i} + x^3\mathbf{j}$ in E_2

(c) $(2xy + z^3)\mathbf{i} + (x^2 + 3z)\mathbf{j} + (3z^2 x + 3y)\mathbf{k}$ in E_3

B EXERCISES

1. Let f and g be continuously differentiable functions in a region R. If C is any piecewise smooth curve in R going from P_1 to P_2, then

$$\int_C f \nabla g \cdot dP = f(P)_2 g(P_2) - f(P_1) g(P_1) - \int_C g \nabla f \cdot dP.$$

2. Show that if ϕ and ψ are both potential functions for a vector field $\mathbf{F}$, then $\phi - \psi = C$, where C is constant.

3. Show that the gravitational field of a point mass (see Section 10.6) is conservative, and find a potential function for it.

4. If $\mathbf{F}$ is continuous on a smooth curve C, show that

$$\left| \int_C \mathbf{F} \cdot d\mathbf{P} \right| \leqslant (\max_C |\mathbf{F}|) L_C,$$

where L_C denotes the length of C.

5. Let $\mathbf{F}$ be a continuous force field. Using Newton's second law ($\mathbf{F} = m\mathbf{a}$), show that the work done by $\mathbf{F}$ on a moving particle is equal to the change in the kinetic energy. Recall that kinetic energy is $\frac{1}{2}m|\mathbf{v}|^2$, where $\mathbf{v}$ is the velocity.

6. Show that $\int_C f(x, y)\, dx = 0$, if C is a segment parallel to the y-axis.

C EXERCISES

1. Let u and v be differentiable functions in a region R in E_2 which satisfy there the relations $u_x = v_y$ and $u_y = -v_x$. Show that if u and v are known to exist, and if u is given, then v can be determined to within an additive constant. Give a formula for v in terms of u, and find v if $u = x^2 - y^2$.

2. Let C be a smooth curve and f be continuous on C. Show that $\int_C f\, dx$ is independent of the parameterization. That is, show that if C is given by

$$\mathbf{P} = \mathbf{P}(t) \qquad \{a \leqslant t \leqslant b\}$$

and by
$$\mathbf{Q} = \mathbf{Q}(\tau) \qquad \{\alpha \leqslant \tau \leqslant \beta\}.$$

where $\mathbf{P}'(t) \neq 0$ and $\mathbf{Q}'(\tau) \neq 0$, then

$$\int_a^b f[\mathbf{P}(t)] \frac{dx}{dt}\, dt = \int_a^\beta f[\mathbf{Q}(\tau)] \frac{dx}{d\tau}\, d\tau.$$

3. Show that the vector field $\mathbf{F} = (-y\mathbf{i} + x\mathbf{j})/(x^2 + y^2)$ in E_2 has local potential function but no global one. In other words, show that in a neighborhood of any point $\mathbf{P}_0 = (a, b) \neq (0, 0)$ in E_2, there is a function ϕ such that $\nabla\phi = \mathbf{F}$, but no function ϕ over the whole of the domain of $\mathbf{F}$ (that is, the plane punctured at the origin) for which $\nabla\phi = \mathbf{F}$.

4. Let f be a continuously differentiable function defined in an open region R. Let $\mathbf{P}$ and $\mathbf{P}_1$ be any two points in R connected by a smooth curve C from $\mathbf{P}$ to $\mathbf{P}_1$. Show that there is a point $\mathbf{Q}$ on C such that $f(\mathbf{P}_1) - f(\mathbf{P}) = \nabla f(\mathbf{Q}) \cdot \mathbf{T}L$, where $\mathbf{T}$ is the unit tangent to C at $\mathbf{Q}$ and L is the length of C.

13.2 GREEN'S THEOREM

An ordinary derivative was defined at a point of an open interval. The idea of a derivative being defined on a closed interval was introduced through the device of a one-sided derivative which took care of the end points. Similarly, partial derivatives have been defined on open regions, but the extension to closed regions is not as easy in higher dimensions as it was in one dimension. For example, if f is defined on a closed circular disk $\{|\mathbf{P} - \mathbf{P}_0| \leqslant a\}$ in E_2, how would you define f_x at the top point on the circle—that is, at the point $\mathbf{P} = \mathbf{P}_0 + \mathbf{j}a$? The device we use is the following: Let f be a continuous function defined on a closed region D, and suppose f_x is continuous in the open region formed by deleting the boundary. Then if there is a function g continuous in D and coinciding with f_x in the open region, we say that f_x is continuous in D and, of course, that $f_x = g$ in D. The other partials are handled in exactly the same way.

In discussing the relation between line integrals and double integrals, we begin by considering a region R of a particularly simple form, which we now describe. Suppose the projection of R onto the x-axis is a closed interval $I:\{a \leqslant x \leqslant b\}$; that is, if (x, y) is in R, then x is in I. And suppose that each line described by $x = x_0$ where x_0 is in I, meets R in

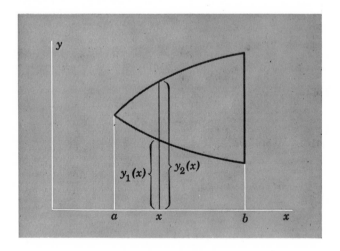

exactly one closed interval, which may degenerate to a point at a or b (or both). Thus R can be given in the form

$$\{y_1(x) \leqslant y \leqslant y_2(x), a \leqslant x \leqslant b\},$$

where we suppose also that $y_1(x)$ and $y_2(x)$ are continuous. Such a region will be called an **x-projectable region**. Similarly, by interchanging the roles of x and y, we can define a **y-projectable region**. A region which is both x- and y-projectable will be called a **standard region**.

Suppose R is a closed standard region with a piecewise smooth boundary, and L and M are two continuously differentiable functions defined on it. Then consider

$$\iint_R \frac{\partial L}{\partial y} \, dA.$$

By Theorem 12.3a, we can write this as an iterated integral, thus

$$\iint_R \frac{\partial L}{\partial y} \, dA = \int_a^b dx \int_{y_1(x)}^{y_2(x)} \frac{\partial L}{\partial y} \, dy$$

$$= \int_a^b \{L[x, y_2(x)] - L[x, y_1(x)]\} \, dx$$

$$= -\int_b^a L[x, y_2(x)] \, dx - \int_a^b L[x, y_1(x)] \, dx.$$

These last integrals can be interpreted as line integrals of L along the curves given by

$$y = y_1(x) \qquad \{a \leqslant x \leqslant b\}$$

and

$$y = y_2(x) \qquad \{a \leqslant x \leqslant b\}.$$

The first of these integrals is an integral from right to left, and the second one is from left to right. Geometrically, we see that this amounts to integration in the counterclockwise direction on the boundary of R, for the integral of L over any vertical segments of R will be zero (why?). Thus we could write the above formula as

$$\iint_R \frac{\partial L}{\partial y} \, dA = -\int_B L \, dx,$$

where the integration in the line integral is taken in the counterclockwise direction around the boundary of R. By a similar calculation,

$$\iint_R \frac{\partial M}{\partial x} \, dA = \int_B M \, dy.$$

Combining these two formulas, we deduce

$$(1) \qquad \int_B L \, dx + M \, dy = \iint_R \left(\frac{\partial M}{\partial x} - \frac{\partial L}{\partial y} \right) dA,$$

where the integral is taken in the counterclockwise direction around the boundary B of R. This is a weak form of what is known as **Green's theorem**, which is a generic term for any theorem which gives sufficient conditions for the validity of formula (1).

We can generalize our result to slightly more complicated domains. Let R be a closed region which can be divided into two standard regions R_1 and R_2 by a piecewise smooth curve C, as illustrated in the figure. Then

(2)
$$\int_{B_1} L\,dx + M\,dy = \iint_{R_1} \left(\frac{\partial M}{\partial x} - \frac{\partial L}{\partial y}\right) dA$$

and

(3)
$$\int_{B_2} L\,dx + M\,dy = \iint_{R_2} \left(\frac{\partial M}{\partial x} - \frac{\partial L}{\partial y}\right) dA,$$

where of course B_1 and B_2 are respectively the boundaries of R_1 and R_2, and the integrals are to be taken in the counterclockwise sense around these boundaries. The curve C occurs in both B_1 and B_2, and hence the line integral along C enters in the left-hand sides of both (2) and (3).

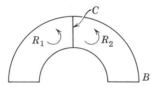

Furthermore, it enters these two formulas with opposite signs, since counterclockwise motion with respect to R_1 gives an orientation to C opposite that induced by counterclockwise motion with respect to R_2. When we add (2) and (3), the contribution from C cancels out, leaving only the integral around B, so that formula (1) is valid for regions which can be cut into two standard regions by a curve C.

By induction, it follows that formula (1) is valid for a closed region which can be cut into a finite number of standard regions by introducing such additional curves as C. However, we have to re-examine the boundary integral. Suppose R has a boundary consisting of more than one simple closed curve and can be decomposed into a finite number of standard regions. We apply (1) to each of the standard regions and add. The contribution to the line integrals arising from the auxiliary curves cancels out, as we would expect; but we also see that the integral over each inside curve is then taken in the clockwise sense. But we see that we can characterize the direction of integration in the following way: the direction of integration along each curve of the boundary should be such as to

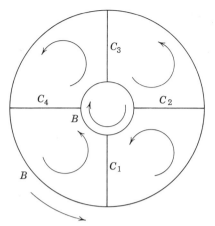

leave the region to the left. This is called the **positive** direction on the boundary.

We can now assert that formula (1) is valid if R can be decomposed by auxiliary curves into a finite number of regions and if the line integral is taken in the positive sense around the boundary.

Thus we have given a geometrical proof for the following form of Green's theorem.

13.2a   Theorem. Let R be a bounded closed region which can be subdivided by a finite number of piecewise smooth curves into a finite number of standard regions. Let L and M be two functions with continuous partial derivatives defined on R. Then

$$\int_B L\, dx + M\, dy = \iint_R \left(\frac{\partial M}{\partial x} - \frac{\partial L}{\partial y} \right) dA,$$

where the line integral is taken over the boundary B of R in the positive sense.

We will not undertake a non-geometrical proof of this theorem, but will be content with the proof given; for a complete proof requires a great deal of detail to place our geometrical arguments on a rigorous basis.

The theorem is true under more general conditions on the region. For example, our proof would not cover all regions whose boundaries consist of a finite number of piecewise smooth, simple closed curves, for they may not be decomposable into a finite number of standard regions. For example, the region in the figure is bounded by a single piecewise

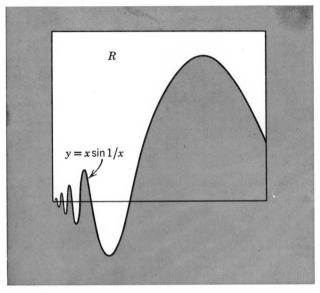

smooth simple closed curve, and it cannot be decomposed into a finite number of standard regions. However, we can approximate such regions by regions for which Green's theorem is valid and, by a limit argument, show that it is valid for these regions also. In fact, we can remove all smoothness requirements from the boundary and require only rectifiability—so that the line integrals make sense—and the formula is still valid.

13.2b Theorem. Let R be a bounded closed region whose boundary consists of a finite number of simple closed rectifiable curves. Let L and M have continuous partials in R. Then

$$\int_B L \, dx + M \, dy = \iint_R \left(\frac{\partial M}{\partial x} - \frac{\partial L}{\partial y} \right) dA.$$

A proof of this theorem can be found in Apostol's *Mathematical Analysis*.

We now return to the question we were discussing at the end of Section 13.1, namely a criterion for determining when a vector field is a gradient field. If we have a continuously differentiable gradient field—that is, if there is a potential ϕ such that $\phi_x = L$ and $\phi_y = M$ then clearly

$$\frac{\partial L}{\partial y} = \phi_{xy} = \phi_{yx} = \frac{\partial M}{\partial x}.$$

Thus we see that, in order for $L\mathbf{i} + M\mathbf{j}$ to be a gradient field, it is necessary that $\partial L/\partial y = \partial M/\partial x$. Now it turns out that this is also sufficient if the region in which the field is defined is sufficiently restricted, for in this case we can integrate to find a potential ϕ, as we shall see. First we define simple connectedness.

We will say that a region is **simply connected** if it has the property that every simple closed curve in R also has its interior in R. Thus, for example, a neighborhood is simply connected, but the annular region $\{r_1 \leqslant |\mathbf{P}| \leqslant r_2\}$ between two concentric circles is not.

13.2c Theorem. Suppose D is a simply connected open region, and L and M have continuous derivatives in D. Then $\int L\,dx + M\,dy$ is independent of the path in R if, and only if,

$$\frac{\partial L}{\partial y} = \frac{\partial M}{\partial x}.$$

Proof. Suppose first that $\int L\,dx + M\,dy$ is independent of the path. Then the vector field $L\mathbf{j} + M\mathbf{j}$ is a gradient field—that is, there is a function ϕ in R such that $L = \partial\phi/\partial x$ and $M = \partial\phi/\partial y$. Then

$$\frac{\partial L}{\partial y} = \frac{\partial^2 \phi}{\partial y\,\partial x}$$

and

$$\frac{\partial M}{\partial x} = \frac{\partial^2 \phi}{\partial x\,\partial y};$$

and, by Theorem 10.1a, these are equal. (Here we did not use the simple connectedness of R.)

Conversely, let us suppose that $\partial L/\partial y = \partial M/\partial x$ throughout R. We want to show that $L\mathbf{i} + M\mathbf{j}$ is a gradient field from which we can conclude by Theorem 13.1b that the integral is independent of the path. Thus it is sufficient to show that $L\mathbf{i} + M\mathbf{j}$ is a gradient field.

Let $\mathbf{P}$ and $\mathbf{Q}$ be any two points in R. There is then a simple (that is, non-self intersecting) polygonal line connecting them (check the definition of a region). We show now that $\int_{\mathbf{P}}^{\mathbf{Q}} L\,dx + M\,dy$ has the same value over all simple polygonal paths connecting $\mathbf{P}$ and $\mathbf{Q}$. Let C_1 and C_2 be two such paths. Then a closed (not necessarily simple) polygon C is formed by C_1, oriented from $\mathbf{P}$ to $\mathbf{Q}$, and C_2, oriented from $\mathbf{Q}$ to $\mathbf{P}$. It is sufficient to show that $\int_C L\,dx + M\,dy = 0$.

It is geometrically clear that C can be decomposed into a finite number of simple closed polygons, together with a finite number of segments which

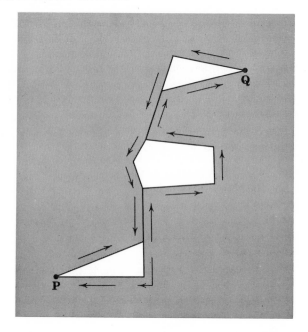

are traversed twice—once in each direction. The contribution to the integral from these segments is zero. Now consider one of the polygons, denoting it by B and its interior by D. By Green's theorem

$$\int_B L\,dx + M\,dy = \iint_D \left(\frac{\partial M}{\partial x} - \frac{\partial L}{\partial y}\right) dA = 0,$$

so that, as desired,

$$\int_C L\,dx + M\,dy = 0.$$

Thus we can say that $\int L\,dx + M\,dy$ is independent of the path as long as we integrate over only simple polygonal paths. This is enough, however, to see that $L\mathbf{i} + M\mathbf{j}$ is a gradient field, for fixing $\mathbf{P_0}$ in R we define ϕ by

$$\phi(\mathbf{P}) = \int_{\mathbf{P_o}}^{\mathbf{P}} L\,dx + M\,dy$$

over a simple polygonal path. This does indeed define a function of $\mathbf{P}$, since we have shown the value is independent of the path. We can now repeat the argument of Theorem 13.1c to see that

$$\frac{\partial \phi}{\partial x} = L, \qquad \frac{\partial \phi}{\partial y} = M.$$

We invoke Theorem 13.1b to complete the proof: since $L\mathbf{i} + M\mathbf{j}$ is a gradient field, $\int L\, dx + M\, dy$ is independent of the path, for all rectifiable curves.   ∎

The reason we need the simple connectedness is to insure that the integral $\int L\, dx + M\, dy$ is independent of the path. To see that $\partial L/\partial y = \partial M/\partial x$ is not in itself sufficient to guarantee that $L\mathbf{i} + M\mathbf{j}$ is a gradient field, let us consider the region $R: \{r_1^2 < x^2 + y^2 < r_2^2\}$. In this annulus, we examine the vector field $(y\mathbf{i} - x\mathbf{j})/(x^2 + y^2)$. By simple calculations, we see that

$$\frac{\partial}{\partial y}\left(\frac{y}{x^2 + y^2}\right) = \frac{\partial}{\partial x}\left(\frac{-x}{x^2 + y^2}\right).$$

Yet this cannot be a gradient field, since $\displaystyle\int_C \frac{y\, dx - x\, dy}{x^2 + y^2}$ taken around a concentric circle is not zero. For if we set $x = r\cos\theta$, $y = r\sin\theta$, then the integral reduces to

$$\int_C d\theta = 2\pi.$$

We can see geometrically why we cannot have a single gradient function for the whole ring. If θ is the angle the radius vector makes with the x-axis, then $\theta = \arctan y/x$, so that

$$d\theta = (y\, dx - x\, dy)/(x^2 + y^2),$$

and we cannot define the angle throughout the whole annulus to be continuous; for if we go once around the inner circle, we increase the angle by 2π.

A EXERCISES

1. Evaluate the following integrals by Green's theorem. The integral is to be taken in the counterclockwise direction around the given curve:

(a) $\displaystyle\int_C (x - y^3)\, dx + x^3\, dy$ $\qquad$ $C: x^2 + y^2 = 1$

(b) $\displaystyle\int_C x\, dy + y\, dx$ $\qquad$ $C: 4x^2 + 9y^2 = 1$

(c) $\displaystyle\int_C e^x \sin y\, dx + e^x \cos y\, dy$ $\qquad$ $C:$ square $x = \pm 1, y = \pm 1$

(d) $\displaystyle\int_C x^2 y\, dx + xy^2\, dy$ $\qquad$ $C: x^2 + y^2 = 4$

(e) $\displaystyle\int_C x^2 y\, dx$ $\qquad$ $C:$ triangle $x = 0, y = 2, x = 2y$

(f) $\displaystyle\int_C f(x)\, dx + g(y)\, dy$ $\qquad$ $C: x^2 + y^2 = 36$

(g) $\displaystyle\int_C \frac{y\,dx - x\,dy}{x^2 + y^2}$ $C: x^2 + (y - 4)^2 = 1$

2. Explain why Green's theorem cannot be used to evaluate the following integral:

$$\int_C \frac{y\,dx - x\,dy}{x^2 + y^2} \qquad C: x^2 + y^2 = 4$$

B EXERCISES

I. Let C be a simple closed piecewise smooth curve.

(a) Show that $\displaystyle\int_C x\,dy = -\int_C y\,dx$ = area enclosed by C. Give a geometrical explanation of this.

(b) Evaluate $\frac{1}{2}\displaystyle\int_C x\,dy - y\,dx$.

(c) Apply (b) to compute the area enclosed by an ellipse $x^2/a^2 + y^2/b^2 = 1$.

2. Use 1(b) to verify the usual formula for the area of a sector bounded by $\theta = \alpha$, $\theta = \beta$, and $\rho = f(\theta)$, where $0 < \beta - \alpha < 2\pi$:

$$A = \frac{1}{2}\int_\alpha^\beta f^2(\theta)\,d\theta = \int_\alpha^\beta d\theta \int_0^{f(\theta)} \rho\,d\rho$$

C EXERCISES

I. Let C be a piecewise smooth curve which forms a positively oriented boundary of a region R. Then the inner normal $\mathbf{n}$ is obtained from the unit $\mathbf{T}$ by a 90°

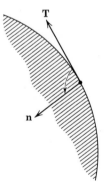

rotation in the counterclockwise direction (see figure). Show that if u has continuous second derivatives in R, then

$$\iint (\Delta u)\,dA = -\int_C \nabla_n u\,ds,$$

2. Show also that:

(a) $$\iint_R (u\Delta v + \nabla u \cdot \nabla v)\, dA = -\int_C u \nabla_n v\, ds$$

(b) $$\iint_R (u\Delta v - v\Delta u)\, dA = -\int_C (u \nabla_n v - v \nabla_n u)\, ds$$

(c) $$\iint_R |\nabla v|^2\, dA = -\int_C v \nabla_n v\, ds, \text{ if } \Delta v = 0.$$

3. From Green's theorem, deduce the following formulas:

(a) $$\iint_R \nabla \cdot \mathbf{F}\, dA = -\int_C \mathbf{F} \cdot \mathbf{n}\, ds$$

(b) $$\iint_R \nabla \times \mathbf{F} \cdot \mathbf{k}\, dA = \int_C \mathbf{F} \cdot \mathbf{T}\, ds$$

13.3 SURFACES. AREA

We have discussed surfaces given explicitly by $z = \phi(x, y)$ and, by means of the implicit function theorem, those given by $f(x, y, z) = 0$. We now want to discuss surfaces which are parametrically described.

Let $\mathcal{D}$ be a region in the plane E_2. We will denote points in $\mathcal{D}$ by $\mathbf{Q} = (u, v)$. And suppose that $\mathbf{F}$ is a three-dimension continuous vector function defined on $\mathcal{D}$:

(1) $$\mathbf{P} = \mathbf{F}(\mathbf{Q})$$

or, in terms of components,

(1') $$x = f(u, v) \qquad y = g(u, v) \qquad z = h(u, v).$$

The range of $\mathbf{F}$ will be called a **surface**, S. However, just as there can be space-filling curves, so can there be space-filling surfaces. Merely under the hypothesis of continuity, then, we would expect very complicated behavior of surfaces. Thus we will restrict ourselves immediately to the consideration of smooth surface elements:

Suppose:

(i) $\mathcal{D}$ is a closed bounded simply connected region whose boundary $\mathcal{B}$ is piecewise smooth.

(ii) S has no double points; that is, if $\mathbf{F}(\mathbf{Q}_1) = \mathbf{F}(\mathbf{Q}_2)$, then $\mathbf{Q}_1 = \mathbf{Q}_2$.

(iii) $\mathbf{F}$ has continuous derivatives in $\mathcal{D}$.

(iv) At no point $\mathbf{Q}$ in $\mathcal{D}$ are all three Jacobians,

$$J_1 \equiv \frac{\partial(y, z)}{\partial(u, v)}, \quad J_2 \equiv \frac{\partial(z, x)}{\partial(u, v)}, \quad J_3 \equiv \frac{\partial(x, y)}{\partial(u, v)},$$

equal to zero.

If $S: \mathbf{P} = \mathbf{F}(\mathbf{Q})$ satisfies all of these conditions, it will be called a **simple smooth surface element.**

13.3a   Theorem. Let $\mathbf{P}_0$ be a point on a simple smooth surface element S. Then there is a neighborhood of $\mathbf{P}_0$ in which S is represented by an equation in which one of $x, y,$ and z is expressed as a function of the other two, for example, $z = \phi(x, y)$.

Proof. Not all the Jacobians J_1, J_2, J_3 vanish at $\mathbf{P}_0$. Suppose $J_3 \neq 0$ there; this is just the condition that $x = f(u, v), y = g(u, v)$ can be solved for (u, v) in terms of (x, y) in a neighborhood of x_0. These solutions may then be substituted into the equations $(1')$. The first two of these reduce to identities (why?) and the third becomes

$$z = h[u(x, y), v(x, y)] = \phi(x, y),$$

where ϕ is differentiable since $u, v,$ and h all are.   ∎

13.3b   Corollary. If S is a simple smooth surface element, then it has a tangent plane at each point $\mathbf{P}_0$ and its normal is given by $J_1\mathbf{i} + J_2\mathbf{j} + J_3\mathbf{k}$.

Proof. S has a tangent plane since, for example, z is a differentiable function of (x, y) near $\mathbf{P}_0$.

Consider the curve C_v through $\mathbf{P}_0$ given by $v = $ constant. Thus C_v has the vector equation

$$\mathbf{P} = f(u, v_0)\mathbf{i} + g(u, v_0)\mathbf{j} + h(u, v_0)\mathbf{k},$$

where $\mathbf{Q}_0 = (u_0, v_0)$ is the point for which $\mathbf{P}_0 = \mathbf{F}(\mathbf{Q}_0)$. Then

$$\frac{\partial \mathbf{P}}{\partial u} = f_1\mathbf{i} + g_1\mathbf{j} + h_1\mathbf{k},$$

where the derivatives are evaluated at $\mathbf{Q}_0$, is tangent to C_v at $\mathbf{P}_0$. Similarly, a tangent to C_u at $\mathbf{P}_0$ is

$$\frac{\partial \mathbf{P}}{\partial v} = f_2\mathbf{i} + g_2\mathbf{j} + h_2\mathbf{k}.$$

Therefore a normal to S at $\mathbf{P}_0$ is given by

$$\mathbf{N} = \frac{\partial \mathbf{P}}{\partial u} \times \frac{\partial \mathbf{P}}{\partial v} = \begin{vmatrix} \mathbf{i} & \mathbf{j} & \mathbf{k} \\ f_1 & g_1 & h_1 \\ f_2 & g_2 & h_2 \end{vmatrix}$$

$$= J_1 \mathbf{i} + J_2 \mathbf{j} + J_3 \mathbf{k}.$$ ∎

Our main objective here is to define surface area. It turns out that certain coefficients occurring in the differential for arc length on a surface have an important connection with area. Consequently, we briefly study smooth curves on a smooth surface.

13.3c Theorem. Let $S: \mathbf{P} = \mathbf{F}(\mathbf{Q})$ for $\mathbf{Q}$ in $\mathscr{D}$ be a simple smooth surface element. Let $\mathscr{C}: \mathbf{Q} = \mathbf{Q}(t)$, $\{a \leqslant t \leqslant b\}$ be a smooth curve in $\mathscr{D}$. Then $C: \mathbf{P} = \mathbf{F}[\mathbf{Q}(t)]$, $\{a \leqslant t \leqslant b\}$ is a smooth curve in S.

Proof. Clearly $\mathbf{P}$ is a differentiable function of t, since $\mathbf{F}$ is a differentiable function of $\mathbf{Q}$, and $\mathbf{Q}$ is a differentiable function of t. It remains to see that $d\mathbf{P}/dt \neq 0$ along C.

To see this, we observe

$$\frac{d\mathbf{P}}{dt} = \frac{\partial \mathbf{P}}{\partial u}\frac{\partial u}{\partial t} + \frac{\partial \mathbf{P}}{\partial v}\frac{\partial v}{\partial t},$$

so that

$$\left(\frac{ds}{dt}\right)^2 = \frac{d\mathbf{P}}{dt} \cdot \frac{d\mathbf{P}}{dt}$$

$$= \left(\frac{\partial \mathbf{P}}{\partial u}\frac{du}{dt} + \frac{\partial \mathbf{P}}{\partial v}\frac{dv}{dt}\right) \cdot \left(\frac{\partial \mathbf{P}}{\partial u}\frac{du}{dt} + \frac{\partial \mathbf{P}}{\partial v}\frac{dv}{dt}\right)$$

$$= \left(\frac{\partial \mathbf{P}}{\partial u} \cdot \frac{\partial \mathbf{P}}{\partial u}\right)\left(\frac{du}{dt}\right)^2 + 2\left(\frac{\partial \mathbf{P}}{\partial u} \cdot \frac{\partial \mathbf{P}}{\partial v}\right)\frac{du}{dt}\frac{dv}{dt} + \left(\frac{\partial \mathbf{P}}{\partial v} \cdot \frac{\partial \mathbf{P}}{\partial v}\right)\left(\frac{dv}{dt}\right)^2$$

$$= E\left(\frac{du}{dt}\right)^2 + 2F\frac{du}{dt}\frac{dv}{dt} + G\left(\frac{dv}{dt}\right)^2,$$

where

$$E = \frac{\partial \mathbf{P}}{\partial u} \cdot \frac{\partial \mathbf{P}}{\partial u} = \left(\frac{\partial x}{\partial u}\right)^2 + \left(\frac{\partial y}{\partial u}\right)^2 + \left(\frac{\partial z}{\partial u}\right)^2$$

$$F = \frac{\partial \mathbf{P}}{\partial u} \cdot \frac{\partial \mathbf{P}}{\partial v} = \frac{\partial x}{\partial u}\frac{\partial x}{\partial v} + \frac{\partial y}{\partial u}\frac{\partial y}{\partial v} + \frac{\partial z}{\partial u}\frac{\partial z}{\partial v}$$

$$G = \frac{\partial \mathbf{P}}{\partial v} \cdot \frac{\partial \mathbf{P}}{\partial v} = \left(\frac{\partial x}{\partial v}\right)^2 + \left(\frac{\partial y}{\partial v}\right)^2 + \left(\frac{\partial z}{\partial v}\right)^2.$$

Not both du/dt and dv/dt can be zero (why?). Thus $(ds/dt)^2 > 0$ if $EG - F^2 > 0$ (why?). By a straightforward calculation (Exercise B4), we see that

$$EG - F^2 = J_1^2 + J_2^2 + J_3^2 > 0.$$

Thus $dP/dt \neq 0$ and C is a smooth curve. ∎

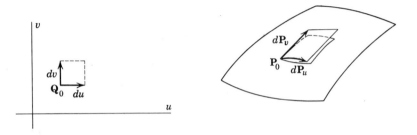

Let $\mathbf{Q}_0$ be a point of $\mathscr{D}$ and $\mathbf{P}_0$ the corresponding point in S. If we make a small change du along the line $v = v_0$ and a small change dv along $u = u_0$ at Q_0, the area of the rectangle in the uv plane so formed is $du\,dv$. These changes induce vector changes in S given approximately as

$$dP_u = \frac{\partial \mathbf{P}}{\partial u}\,du = \left(\frac{\partial x}{\partial u}\mathbf{i} + \frac{\partial y}{\partial u}\mathbf{j} + \frac{\partial z}{\partial u}\mathbf{k}\right)du$$

and
$$dP_v = \frac{\partial \mathbf{P}}{\partial v}\,dv = \left(\frac{\partial x}{\partial v}\mathbf{i} + \frac{\partial y}{\partial v}\mathbf{j} + \frac{\partial z}{\partial v}\mathbf{k}\right)dv.$$

These differentials dP_u and dP_v approximate the sides of an small parallelogram in S, whose area $d\sigma$ is given by

$$d\sigma = |dP_u \times dP_v| = \left|\frac{\partial \mathbf{P}}{\partial u} \times \frac{\partial \mathbf{P}}{\partial v}\right|du\,dv$$

$$= |J_1\mathbf{i} + J_2\mathbf{j} + J_3\mathbf{k}|\,du\,dv$$

$$= \sqrt{J_1^2 + J_2^2 + J_3^2}\,du\,dv$$

or
$$d\sigma = \sqrt{EG - F^2}\,du\,dv.$$

If the surface is given in the form $z = f(x, y)$, this reduces to

$$d\sigma = \sqrt{1 + \left(\frac{\partial z}{\partial x}\right)^2 + \left(\frac{\partial z}{\partial y}\right)^2}\,dx\,dy.$$

This last formula has a simple geometrical meaning. For if S is described by $z = f(x, y)$, the vector equation of S is

$$\mathbf{P} = x\mathbf{i} + y\mathbf{j} + f(x, y)\mathbf{k},$$

so that

$$\frac{\partial \mathbf{P}}{\partial x} = \mathbf{i} + f_1\mathbf{k}$$

$$\frac{\partial \mathbf{P}}{\partial y} = \mathbf{j} + f_2\mathbf{k}$$

and

$$\mathbf{N} = \frac{\partial \mathbf{P}}{\partial x} \times \frac{\partial \mathbf{P}}{\partial y} = \mathbf{k} - \mathbf{j}f_2 - \mathbf{i}f_1.$$

The unit vector in the direction of $\mathbf{N}$ we will denote by $\mathbf{n}$:

$$\mathbf{n} = \frac{\mathbf{N}}{|\mathbf{N}|} = \frac{\mathbf{k} - \mathbf{j}f_2 - \mathbf{i}f_1}{\sqrt{1 + f_1^2 + f_2^2}}.$$

Thus if γ is the angle between $\mathbf{k}$ and $\mathbf{n}$,

$$\cos \gamma = \mathbf{n} \cdot \mathbf{k} = 1/\sqrt{1 + f_1^2 + f_2^2} = 1 \Big/ \sqrt{1 + \left(\frac{\partial z}{\partial x}\right)^2 + \left(\frac{\partial z}{\partial y}\right)^2},$$

so that

$$d\sigma = \sec \gamma \, dx \, dy = \sec \gamma \, dA_{xy}.$$

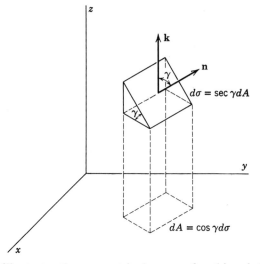

The figure illustrates the geometrical reason for this relationship. The fact that $\mathbf{n} \cdot \mathbf{k} > 0$ means that $\mathbf{n}$ is the upward normal. If we use the downward normal, namely $\mathbf{n}' = -\mathbf{n}$, the angle between between $\mathbf{n}'$ and $\mathbf{k}$ is obtuse, so that $\cos \gamma < 0$. Then we could express $d\sigma$ in terms of $dx \, dy$ by the formula

$$d\sigma = \sec(\pi - \gamma) \, dx \, dy.$$

This heuristic argument indicates that an element of area $du\, dv$ maps onto an element of area $\sqrt{J_1{}^2 + J_2{}^2 + J_3{}^2}\, du\, dv$ when $\mathscr{D}$ is mapped onto S by $\mathbf{P} = \mathbf{F}(\mathbf{Q})$. Accordingly, we define the **area of a simple smooth surface element** by

$$A = \int_{\mathscr{D}} \sqrt{J_1{}^2 + J_2{}^2 + J_3{}^2}\, du\, dv.$$

If S is a surface which can be decomposed by piecewise smooth curves into a finite number of simple smooth surface elements, we say that it is a piecewise smooth surface. The area of a piecewise smooth surface is defined as the sum of the areas of the smooth pieces.

In order that this definition may be useful, even sensible, we must know that it is independent of the manner of decomposition of the surface. It is sufficient to show that if a smooth simple surface element is cut up into smaller pieces by piecewise smooth lines, then the area of the element is the sum of the areas of the pieces. This is equivalent to showing that the integral over $\mathscr{D}$ giving the area is additive, a situation covered by Theorem 12.4g.

You might think it more natural to approximate the surface by polyhedra, as we approximated curves by polygons. However, a little reflection will show you that it is a difficult matter to inscribe a polyhedron in a surface. Certainly there is no easy, general method of doing this. Moreover, after an approximation method has been settled on, the areas of the approximating polyhedra do not always converge to the area of the surface. There is an example showing that even in as smooth a surface as a cylinder the areas of the polyhedra may become infinite instead of approaching the surface area.

EXAMPLE. Compute the area of the surface S given by

$$S: \quad z = x^2 + y^2 \qquad \mathscr{D}: \{x^2 + y^2 \leqslant 1\}.$$

Here $\partial z/\partial x = 2x$, $\partial z/\partial y = 2y$, so that

$$A = \int\int_{\mathscr{D}} \sqrt{1 + 4x^2 + 4y^2}\, dx\, dy$$

$$= \int_0^1 d\rho \int_0^{2\pi} \sqrt{1 + 4\rho^2}\, \rho\, d\theta$$

$$= 2\pi \int_0^1 \sqrt{1 + 4\rho^2}\, \rho\, d\rho$$

$$= \frac{\pi}{4} (\sqrt{125} - 1).$$

13.4 SURFACE INTEGRALS.   THE DIVERGENCE THEOREM

We are now in a position to define what is meant by an integral over a surface. Let S be a smooth simple surface element, given by $\mathbf{P} = \mathbf{F}(\mathbf{Q})$ for $\mathbf{Q}$ in $\mathscr{D}$, and let ϕ be a function defined on S. Then by $\displaystyle\int\int_S \phi(\mathbf{P})\, d\sigma$ we mean

$$\int\int_{\mathscr{D}} \phi[\mathbf{F}(\mathbf{Q})]\sqrt{J_1{}^2 + J_2{}^2 + J_3{}^2}\, dA_{\mathbf{Q}},$$

whenever this integral exists. (In particular, it will exist when ϕ is continuous.) Where S is given in the form $z = f(x, y)$, we write this as

$$\int\int_{\mathscr{D}} \phi(x, y, z)\sec\gamma\, dA_{xy}.$$

There is a three-dimensional analogue of Green's theorem which expresses a relation between volume and surface integrals. And again, as in Green's theorem, we give a geometrical argument.

Let us suppose first that D is a closed region in three-space with a boundary which is a piecewise smooth surface, and that its projection $\mathscr{D}$ in the xy plane is a closed two-dimensional region with a piecewise smooth boundary. We suppose further that any vertical line through $\mathscr{D}$ intersects D in exactly one interval:

$$\{z_1(x, y) \leqslant z \leqslant z_2(x, y)\}.$$

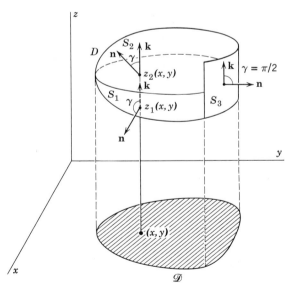

The boundary of D then consists of three parts: S_1, given by $z = z_1(x, y)$; S_2 given by $z = z_2(x, y)$; and S_3, a surface (or surfaces) parallel to the z-axis. Such a region will be said to be xy-**projectable**. Similar definitions hold for yz- and xz-**projectable** regions. If a region is projectable on all coordinate three planes, it will be called a **standard region.**

Suppose now that N is a function which has continuous partial derivatives in a standard region D, whose projection in the xy plane is $\mathscr{D}$. We then have

$$\iiint_D \frac{\partial N}{\partial z}\, dV = \iint_{\mathscr{D}} dA_{xy} \int_{z_1}^{z_2} \frac{\partial N}{\partial z}\, dz$$

$$= \iint_{\mathscr{D}} N[x, y, z_2(x, y)]\, dA_{xy} - \iint_{\mathscr{D}} N[x, y, z_1(x, y)]\, dA_{xy}$$

If we denote by $\mathbf{n}$ the unit vector in the direction of the outer normal and by γ the angle between $\mathbf{n}$ and $\mathbf{k}$ we get

$$\iint_{\mathscr{D}} N[x, y, z_2(x, y)]\, dA = \iint_{\mathscr{D}} N[x, y, z_2(x, y)] \cos \gamma \sec \gamma\, dA$$

$$= \iint_{S_2} N \cos \gamma\, d\sigma.$$

On S_1, the outer normal points downward, so that $d\sigma = \sec(\pi - \gamma)\, dA$. Thus we get

$$-\iint_{\mathscr{D}} N[x, y, z_1(x, y)]\, dA = \iint_{\mathscr{D}} N \cos \gamma \sec(-\gamma)\, dA$$

$$= \iint_{S_1} N \cos \gamma\, d\sigma.$$

And finally,

$$\iint_{S_3} N \cos \gamma\, d\sigma = 0,$$

since $\gamma = \pi/2$ on S_3. Thus, combining all these surface integrals we see that

$$\iiint_D \frac{\partial N}{\partial z}\, dV = \iint_S N \cos \gamma\, d\sigma.$$

Similarly,

$$\iiint_D \frac{\partial L}{\partial x}\, dV = \iint_S L \cos \alpha\, d\sigma$$

and

$$\iiint_D \frac{\partial M}{\partial y}\, dV = \iint_S M \cos \beta\, d\sigma,$$

where L and M have continuous derivatives in D, and where $\cos \alpha = \mathbf{n} \cdot \mathbf{i}$ and $\cos \beta = \mathbf{n} \cdot \mathbf{j}$. Adding these three formulas, we express the results in the form

$$\iiint_D \left(\frac{\partial L}{\partial x} + \frac{\partial M}{\partial y} + \frac{\partial N}{\partial z} \right) dV = \iint_S (L\mathbf{i} \cdot \mathbf{n} + M\mathbf{j} \cdot \mathbf{n} + N\mathbf{k} \cdot \mathbf{n}) \, d\sigma$$

$$= \iint_S (L\mathbf{i} + M\mathbf{j} + N\mathbf{k}) \cdot \mathbf{n} \, d\sigma$$

or, in vector notation,

(1) $$\iiint_D \nabla \cdot \mathbf{F} \, dV = \iint_S \mathbf{F} \cdot \mathbf{n} \, d\sigma,$$

where $\mathbf{F} = L\mathbf{i} + M\mathbf{j} + N\mathbf{k}$ and $\mathbf{n}$ is the exterior normal.

It should also be clear that if D is any region which can be decomposed into standard regions by piecewise smooth surfaces, formula (1) holds for D. Formula (1) holds for each standard region. If S_a is an auxiliary surface lying between two standard regions, the exterior normal for one is the negative of the exterior region for the other. Thus the contribution to the surface integrals over these auxiliary surfaces cancels out, leaving just formula (1). Thus we get the following theorem, known as Green's theorem, as Gauss' theorem, or, because of the presence of $\nabla \cdot \mathbf{F}$ in the integrand of the volume integral, as the **divergence theorem**.

13.4a Theorem. Let D be a bounded closed region in E_3 which can be subdivided into a finite number of standard regions. Let $\mathbf{F}$ be a continuously differentiable function on D. Then

$$\iiint_D \nabla \cdot \mathbf{F} \, dV = \iint_S \mathbf{F} \cdot \mathbf{n} \, d\sigma,$$

where $\mathbf{n}$ is the exterior normal.

As in the case of Green's theorem, we will content ourselves with the geometrical argument we have given. While it is true that this is by no means the strongest form of the theorem, nevertheless it is a useful theorem that serves very well for most purposes of analysis. For example, in potential theory and the theory of partial differential equations, we can usually restrict our use of the divergence theorem to very simple regions covered by Theorem 13.4a.

A EXERCISES

1. Find the areas of the following surfaces:

    (a) $z = \sqrt{1 - x^2 - y^2}$ $\mathscr{D}: \{x^2 + y^2 \leqslant 1\}$

(b) $z = \sqrt{x^2 + y^2}$ $\mathscr{D}: \{x^2 + y^2 \leqslant 1\}$

(c) $2z = 4 - x^2 - y^2$ $\mathscr{D}: \{1 < x^2 + y^2 < 2\}$

(d) $z = xy$ $\mathscr{D}: \{x^2 + y^2 \leqslant 1\}$

2. Find the area cut off the tip of the paraboloid $x = y^2 + z^2$ by the plane $x + z = 1$.

3. Compute the following surface integrals:

(a) $\displaystyle\iint_S x^2 \, d\sigma$ S:the cylinder $\{x^2 + y^2 = 1, 0 < z < 1\}$

(b) $\displaystyle\iint_S x(z^2 + y^2) \, d\sigma$ $S: x = \sqrt{9 - y^2 - z^2}$

(c) $\displaystyle\iint_S (z^2 + y^2) \, d\sigma$ $S: x = \sqrt{4 - y^2 - z^2}$

(d) $\displaystyle\iint_S \mathbf{P} \cdot \mathbf{n} \, d\sigma$ $S: z = \sqrt{1 - x^2 - y^2}$

4. Tell why $\displaystyle\iint_S x \, d\sigma = 0$ if S is symmetric about the origin.

5. Compute the following surface integrals by the divergence theorem:

(a) $\displaystyle\iint_S \mathbf{P} \cdot \mathbf{n} \, d\sigma$ $S: x^2 + y^2 + z^2 = 1$

(b) $\displaystyle\iint_S (x^2\mathbf{i} + y^2\mathbf{j} + z^2\mathbf{k}) \cdot \mathbf{n} \, d\sigma$, where S is the surface of the cube $\{-1 \leqslant x \leqslant 1, -1 \leqslant y \leqslant 1, -1 \leqslant z \leqslant 1\}$.

(c) $\displaystyle\iint_S (x \cos \alpha - y \cos \beta - z \cos \gamma) \, d\sigma$ over the sphere $x^2 + y^2 + (z - 1)^2 = 1$, where $\mathbf{n} = (\cos \alpha, \cos \beta, \cos \gamma)$.

B EXERCISES

1. Let S be defined implicitly by $f(x, y, z)$, where f is continuously differentiable; and suppose that $f_3 \neq 0$, so that the equation can be solved for z in terms of x and y, for (x, y) in $\mathscr{D}$. Show that for ϕ continuous on S:

$$\iint_S \phi \, d\sigma = \iint_{\mathscr{D}} \phi \, \frac{\sqrt{f_1^2 + f_2^2 + f_3^2}}{|f_3|} \, dA$$

$$\iint_S \mathbf{F} \cdot \mathbf{n} \, d\sigma = \iint_{\mathscr{D}} \frac{\mathbf{F} \cdot \nabla f}{|f_3|} \, dA$$

2. Let D be a standard region and S its boundary. If **O** is not in D, how that:

(a) $\displaystyle\iint_S \mathbf{P} \cdot \mathbf{n} \, d\sigma = 3 \iiint_D dV$

(b) $\displaystyle\iint_S \frac{\mathbf{P} \cdot \mathbf{n}}{|\mathbf{P}|} \, d\sigma = 2 \iiint_D \frac{dV}{|\mathbf{P}|}$

(c) $\displaystyle\iint_S \frac{\mathbf{P} \cdot \mathbf{n}}{|\mathbf{P}|^2} \, d\sigma = \iiint_D \frac{dV}{|\mathbf{P}|^2}$

3. If V equals the volume of D in 2 above, show that:

$$V = \iint_S x(\mathbf{i} \cdot \mathbf{n}) \, d\sigma = \iint_S y(\mathbf{j} \cdot \mathbf{n}) \, d\sigma = \iint_S z(\mathbf{k} \cdot \mathbf{n}) \, d\sigma.$$

4. Show that $EG - F^2 = J_1^2 + J_2^2 + J_3^2$, and thus complete the proof of Theorem 13.3c.

C EXERCISES

I. Let S be a smooth surface element which intersects each ray from the origin in at most one point. The set of rays which intersect S will pierce the unit

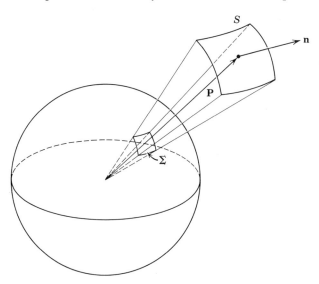

sphere centered at the origin in a set Σ. The area of Σ is called the **solid angle**, subtended by S. Show that the solid angle is given by

$$\iint_S \frac{\mathbf{P} \cdot \mathbf{n}}{|\mathbf{P}|^3} \, d\sigma,$$

where **n** is the outward normal on S. (Apply the divergence theorem to the volume between Σ and S.)

2. Let D be a standard region with surface S, and let u and v both have second-order continuous derivatives in D. Show that:

(a) $\displaystyle\iiint_D (u\Delta v + \nabla u \cdot \nabla v)\, dV = \iint_S u\nabla v \cdot \mathbf{n}\, d\sigma$

(b) $\displaystyle\iiint_D (u\Delta v - v\Delta u)\, dV = \iint_S (u\nabla v \cdot \mathbf{n} - v\nabla u \cdot \mathbf{n})\, d\sigma$

(c) $\displaystyle\iiint_D \Delta u\, dV = \iint_S \nabla u \cdot \mathbf{n}\, d\sigma$

(d) $\displaystyle\iiint_D |\nabla u|^2\, dV = \iint_S u(\nabla u \cdot \mathbf{n})\, d\sigma$, if $\Delta u = 0$.

3. Prove the converse of Theorem 13.3c: If C is a smooth curve on a simple smooth surface element, then $\mathscr{C}$, the image of C back in $\mathscr{D}$, is a smooth curve.

13.5 STOKES' THEOREM. ORIENTABLE SURFACES

Let S be a simple smooth surface element described by $\mathbf{P} = \mathbf{F}(\mathbf{Q})$ for $\mathbf{Q}$ in $\mathscr{D}$. Let $\mathscr{B}: \mathbf{Q} = \mathbf{Q}(t)$, $\{a \leqslant t \leqslant b\}$ be the boundary of $\mathscr{D}$ oriented

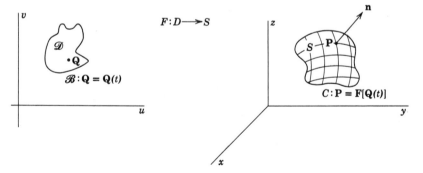

positively with respect to $\mathscr{D}$. This induces a parameterization, and thereby an orientation of C, the boundary of S, given by $\mathbf{P} = \mathbf{F}[\mathbf{Q}(t)]$. (The unit normal, as defined by $\mathbf{n} = (J_1\mathbf{i} + J_2\mathbf{j} + J_3\mathbf{k})/\sqrt{J_1^2 + J_2^2 + J_3^2}$, will then point so that the curve $\mathscr{C}$ is oriented in a counterclockwise manner around it, the rotation being viewed from the end of the normal vector.)

Now suppose L, M, and N are differentiable functions defined in a region R in which S is contained (what we really use is the existence of

∇L, ∇M, ∇N on S), and that the vector function **F** has continuous second derivatives on $\mathscr{D}$. Then consider

$$\int_C L\,dx = \int_{\mathscr{B}} L\frac{\partial x}{\partial u}\,du + L\frac{\partial x}{\partial v}\,dv.$$

By Green's theorem, this becomes

$$\iint_{\mathscr{D}} \left[\frac{\partial}{\partial u}\left(L\frac{\partial x}{\partial v}\right) - \frac{\partial}{\partial v}\left(L\frac{\partial x}{\partial u}\right)\right] dA_{uv} = \iint_{\mathscr{D}} \left(\frac{\partial L}{\partial u}\frac{\partial x}{\partial v} - \frac{\partial L}{\partial v}\frac{\partial x}{\partial u}\right) dA_{uv}.$$

Since $\partial^2 x/\partial u\,\partial v = \partial^2 x/\partial v\,\partial u$, the terms involving these derivatives cancel out. Now

$$\frac{\partial L}{\partial u} = \frac{\partial L}{\partial x}\frac{\partial x}{\partial u} + \frac{\partial L}{\partial y}\frac{\partial y}{\partial u} + \frac{\partial L}{\partial z}\frac{\partial z}{\partial u}$$

and

$$\frac{\partial L}{\partial v} = \frac{\partial L}{\partial x}\frac{\partial x}{\partial v} + \frac{\partial L}{\partial y}\frac{\partial y}{\partial v} + \frac{\partial L}{\partial z}\frac{\partial z}{\partial v},$$

so that when we multiply these respectively by $\partial x/\partial v$ and $\partial x/\partial u$, and add we get

$$\frac{\partial L}{\partial u}\frac{\partial x}{\partial v} - \frac{\partial L}{\partial v}\frac{\partial x}{\partial u} = -\frac{\partial L}{\partial y}J_3 + \frac{\partial L}{\partial z}J_2,$$

where

$$J_1 = \frac{\partial(y,\,z)}{\partial(u,\,v)}, \qquad J_2 = \frac{\partial(z,\,x)}{\partial(u,\,v)}, \qquad J_3 = \frac{\partial(x,\,y)}{\partial(u,\,v)}.$$

But the normal **n** is given by

$$\mathbf{n} = \frac{J_1\mathbf{i} + J_2\mathbf{j} + J_3\mathbf{k}}{\sqrt{J_1^{\,2} + J_2^{\,2} + J_3^{\,2}}} = \cos\alpha\,\mathbf{i} + \cos\beta\,\mathbf{j} + \cos\gamma\,\mathbf{k},$$

so that

$$J_1 = \cos\alpha\sqrt{J_1^{\,2} + J_2^{\,2} + J_3^{\,2}}$$

and so forth. The integral then becomes

$$\int_C L\,dx = \iint_{\mathscr{D}} \left(-\frac{\partial L}{\partial y}\cos\gamma + \frac{\partial L}{\partial z}\cos\beta\right)\sqrt{J_1^{\,2} + J_2^{\,2} + J_3^{\,2}}\,dA_{uv}$$

$$= \iint_S \left(-\frac{\partial L}{\partial y}\cos\gamma + \frac{\partial L}{\partial z}\cos\beta\right)d\sigma.$$

Similarly,

$$\int_C M\,dy = \iint_S \left(-\frac{\partial M}{\partial z}\cos\alpha + \frac{\partial M}{\partial x}\cos\gamma\right)d\sigma$$

and

$$\int_C N\,dz = \iint_S \left(-\frac{\partial N}{\partial x}\cos\beta + \frac{\partial N}{\partial y}\cos\alpha\right)d\sigma.$$

By addition, we get

$$\int_C L\, dx + M\, dy + N\, dz = \int\!\!\int_S \left[\left(\frac{\partial N}{\partial y} - \frac{\partial M}{\partial z} \right) \cos \alpha \right.$$
$$\left. + \left(\frac{\partial L}{\partial z} - \frac{\partial N}{\partial x} \right) \cos \beta + \left(\frac{\partial M}{\partial x} - \frac{\partial L}{\partial y} \right) \cos \gamma \right] d\sigma.$$

In vector notation, this becomes

(1) $$\int_C \mathbf{F} \cdot d\mathbf{P} = \int\!\!\int_S \nabla \times \mathbf{F} \cdot \mathbf{n}\, d\sigma.$$

This is **Stokes' theorem** for a simple smooth surface element.

To extend this formula to a surface which can be decomposed into simple smooth surface elements, we must see how these elements are put together to form the complete surface. The idea is this: Suppose S is composed of S_1 with boundary C_1, and S_2 with boundary C_2, where C_1 and C_2 have one or more common arcs. If formula (1) is applicable to both S_1 and S_2, we would like to add the results, have the line integrals

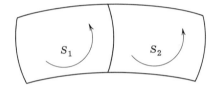

over the common arcs cancel out, and have (1) valid for S itself. Unfortunately, this cannot always happen. This distinction separates surfaces into two classes: those for which such a decomposition can be achieved, and those for which it cannot. Stokes' theorem extends to the one class of surfaces and not to the other.

Suppose S consists of two simple smooth surface elements S_1 and S_2, with positively oriented boundaries C_1 and C_2 respectively, and that S_1 and S_2 join along at most a finite number of arcs which are common to C_1 and C_2. Each of these common arcs will inherit an orientation from C_1 and from C_2. If these two orientations are in opposite directions, we say that the surface S is an **orientable surface**; otherwise it is **non-orientable**. In general, suppose S can be decomposed into a finite number of simple smooth surface elements $S_1, S_2, \ldots, S_n$, with boundaries $C_1, C_2, \ldots, C_n$ respectively. If each C_j has at most a finite number of arcs in common with all other C_k's, and if the two orientations induced on each of these arcs by C_j and C_k are opposite, then we say that S is **orientable**; otherwise it is **non-orientable**. It is a fact, though we will not show it, that orientability is a property of the surface and not the decomposition; that is, if a surface is orientable under one decomposition, it will also be orientable under all other decompositions.

To convince yourself that there do exist non-orientable surfaces, you should study the diagrams of the Möbius strip. This one-sided surface is

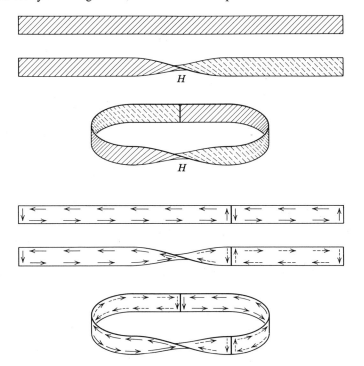

constructed as follows: Take a long rectangular piece of paper, give it a half twist (*H*), bend the ends together, and glue them. The resulting surface will be one-sided, will have one edge, and will be non-orientable.

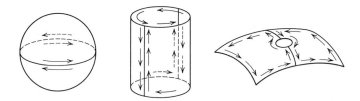

Stokes' theorem extends immediately to orientable surfaces; for, as indicated earlier, the line integrals over the common parts of the boundary cancel out, leaving just the integral around the boundary of *S*. Thus we have the following theorem.

13.5a   Theorem. Let S be an orientable surface with boundary C, where the equations defining each simple smooth part of S have two continuous derivatives. Suppose further that F is a differentiable function defined in a region containing S. Then

$$\iint_S \nabla \times \mathbf{F} \cdot \mathbf{n} \, d\sigma = \int_C \mathbf{F} \cdot d\mathbf{P}.$$

We can use Stokes' theorem to establish a three-dimensional analogue of Theorem 13.2c, which gives a derivative test that a vector field be a gradient field. The idea of the test is as follows: If ϕ is a twice continuously differentiable function, its mixed derivatives are independent of the order of differentiation. Thus, for example,

$$\phi_{12} = \phi_{21}.$$

This is expressed vectorially by

$$\nabla \times \nabla \phi = \mathbf{O}.$$

Now it turns out that, in simply connected regions, this is also sufficient. (The necessity for simple connectedness is somewhat the same as in two dimensions.)

Simple connectedness is a difficult concept in three dimensions, so we prove the theorem under the more restrictive condition of convexity. A set D is said to be **convex** if any two points in D can be joined by a segment lying in D.

13.5b   Theorem. Let D be a convex region, and let $\mathbf{F} = L\mathbf{i} + M\mathbf{j} + N\mathbf{k}$ be continuously differentiable in D. Then for $\mathbf{F}$ to be a gradient field, it is necessary and sufficient that $\nabla \times \mathbf{F} = \mathbf{O}$.

Proof: Necessity. If there is a ϕ such that $\mathbf{F} = \nabla \phi$, then

$$\nabla \times \mathbf{F} = \nabla \times \nabla \phi = \mathbf{O}.$$

Sufficiency. If $\nabla \times \mathbf{F} = \mathbf{O}$, then we define ϕ in D by

$$\phi(\mathbf{P}) = \int_{\mathbf{P}_0}^{\mathbf{P}} \mathbf{F} \cdot d\mathbf{P},$$

where $\mathbf{P}_0$ is a fixed point and the integral is taken over the segment from $\mathbf{P}_0$ to $\mathbf{P}$.

We first show that, for any $\mathbf{P}$ and $\mathbf{Q}$ in D,

$$\phi(\mathbf{P}) - \phi(\mathbf{Q}) = \int_{\mathbf{Q}}^{\mathbf{P}} \mathbf{F} \cdot d\mathbf{P},$$

where the integral is taken along the segment connecting $\mathbf{Q}$ to $\mathbf{P}$. To see this, we consider

(1)
$$\int_{\mathbf{P}_0}^{\mathbf{P}} \mathbf{F} \cdot d\mathbf{P} + \int_{\mathbf{P}}^{\mathbf{Q}} \mathbf{F} \cdot d\mathbf{P} + \int_{\mathbf{Q}}^{\mathbf{P}_0} \mathbf{F} \cdot d\mathbf{P} = \int_C \mathbf{F} \cdot d\mathbf{P},$$

where C is the triangle with vertices $\mathbf{P}_0$, $\mathbf{P}$, and $\mathbf{Q}$. If S is the triangular surface bounded by C, then S is in D (why?) and, by Stokes' theorem, this line integral is equal to

$$\iint_S (\nabla \times \mathbf{F}) \cdot \mathbf{n} \, d\sigma = 0.$$

Thus the right-hand side of (1) vanishes, so that

$$\int_{\mathbf{P}_0}^{\mathbf{P}} \mathbf{F} \cdot d\mathbf{P} + \int_{\mathbf{P}}^{\mathbf{Q}} \mathbf{F} \cdot d\mathbf{P} + \int_{\mathbf{Q}}^{\mathbf{P}_0} \mathbf{F} \cdot d\mathbf{P} = 0.$$

This is equivalent to

$$\phi(\mathbf{P}) - \phi(\mathbf{Q}) = \int_{\mathbf{Q}}^{\mathbf{P}} \mathbf{F} \cdot d\mathbf{P}.$$

We apply this formula in the following manner. We set

$$\mathbf{Q} = (x, y, z)$$

$$\mathbf{P} = (x + h, y, z).$$

Thus
$$\frac{1}{h} [\phi(x + h, y, z) - \phi(x, y, z)] = \frac{1}{h} \int_x^{x+h} L \, dx$$

$$= L(x', y, z)$$

by the mean-value theorem, where x' is between x and $x + h$.
As $h \to 0$, we get

$$\phi_1(\mathbf{Q}) = L(\mathbf{Q}).$$

Similarly,
$$\phi_2(\mathbf{Q}) = M(\mathbf{Q}),$$

and
$$\phi_3(\mathbf{Q}) = N(\mathbf{Q}).$$

Thus
$$\nabla \phi = \mathbf{F}. \qquad \blacksquare$$

This theorem can be restated as a corollary.

13.5c Corollary. Let D be a convex region, and let $\mathbf{F} = L\mathbf{i} + M\mathbf{j} + N\mathbf{k}$ be continuously differentiable in D. Then for $\int \mathbf{F} \cdot d\mathbf{P}$ to be independent of the path, it is necessary and sufficient that $\nabla \times \mathbf{F} = \mathbf{O}$.

13.6 SOME PHYSICAL HEURISTICS

Let $\mathbf{F} = L\mathbf{i} + M\mathbf{j} + N\mathbf{k}$ be a differentiable vector field in a region D, and $\mathbf{P}_0$ be a point in D. If D_r is a sphere of radius r centered at $\mathbf{P}_0$, then by the mean-value theorem

$$(1) \qquad \iiint_{D_r} \nabla \cdot \mathbf{F} \, dV = \nabla \cdot \mathbf{F}(\mathbf{P}')V_r,$$

where V_r is the volume of D_r and $\mathbf{P}'$ is a point of D_r. Also, by the divergence theorem,

$$(2) \qquad \iiint_{D_r} \nabla \cdot \mathbf{F} \, dV = \iint_{S_r} \mathbf{F} \cdot \mathbf{n} \, d\sigma,$$

where S_r is the surface of D_r and $\mathbf{n}$ is the exterior normal. By combining (1) and (2), dividing by V_r, and letting $r \to 0$, we get

$$(3) \qquad \nabla \cdot \mathbf{F}(\mathbf{P}_0) = \lim_{r \to 0} \frac{1}{V_r} \iint_{S_r} \mathbf{F} \cdot \mathbf{n} \, d\sigma.$$

This gives an interpretation of the divergence of a vector field which is coordinate-free. For this reason it is frequently used as the definition of divergence, from which one can show that in any rectangular coordinate system the divergence is given by

$$\nabla \cdot \mathbf{F} = \frac{\partial L}{\partial x} + \frac{\partial M}{\partial y} + \frac{\partial N}{\partial z}.$$

Let us suppose that a fluid moves in a region D and that at a given instant the particle of fluid at the point $\mathbf{P}$ has a velocity vector $\mathbf{F}$. The vector field so defined is called the **velocity field** of the fluid at the instant in question. If α is a unit vector, then $\mathbf{F}(\mathbf{P}) \cdot \alpha$ is the component of velocity at $\mathbf{P}$ in the direction α.

Let us fix our attention again on the sphere D_r, centered at a point $\mathbf{P}_0$ in D. Since $\mathbf{n}$ is the exterior normal, $\mathbf{F}(\mathbf{P}) \cdot \mathbf{n}$ is the rate of flow of the fluid out of the sphere at the point $\mathbf{P}$, and the integral $\iint_{S_r} \mathbf{F} \cdot \mathbf{n} \, d\sigma$ gives the net rate of flow (net flux) of the fluid out of the sphere. Dividing by V_r yields the net rate of flow of fluid out of D_r per unit volume. Thus $(1/V_r)\iint_{S_r} \mathbf{F} \cdot \mathbf{n} \, d\sigma$ is a measure of the rate at which the fluid is expanding or diverging near the point $\mathbf{P}_0$. This, of course, is the reason the name "divergence" is applied to $\nabla \cdot \mathbf{F} = L_1 + M_2 + N_3$.

We consider now a plane passing through the point P_0. Let C_r be a circle of radius r in this plane centered at P_0, with the disk bounded by C_r denoted by S_r. Then, by Stokes' theorem,

$$(4) \qquad \int_{C_r} \mathbf{F} \cdot d\mathbf{P} = \int\int_{S_r} (\nabla \times \mathbf{F}) \cdot \mathbf{n} \, d\sigma.$$

By the mean-value theorem, we get

$$(5) \qquad \int_{C_r} \mathbf{F} \cdot d\mathbf{P} = \nabla \times \mathbf{F}(\mathbf{P'}) \cdot \mathbf{n} A_r,$$

where $\mathbf{P'}$ is in S_r and A_r is the area of the circle. From (4) and (5), we get

$$(6) \qquad \mathbf{n} \cdot \nabla \times \mathbf{F}(\mathbf{P_0}) = \lim_{r \to 0} \frac{1}{A_r} \int_{C_r} \mathbf{F} \cdot d\mathbf{P}.$$

Now $\mathbf{F} \cdot d\mathbf{P} = \mathbf{F} \cdot \mathbf{T} \, ds$ is the component of $\mathbf{F}$ along C_r in the positive direction along C_r, times the element of arc length. Integrated over C_r, this gives the net component of $\mathbf{F}$ in the positive direction around C_r, which measures the tendency of the fluid to rotate or to curl about an axis in the direction $\mathbf{n}$ at the point P_0. From this comes the name **curl F** for $\nabla \times \mathbf{F}$. This is also sometimes called the **rotation** of $\mathbf{F}$ and denoted by **rot F**.

A EXERCISES

1. Evaluate by Stokes' theorem:

(a) $\displaystyle\int_C 2y \, dx - 2x \, dy + z^2 x \, dz$

$C: \mathbf{P} = \cos \theta \mathbf{i} + \sin \theta \mathbf{j} + 5\mathbf{k} \qquad \{0 < \theta < 2\pi\}$

(b) $\displaystyle\int_C yz^2 \, dx + (xz^2 - 2y) \, dy + 2xyz \, dz$

$C: \mathbf{P} = \cos \theta \mathbf{i} + \sin \theta \mathbf{j} + \cos \theta \mathbf{k} \qquad \{0 < \theta < 2\pi\}$

B EXERCISES

1. Show that if S is a piecewise smooth simple surface, bounded by C, then

$$\int\int_S \mathbf{a} \cdot \mathbf{n} \, d\sigma = \tfrac{1}{2} \int_C \mathbf{a} \times \mathbf{P} \cdot d\mathbf{P}.$$

2. Show that, if u is continuously differentiable on S,

$$\int\int_S \mathbf{n} \cdot \nabla u \times \nabla v \, d\sigma = \int_C u \nabla v \cdot d\mathbf{P}.$$

13.7 CHANGE OF VARIABLES IN MULTIPLE INTEGRALS

In the integral

$$I = \int_a^b f(y) \, dy$$

a change of variables given by $y = v(x)$ led to the formula

$$I = \int_c^d f[v(x)]v'(x) \, dx,$$

where $v(c) = a$ and $v(d) = b$. To simplify our picture of what is involved, let us suppose that $v(x)$ is an increasing function, so that the equation $y = v(x)$ gives a one-to-one map of the interval $\{c \leqslant x \leqslant d\}$ onto the interval $\{a \leqslant y \leqslant b\}$. Then $v(x + h) - v(x)$ is the length of the interval on the y-axis, which is the image of the interval from x to $x + h$ on the x-axis. The ratio of these intervals is $[v(x + h) - v(x)]/h$. As $h \to 0$, this difference quotient tends to $v'(x)$. Thus we see $v'(x)$ as a "local magnification factor," by which the interval of length dx must be multiplied in order to become the same length as its image of length dy on the y-axis. The change of variables in I is then seen heuristically as a replacement of equals by equals: $f(y) = f[v(x)]$ and $dy = v'(x) \, dx$.

We are thus led to expect a similar formula in the case of a multiple integral. Let

$$I = \int\!\!\int_D f(\mathbf{P}) \, dA_\mathbf{P}.$$

If $\mathbf{P} = \mathbf{F}(\mathbf{Q})$ gives a one-to-one mapping of a domain $\mathscr{D}$ onto D, we should then expect a formula of the form

$$I = \int\!\!\int_\mathscr{D} f[\mathbf{F}(\mathbf{Q})]|J(\mathbf{Q})| \, dA_\mathbf{Q},$$

where $|J(\mathbf{Q})|$ is the "local magnification factor" by which the element of area $dA_\mathbf{Q}$ must be multiplied to make it equal to the area $dA_\mathbf{P}$, into which it is carried by the mapping $\mathbf{P} = \mathbf{F}(\mathbf{Q})$. We know (at least heuristically, by Section 11.5) of such a factor, namely the absolute value of the Jacobian of the transformation $\mathbf{F}$.

The same reasoning applies equally well in any number of dimensions, so that we would expect that

$$\int\!\!\int\!\!\int_D f(\mathbf{P}) \, dV_\mathbf{P} = \int\!\!\int\!\!\int_\mathscr{D} f[\mathbf{F}(\mathbf{Q})]|J(\mathbf{Q})| \, dV_\mathbf{Q}$$

The object of this section is to determine conditions under which these formulas are valid. Let R be an open region in the (x, y) plane, and suppose that the equation $\mathbf{P} = \mathbf{F}(\mathbf{Q})$, given in coordinates by $x = f(u, v)$, $y = g(u, v)$, is a continuously differentiable one-to-one mapping of an open region $\mathscr{R}$ in the (u, v) plane onto R. Suppose now that $\mathbf{F}$ and its inverse map regions to which Green's theorem applies onto regions to which Green's theorem applies. We suppose further that the Jacobian

$$J(\mathbf{Q}) = \frac{\partial(x, y)}{\partial(u, v)}$$

is never zero in $\mathscr{R}$.

13.7a **Lemma.** Let D be a closed bounded sub-region of R, to which Green's theorem applies. And suppose in addition that g is twice continuously differentiable. Then the area of D is given by

$$A_D = \int\int_{\mathscr{D}} |J(\mathbf{Q})| \, dA_\mathbf{Q},$$

where $\mathscr{D}$ is the image in $\mathscr{R}$ of D under the inverse mapping.

Proof. Let B be the boundary of D. Then, by Green's theorem,

$$\int_B x \, dy = \int\int_D dA_\mathbf{P} = A_D.$$

But if $\mathscr{B}$ is the boundary of $\mathscr{D}$, we have

$$\int_B x \, dy = \int_{\pm\mathscr{B}} f \frac{\partial g}{\partial u} \, du + f \frac{\partial g}{\partial v} \, dv,$$

where the integral is taken in the positive or negative sense according as the orientation is preserved or reserved by the mapping. But

$$\int_{\pm\mathscr{B}} \left(f \frac{g}{u} \, du + f \frac{g}{v} \, dv \right) = \pm \int_{\mathscr{B}} \left(f \frac{g}{u} \, du + f \frac{g}{v} \, dv \right)$$

$$= \pm \int\int_{\mathscr{D}} \left(\frac{\partial}{\partial u} \left(f \frac{\partial g}{\partial v} \right) - \frac{\partial}{\partial v} \left(f \frac{\partial g}{\partial u} \right) \right) \, dA_\mathbf{Q}$$

$$\int\int (f_\sigma - f_v g_u) \, dA_\mathbf{Q} = \pm \int\int J(\mathbf{Q}) \, dA_\mathbf{Q}$$

If it should happen that g is not twice continuously differentiable, but f is, then the proof can be carried through by starting from

$$A_D = -\int_B y\, dx.$$

In most instances both f and g will be highly differentiable; for example, the equations introducing polar coordinates are infinitely differentiable.

13.7b   Theorem. Let D and $\mathscr{D}$ be related as in Lemma 13.7a, and let ϕ be continuous in D. Then

$$\iint_D \phi(\mathbf{P})\, dA_\mathbf{P} = \iint_{\mathscr{D}} \phi[\mathbf{F}(\mathbf{Q})]|J(\mathbf{Q})|\, dA_\mathbf{Q}.$$

Proof. Form a curvilinear partition Δ of D, of which each sub-region D_k is a region to which Green's theorem applies. Let $\mathscr{D}_k$ be the image of D_k in the (u, v) plane. Then, by Lemma 13.7a and the mean-value theorem,

$$A_{D_k} = \iint_{\mathscr{D}_k} |J(\mathbf{Q})|\, dA_\mathbf{Q} = |J(\mathbf{Q}_k)| A_{\mathscr{D}_k},$$

where $\mathbf{Q}_k$ is a point in $\mathscr{D}_k$. Let $\mathbf{P}_k = \mathbf{F}(\mathbf{Q}_k)$, and observe that

$$\sum_\Delta \phi(\mathbf{P}_k) A_{D_k} = \sum_\Delta \phi[\mathbf{F}(\mathbf{Q}_k)]|J(\mathbf{Q}_k)| A_{\mathscr{D}_k}$$

where Δ' is the partition of $\mathscr{D}$ induced by Δ. Then, by uniform continuity,

$$\|\Delta'\| \to 0 \quad \text{as} \quad \|\Delta\| \to 0;$$

so passing to the limit, we get by Theorem 12.4h

$$\iint_D \phi(\mathbf{P})\, dA_\mathbf{P} = \iint_{\mathscr{D}} \phi[\mathbf{F}(\mathbf{Q})]|J(\mathbf{Q})|\, dA_\mathbf{Q} \qquad \blacksquare$$

The same results extend to three dimensions. We assume that the transformation is given by $\mathbf{P} = \mathbf{F}(\mathbf{Q})$ or in coordinates by $x = f(u, v, w)$, $y = g(u, v, w)$, $z = h(u, v, w)$. As before, we assume that $\mathbf{F}$ maps an open region $\mathscr{R}$ in the $\mathbf{Q} = (u, v, w)$ space onto an open region R of the $\mathbf{P} = (x, y, z)$ space in a one-to-one manner. Further, we assume that $\mathbf{F}$ is twice continuously differentiable. We let D be a closed sub-region of R whose boundary B is a piecewise smooth surface and $\mathscr{D}$ be the image of D in $\mathscr{R}$ under the inverse mapping. Then the boundary $\mathscr{B}$ of $\mathscr{D}$ is piecewise smooth. (The argument is much the same as in Theorem 13.3c.) Finally, we suppose that the divergence theorem is applicable to both D and $\mathscr{D}$.

13.7c   Theorem. Let D and $\mathscr{D}$ be related as above. Then, if $J(\mathbf{Q}) \neq 0$, the volume of D is given by

$$V_D = \iiint_{\mathscr{D}} |J(\mathbf{Q})| \, dV_\mathbf{Q},$$

where $J(\mathbf{Q})$ is the Jacobian of $\mathbf{F}$.

Proof. By the divergence theorem,

$$V_D = \iiint_D dV_\mathbf{P} = \iint_B z \cos \gamma \, d\sigma_\mathbf{P}.$$

Let S be a simple smooth surface element on B and $\mathscr{S}$ its image on $\mathscr{B}$. If $\mathscr{S}$ is given by $\mathbf{Q} = \mathbf{Q}(r, t)$; that is, $u = u(r, t)$, $v = v(r, t)$, and $w = w(r, t)$ for (r, t) in a plane region M of the (r, t) plane, then S is given by $\mathbf{P} = \mathbf{F}[\mathbf{Q}(r, t)]$. Now consider

$$\iint_S z \cos \gamma \, d\sigma_\mathbf{P} = \pm \iint_M z \, \frac{J_3}{\sqrt{J_1^{\,2} + J_2^{\,2} + J_3^{\,2}}} \sqrt{J_1^{\,2} + J_2^{\,2} + J_3^{\,2}} \, dA_{r,t}$$

$$= \pm \iint_M z J_3 \, dA_{r,t} = \pm \iint_M z \, \frac{\partial(x, y)}{\partial(r, t)} \, dA_{r,t}$$

But $\dfrac{\partial(x, y)}{\partial(r, t)} = \dfrac{\partial(x, y)}{\partial(v, w)} \dfrac{\partial(v, w)}{\partial(r, t)} + \dfrac{\partial(x, y)}{\partial(w, u)} \dfrac{\partial(w, u)}{\partial(r, t)} + \dfrac{\partial(x, y)}{\partial(u, v)} \dfrac{\partial(u, v)}{\partial(r, t)}.$

(See Exercise B5 of Section 11.3. This can also be verified by direct calculation.) Thus

$$\frac{\partial(x, y)}{\partial(r, t)} = \frac{\partial(x, y)}{\partial(u, w)} \mathscr{J}_1 + \frac{\partial(x, y)}{\partial(w, v)} \mathscr{J}_2 + \frac{\partial(x, y)}{\partial(u, v)} \mathscr{J}_3,$$

where the script $\mathscr{J}$'s refer to the surface $\mathscr{S}$. Substituting this together with $x = f$, $y = g$, $z = h$ into our integral, we get

$$\pm \iint_M \left[h \, \frac{\partial(f, g)}{\partial(v, w)} \mathscr{J}_1 + h \, \frac{\partial(f, g)}{\partial(w, u)} \mathscr{J}_2 + h \, \frac{\partial(f, g)}{\partial(u, v)} \mathscr{J}_3 \right] dA_{r,t}$$

Next we denote $\mathscr{J}_1 / \sqrt{\mathscr{J}_1^{\,2} + \mathscr{J}_2^{\,2} + \mathscr{J}_3^{\,2}} = \cos \alpha'$, and so forth, so that this integral becomes

$$\pm \iint_{\mathscr{S}} \left[h \, \frac{\partial(f, g)}{\partial(v, w)} \cos \alpha' + h \, \frac{\partial(f, g)}{\partial(w, u)} \cos \beta' + h \, \frac{\partial(f, g)}{\partial(u, v)} \cos \gamma' \right] d\sigma_\mathbf{Q}.$$

Combining the integrals over all smooth pieces gives

$$V_D = \pm \int\int_{\mathscr{S}} \left[h \frac{\partial(f, g)}{\partial(v, w)} \cos \alpha' + h \frac{\partial(f, g)}{\partial(w, u)} \cos \beta' + h \frac{\partial(f, g)}{\partial(u, v)} \cos \gamma \right] d\sigma_Q.$$

We will apply the divergence theorem to this integral with

$$L = h \frac{\partial(f, g)}{\partial(v, w)}, \quad M = h \frac{\partial(f, g)}{\partial(w, u)}, \quad N = h \frac{\partial(f, g)}{\partial(u, v)}.$$

We find, after a calculation in which some second derivatives cancel out, that

$$\frac{\partial L}{\partial u} + \frac{\partial M}{\partial v} + \frac{\partial N}{\partial w} = \frac{\partial(f, g, h)}{\partial(u, v, w)} = J(Q).$$

Thus we finally get

$$V_D = \pm \int\int\int_{\mathscr{D}} J(Q) \, dV_Q.$$

The sign must be chosen as before. Thus the proof is complete. ∎

13.7d Theorem. Let D and $\mathscr{D}$ be related as above, and let ϕ be continuous in D. Then

$$\int\int\int_D \phi(P) \, dV_P = \int\int\int_{\mathscr{D}} \phi[F(Q)]|J(Q)| \, dV_Q.$$

Proof. The proof of Theorem 13.7b can be taken over almost word for word. ∎

Perhaps the most common changes of variables are the introduction of polar coordinates in the plane, and of spherical and cylindrical coordinates in three-space. We will discuss polar coordinates in the plane given by $x = r \cos \theta$, $y = r \sin \theta$ as presenting difficulties typical of all three.

There are two main difficulties with which we have to deal. The first, and lesser, arises from the fact that the inverse transformation given by $r = \sqrt{x^2 + y^2}$, $\theta = \text{arc tan } y/x$ is not single-valued. This is easily handled by dividing the plane up into quadrants in which it is single-valued. (A minor difficulty does arise from the fact that arc tan y/x is not defined for $x = 0$. However, we can then use an equivalent formula arc cot x/y.)

The main trouble arises from the fact that the Jacobian $\partial(x, y)/\partial(r, \theta) = r$ vanishes at the origin. By the remarks of the previous paragraph, it is clear that we need consider only the neighborhood of the origin. Thus let f be a continuous function defined in D: $\{x^2 + y^2 \leqslant a^2\}$. Then certainly

$$\int\int_D f(x, y) \, dx \, dy \text{ exists. Now } f \text{ is bounded, let us say by } M, \text{ so that if}$$

we delete an ϵ-neighborhood of the origin from D we have

$$\left| \iint\limits_{D} f \, dx \, dy - \iint\limits_{D_\epsilon} f \, dx \, dy \right| \leqslant M\pi\epsilon^2,$$

where D_ϵ is the annulus which remains after the deletion. If we divide this annulus up by the axes into four parts, each is mapped in a one-to-one manner onto a rectangle in the (r, θ) plane. Thus we see that the annulus

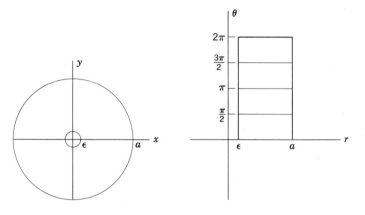

itself is mapped onto the rectangle R_ϵ: $\{\epsilon \leqslant r \leqslant a, 0 \leqslant \theta \leqslant 2\pi\}$. The mapping is one to one except that the top and bottom of the rectangle both map onto the segment of the x-axis. Thus

$$\iint\limits_{D_\epsilon} f(x, y) \, dx \, dy = \iint\limits_{R_\epsilon} f(r \cos \theta, r \sin \theta) r \, dr \, d\theta.$$

Now if R is the rectangle $\{0 \leqslant r \leqslant a, 0 \leqslant \theta \leqslant 2\pi\}$, clearly the function defined by $rf(r \cos \theta, r \sin \theta)$ is integrable over R and

$$\left| \iint\limits_{R} rf(r \cos \theta, r \sin \theta) \, dr \, d\theta - \iint\limits_{R_\epsilon} rf(r \cos \theta, r \sin \theta) \, dr \, d\theta \right| \leqslant M\epsilon\pi\epsilon.$$

Thus, symbolically,

$$\left| \iint\limits_{D} - \iint\limits_{R} \right| \leqslant \left| \iint\limits_{D} - \iint\limits_{D_\epsilon} \right| + \left| \iint\limits_{D_\epsilon} - \iint\limits_{R} \right|$$

$$= \left| \iint\limits_{D} - \iint\limits_{D_\epsilon} \right| + \left| \iint\limits_{R_\epsilon} - \iint\limits_{R} \right| \leqslant 2M\pi\epsilon^2.$$

Since this holds for every $\epsilon > 0$, we have

$$\iint\limits_{D} f(x, y)\, dx\, dy = \iint\limits_{R} f(r \cos \theta, r \sin \theta) r\, dr\, d\theta.$$

A EXERCISES

1. Evaluate $\displaystyle\iint\limits_{D} \left(\dfrac{x^2}{a^2} + \dfrac{y^2}{b^2}\right) dx\, dy$ $D: \left\{\dfrac{x^2}{a^2} + \dfrac{y^2}{b^2} \leqslant 1\right\}$. Set $x = au, y = bv$, and use polar coordinates.

2. Transform the integral $\displaystyle\iint\limits_{D} f(x, y)\, dx\, dy$ $D: \{x^2 + y^2 \leqslant a^2\}$ as indicated and describe the new domain of integration:

(a) $x = u + 1, y = v - 2$ (b) $x = au + bv, y = cu + dv$

3. Let f be continuously differentiable over $D: \{(x - 2)^2 + (y - 3)^2 \leqslant 1\}$. Transform $\displaystyle\iint\limits_{D} (f_x^{\,2} + f_y^{\,2})\, dx\, dy$ by $x = u/(u^2 + v^2), y = v/(u^2 + v^2)$.

4. Find the volume below $z = x$ and above $z = x^2 + y^2$

(a) by rectangular coordinates;   (b) by cylindrical coordinates.

5. Compute $\displaystyle\iint\limits_{R} \exp\left(\dfrac{x - y}{x + y}\right) dx\, dy$, where R is the triangle bounded by $x = 0$, $y = 0, x + y = 1$. Make the substitution $u = x + y, v = x - y$.

6. Let R be the triangle bounded by $x = 0, y = 0, x + y = 1$. Make the substitution $x + y = u, y = uv$, and show that $\displaystyle\iint\limits_{R} e^{-x-y} x^{a-1} y^{b-1}\, dx\, dy$ can be reduced to the product of two simple integrals.

B EXERCISES

1. Let f be continuous in $D: \{x^2 + y^2 + z^2 \leqslant a^2\}$. Show that

$$\iiint\limits_{D} f(x, y, z)\, dx\, dy\, dz$$

$$= \iiint\limits_{R} f(r \cos \theta \sin \phi, r \sin \theta \sin \phi, r \cos \phi) r^2 \sin\, dr\, d\theta\, d\phi,$$

where R is the rectangle $\{0 \leqslant r \leqslant a, 0 \leqslant \theta \leqslant 2\pi, 0 \leqslant \phi \leqslant \pi\}$.

2. Find the value of $\displaystyle\int\int_R \{(x - y)^2 + 2(x + y) + 1\}^{-1/2}\,dx\,dy$, by substituting $x = u(1 + v)$ and $y = v(1 + u)$, where R is the triangle bounded by $x = 0$, $x = 2$, and $x = y$.

3. Transform $\displaystyle\int\int_R f(x, y)\,dx\,dy$ $R: \{|x|^{2/3} + |y|^{2/3} \leqslant a^{2/3}\}$ by $x = r \cos^3 \theta$, $y = r \sin^3 \theta$.

part **III**

THEORY
OF CONVERGENCE

14

Infinite Series (special kind of sequences — sequences of partial sums)
KNOPP: Theory + Application of Infinite Series

14.1 CONVERGENCE, ABSOLUTE AND CONDITIONAL

From here on we will discuss infinite series and related topics. We begin with definitions.

Let $\{a_n\}$ be a sequence of numbers. Then the formal sum

$$a_0 + a_1 + a_2 + \cdots + a_n + \cdots$$

or

$$\sum_{n=0}^{\infty} a_n$$

is called an **infinite series**. The numbers $a_0, a_1, \ldots a_n, \ldots$ are its **terms**, and the numbers $S_n = \sum_{k=0}^{n} a_k$ its **partial sums**.

If $\lim S_n$ exists, its value S is called the **sum of the series**. In this case, we say that the series **converges** and we write

$$S = \sum_{n=0}^{\infty} a_n.$$

If $\lim S_n$ does not exist, we say that the series **diverges**.

A series may begin with the first, second, or other terms, as for example $\sum_{n=1}^{\infty} a_n, \sum_{n=2}^{\infty} a_n, \ldots$ Sometimes we will write these as $\sum_{1}^{\infty} a_n, \sum_{2}^{\infty} a_n, \ldots$, and where there is no danger of ambiguity we will write simply Σa_n,

EXAMPLE 1. Prove that $\sum_{0}^{\infty} x^n = \dfrac{1}{1-x}$ for $|x| < 1$.

Solution:

Since convergence is defined in terms of partial sums, we look at

$$S_n = 1 + x + \cdots + x^n = \sum_{0}^{n} x^k.$$

From algebra, we have that

$$S_n = \frac{1 - x^{n+1}}{1 - x} = \frac{1}{1 - x} - \frac{x^{n+1}}{1 - x}.$$

From our study of limits, we know that $x^{n+1} \to 0$ if $|x| < 1$. Hence

$$\lim S = \frac{1}{1 - x}.$$

It is also clear that, if $|x| \geqslant 1$, the series diverges.

Our second example illustrates a technique useful in certain simple series.

EXAMPLE 2. Prove that $\sum_1^\infty \frac{1}{n(n + 1)}$ converges, and find its sum.

Solution:

We decompose $\dfrac{1}{n(n + 1)}$ by partial fractions:

$$\frac{1}{n(n + 1)} = \frac{1}{n} - \frac{1}{n + 1}.$$

Thus $S_n = \sum_1^n \dfrac{1}{k(k + 1)} = \sum_1^n \left(\dfrac{1}{k} - \dfrac{1}{k + 1} \right) = \left(1 - \dfrac{1}{2} \right) + \left(\dfrac{1}{2} - \dfrac{1}{3} \right) + \cdots$

$$+ \left(\frac{1}{n - 1} - \frac{1}{n} \right) + \left(\frac{1}{n} - \frac{1}{n + 1} \right) = 1 - \frac{1}{n + 1}.$$

From this, it is clear that

$$S = \lim S_n = 1.$$

Our first theorem on series establishes what is really a divergence test.

14.1a Theorem. Suppose Σa_n converges. Then $\lim a_n = 0$.

Proof. Note first that, if $\lim S_n = S$, then $\lim S_{n-1} = S$. Now $a_n = S_n - S_{n-1}$, so

$$\lim a_n = \lim (S_n - S_{n-1}) = \lim S_n - \lim S_{n-1} = S - S = 0. \quad \blacksquare$$

This does not say that, if $\lim a_n = 0$, then Σa_n converges. Indeed this is not correct, as we shall see later. It says that convergence of Σa_n implies $a_n \to 0$. Hence if a_n does not tend to zero, the series cannot converge. Thus, in a given series Σa_n, we can examine $\lim a_n$. If $\lim a_n = 0$, we have no information about convergence or divergence; but if $\lim a_n \neq 0$, either because it fails to exist or because it exists and has another value, then Σa_n diverges.

EXAMPLE 3. Test $\displaystyle\sum_1^\infty \frac{n^n}{n!}$.

Solution:

$$\frac{n^n}{n!} = \frac{n \cdot n \cdot n \cdots n}{1 \cdot 2 \cdot 3 \cdots n} = \left(\frac{n}{1}\right)\left(\frac{n}{2}\right)\cdots\left(\frac{n}{n}\right) > 1.$$

Hence $\lim n^n/n! \neq 0$, and the series diverges.

Since convergence of a series is defined in terms of the convergence of the sequence of partial sums, any information about the convergence of sequences is useful in discussing series. Of particular importance in this connection is the Cauchy criterion, which takes the following form.

14.1b   Theorem. A necessary and sufficient condition that a series Σa_n converge is that, for each $\epsilon > 0$, there is an $N(\epsilon)$ for which

$$|a_{n+1} + a_{n+2} + \cdots + a_m| < \epsilon \qquad \text{if } m > n > N.$$

Proof. Apply the Cauchy criterion for sequences to the sequence of partial sums.   ∎

The ϵ-condition above is sometimes written

$$|a_{n+1} + a_{n+2} + \cdots + a_{n+p}| < \epsilon \qquad \text{if } n > N, p \geqslant 1.$$

This comes from setting $p = m - n$.

EXAMPLE 4. Test $\displaystyle\sum_0^\infty \frac{1}{n!}$. (Compare Section 2.6.)

Solution. We observe that

$$\frac{1}{n!} = \frac{1}{1 \cdot 2 \cdot 3 \cdots n} \leqslant \frac{1}{1 \cdot 2 \cdot 2 \cdots 2} = \frac{1}{2^{n-1}}.$$

Then
$$\left|\sum_{n+1}^{n+p} \frac{1}{k!}\right| = \sum_{n+1}^{n+p} \frac{1}{k!} < \sum_{n+1}^{n+p} \frac{1}{2^{k-1}} = \frac{1}{2^n}\left[1 + \frac{1}{2} + \cdots + \frac{1}{2^{p-1}}\right]$$

$$= \frac{1}{2^n}\frac{1 - (1/2)^p}{1 - 1/2} < \frac{1}{2^n}\frac{1}{1 - 1/2} = \frac{1}{2^{n-1}} = 2(1/2)^n$$

Now we know (Theorem 2.2a) that $(1/2)^n \to 0$. Hence, for each $\epsilon > 0$, there is an N for which

$$2(1/2)^n < \epsilon \qquad \text{if } n > N.$$

Thus
$$\left|\sum_{n+1}^{n+p} \frac{1}{k!}\right| < \epsilon \qquad \text{if } n > N, p \geqslant 1,$$

and the series converges by the Cauchy criterion.

It sometimes happens that a series Σa_n converges while the series $\Sigma |a_n|$ diverges. In this case, we say that the series Σa_n **converges conditionally.** When the series $\Sigma |a_n|$ converges, we say that the series Σa_n **converges absolutely.** An important fact about absolutely convergent series is that they are also convergent.

14.1c Theorem. If $\Sigma |a_n|$ converges, so does Σa_n.

Proof. The basic inequality involved in the proof is the following:

(1) $\quad |a_{n+1} + a_{n+2} + \cdots + a_{n+p}| \leqslant |a_{n+1}| + |a_{n+2}| + \cdots + |a_{n+p}|.$

We make a double application of the Cauchy criterion, using both the necessity and the sufficiency: Now $\Sigma |a_n|$ converges. So for each $\epsilon > 0$ there is an $N(\epsilon)$ for which

(2) $\qquad |a_{n+1}| + |a_{n+2}| + \cdots + |a_{n+p}| < \epsilon \qquad$ if $n > N, p \geqslant 1,$

this being true by the necessity part of the criterion. But (1) and (2) imply

(3) $\qquad |a_{n+1} + a_{n+2} + \cdots + a_{n+p}| < \epsilon \qquad$ if $n > N, p \geqslant 1.$

Then, by the sufficiency part of the criterion, (3) implies that Σa_n converges. ∎

EXAMPLE 5. Test $\displaystyle\sum_1^\infty \frac{(-1)^n}{n(n+1)}$.

Solution. We have seen in Example 2 that $\displaystyle\sum_1^\infty \frac{1}{n(n+1)}$ converges. Hence, by Theorem 14.1c, so does the given series.

A EXERCISES

hand all in

1. Sum the following series:

(a) $\displaystyle\sum_0^\infty (-1)^n \frac{2n+3}{(n+1)(n+2)}$ (b) $\displaystyle\sum_1^\infty \frac{1}{n(n+1)(n+2)}$ (c) $\displaystyle\sum_2^\infty \frac{n-1}{n!}$

2. Test $\Sigma(-1)^n n!/n^n$ for absolute convergence.

B EXERCISES

1. Show that if Σa_n converges absolutely and $\{b_n\}$ is a bounded sequence, then $\Sigma a_n b_n$ converges absolutely.

2. Show that if Σa_n converges to a sum S, then for any c the series $\Sigma c a_n$ converges to cS.

3. Show that if Σa_n is convergent, any new series formed by grouping the terms arbitrarily, such as, $(a_1 + a_2 + \cdots + a_{m_1}) + (a_{m_1+1} + a_{m_1+2} + \cdots + a_{m_2}) + (\cdots \quad) \cdots$ is also convergent.

14.2 SERIES WITH NON-NEGATIVE TERMS: COMPARISON TESTS

One of the significant implications of the last theorem is that, for many purposes, it is sufficient to study series with non-negative terms. Consequently we now give our attention to a set of theorems on such series. As you study this section, keep in mind that all the tests given here can be used to test for absolute convergence of series with variable signs.

14.2a Theorem. If Σa_n has non-negative terms, it converges if, and only if, the sequence of partial sums is bounded.

Proof. The sequence of partial sums is non-decreasing, and hence has a limit if, and only if, it is bounded. ∎

EXAMPLE 1. Show that the k series, $\sum_{n=1}^{\infty} \dfrac{1}{n^k}$, converges if $k > 1$ and diverges if $k \leqslant 1$. This series is useful for comparison tests.

Solution:

(a) Suppose $k > 1$. We show that $\sum \dfrac{1}{n^k}$ converges. We examine partial sums of order $2^n - 1$:

$$S_{2^n-1} = 1 + \left(\frac{1}{2^k} + \frac{1}{3^k}\right) + \left(\frac{1}{4^k} + \cdots + \frac{1}{7^k}\right) + \left(\frac{1}{8^k} + \cdots + \frac{1}{15^k}\right)$$

$$+ \cdots + \left(\frac{1}{(2^{n-1})^k} + \cdots + \frac{1}{(2^n - 1)^k}\right)$$

$$\leqslant 1 + \left(\frac{1}{2^k} + \frac{1}{2^k}\right) + \left(\frac{1}{4^k} + \cdots + \frac{1}{4^k}\right) + \left(\frac{1}{8^k} + \cdots + \frac{1}{8^k}\right)$$

$$+ \cdots + \left(\frac{1}{(2^{n-1})^k} + \cdots + \frac{1}{(2^{n-1})^k}\right)$$

$$= 1 + \frac{1}{2^{k-1}} + \frac{1}{(2^{k-1})^2} + \frac{1}{(2^{k-1})^3} + \cdots + \frac{1}{(2^{n-1})^{k-1}}$$

$$= \frac{1 - [1/(2^{k-1})^n]}{1 - (1/2^{k-1})} \frac{1}{1 - (1/2^{k-1})} = \frac{2^{k-1}}{2^{k-1} - 1} = \text{constant.}$$

Now, for any integer m, there is an n for which $2^n - 1 > m$. So also

$$S_m \leqslant S_{2^n-1} < \frac{2^{k-1}}{2^{k-1} - 1}.$$

Hence all partial sums are bounded, and the series therefore converges.

(b) Suppose $k \leqslant 1$. We show that $\sum\limits_1^\infty \dfrac{1}{n^k}$ diverges. First let us observe that $n^k \leqslant n$, since $k \leqslant 1$. Then:

$$S_{2^n} = 1 + \frac{1}{2^k} + \left(\frac{1}{3^k} + \frac{1}{4^k}\right) + \left(\frac{1}{5^k} + \cdots + \frac{1}{8^k}\right)$$

$$+ \cdots + \left(\frac{1}{(2^{n-1}+1)^k} + \cdots + \frac{1}{(2^n)^k}\right)$$

$$\geqslant 1 + \frac{1}{2} + \left(\frac{1}{3} + \frac{1}{4}\right) + \left(\frac{1}{5} + \cdots + \frac{1}{8}\right)$$

$$+ \cdots + \left(\frac{1}{2^{n-1}+1} + \cdots + \frac{1}{2^n}\right)$$

$$\geqslant 1 + \frac{1}{2} + \left(\frac{1}{4} + \frac{1}{4}\right) + \left(\frac{1}{8} + \cdots + \frac{1}{8}\right)$$

$$+ \cdots + \left(\frac{1}{2^n} + \cdots + \frac{1}{2^n}\right)$$

$$= 1 + \frac{1}{2} + \frac{1}{2} + \frac{1}{2} + \cdots + \frac{1}{2} = 1 + \frac{n}{2}.$$

Hence the partial sums are unbounded, and therefore the series diverges.

Where $k = 1$, the series becomes

$$1 + \frac{1}{2} + \frac{1}{3} + \frac{1}{4} + \cdots + \frac{1}{n} + \cdots = \sum_1^\infty \frac{1}{k}.$$

This series is called the **harmonic series.** It diverges, as the above proof shows.

We come now to a group of comparison tests. These are tests by which knowledge of the behavior of one series (namely, its convergence or divergence) can be used to study the behavior of another, provided the terms of the two series are appropriately related. The precise nature of this relationship is made clear in the statements of the following theorems. The most common of these theorems is called the **comparison test.**

14.2b   Theorem. Suppose Σa_n and Σb_n are two series with non-negative terms, and there is an N such that $a_n \leqslant b_n$ if $n > N$. Then
(i) if Σb_n converges, so does Σa_n;
(ii) if Σa_n diverges, so does Σb_n.

Proof. The basic inequality is

$$a_{N+1} + a_{N+2} + \cdots + a_{N+p} \leqslant b_{N+1} + b_{N+2} + \cdots + b_{N+p}$$

or

$$S_{N+p} - S_N \leqslant S'_{N+p} - S_N',$$

where the S_n refers to Σa_n and $S_n{}'$ to Σb_n. The result follows immediately from the previous theorem. ∎

EXAMPLE 2. Test $\displaystyle\sum_2^\infty \frac{1}{\sqrt{n(n-1)}}$.

Solution:

$$\frac{1}{n(n-1)} > \frac{1}{n \cdot n} = \frac{1}{n^2},$$

so that

$$\frac{1}{\sqrt{n(n-1)}} > \frac{1}{n}.$$

Hence $\displaystyle\sum_2^\infty \frac{1}{\sqrt{n(n-1)}}$ diverges by comparison with the harmonic series.

The next theorem is called the **limit form of the comparison test.**

14.2c Theorem. If Σa_n and Σb_n both have positive terms, and if

$$0 < \lim_{n \to \infty} \frac{a_n}{b_n} < \infty,$$

then either they both diverge or they both converge.

Proof. Since $\lim a_n/b_n = A$ exists, there is an N such that

$$\left| \frac{a_n}{b_n} - A \right| < \frac{A}{2} \qquad \text{if } n > N.$$

Then

$$-\frac{A}{2} < \frac{a_n}{b_n} - A < \frac{A}{2}$$

or

$$\tfrac{1}{2}A < \frac{a_n}{b_n} < \tfrac{3}{2}A < 2A,$$

so that

$$b_n < \left(\frac{2}{A}\right) a_n, \qquad a_n < (2A)b_n \qquad \text{if } n > N.$$

Hence the result follows by the previous comparison test. ∎

EXAMPLE 3. Test $\displaystyle\sum_1^\infty \frac{1}{\sqrt{n(2n+1)}}$.

Solution:

$$\frac{1}{\sqrt{n(2n+1)}} \Big/ \frac{1}{n} = \frac{n}{\sqrt{n(2n+1)}} = \frac{1}{\sqrt{2 + 1/n}} \to \frac{1}{\sqrt{2}}.$$

Hence the series diverges by comparison with the harmonic series in the limit form of the comparison test.

The next test, called the **integral test,** is also a comparison-type test, but this time the comparison is made between an integral and a series, rather than between two series.

14.2d Theorem. Let Σa_n be a series of positive non-increasing terms. Let $f(x)$ be a non-increasing function defined for $n \geqslant N$, for which

$$f(n) = a_n \qquad n \geqslant N.$$

Then the series Σa_n and the integral $\int_N^\infty f(x)\,dx$ both converge or both diverge.

Proof. For $k \geqslant N$, in the interval $k \leqslant x \leqslant k+1$, we have

$$a_k = f(k) \geqslant f(x) \geqslant f(k+1) = a_{k+1}.$$

Integrating from k to $k+1$,

$$a_k \geqslant \int_k^{k+1} f(x)\,dx \geqslant a_{k+1}.$$

Then we have both

(1)
$$\sum_N^{n-1} a_k \geqslant \int_N^n f(x)\,dx.$$

and

(2)
$$\int_N^n f(x)\,dx \geqslant \sum_N^{n-1} a_{k+1} = \sum_{N+1}^n a_k.$$

In terms of partial sums, inequality (1) says

$$S_{n-1} - S_{N-1} \geqslant \int_N^n f(x)\,dx.$$

But if the series converges to a sum S, then $S \geqslant S_{n-1}$, so that

$$S - S_{N-1} \geqslant \int_N^n f(x)\,dx.$$

Since the right-hand side is an increasing bounded sequence, the integral converges.

If the integral converges then inequality (2) implies

$$\int_N^\infty f(x)\,dx \geqslant \int_N^n f(x)\,dx \geqslant S_{n+1} - S_N,$$

or
$$S_{n+1} \leqslant A + S_N.$$

Hence the partial sums are bounded and the series converges. ∎

As our symbol indicates, the proof is now complete. But we have not discussed the case where the series and the integral are divergent. Why is this not necessary? (See Exercise B3.)

EXAMPLE 4. (a) We re-examine the k series

$$\sum 1/n^k \qquad k > 1.$$

Solution. We choose $f(x) = 1/x^k$ and consider

$$\int_1^n \frac{dx}{x^k} = \int_1^n x^{-k}\,dx = \frac{x^{1-k}}{1-k}\Big|_1^n$$

$$= \frac{n^{1-k}}{1-k} - \frac{1}{1-k}$$

$$= \frac{1}{k-1} - \frac{1}{k-1}\frac{1}{n^{k-1}}.$$

Now $k - 1 > 0$; hence

$$\frac{1}{n^{k-1}} \to 0 \qquad \text{as } n \to \infty.$$

Thus the integral converges, and so does the series.
(b) We re-examine the k series

$$\sum 1/n^k \qquad k < 1.$$

Solution. We calculate as before and get

$$\int_1^n \frac{dx}{x^k} = \frac{n^{1-k}}{1-k} - \frac{1}{1-k}.$$

But this time $1 - k > 0$, so that

$$n^{1-k} \to +\infty \qquad \text{as } n \to \infty.$$

Thus the integral diverges, and so does the series.

The harmonic series, corresponding to the case $k = 1$, has to be treated separately. The details are left as an exercise.

A EXERCISES

1. Use the integral test to show that the harmonic series diverges.

2. Test Σa_n for absolute convergence if a_n is

(a) $\dfrac{(-1)^n}{n^{1+1/n}}$

(b) $(-1)^n\left[\dfrac{\sqrt{n+1}-\sqrt{n}}{n}\right]$

(c) $\dfrac{(-1)^n n^{(-1)^n}}{n}$

(d) $\dfrac{n\cos(n\pi/2)}{\sqrt{n^4+n^3-2}}$

(e) $\dfrac{(-1)^n \log n}{n}$

(f) $\dfrac{3^n}{n}$

(g) $\dfrac{\sin n}{n^2+1}$

(h) $\dfrac{3^n+2n}{4^n+5}$

(i) $\dfrac{n}{n^2+2n+1}$

in notes

(j) $\dfrac{(-1)^n}{n \log n}$ (k) $\dfrac{(-1)^n}{n (\log n)^2}$ (l) $\dfrac{(-1)^n}{\log n}$

(m) $\dfrac{1}{3} - \dfrac{1 \cdot 2}{3 \cdot 5} + \dfrac{1 \cdot 2 \cdot 3}{3 \cdot 5 \cdot 7} - \dfrac{1 \cdot 2 \cdot 3 \cdot 4}{3 \cdot 5 \cdot 7 \cdot 9} + - \cdots .$

3. For what values of x does $\dfrac{x}{x+1} - \left(\dfrac{x}{x+1}\right)^2 + \left(\dfrac{x}{x+1}\right)^3 - + \cdots .$
converge, and what is its sum?

B EXERCISES

1. Establish the polynomial test: if $P(n)$ and $Q(n)$ are polynomials in n and $Q(n) \neq 0$, $n = 1, 2, 3, \ldots,$ then $\sum\limits_{1}^{\infty} \dfrac{P(n)}{Q(n)}$ converges if, and only if, the degree of Q exceeds that of P by 2 or more.

2. For what values of x does Σe^{-nx} converge?

3. In the proof of the integral test, why was it not necessary to discuss the case when either the series or the integral was divergent?

4. Test $\Sigma \sin \{\pi(n + 1/n\}$ and $\Sigma \sin^2 \left\{\pi\left((n + \dfrac{1}{n}\right)\right\}$ for absolute convergence.

5. For which values of k does $\sum\limits_{2}^{\infty} \dfrac{1}{n (\log n)^k}$ converge?

6. For which values of x does $\sum\limits_{n=1}^{\infty} \dfrac{x^n}{x^{2n} - 1}$ converge?

C EXERCISES

1. Suppose $a_n \geqslant 0$ and the sequence $\{a_n\}$ is non-increasing, and Σa_n converges. Show that $na_n \to 0.$ *as $n \to \infty$*

2. We know that the harmonic series diverges, that is, $H_n \to +\infty$ if $H_n = \sum\limits_{1}^{n} \dfrac{1}{k}.$
Show that H_n grows like $\log n$. In particular, show that $0 < H_n - \log n < 1$. Show further that $H_n - \log n$ is a non-increasing sequence and hence has a limit. (The value of this limit is approximately .577. It is known as the **Euler-Mascheroni constant** and is denoted by γ. It is not known whether γ is rational or irrational.)

3. Show that if a and b are any two positive numbers such that $a \geqslant b$, then

$$H_{[na]} - H_{[nb]} \to \log \dfrac{a}{b} .$$

(See Exercise 2, above.)

4. Let Σa_n and Σb_n have positive terms, and suppose $b_{n+1}/b_n \leqslant a_{n+1}/a_n.$ Show that Σb_n converges if Σa_n converges.

5. Extend the limit form of the ratio test to the following:

(a) If there are three positive constants a, A, and N such that $a \leqslant a_n/b_n \leqslant A$ when $n > N$, then Σa_n and Σb_n both diverge or both converge.

(b) If $a_n/b_n \to 0$ and Σb_n converges, then so does Σa_n.

(c) If $a_n/b_n \to \infty$ and Σb_n diverges, then so does Σa_n.

6. Suppose you have an inexhaustible supply of uniform rectangular cards. Show that, given any distance d, a finite number of these cards can be stacked on a table so that the outside edge of the top card projects a distance d beyond the edge of the table.

14.3 SERIES WITH NON-NEGATIVE TERMS: RATIO AND ROOT TESTS. REMAINDERS

We come now to a test which is still partly a comparison test, but goes by the name **Cauchy's root test.**

14.3a Theorem. Let Σa_n be a series of non-negative terms.

(i) If there is an $r < 1$ and an N such that

$$\sqrt[n]{a_n} \leqslant r \qquad \text{for } n > N,$$

then Σa_n converges.

(ii) If there are infinitely many n's for which

$$\sqrt[n]{a_n} \geqslant 1,$$

then Σa_n diverges.

Proof:

(i) For all $n > N$, we have $\sqrt[n]{a_n} \leqslant r$ or $a_n \leqslant r^n$. The series then converges, by comparison with the geometric progression.

(ii) For infinitely many n's, we have $\sqrt[n]{a_n} \geqslant 1$. Thus $a_n \geqslant 1$ for infinitely many n's and so $\lim a_n \neq 0$. ∎

Another slightly weaker form of the root test is given by the following theorem.

14.3b Theorem. Let Σa_n be a series of non-negative terms. Define ρ by

$$\rho = \lim \sup \sqrt[n]{a_n}.$$

(i) If $\rho < 1$, Σa_n converges.

(ii) If $\rho > 1$, Σa_n diverges.

(iii) If $\rho = 1$, the test fails. (That is, some series for which $\rho = 1$ diverge and others converge.)

Proof:
(i) By the definition of the limit superior (see Section 6.3), if $\rho < 1$, there is an N such that

$$\sqrt[n]{a_n} \leqslant \frac{\rho + 1}{2} < 1 \qquad \text{if } n > N,$$

and Σa_n then converges by part (1) of Theorem 14.3a.

(ii) Again by the definition, if $\rho > 1$ there is a subsequence a_{n_k} such that $(a_{n_k})^{1/n_k} \to \rho$. Then, if k is sufficiently large $(a_{n_k})^{1/n_k} \geqslant 1$, and Σa_n diverges by part (2) of Theorem 14.3a.

(iii) See Exercise B2.   ∎

Of course if $\lim \sqrt[n]{a_n}$ exists, then $\lim \sup \sqrt[n]{a_n} = \lim \sqrt[n]{a_n}$ and the previous theorem applies.

It is often important to know how closely the partial sums of a convergent series approximate the sum. We can get an estimate of the difference between these two in the convergent case of Theorem 14.3a.

14.3c Corollary. In case (1) of Theorem 14.3a, we have

$$0 \leqslant S - S_n \leqslant \frac{r^{n+1}}{1 - r} \qquad \text{for all } n > N.$$

Proof:

$$S - S_n = \sum_{n+1}^{\infty} a_k \leqslant \sum_{n+1}^{\infty} r^k$$
$$= r^{n+1} + r^{n+2} + \cdots$$
$$= r^{n+1}[1 + r + r^2 + \cdots]$$
$$= r^{n+1}/(1 - r).$$ ∎

EXAMPLE 1. Prove that $\sum_{1}^{\infty} [n/(n + 1)]^{n^2}$ converges, and estimate the error in using S_n as an approximation for S.

Solution. We apply Theorem 14.3a and Corollary 14.3b,

$$\sqrt[n]{\left(\frac{n}{n + 1}\right)^{n^2}} = \left(\frac{n}{n + 1}\right)^{n} = \frac{1}{(1 + 1/n)^n}.$$

But
$$\left(1 + \frac{1}{n}\right)^n > 2.$$

Hence
$$\sqrt[n]{\left(\frac{n}{n + 1}\right)^{n^2}} < \frac{1}{2}$$

or
$$\left(\frac{n}{n + 1}\right)^{n^2} < \left(\frac{1}{2}\right)^{n}.$$

Now that we have convergence by the root test, we apply the corollary
and get

$$S - S_n \leqslant \frac{(1/2)^{n+1}}{1 - 1/2} = \frac{1}{2^n}.$$

The next theorem is known as the **ratio test.**

14.3d   Theorem. Let Σa_n be a series of positive terms for which
$\lim a_{n+1}/a_n = q$ exists. Then:

(i) Σa_n converges if $q < 1$.
(ii) Σa_n diverges if $q > 1$.
If $q = 1$, the test fails.

Proof:
(i) Define $r = \frac{1}{2}(1 + q)$ so that $q < r < 1$. Now there exists an N
such that

$$\frac{a_{n+1}}{a_n} < r \qquad \text{if } n \geqslant N. \qquad \text{(Why?)}$$

Then

$$a_k = \frac{a_k}{a_{k-1}} \cdot \frac{a_{k-1}}{a_{k-2}} \cdots \frac{a_{N+1}}{a_N} \cdot a_N \leqslant r \cdot r \cdots r \cdot a_N = r^{k-N} a_N.$$

Hence the series converges, by comparison with the geometric progression
with $r < 1$.

(ii) Define $r = \frac{1}{2}(1 + q)$ so that $q > r > 1$. Now there exists an N
such that

$$\frac{a_{n+1}}{a_n} \geqslant r \qquad \text{if } n \geqslant N.$$

Then $\{a_n\}$ is an increasing sequence for $n > N$. Thus $\lim a_n \neq 0$.   ∎

Again we can estimate the remainder—that is, the difference $S - S_n$.

14.3e   Corollary. In case (1) of Theorem 14.3d,

$$0 \leqslant S - S_n \leqslant \frac{a_N r^{n-N}}{1 - r} \qquad \text{if } n > N.$$

Proof:

$$S - S_n = \sum_{n+1}^{\infty} a_k = a_{n+1} + a_{n+2} + \cdots$$
$$\leqslant a_N r^{n-N} + a_N r^{n-N+1} + \cdots$$
$$= a_N r^{n-N}(1 + r + \cdots)$$
$$= a_N r^{n-N}/(1 - r). \qquad \blacksquare$$

EXAMPLE 2.   Prove that $\sum_1^\infty \dfrac{(-1)^n n}{2^n}$ is absolutely convergent, and estimate the remainder.

Solution. We study the series $\sum_1^\infty \left| \dfrac{(-1)^n n}{2^n} \right| = \sum_1^\infty \dfrac{n}{2^n}$. By the ratio test,

$$\left| \frac{a_{n+1}}{a_n} \right| = \frac{n+1}{2n} = \frac{1}{2}\left(1 + \frac{1}{n} \right) \leqslant 0.6 \qquad \text{if } n \geqslant 5.$$

The series is thus absolutely convergent.

Let S be its sum. Then

$$|S - S_n| = \left| \sum_{n+1}^\infty \frac{(-1)^k k}{2^k} \right|$$

$$\leqslant \sum_{n+1}^\infty \frac{k}{2^k}$$

$$\leqslant \frac{|a_5|(0.6)^{n-5}}{0.4}$$

$$= \frac{5}{2^5} \frac{(0.6)^{n-5}}{0.4}$$

$$= \frac{25}{64} (0.6)^{n-5}.$$

14.4   SERIES WITH VARIABLE SIGNS

All of the preceding serve to establish the absolute convergence of series with variable signs. But for series that are conditionally convergent —and there are many of them—these tests will not reveal their convergence. In fact, the only tests we have presently available for such series are the definition itself and the Cauchy criterion, both of which are frequently awkward to apply directly. We now give the simplest theorem for dealing with such series. It is called the **alternating series test.**

14.4a   Theorem. Let $\{b_n\}$ be a sequence of positive terms decreasing monotonically to zero. Then $\Sigma(-1)^n b_n$ converges and

$$|S - S_n| \leqslant b_{n+1}.$$

Proof. We examine the odd partial sums. Clearly

$$S_{2n-1} = (b_0 - b_1) + (b_2 - b_3) + \cdots + (b_{2n-2} - b_{2n-1})$$

and
$$S_{2n+1} = S_{2n-1} + (b_{2n} - b_{2n+1}) \geqslant S_{2n-1}.$$

Thus the odd sums form a non-decreasing sequence. Furthermore, they are bounded:

$$S_{2n-1} = b_0 - (b_1 - b_2) - \cdots - (b_{2n-3} - b_{2n-2}) - b_{2n-1} \leqslant b_0. \text{ (Why?)}$$

Hence $\lim S_{2n-1} = S$ exists.

Now
$$S_{2n} = S_{2n-1} + b_{2n},$$

so that
$$\lim S_{2n} = \lim S_{2n-1} + \lim b_{2n} = S.$$

Since both even and odd partial sums converge to the same limit, the series must converge to S as its sum.

To obtain the estimate, we note that

$$|S - S_n| = |b_{n+1} - b_{n+2} + b_{n+3} \cdots|$$
$$= (b_{n+1} - b_{n+2}) + (b_{n+3} - b_{n+4}) + \cdots$$

which is positive since each parenthesis is positive. Thus

$$|S - S_n| = b_{n+1} - b_{n+2} + b_{n+3} - + \cdots$$
$$= b_{n+1} - (b_{n+2} - b_{n+3}) - (\quad) \cdots$$
$$\leqslant b_{n+1}.$$

An important example is given by the alternating harmonic series

$$1 - \tfrac{1}{2} + \tfrac{1}{3} - \tfrac{1}{4} + \tfrac{1}{5} - \tfrac{1}{6} + - \cdots,$$

which clearly satisfies the conditions and therefore converges. Its sum is log 2, but we cannot prove this until later. In general, the alternating k series is convergent if $k > 0$.

For two other tests, namely Dirichlet's and Abel's, refer to the next chapter, where these tests are discussed in connection with uniform convergence of series of functions. The special case of functions that are constants leads to a test for convergence of series of constants.

A   EXERCISES

1. Test Σa_n for convergence and absolute convergence, where a_n is

(a) $\dfrac{(-1)^n}{2n}$ (b) $\dfrac{(-1)^n}{\log n}$ (c) $(-1)^n(\sqrt{n+1} - \sqrt{n})$

(d) $\dfrac{(-1)^n}{n^{1+1/n}}$ (e) $\dfrac{(-1)^n \log n}{n}$ (f) $\dfrac{(-1)^n n}{n^2 - 5n + 1}$

(g) $\dfrac{(-1)^n}{\sqrt{n} + 1/n}$ (h) $\sin\left\{\pi\left(n + \dfrac{1}{n}\right)\right\}$ (i) $n^k e^{-nx}$

(j) $\log\left(1 + \dfrac{1}{n}\right)$ (k) $\left(1 - \dfrac{1}{n}\right)^{n^2}$ (l) $\dfrac{1}{x^n - y^n}$ $x > y > 0$

2. In 1 (b), (c), (e), and (g), how many terms must be taken to be sure that the remainder is smaller than 10^{-10}?

3. Determine for which values of x the following series converge:

(a) $\displaystyle\sum_{1}^{\infty} nx^n$ (b) $\displaystyle\sum_{1}^{\infty} n^k x^n$ (c) $\displaystyle\sum_{1}^{\infty} \frac{1}{x^n - 1}$

(d) $\displaystyle\sum_{1}^{\infty} n^n x^n$ (e) $\displaystyle\sum_{1}^{\infty} \frac{x^n}{n}$

4. In 3(a), (b), and (e), give a formula for the remainder after the Nth term.

5. Test Σa_n for convergence or divergence where a_n is

(a) $\dfrac{n!}{3 \cdot 5 \cdots (2n - 1)}$ (b) $\dfrac{3 \cdot 5 \cdots (2n + 1)}{2 \cdot 4 \cdots 2n}$

(c) $\dfrac{n!}{3^n}$ (d) $\dfrac{3^n}{n!}$ (e) $\dfrac{3 \cdot 5 \cdots (2n + 1)}{4 \cdot 7 \cdots (3n + 1)}$

(f) $\dfrac{n^{n^2}}{(n + 1)^{n^2}}$ (g) $\dfrac{(n + 1)^n}{(3n)^n}$

6. Estimate the remainders in 5(a), (d), and (e) after 100 terms.

B EXERCISES

use ratio test on these (a), (b),(c) then and ...(f), ... (h)n

1. Show that if Σa_k converges and $a_k \geqslant 0$, then $\Sigma a_k{}^2$ converges. Give an example showing that the condition $a_k \geqslant 0$ cannot be omitted.

2. Give examples to prove part (3) of Theorem 14.3b.

3. (a) Show that if $a_n > 0$, and if there is an N such that $a_{n+1}/a_n \geqslant 1$ for all $n > N$, then Σa_n diverges.

(b) If there is an N and a q, $0 < q < 1$ such that $a_{n+1}/a_n \leqslant q$ for all $n > N$, then Σa_n converges.

(c) Give examples to show that $\displaystyle\lim_{n \to \infty} \frac{a_{n+1}}{a_n} = 1$ is indecisive, that is, under this condition Σa_n may either converge or diverge.

C EXERCISES

1. Suppose Σa_n is a series of positive terms. Show that $\displaystyle\lim \inf \frac{a_{n+1}}{a_n} \leqslant \lim \inf \sqrt[n]{a_n} \leqslant \lim \sup \sqrt[n]{a_n} \leqslant \lim \sup \frac{a_{n+1}}{a_n}$.

2. Prove that if $\Sigma a_n{}^2$ and $\Sigma b_n{}^2$ converge, then so do $\Sigma a_n b_n$ and $\Sigma (a_n + b_n)^2$.

3. Prove that if $\Sigma a_n{}^2$ and $\Sigma b_n{}^2$ converge, then $|\Sigma a_n b_n| < \frac{1}{2}(\Sigma a_k{}^2 + \Sigma b_k{}^2)$.

4. Prove the Cauchy-Schwarz inequality for infinite series: if $\Sigma a_n{}^2$ and $\Sigma b_n{}^2$ converge, then $(\Sigma a_n b_n)^2 \leqslant (\Sigma a_n{}^2)(\Sigma b_n{}^2)$, and equality holds if, and only if, $a_n = k b_n$.

5. Prove the "triangle" inequality for infinite series: if $\Sigma a_n{}^2$ and $\Sigma b_n{}^2$ converge, then $\sqrt{\Sigma (a_n + b_n)^2} \leqslant \sqrt{\Sigma a_n{}^2} + \sqrt{\Sigma b_n{}^2}$, and equality holds if, and only if, $a_n = k b_n$, where $k \geqslant 0$.

14.5 MORE DELICATE TESTS

In this section we collect a few convergence tests which are designed primarily to study series for which the ratio test fails—that is, series for, which $\lim\limits_{n\to 1} a_{n+1}/a_n = 1$. We begin with **Kummer's test.**

14.5a Theorem. Let Σa_n be a series of positive terms.

(i) If there is a positive sequence $\{b_n\}$, a positive constant α, and an N for which

$$c_n = \frac{a_n}{a_{n+1}} \cdot b_n - b_{n+1} \geqslant \alpha \qquad \text{for all } n \geqslant N,$$

then Σa_n converges.

(ii) If $c_n \leqslant 0$ for all $n \geqslant N$, then Σa_n diverges if $\Sigma 1/b_n$ diverges. An alternative formulation of the conclusion is

(i) Σa_n is convergent if $\lim \inf c_n > 0$.

(ii) Σa_n is divergent if $\lim \sup c_n < 0$ and $\Sigma 1/b_n$ is divergent.

Proof:

(i) Since $a_{n+1} > 0$,

$$b_n a_n - b_{n+1} a_{n+1} \geqslant \alpha a_{n+1} \qquad \text{if } n \geqslant N,$$

so that

$$b_N a_N - b_{N+1} a_{N+1} \geqslant \alpha a_{N+1}$$

$$b_{N+1} a_{N+1} - b_{N+2} a_{N+2} \geqslant \alpha a_{N+2}$$

$$\cdot$$
$$\cdot$$
$$\cdot$$

$$b_{N+p-1} a_{N+p-1} - b_{N+p} a_{N+p} \geqslant \alpha a_{N+p}.$$

Adding, we get

$$b_N a_N - b_{N+p} a_{N+p} \geqslant \alpha(a_{N+1} + \cdots + a_{N+p}).$$

That is,

$$S_{N+p} - S_N \leqslant \frac{1}{\alpha}(b_N a_N - b_{N+p} a_{N+p}) \leqslant \frac{1}{\alpha} b_N a_N$$

or

$$S_{N+p} \leqslant S_N + \frac{1}{\alpha} b_N a_N.$$

The partial sums are therefore bounded, and hence the series converges.

(ii) If the condition of part (ii) of the theorem is satisfied, then

$$b_n a_n - b_{n+1} a_{n+1} \leqslant 0 \qquad \text{for } n \geqslant N.$$

Thus $\{a_n b_n\}$ is a non-decreasing sequence. Hence

$$b_n a_n \geqslant b_{n-1} a_{n-1} \geqslant \cdots \geqslant b_N a_N \equiv k$$

or

$$a_n \geqslant k/b_n,$$

and Σa_n diverges, by comparison with $\Sigma 1/b_n$. ∎

From this, **Raabe's test** follows immediately.

14.5b   Theorem. Let Σa_n be a series with positive terms, and suppose

$$\lim_{n \to \infty} n\left(\frac{a_n}{a_{n+1}} - 1\right) = r$$

exists. Then
(i) Σa_n converges if $r > 1$.
(ii) Σa_n diverges if $r < 1$.
And of course the test is inconclusive if $r = 1$.

Proof. The proof of this theorem is left as an exercise. ∎

Also as a consequence of Kummer's test, we can obtain **Gauss's test**.

14.5c   Theorem. If Σa_n is a series with positive terms, and if there is a bounded sequence $\{A_n\}$ such that for $n > N$,

$$\frac{a_n}{a_{n+1}} = 1 + \frac{r}{n} + \frac{A_n}{n^2},$$

then
(i) Σa_n converges if $r > 1$.
(ii) Σa_n diverges if $r \leqslant 1$.
This proof is also left as an exercise.

EXAMPLE. Test the series

$$\frac{1}{2} + \frac{1 \cdot 3}{2 \cdot 4} + \frac{1 \cdot 3 \cdot 5}{2 \cdot 4 \cdot 6} + \cdots + \frac{1 \cdot 3 \cdot 5 \cdots (2n - 1)}{2 \cdot 4 \cdot 6 \cdots (2n)} + \cdots.$$

Solution. We try the ratio test:

$$\frac{a_{n+1}}{a_n} = \frac{2n + 1}{2n + 2} = \frac{1 + 1/2n}{1 + 1/n} \to 1.$$

The ratio test fails, so we try Gauss's test:

$$\frac{a_n}{a_{n+1}} = \frac{2n + 2}{2n + 1}$$

$$= 1 + \frac{1}{2n} - \frac{1}{2n(2n + 1)}$$

$$= 1 + \frac{1}{2} \cdot \frac{1}{n} - \frac{1}{n^2} \cdot \frac{n}{2(2n + 1)}.$$

This is in the form where Gauss's theorem applies with

$$r = 1/2, \quad A_n = -\frac{n}{2(2n + 1)}.$$

Since $r < 1$ and $|A_n| \leqslant 1/4$, the series diverges by Gauss's test.

14.6 REARRANGEMENTS

In arithmetic, you are familiar with the commutative property of addition which states that a sum is independent of the order of the terms in the sum. For example,

$$a + b + c + d = c + b + d + a = d + a + c + b = \cdots.$$

However, in infinite series the sum is defined in a new way, namely as a limit. We want to inquire if, under this extended definition, the independence of the order of the terms is preserved. For example, we rearrange the terms of the alternating harmonic series

$$S = 1 - \tfrac{1}{2} + \tfrac{1}{3} - \tfrac{1}{4} + \tfrac{1}{5} - \tfrac{1}{6} + \cdots$$

into the new series

$$\sigma = 1 - \tfrac{1}{2} - \tfrac{1}{4} + \tfrac{1}{3} - \tfrac{1}{6} - \tfrac{1}{8} + \tfrac{1}{5} - \tfrac{1}{10} - \tfrac{1}{12} + \tfrac{1}{7} - - + - - + \cdots,$$

where we take two negative terms in order, then one positive one.

Two question arise:

(1) Does the new series converge?

(2) If so, does $\sigma = S$?

We denote the partial sums of S by S_n of σ by σ_n and examine the partial sums of σ of order $3n$:

$$\sigma_{3n} = \sum_{1}^{n} \left(\frac{1}{2k - 1} - \frac{1}{4k - 2} - \frac{1}{4k} \right)$$

$$= \sum_{k=1}^{n} \left(\frac{1}{2k - 1} - \frac{1}{2} \frac{1}{2k - 1} - \frac{1}{4} \cdot \frac{1}{k} \right)$$

$$= \sum_{k=1}^{n} \left(\frac{1}{2} \frac{1}{2k - 1} - \frac{1}{4} \frac{1}{k} \right) = \frac{1}{2} \sum_{k=1}^{n} \frac{1}{2k - 1} - \frac{1}{4} \sum_{1}^{n} \frac{1}{k}.$$

Now, in the first sum of our last expression, we fill in the even terms with negative signs and then add them on again:

$$\sigma_{3n} = \frac{1}{2}\left(\sum_{j=1}^{2n} \frac{(-1)^{j+1}}{j} + \sum_{1}^{n} \frac{1}{2k}\right) - \frac{1}{4}\sum_{1}^{n}\frac{1}{k}$$

$$= \frac{1}{2}\sum_{1}^{2n} \frac{(-1)^{j+1}}{j} + \frac{1}{4}\sum_{1}^{n}\frac{1}{k} - \frac{1}{4}\sum_{1}^{n}\frac{1}{k}$$

$$= \tfrac{1}{2}S_{2n}$$

Then, as $n \to \infty$,

$$S_{2n} \to S,$$

so that

$$\sigma_{3n} \to \tfrac{1}{2}S.$$

But any partial sum of σ differs from a third-order one by at most two terms, which tend to zero as $n \to \infty$. Hence $\sigma_n \to \frac{1}{2}S$.

That is, $\quad \frac{1}{2}S = 1 - \frac{1}{2} - \frac{1}{4} + \frac{1}{3} - \frac{1}{6} - \frac{1}{8} + \frac{1}{5} - - + - \cdots.$

It is therefore clear that the sum may be dependent on the order of the terms. We now prove two theorems which are concerned with this phenomenon.

First, we set up a convenient notation: If Σa_k is a series with variable signs, we designate the first positive a by p_1, the next by $p_2, \ldots$; the first negative one by $-n_1$, the next by $-n_2, \ldots$. Then any partial sum can be written

$$\sum_{1}^{n} a_k = \sum_{1}^{m} p_k - \sum_{1}^{r} n_k \qquad m + r = n.$$

Our first theorem now follows.

14.6a Theorem. If Σa_k is conditionally convergent, then both Σp_k and Σn_k are divergent.

Proof. Suppose one of them were convergent. To fix ideas, we may say that Σp_k is convergent and we write

$$\sum^{r} n_k = \sum^{m} p_k - \sum^{n} a_k.$$

Since both sums on the right have limits, so then does the sum on the left. Hence both Σn_k and Σp_k converge.

$$\sum_{1}^{n} |a_k| = \sum_{1}^{m} p_k + \sum_{1}^{r} n_k.$$

Again both sums on the right have limits. Hence $\Sigma|a_k|$ converges.

But this contradicts our hypothesis that Σa_k is conditionally convergent. Hence both Σp_k and Σn_k must diverge. ∎

We are now in a position to observe a very strange phenomenon of conditionally convergent series.

14.6b **Theorem.** Let Σa_k be a conditionally convergent series and A any real number. Then there is a rearrangement of Σa_k which converges to A.

Proof. Instead of giving a rigorous proof, we shall outline the procedure and try to make the result reasonable. First, let us note that the associated Σp_k and Σn_k both diverge to $+\infty$, since all terms in each series are positive. The procedure is as follows, supposing for definiteness that $A > 0$:

(i) Form successive partial sums of Σp_k until you get to the *first* one which is greater than A. This can be done, since $\sum^{m} p_k \to +\infty$.

(ii) Start subtracting partial sums of Σn_k until you get to the *first* one which brings the sum below A.

(iii) Add more terms of Σp_k to bring the sum just above A again.

.

.

.

To convince yourself that this procedure produces a convergent series, observe that $a_k \to 0$, since Σa_k converges. Hence $p_k \to 0$ and $n_k \to 0$. Now at each turning point in the above procedure the sum differs from A by less than a single p_k or n_k. As the procedure continues, these differences tend to zero. All intermediate partial sums are closer than the ones at the turning points. Hence the partial sums in this construction tend to A. ∎

14.6c **Theorem.** If Σa_k is absolutely convergent, Σp_k and Σn_k converge.

Proof. Suppose one diverges say, $\sum^{m} p_k \to +\infty$. Then

$$\sum^{r} n_k = -\sum^{n} a_k + \sum^{m} p_k,$$

Then, since $\sum^{n} a_k$ converges as $n \to \infty$, we see that also $\sum^{r} n_k \to +\infty$.

$$\sum^{n} |a_k| = \sum^{m} p_k + \sum^{r} n_k \to +\infty,$$

which contradicts the assumption that $\sum^{n} |a_k|$ converges. ∎

Yet all is not chaos in the rearrangement of series, for absolutely convergent ones save the day.

14.6d **Theorem.** If Σa_k is absolutely convergent, then any rearrangement is also absolutely convergent, and furthermore all rearrangements of this series have the same sum.

Proof. We prove the above theorem first for positive terms. Let Σb_k be the rearrangement. Let $S = \Sigma a_k$, $S_n = \overset{n}{\Sigma} a_k$, and $\sigma_n = \overset{n}{\Sigma} b_k$. Now for any σ_n, all the b's forming the partial sum occur as a's. Hence they occur, together with some others, in S so that

$$\sigma_n \leqslant S \qquad \text{for all } n.$$

Hence, since $\{\sigma_n\}$ is a monotone sequence,

$$\sigma_n \to \sigma \qquad \text{where } \sigma \leqslant S.$$

But the argument is symmetric; it applies also when the a's and b's are interchanged so that

$$\sigma \geqslant S.$$

Hence
$$\sigma = S,$$

and the proof is complete for positive a's.

Suppose now that Σa_k has variable signs. Then

$$\Sigma a_k = \Sigma p_k - \Sigma n_k.$$

Any rearrangement of the a's leads to a rearrangement of the p's and n's. But, by the first part, these sums are independent of the order. Hence the sum is left unchanged by the rearrangement.   ■

A   EXERCISES

1. For which values of a and b will

$$\frac{a}{b} + \frac{a(a+1)}{b(b+1)} + \cdots + \frac{a(a+1)\cdots(a+n-1)}{b(b+1)\cdots(b+n-1)} + \cdots$$

converge?

2. Test the following series for convergence:

use Raabe's test

(a) $\displaystyle\sum_1^\infty \frac{1 \cdot 3 \cdot 5 \cdots (2n-1)}{2 \cdot 4 \cdot 6 \cdots (2n)}$

(b) $\displaystyle\sum_1^\infty \frac{1 \cdot 3 \cdots (2n+1)}{2 \cdot 4 \cdots (2n)} \cdot \frac{1}{2n+5}$

(c) $\displaystyle\sum_1^\infty \frac{1 \cdot 3 \cdots (2n-1)}{2 \cdot 4 \cdots 2n} \cdot \frac{4n+3}{2n+2}$

3. For different values of k, test $\displaystyle\sum_1^\infty \left(\frac{1 \cdot 3 \cdots (2n-1)}{2 \cdot 4 \cdots 2n} \right)^k$

4. In the doubtful case in Exercise 3 above, use Kummer's test with $b_n = n \log n$.

5. Let $S = \displaystyle\sum_1^\infty 1/k^2$. Show that $\displaystyle\sum_0^\infty \frac{1}{(2k+1)^2} = \frac{3}{4} S$ and $\displaystyle\sum_1^\infty (-1)^k/k^2 = -\frac{1}{2} S$.

B EXERCISES

1. (a) Prove Raabe's theorem, applying Kummer's test with $b_n = n$.
(b) Prove Gauss's test.

2. Discuss the convergence of the binomial series

$$1 + ax + \frac{a(a-1)}{2!} x^2 + \cdots + \frac{a(a-1)(a-2)\cdots(a-n+1)}{n!} x^2 + \cdots$$

for all x's and all a's.

3. Show that

$$\{(1+\tfrac{1}{2})^2 - (1+\tfrac{1}{3})^2\} + \{(1+\tfrac{1}{4})^2 - (1+\tfrac{1}{5})^2\} + \cdots$$

$$+ \left\{\left(1+\frac{1}{2n}\right)^2 - \left(1+\frac{1}{2n+1}\right)^2\right\} + \cdots$$

converges, but that the series formed by removing the braces is divergent.

4. Give arguments similar to those used in the proof of Theorem 14.6b to show that the terms of a conditionally convergent series can be rearranged so that the partial sums (a) tend to $+\infty$; (b) tend to $-\infty$. (c) oscillate boundedly; (d) oscillate unboundedly.

C EXERCISES

1. Let

$$S_n = \sum_{k=1}^{n} \frac{(-1)^{k+1}}{k}.$$

Show that $S_{2n} = \sum_{k=1}^{n} \frac{1}{n+k}$, and hence deduce that $\sum_{1}^{\infty} \frac{(-1)^{k+1}}{k} = \log 2$.

2. Rearrange the alternating harmonic series to converge to zero.

3. Show that any convergent series of positive terms can be rearranged so that the terms occur in decreasing order.

4. Let

$$S = \sum_{1}^{\infty} \frac{(-1)^{k+1}}{k} = 1 - \tfrac{1}{2} + \tfrac{1}{3} - \tfrac{1}{4} + \tfrac{1}{5} - + \cdots$$

$$\sigma = 1 + \tfrac{1}{3} - \tfrac{1}{2} + \tfrac{1}{5} + \tfrac{1}{7} - \tfrac{1}{4} + + - + + - \cdots.$$

Show that $\sigma = \dfrac{3}{2} S.$

15

Sequences and Series of Functions. Uniform Convergence

15.1 INTRODUCTION

In the chapter on elementary functions, we commented on the scarcity of functions which we can write down. There are polynomials, rational functions, algebraic functions, and elementary transcendental functions. We can make compositions of these and piece them together on abutting intervals.

But many other kinds of functions are important in analysis. To use these we need some way of writing them down; that is, we need a representation for any function we want to use, and we need this representation to be amenable to the operations of analysis. One such representation is by means of an integral, as we have seen, especially in the case of the circular functions and their inverses. Another possible representation, and it is the one we want to study here, is as a convergent series of functions, or what amounts to the same thing, as the limit of a sequence of functions. In general, the terms of the series, or the approximants in the sequence, are expected to be simple functions whose properties we are presumed to know something about. From these properties of the terms of the series, we expect to deduce properties of the limit function. The two types of series to which we will give our closest attention will be series of powers of x or of $x - c$, where c is some appropriate constant:

$$\Sigma a_n (x - c)^n,$$

and Fourier series whose terms are sines and cosines of multiples of x:

$$a_0/2 + \Sigma(a_n \cos nx + b_n \sin nx).$$

It turns out that such series are useful, not only for writing down functions not otherwise easily representable, but also as tools for investigating the properties of known functions.

In the present chapter we will not be concerned with such special series as these, but will obtain some general results pertaining to series whose terms may be any reasonable functions, where reasonableness will be clarified as the discussion proceeds.

15.2 UNIFORM CONVERGENCE

It turns out that an important tool in the study of series and sequences of functions is the concept of uniform convergence.

For each integer n, let u_n be a function defined on some fixed interval I of the x-axis. The interval I may be open, closed, half open, semi-infinite, infinite, or what have you. (In fact, we can take the domains of our functions to be quite general sets, but for our purposes it is sufficient to restrict ourselves to intervals.) At each point x_1 in I, the numbers $u_n(x_1)$ form a sequence $\{u_n(x_1)\}$, and we can inquire as to the convergence of this sequence. If for each x in I the sequence $\{u_n(x)\}$ converges, the limit will of course generally depend upon the point x. Hence the limit defines a function which will be denoted by u.

These remarks apply equally well to a series Σu_n. We simply examine the sequence of partial sums $S_n = \sum_1^n u_k$. The sum S, if it exists, will depend on x, thus defining a function. In general, we will denote the value of this sum at the point x by $S(x)$.

Since any series Σu_k generates a sequence S_n of partial sums, and every sequence S_n generates a series of which it is the partial sum, namely,

$$u_1 = S_1, \, u_n = S_n - S_{n-1} \qquad n \geqslant 2,$$

we will generally restrict our remarks to sequences. In the case of series, it will be understood that $\{S_n\}$ is the sequence of partial sums.

In order that the sequence $\{S_n\}$ converge to a limit function S on an interval I, we must have at each x in I and for each $\epsilon > 0$ an $N(\epsilon, x)$ for which

$$|S_n(x) - S(x)| < \epsilon \qquad \text{if } n > N,$$

for this is the definition of convergence. Now at two distinct x's, say x_1 and x_2 in I, we are really dealing with two distinct sequences of numbers

$\{S_n(x_1)\}$ and $\{S_n(x_2)\}$, so we would certainly expect the index N to depend on x. Thus to get $S_n(x)$ to approximate $S(x)$ to within a prescribed tolerance ϵ, it may be necessary to take n larger at one point than at another. Of course, with just two points x_1 and x_2 we could always take n larger than both $N(\epsilon, x_1)$ and $N(\epsilon, x_2)$, and thus have $S_n(x)$ approximate $S(x)$ to within ϵ at both points. But if we try to achieve such a uniform approximation at all points in an interval, we have greater difficulties. When this is possible, we say that the sequence **converges uniformly** to S; or, if S_n is the partial sum of a series, we say that the series converges uniformly. The precise formulation follows.

Let $\{S_n\}$ be a sequence of functions on an interval I. We say $\{S_n\}$ **converges uniformly** to S if for each $\epsilon > 0$ there is an $N(\epsilon, I)$, where N is independent of the particular x in I, such that

$$|S_n(x) - S(x)| < \epsilon \qquad \text{if } n > N \text{ for all } x \text{ in } I.$$

The geometrical meaning of this is quite simple. If one draws the graph of $y = S(x)$ and centers a band of vertical width 2ϵ on this curve then for uniform convergence, there must be an N such that for $n > N$ the graph of $y = S_n(x)$ lies everywhere in this band. The determining quantity is clearly the maximum difference between $S_n(x)$ and $S(x)$. If this is $< \epsilon$,

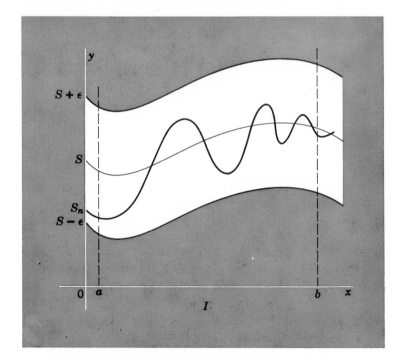

then the curve lies in the 2ϵ band. This leads immediately to the following considerations.

We define the sequence of constants M_n by

$$M_n = \sup_I |S_n(x) - S(x)|.$$

15.2a Theorem. A necessary and sufficient condition that $\{S_n\}$ converge uniformly to S in I is that the sequence M_n converge to zero.

Proof: Sufficiency. Suppose $M_n \to 0$. This means that for each $\epsilon > 0$ there is an $N(\epsilon)$ for which $0 \leqslant M_n < \epsilon$ if $n > N$. But since $|S_n(x) - S(x)| \leqslant M_n$ for all x in I, we have

$$0 \leqslant |S_n(x) - S(x)| \leqslant \epsilon \qquad \text{if } n > N.$$

Necessity. Suppose $S_n \to S$ uniformly. Then for each $\epsilon > 0$ there is an $N(\epsilon)$, independent of x, for which

$$|S_n(x) - S(x)| < \epsilon \qquad \text{if } n > N.$$

This ϵ is an upper bound for the numbers $|S_n(x) - S(x)|$. Hence the least upper bound, namely M_n, is also $\leqslant \epsilon$.

That is, $\qquad\qquad 0 \leqslant M_n \leqslant \epsilon \qquad \text{if } n > N.$

Thus $\qquad\qquad\qquad\qquad M_n \to 0$ ∎

EXAMPLE 1. Let $S_n(x) = \dfrac{\sin nx}{\sqrt{n}}$ $\qquad I: \{0 \leqslant x \leqslant \pi\}$.

Solution:

$$|S_n(x)| = |S_n(x) - 0| \leqslant M_n = \frac{1}{\sqrt{n}}. \qquad\qquad \text{(Why?)}$$

Thus $M_n \to 0$; hence $S_n(x) \to 0$ uniformly.

EXAMPLE 2. Let $S_n(x) = \dfrac{nx^2}{1 + nx}$ $\qquad I: \{0 \leqslant x \leqslant 1\}$.

Solution. For each fixed x, $S_n(x) \to x$,

$$S_n(x) = \frac{x^2}{x + 1/n} \to x \qquad \text{as } n \to \infty.$$

Is the convergence uniform?

$$|S_n(x) - x| = \left| \frac{x^2}{x + 1/n} - x \right| = \frac{x/n}{x + 1/n} = \frac{1}{n}\left(\frac{nx}{nx + 1} \right)$$

$$= \frac{1}{n}\left(1 - \frac{1}{nx + 1} \right) \leqslant \frac{1}{n}.$$

Thus $M_n \leqslant 1/n$, $M_n \to 0$; hence $S_n(x) \to x$ uniformly.

EXAMPLE 3. $S(x) = x^n$ $\{0 \leqslant x < 1\}$.

Solution. For each x, $S_n(x) \to 0$, but

$$M_n = \sup_{0 \leqslant x < 1} x^n = 1.$$

Since M_n does not converge to zero, the sequence $\{S_n\}$ does not converge uniformly, even though it converges at each point.

As you might expect after seeing it occur in so many other convergence settings, there is a Cauchy criterion for uniform convergence.

15.2b Theorem. Let $\{S_n\}$ be a sequence of functions defined on an interval I. In order that the sequence converge uniformly in I, it is necessary and sufficient that for each $\epsilon > 0$ there is an $N(\epsilon)$ (independent of x in I) for which

$$|S_n(x) - S_m(x)| < \epsilon \qquad \text{if } n > N, m > N.$$

Proof. The proof is left as an exercise (B1).

We turn now to a test for uniform convergence of series known as the **Weierstrass M-test**.

15.2c Theorem. Suppose $\{u_n\}$ is a sequence of functions defined on an interval I, and there is a sequence of positive constants M_n with $|u_n(x)| \leqslant M_n$ for all x in I and all n. If the series ΣM_n converges, then the series Σu_n converges uniformly in I.

Proof. Since ΣM_n converges, for any $\epsilon > 0$ there is an $N(\epsilon)$ for which

$$\sum_{n+1}^{m} M_k < \epsilon \qquad \text{if } n > N. \text{ Then if } S_n(x) = \sum_{1}^{n} u_k(x), \text{ we have for all } x \text{ in } I$$

$$|S_m(x) - S_n(x)| = \Big| \sum_{n+1}^{m} u_k(x) \Big| \leqslant \sum_{n+1}^{m} |u_k(x)| \leqslant \sum_{n+1}^{m} M_n < \epsilon.$$

Hence the series converges uniformly in I, by the Cauchy criterion. ∎

A EXERCISES

1. Set $S_n(x) = 1/x + (1/n) \sin 1/nx$. Does $\{S_n\}$ converge uniformly on $\{0 < x \leqslant 1\}$?

2. Show that $\{x^n\}$ converges uniformly in each closed sub-interval of $\{-1 < x < 1\}$.

3. Discuss the convergence, both pointwise and uniform of $\{nxe^{-nx^2}\}$ on:

   (a) $\{0 \leqslant x \leqslant 1\}$ (b) $\{1 \leqslant x < \infty\}$

4. Determine whether $\left\{\dfrac{n^2 x}{1 + n^3 x^2}\right\}$ converges (i) uniformly (ii) pointwise on:

   (a) $\{-1 \leqslant x \leqslant 1\}$ (b) $\{1 \leqslant x \leqslant 2\}$ (c) $\{x \geqslant 0\}$

5. Discuss the convergence of $\left(\dfrac{nx}{1 + n^2x^2}\right)$ on:

(a) $\{-1 \leqslant x \leqslant 1\}$ (b) $\{a \leqslant x \leqslant b\}$, where $a > 0$.

6. Show that $\displaystyle\sum_0^\infty x^n$ converges uniformly on $\{-a \leqslant x \leqslant a\}$ for every a, $0 < a < 1$, but not on $\{-1 < x < 1\}$.

7. Show that $\displaystyle\sum_0^\infty \dfrac{x^n}{n!}$ converges uniformly on every interval $\{-a \leqslant x \leqslant a\}$, but not on $\{-\infty < x < \infty\}$.

8. Discuss the convergence of $\displaystyle\sum_{n=1}^\infty \dfrac{x^{2n} - 1}{x^{2n} + 1} \cdot \dfrac{1}{n^2}$.

9. Let $\{a_n\}$ be a sequence of constants such that Σa_n converges absolutely. Show that $\Sigma a_n \sin nx$ and $\Sigma a_n \cos nx$ both converge uniformly on $\{-\infty < x < \infty\}$.

10. Show that if Σu_n converges uniformly on an interval I, then the sequence $\{u_n\}$ converges uniformly to zero on I.

11. Discuss the convergence of $\displaystyle\sum_0^\infty (x \log x)^n$ on $\{0 < x \leqslant 1\}$.

12. Let $u_n(x) = a_n$ for all x in I and all n, where $\{a_n\}$ is a sequence of constants. What does it mean that $\{u_n(x)\}$ converges uniformly on I?

13. Discuss the convergence, pointwise and uniform, for $\displaystyle\sum_0^\infty n^{75}e^{-nx}$ and $\displaystyle\sum_0^\infty nxe^{-nx}$ on $\{x \geqslant 0\}$.

B EXERCISES

1. Prove the Cauchy criterion for uniform convergence.

2. Suppose $\{S_n\}$ converges uniformly on a bounded interval I: $\{a < x \leqslant b\}$ to a function S. Suppose also that S and all the S_n's are integrable on I. Show that

$$\lim \int_a^b S_n(x)\, dx = \int_a^b S(x)\, dx.$$

3. Show that $\displaystyle\sum_0^\infty (-1)^n(1 - x)x^n$ converges uniformly on $\{0 < x \leqslant 1\}$.

4. How big can a be if $\displaystyle\sum_0^\infty (x \log x)^n$ converges uniformly on $\{0 \leqslant x \leqslant a\}$?

5. If $\{S_n\}$ converges uniformly on I and the limit function S is bounded on I, show that $\{S_n\}$ is uniformly bounded on I; that is, there is a constant M for which $|S_n(x)| \leqslant M$ for all n and all x in I.

6. If $\{f_n\}$ and $\{g_n\}$ converge uniformly on I, show that $\{h_n\}$ defined by $h_n = f_n \cdot g_n$ converges uniformly on I, if both $\{f_n\}$ and $\{g_n\}$ are uniformly bounded.

7. Suppose $0 \leqslant u_{n+1}(x) \leqslant u_n(x)$ and the sequence $\{u_n\}$ converges to 0 uniformly on an interval I. Show that $\displaystyle\sum_0^\infty (-1)^n u_n(x)$ converges uniformly on I.

C EXERCISES

1. Show that if $\Sigma a_n x^n$ converges for $x = x_0$, then it converges uniformly on any closed interval in $\{|x| < |x_0|\}$.

2. Show that $\displaystyle\sum_1^\infty \left[1 - \cos\left(\frac{x}{n}\right)\right]$ converges uniformly in $\{-a \leqslant x \leqslant a\}$ for every a, but not in $\{-\infty < x < \infty\}$.

15.3 CONSEQUENCES OF UNIFORM CONVERGENCE

At the beginning of this chapter we remarked that uniform convergence is a useful tool for investigating the operations of analysis on limiting functions or on sums of series. Having seen the basic simple criteria for testing uniform convergence, we now turn to its application to these problems of analysis. We will see that we are basically concerned with the problem of the interchange of the order of limiting operations.

Let us consider the sequence of functions given by

$$S_n(x) = x^n \qquad \{0 \leqslant x \leqslant 1\}.$$

Now at $x = 1$, $S_n(1) = 1$; hence $S_n(1) \to 1$. For all x in $\{0 \leqslant x < 1\}$, $S_n(x) \to 0$. Hence the limit functions S is given by

$$S(x) = \begin{cases} 0 & \{0 \leqslant x < 1\} \\ 1 & x = 1. \end{cases}$$

Clearly this function is discontinuous, so that $\lim\limits_{x \to 1} S(x) = 0$ and $S(1) = 1$.

Hence

$$\lim_{n \to \infty} \lim_{x \to 1} S_n(x) = 1$$

and

$$\lim_{x \to 1} \lim_{n \to \infty} S_n(x) = 0.$$

That is, the two limits are not interchangeable as they would be if S were continuous at $x = 1$.

We would then like to know what conditions on S_n will insure that S will be continuous, if the approximating functions are themselves continuous. Uniform convergence provides a sufficient condition to guarantee this result.

15.3a Theorem. Let $\{S_n\}$ be a sequence of functions on an interval I, each of which is continuous on I. If $\{S_n\}$ converges uniformly to a limit function S on I, then S is continuous.

Proof. Let x_0 be any point in I. Then we must show that, for each $\epsilon > 0$, there is a $\delta(\epsilon)$ for which

$$|S(x) - S(x_0)| < \epsilon \qquad \text{if } |x - x_0| < \delta.$$

For any n,

$$|S(x) - S(x_0)| = |S(x) - S_n(x) + S_n(x) - S_n(x_0) + S_n(x_0) - S(x_0)|$$

or

(1) $|S(x) - S(x_0)| \leqslant |S(x) - S_n(x)| + |S_n(x) - S_n(x_0)| + |S_n(x_0) - S(x_0)|.$

By uniform convergence, there is an $N(\epsilon)$, independent of x, for which

(2) $\qquad |S_n(x) - S(x)| < \epsilon/3 \qquad$ if $n > N \qquad$ for all x in I.

Choose such an n and keep it fixed. From (1) and (2), we then have

(3) $\qquad |S(x) - S(x_0)| < \epsilon/3 + |S_n(x) - S_n(x_0)| + \epsilon/3.$

But $S_n(x)$ is a continuous function. Hence there is a $\delta(\epsilon)$ for which

(4) $\qquad |S_n(x) - S_n(x_0)| < \epsilon/3 \qquad$ if $|x - x_0| < \delta.$

Putting all this together, we have

$$|S(x) - S(x_0)| < \epsilon \qquad \text{if } |x - x_0| < \delta. \qquad \blacksquare$$

By applying this theorem to the partial sums of series, we get the following.

15.3b Corollary. If $\{u_n\}$ is a sequence of functions each of which is continuous on an interval, and if Σu_n converges uniformly, then its sum is a continuous function.

Another important operation is integration. We are led to inquire, when do we have

$$\lim \int_a^b S_n(x)\, dx = \int_a^b S(x)\, dx,$$

that is, $\qquad \lim \int_a^b S_n(x)\, dx = \int_a^b \lim S_n(x)\, dx?$

This again is a question of interchanging the order of two limits, for the integral itself, you will recall, is a rather complicated type of limit. Again the answer is that uniform convergence is sufficient.

Before stating and proving the theorem let us see that we need some sort of conditions since it is not always true that limits and integration can be interchanged. Consider the sequence given by

$$S_n(x) = 2nxe^{-nx^2} \qquad \{0 \leqslant x \leqslant 1\}.$$

These functions are all continuous; the sequence has a limit function $S(x) = 0$. (See Exercise A3 of the previous set of exercises.) Hence

$$\int_0^1 \lim S_n(x)\, dx = \int_0^1 0 \cdot dx = 0.$$

But

$$\int_0^1 S_n(x)\, dx = \int_0^1 e^{-nx^2}\, 2nx\, dx = \left. -e^{-nx^2}\right]_0^1 = 1 - e^{-n},$$

From which it is clear that

$$\lim \int_0^1 S_n(x)\, dx = 1.$$

We proceed to the result stated. (See Exercise B2 of the previous set of exercises.)

15.3c   Theorem. Let $\{S_n\}$ be a sequence of integrable functions on an interval $I: \{a \leqslant x \leqslant b\}$. If $\{S_n\}$ converges uniformly to a limit function S which is also integrable on I, then

$$\lim \int_a^b S_n(x)\, dx = \int_a^b S(x)\, dx.$$

Proof. Let $\epsilon > 0$ be given. Then there is an $N(\epsilon)$ for which

$$|S_n(x) - S(x)| < \epsilon/(b - a) \qquad \text{if } n > N.$$

Then, for $n > N$,

$$\left| \int_a^b S_n(x)\, dx - \int_a^b S(x)\, dx \right| = \left| \int_a^b [S_n(x) - S(x)]\, dx \right|$$

$$\leqslant \int_a^b |S_n(x) - S(x)|\, dx \leqslant \int_a^b \frac{\epsilon}{b - a}\, dx = \frac{\epsilon}{b - a}(b - a) = \epsilon. \qquad \blacksquare$$

We point out two important special cases.

15.3d   Corollary. Let $\{S_n\}$ be a sequence of functions on an interval I, $\{a \leqslant x \leqslant b\}$, and suppose that each of them is continuous on I. If $\{S_n\}$ converges uniformly to S on I, then

$$\lim \int_a^b S_n(x)\, dx = \int_a^b S(x)\, dx.$$

15.3e   Corollary. Let $\{S_n\}$ be a sequence of functions on an interval I, $\{a \leqslant x \leqslant b\}$, and suppose that each of them is non-decreasing on I. If $\{S_n\}$ converges uniformly to S on I, then

$$\lim \int_a^b S_n(x)\, dx = \int_a^b S(x)\, dx.$$

All of these have immediate extensions to series.

15.3f Corollary. Let $\{u_n\}$ be a sequence of integrable (for example, continuous or non-decreasing) functions on an interval $I\colon\{a \leqslant x \leqslant b\}$. If $\Sigma u_n(x)$ converges uniformly on I to an integrable sum, then

$$\int_a^b \sum_0^\infty u_n(x)\, dx = \sum_0^\infty \int_a^b u_n(x)\, dx.$$

EXAMPLE. Suppose $|x| \leqslant r < 1$.

$$\frac{1}{1 + x^2} = 1 - x^2 + x^4 - x^6 + - \cdots \pm x^{2n} \mp \frac{x^{2n+2}}{1 + x^2}.$$

Then

$$\left|\frac{1}{1 + x^2} - 1 + x^2 \cdots \pm x^{2n}\right| \leqslant \frac{|x|^{2n+2}}{1 + x^2} \leqslant r^{2n+2}$$

Note that the estimate is independent of x. And as $n \to \infty$, $r^{2n+2} \to 0$, so that

$$\sum_0^\infty (-1)^n x^{2n} = \frac{1}{1 + x^2} \qquad \{|x| \leqslant r\},$$

and the convergence is uniform for each $r < 1$. Then for any y, when $|y| \leqslant r$,

$$\text{arc tan } y = \int_0^y \frac{dx}{1 + x^2} = \int_0^y \sum_0^\infty (-1)^n x^{2n}\, dx = \sum_0^\infty (-1)^n \int_0^y x^{2n}\, dx,$$

the last equality being assured by the last corollary. Then

$$\text{arc tan } y = \sum_0^\infty (-1)^n \frac{y^{2n+1}}{2n + 1} \qquad \{|y| \leqslant r\}.$$

But for any $|y| < 1$ there is an $r < 1$ for which $|y| \leqslant r < 1$, namely $|y|$ itself, so that

$$\text{arc tan } y = \sum_0^\infty \frac{(-1)^n y^{2n+1}}{(2n + 1)} \qquad \{|y| < 1\}.$$

Question: In the above equation for $|y| < 1$, we observe that both sides make sense for $y = \pm 1$. That is, the series converges for these values of y. Can we extend this equality to include $y = \pm 1$?; that is, can we say

$$\frac{\pi}{4} = \sum_0^\infty \frac{(-1)^n}{2n + 1} \, ?$$

We will come back to this question in the next section.

Another important operation of analysis is differentiation. Let us look at the sequence given by

$$S_n(x) = x e^{-nx^2} \qquad \{-1 \leqslant x \leqslant 1\}.$$

It is easy to see that $\{S_n\}$ converges uniformly to zero on $\{-1 \leqslant x \leqslant 1\}$. So $S'(x) = 0$ for all x. But

$$S_n{}'(x) = e^{-nx^2}[1 - 2nx^2].$$

In particular, at $x = 0$, $S_n{}'(0) = 1$ for all n. Thus $S_n{}'(0) \to 1$ and $S'(0) = 0$. Hence we see that uniform convergence is not enough to guarantee that

$$\frac{d}{dx} \lim S_n(x) = \lim \frac{d}{dx} S_n(x).$$

Again we see that it is a question of the interchange to two limiting operations. The theorem we prove is the following.

15.3g   Theorem. Suppose $\{S_n\}$ is a sequence of functions each of which is continuously differentiable on an interval $I:\{a \leqslant x \leqslant b\}$; that is, $S_n{}'(x)$ are all continuous on I. Suppose, further, that $\{S_n\}$ converges at one point x_0 in I and that $\{S_n{}'\}$ converges uniformly in I. Then $\{S_n\}$ converges uniformly in I, to a function S, and $S' = \lim S_n{}'$.

Proof. By the fundamental theorem of calculus, we have for any x in I

$$S_n(x) = \int_{x_0}^{x} S_n{}'(t)\, dt + S_n(x_0).$$

Thus

$$S_n(x) - S_m(x) = \int_{x_0}^{x} [S_n{}'(t) - S_m{}'(t)]\, dt + [S_n(x_0) - S_m(x_0)]$$

$$|S_n(x) - S_m(x)| \leqslant \int_{x_0}^{x} |S_n{}'(t) - S_m{}'(t)|\, dt + |S_n(x_0) - S_m(x_0)|.$$

By the Cauchy criterion for the convergence of a sequence of constants and the Cauchy criterion for the uniform convergence of a sequence of functions, there is an $N(\epsilon)$ such that if $m, n > N$,

$$|S_n{}'(t) - S_m{}'(t)| < \epsilon$$

and

$$|S_n(x_0) - S_m(x_0)| < \epsilon.$$

Thus

$$|S_n(x) - S_m(x)| \leqslant \epsilon(x - x_0) + \epsilon \leqslant \epsilon(b - a + 1).$$

By the sufficiency part of the Cauchy criterion, $\{S_n\}$ converges uniformly in I. The above argument assumes that $x \geqslant x_0$. For those x's less than x_0, a sign change effects the same estimate.

Denote the limit function by S and denote the limit of $S_n{}'$ by σ. It remains to show $S' = \sigma$. We see that

$$S_n(x) - S_n(x_0) = \int_{x_0}^{x} S_n{}'(t)\, dt.$$

After taking the limits of both sides, we get

$$S(x) - S(x_0) = \int_{x_0}^{x} \sigma(t)\, dt.$$

But σ is continuous, so by the fundamental theorem of calculus,

$$S'(x) = \sigma(x). \qquad \blacksquare$$

EXAMPLE. $S(x) = \sum_{1}^{\infty} \dfrac{\sin nx}{n^{5/2}}$.

Solution. This series converges uniformly for all x by the M-test:

$$\left| \frac{\sin nx}{n^{5/2}} \right| \leqslant \frac{1}{n^{5/2}} = M_n,$$

and ΣM_n converges since it is a k series with $k > 1$. Furthermore, by the same test, the differentiated series $\sum_{1}^{\infty} \dfrac{\cos nx}{n^{3/2}}$ also converges uniformly for all x:

$$\left| \frac{\cos nx}{n^{3/2}} \right| \leqslant \frac{1}{n^{3/2}} = M_n.$$

Hence the differentiated series is the derivative of the original series.

A EXERCISES

1. Letting $S(x) = \sum_{1}^{\infty} \dfrac{\cos nx}{n^{1/3}}$, verify $S'(x) = -\sum_{1}^{\infty} \dfrac{\sin nx}{n^{1/3}}$ for all x.

3 out of the 4 circled

2. Let $S(x) = \sum_{1}^{\infty} \dfrac{1}{n} \left(\dfrac{x}{1-x} \right)^n$. Where is $S'(x) = \sum_{0}^{\infty} \left(\dfrac{x}{1-x} \right)^n \cdot \dfrac{1}{(1-x)^2}$?

3. Let $S(x) = \sum_{1}^{\infty} n^{-x}$. Where is $S'(x) = -\sum_{1}^{\infty} n^{-x} \log n$?

4. Let $S_n(x) = \dfrac{nx^n}{1+nx^n}$. Compute the pointwise limit in the interval $\{0 < x < 2\}$.
How can you tell that the convergence is not uniform?

5. Let $S(x)$ be defined as in Exercise 1 above. Compute a series for $\displaystyle\int_{0}^{x} S(t)\, dt$.

6. Let $S_n(x) = \dfrac{nx}{nx + 1}$.

(a) Compute the pointwise limit on $\{0 < x < 1\}$. Is the convergence uniform?

(b) Compute $\displaystyle\lim \int_{0}^{1} S_n(x)\, dx$ and $\displaystyle\int_{0}^{1} \lim S_n(x)\, dx$. Explain.

7. Let $\Sigma n a_n$ be absolutely convergent, and let $f(x) = \sum_{1}^{\infty} a_n \cos nx$ and $g(x) = \Sigma a_n \sin nx$. Show that, for all x, $f'(x) = -\Sigma n a_n \sin nx$, and $g'(x) = \Sigma n a_n \cos nx$.

8. Let $f(x) = \sum_{1}^{\infty} n e^{-nx}$. Where is f continuous? Compute $\int_{1}^{2} f(x)\, dx$.

B   EXERCISE

1. Let Σu_n be a series of positive non-decreasing functions on I: $\{a \leqslant x \leqslant b\}$. Show that $\int_{a}^{b} \Sigma u_n(x)\, dx = \Sigma \int_{a}^{b} u_n(x)\, dx$, provided only that $\Sigma u_n(b)$ converges.

C   EXERCISES

1. Let $\{S_n\}$ be a sequence of continuous function on $\{a \leqslant x \leqslant b\}$, which converges uniformly to a limit function S on $\{a \leqslant x \leqslant c\}$ for every c in $\{a \leqslant x < b\}$. If S and S_n are all uniformly bounded on $\{a \leqslant x \leqslant b\}$, show that

$$\lim \int_{a}^{b} S_n(x)\, dx = \int_{a}^{b} S(x)\, dx.$$

2. Let ϕ and S_0 be continuous on I: $\{a \leqslant x \leqslant b\}$: Define the sequence S_n by

$$S_n(x) = \alpha + \int_{a}^{x} \phi(t)\, S_{n-1}(t)\, dt \qquad n \geqslant 1, \qquad \{a \leqslant x \leqslant b\}.$$

(a) Show that $\{S_n\}$ converges uniformly on I to a function S, which is a solution of the problem $S'(x) = \phi(x)\, S(x)$, $S(a) = \alpha$.

(b) Deduce that $S(x) = \alpha \exp \int_{a}^{x} \phi(t)\, dt$.

3. If $S(x) = \sum_{1}^{\infty} a_n x^n$ converges for $x = x_0 \neq 0$, show that

$$S'(x) = \sum_{1}^{\infty} n a_n x^{n-1} \qquad \text{in } \{|x| < |x_0|\}.$$

4. Let $S(x) = \sum_{1}^{\infty} \frac{1}{n} e^{-nx}$. Show that $\lim_{x \to 0+} S(x) = +\infty$.

15.4   ABEL'S AND DIRICHLET'S TESTS

We return now to the problem of sufficient conditions for uniform convergence of a series. The M-test, although very useful, requires that the convergence be absolute as well as uniform. We present here two tests which are more delicate that the M-test in that they do not require absolute convergence. They depend upon the following lemma, which we will call **Abel's identity**. It is analogous to integration by parts.

15.4a Lemma. Let $\{u_n\}$ and $\{v_n\}$ be two sequences, and $\{U_n\}$ be a sequence with the property that $U_n - U_{n-1} = u_n$. Then

$$\sum_{k=n+1}^{m} u_k v_k = U_m v_m - U_n v_{n+1} - \sum_{k=n+1}^{m-1} U_k(v_{k+1} - v_k).$$

Proof. We write

$$\sum_{n+1}^{m} u_k v_k = \sum_{n+1}^{m} v_k(U_k - U_{k-1})$$

$$= v_{n+1}(U_{n+1} - U_n) + v_{n+2}(U_{n+2} - U_{n+1}) + \cdots + v_m(U_m - U_{m-1})$$

$$= -U_n v_{n+1} - U_{n+1}(v_{n+2} - v_{n+1}) - U_{n+2}(v_{n+3} - v_{n+2}) - \cdots$$

$$-U_{m-1}(v_m - v_{m-1}) + U_m v_m. \qquad \blacksquare$$

We now apply this identity to the proof of two theorems which are modifications of Abel's and Dirichlet's tests. These formulations are by a British mathematician, G. H. Hardy. The first we will call the **modified Dirichlet test**.

15.4b Theorem. Let $\{u_n\}$ and $\{v_n\}$ be two sequences of functions defined on an interval I. And suppose

(i) $\sum_{0}^{\infty} u_n(x)$ converges uniformly on I.

(ii) $\sum_{1}^{\infty} |v_n(x) - v_{n-1}(x)| < K$ (constant) on I.

(iii) $|v_0(x)| \leqslant K$ on I.

Then $\sum_{0}^{\infty} u_n(x)v_n(x)$ converges uniformly on I.

Proof. Let $U(x) = \sum_{0}^{\infty} u_n(x)$, and define

$$U_n(x) = \sum_{0}^{n} u_k(x) - U(x) = - \sum_{k=n+1}^{\infty} u_k(x).$$

We observe also that

$$v_n(x) = \sum_{1}^{n} [v_k(x) - v_{k-1}(x)] + v_0(x),$$

so that

$$|v_n(x)| \leqslant \sum_{1}^{n} |v_k(x) - v_{k-1}(x)| + |v_0(x)|$$

$$\leqslant \sum_{1}^{\infty} |v_k(x) - v_{k-1}(x)| + |v_0(x)|$$

$$\leqslant 2K.$$

From the uniform convergence of $\Sigma u_k(x)$, we have that $U_n \to 0$ uniformly in I. Thus given an $\epsilon > 0$, there is an $N(\epsilon)$, independent of x, for which $|U_n(x)| < \epsilon$ if $n > N$. And from Abel's identity, we get

$$\left| \sum_{n+1}^{m} u_k(x)v_k(x) \right| = \left| U_m v_m - U_n v_{n+1} - \sum_{k=n+1}^{m-1} U_k(v_{k+1} - v_k) \right|$$

$$\leqslant |U_m| \cdot |v_m| + |U_n| \, |v_{n+1}| + \sum_{n+1}^{m-1} |U_k| \, |v_{k+1} - v_k|$$

$$< 2K\epsilon + 2K\epsilon + K\epsilon = 5K\epsilon$$

if $m > n > N$. Hence, by the Cauchy criterion, $\Sigma u_n(x)v_n(x)$ converges uniformly. ∎

Our next theorem is a **modified Abel's theorem.**

15.4c Theorem. Let $\{u_n\}$ and $\{v_n\}$ be two sequences of functions defined on an interval I. And suppose

(i) the partial sums of $\Sigma u_n(x)$ are bounded; that is, there is a constant M for which $\left| \sum_{0}^{n} u_k(x) \right| < M$ in I;

(ii) $\sum_{0}^{\infty} |v_n(x) - v_{n-1}(x)|$ converges uniformly in I;

(iii) $v_n(x) \to 0$ uniformly in I.

Then $\Sigma u_n(x)v_n(x)$ converges uniformly in I.

Proof. Given an $\epsilon > 0$, there is by hypothesis (iii) a uniform N_1 such that

$$|v_n(x)| < \epsilon \qquad \text{if } n > N_1$$

and by (ii) there is a uniform N_2 such that

$$\sum_{n+1}^{m-1} |v_{k+1}(x) - v_k(x)| < \epsilon \qquad \text{if } n > N_2.$$

We suppose now that $n > N = \max [N_1, N_2]$. Then, by Abel's identity and with $U_n = \sum_{0}^{n} u_k$, we get,

$$\left| \sum_{n+1}^{m} u_k(x)v_k(x) \right| \leqslant |U_m| \, |v_m| + |U_n| \, |v_{n+1}| + \sum_{n+1}^{m-1} |U_k| \cdot |v_{k+1} - v_k|$$

$$\leqslant M \left[|v_m| + |v_{n+1}| + \sum_{n+1}^{m-1} |v_{k+1} - v_k| \right]$$

$$\leqslant 3\epsilon M.$$

By the Cauchy criterion, the proof is complete. ∎

EXAMPLE. Let us return to the question we raised in the last section. We have seen that

$$\sum_{0}^{\infty} \frac{(-1)^n x^{2n+1}}{2n+1}$$ converges for $|x| \leq 1$, and hence represents a function of x on that interval. Let us denote this function by $f(x)$:

$$f(x) = \sum_{0}^{\infty} \frac{(-1)^n x^{2n+1}}{(2n+1)} \qquad \{|x| \leq 1\}.$$

We have seen also that $f(x) = $ arc tan x for $|x| < 1$, and there is a question as to the persistence of the equality when $x = \pm 1$. This is equivalent to the question of continuity (one-sided continuity, of course) of $f(x)$, for we have

$$f(x) = \begin{cases} \sum_{0}^{\infty} (-1)^n/(2n+1) & x = 1 \\ \text{arc tan } x & |x| < 1. \end{cases}$$

Then if $f(x)$ were known to be continuous, we would have

$$f(1) = \lim_{x \to 1} f(x) = \lim_{x \to 1} \text{arc tan } x.$$

But arc tan x *is* continuous; hence

$$f(1) = \lim_{x \to 1} \text{arc tan } x = \text{arc tan } 1 = \pi/4.$$

Thus everything turns on the continuity of the function $f(x)$.

Now $f(x)$ is continuous at $x = 1$ if the series is uniformly convergent for $|x| \leq 1$. To see that this is the case, we apply Abel's test. We make the identification $u_n(x) = (-1)^n x^{2n+1}$, $v_n(x) = 1/(2n+1)$. We verify the hypotheses:

(i) $|U_n(x)| = \left| \sum_{0}^{n} (-1)^k x^{2k+1} \right| \leq 2$ for $|x| \leq 1$.

$$U_n(x) = \frac{x[1 - x^2 + x^4 - + \cdots + (-1)^n x^{2n}](1 + x^2)}{(1 + x^2)}$$

$$= \frac{x[1 + (-1)^n x^{2n+2}]}{1 + x^2}.$$

Hence $$|U_n(x)| \leq \frac{1 \cdot [1 + 1]}{1} = 2 \qquad \text{if } |x| \leq 1.$$

(ii) $\sum_{1}^{\infty} |v_k(x) - v_{k-1}(x)|$ converges uniformly for $|x| \leq 1$. Since v_k's are constants, uniform convergence means simply convergence (see Exercise A9 of Section 15.2):

$$|v_k - v_{k-1}| = \left| \frac{1}{2k+1} - \frac{1}{2k-1} \right| = \frac{2}{4k^2 - 1}$$

and $$\frac{2}{4k^2 - 1} \bigg/ \frac{1}{k^2} = \frac{2k^2}{4k^2 - 1} \to \frac{1}{2} \neq 0.$$

Hence by the limit form of the comparison test, the series converges; and since it is independent of x, it converges uniformly.

(iii) $v_k(x) \to 0$ uniformly. But

$$v_k = \frac{1}{2k + 1} \to 0.$$

Hence all the hypotheses are satisfied, and the convergence is uniform. Therefore $f(x)$ is continuous, and we have finally proved that

$$\frac{\pi}{4} = \sum_0^\infty \frac{(-1)^n}{2n + 1}.$$

Now, as we have seen in the application of Abel's test to our example, $v_n(x)$ need not depend on x. In fact, both $u_n(x)$ and $v_n(x)$ can be constants. Then both Abel's and Dirichlet's tests become tests for convergence of sequences of constants. In such an application of the theorems, a hypothesis which calls for uniform convergence reduces simply to a hypothesis asking for ordinary convergence, and the conclusion becomes a conclusion about ordinary convergence. (See Exercise A1.)

15.5 A THEOREM OF DINI

As we have seen in numerous examples and exercises, it can very well happen that a sequence of continuous functions may converge to a continuous limit even though the convergence is not uniform. But there is an important situation in which this cannot happen, that is, in which we can deduce the uniformity of the convergence from the continuity of the limit function. This is the case when the convergence is monotone; that is, when for each fixed x in the interval (a bounded closed interval) the sequence is non-decreasing (or non-increasing).

15.5a Theorem. Let $\{S_n\}$ be a non-decreasing sequence of continuous functions in the interval $I: \{a \leqslant x \leqslant b\}$. Suppose $\{S_n\}$ converges to a limit function S, which is also continuous in I. Then $\{S_n\}$ converges uniformly to S

Proof. The proof is similar to those of the theorems in Chapter 6.

Suppose the convergence were not uniform. Then that would mean the sequence of suprema

$$M_n = \sup_I |S_n(x) - S(x)| = \sup_I [S(x) - S_n(x)]$$

does not tend to zero. Hence there is an exceptional ϵ_0 such that $M_n \geqslant \epsilon_0$ for a subsequence $\{n_k\}$. Now to simplify notation, let us set $S_{n_k}(x) = \sigma_k(x)$,

$M_{n_k} = \mathcal{M}_k$, and $S(x) = \sigma(x)$. Since σ_k and σ are continuous, so is $\sigma - \sigma_k$. Thus there is a point x_k in I at which $\mathcal{M}_k = \sigma(x_k) - \sigma_k(x_k)$. But $\{x_k\}$ is a bounded sequence, and so has a limit point in I. That is, there is a subsequence of $\{x_k\}$, say $\{x_{k_j}\}$, such that $x_{k_j} \to \xi$ in I.

Let $R_k = \sigma - \sigma_k$. Then $\{R_k\}$ converges in a non-increasing manner to 0 at each point, in particular ξ. So there is an N for which

$$0 \leqslant R_k(\xi) \leqslant \epsilon_0/2 \qquad \text{if } k > N.$$

And also $R_{k_j}(x_{k_j}) \geqslant \epsilon_0.$

By the monotone character of R_k, we have for $m < k_j$ that

$$R_m(x_{k_j}) \geqslant R_{k_j}(x_{k_j}) \geqslant \epsilon_0.$$

Now let $j \to \infty$. By continuity $R_m(x_{k_j}) \to R_m(\xi)$ and we get

$$R_m(\xi) \geqslant \epsilon_0 \qquad \text{for every } m.$$

This contradiction completes the proof.   ■

A EXERCISES

1. Write out the modified Abel's and Dirichlet tests for the convergence of a series of constants of the form $\Sigma a_n b_n$.

2. Let $f(x) = \sum_1^\infty (-1)^n e^{-nx}/n^2$, $\{x > 0\}$, Show that

$$f'(x) = \sum_1^\infty (-1)^{n+1} e^{-nx}/n \qquad \{x > 0\}.$$

3. Show that $\sum_2^\infty (-1)^n e^{-nx}/\log n$ is continuous on $\{x \geqslant 0\}$.

4. Show that $\sum_2^\infty \dfrac{(-1)^n e^{-nx} x^n}{\log n}$ converges uniformly on $\{0 \leqslant x \leqslant \frac{1}{2}\}$.

5. Show that $f(x) = \sum_1^\infty \dfrac{(-1)^n}{n + x^2}$ converges uniformly for all x, and compute $f'(x)$ by termwise differentiation.

6. For the function f in Exercise 5, compute $\displaystyle\int_0^x 2tf(t)\,dt$. Does this series converge uniformly for all x's?

7. Show that the sequence $\{e^{-nx}\}$ converges monotonically to zero for $x > 0$, and deduce that the convergence is uniform in $\{a \leqslant x \leqslant b\}$ for any $a > 0$.

8. Show that $\{x^n\}$ converges monotonically to zero in $\{0 \leqslant x < 1\}$, and deduce that the convergence is uniform in any closed sub-set.

9. Let $S_n(x) = \dfrac{nx^2}{1 + nx}$. Show that $\{S_n\}$ converges pointwise to $S(x) = x$ on $\{0 \leqslant x \leqslant 1\}$ in a monotone way, and deduce that the convergence is uniform.

B EXERCISES

1. Let $S_n(x) = \sum_1^n \sin kx$. Multiply by $2 \sin \frac{1}{2}x$, use the identity $2 \sin a \sin b = \cos (a - b) - \cos (a + b)$, and show that

$$S_n(x) = \frac{\cos \frac{1}{2}x - \cos (n + \frac{1}{2})x}{2 \sin \frac{1}{2}x}.$$

2. Let $S_n(x) = \sum_1^n \cos kx$. Multiply by $2 \sin \frac{1}{2}x$, use the identity $2 \cos a \sin b = \sin (a + b) - \sin (a - b)$, and show that

$$S_n(x) = \frac{\sin (n + 1/2)x - \sin 1/2x}{\sin 1/2 \, x}.$$

3. Show that $\sum_1^\infty \dfrac{\sin nx}{n^\alpha}$ converges for all x's, and that it converges uniformly on any closed sub-interval of $\{0 < x < 2\pi\}$ for any $\alpha > 0$.

4. For any $\alpha > 0$, show that $\sum_1^\infty \dfrac{\cos nx}{n^\alpha}$ converges for all x's, except multiples of 2π, and that it converges uniformly on any closed sub-interval of $\{0 < x < 2\pi\}$.

5. Show that if $S = \sum_1^\infty u_n$ converges uniformly on $\{a < x < b\}$, then we may integrate termwise as many times as we please.

6. Show that $(1 + x/n)^n$ tends in a monotone fashion to e^x in $\{0 < x < b\}$, and deduce the uniformity of the convergence.

7. Let $\{u_n\}$ be a sequence of continuous functions on $I: \{a < x < b\}$. Suppose $0 < u_{n+1}(x) < u_n(x)$ and $S(x) = \Sigma(-1)u_n(x)$ is continuous on I. Show that the convergence is uniform.

C EXERCISES

1. Let Σu_n converge uniformly on an interval I, and let the sequence $\{v_n\}$ be uniformly bounded and monotone on I. Show that $\Sigma u_n v_n$ converges uniformly on I.

2. Let $\sum_1^n u_k$ be uniformly bounded in I, and let the sequence $\{v_n\}$ be monotone in n and converging uniformly to zero. Show that $\Sigma u_n v_n$ converges uniformly in I.

3. Justify the equation

$$\sum_{n=0}^\infty \frac{(-1)^n}{m + nk} = \int_0^1 \frac{t^{m-1} \, dt}{1 + t^k} \qquad m > 0.$$

16

The Taylor Series

16.1 POWER SERIES. INTERVAL OF CONVERGENCE

At the beginning of the previous chapter, we discussed the importance of series for the representation of functions. One of the most important types of series for this purpose is **power series**. These are series whose terms are powers of $x - x_0$ multiplied by constants:

$$\sum_0^\infty a_n(x - x_0)^n.$$

To study power series, it is sufficient to assume that $x_0 = 0$, since by the substitution $x' = x - x_0$ we can bring our series into the form

$$\sum_0^\infty a_n x'^n.$$

Any power series, $\Sigma a_n x^n$, converges for at least *one* value of x, namely $x = 0$; for all terms except a_0 vanish when $x = 0$, so that the partial sums S_n are all equal to a_0. There are series which converge for no other values of x; for example,

$$\Sigma n!\, x^n = 1 + x + 2!\, x^2 + 3!\, x^3 + \cdots.$$

Let us apply the ratio test. We choose any fixed value of x, say $x_0 \neq 0$, and compare $(n + 1)!\, x_0^{n+1}$ with $n!\, x_0^n$.

$$|(n + 1)!\, x_0^{n+1}/n!\, x_0^n| = (n + 1)|x_0|.$$

Since $x_0 \neq 0$, this will eventually become greater than 1; in fact it diverges to $+\infty$ as $n \to \infty$. Hence the series diverges for any $x_0 \neq 0$.

There are other power series which converge for all values of x, for example,

$$\Sigma \frac{x^n}{n!} = 1 + x + \frac{x^2}{2!} + \frac{x^3}{3!} + \cdots + \frac{x^n}{n!} + \cdots$$

Again we apply the ratio test at some fixed $x_0 \neq 0$:

$$\left| \frac{x_0^{n+1}}{(n+1)!} \middle/ \frac{x_0^n}{n!} \right| = \frac{|x_0|}{n+1} \to 0 < 1.$$

Hence the series converges by the ratio test no matter what x_0 is.

There are other series which converge for certain x's and diverge for others. For example, we already know that the geometric progression

$$\sum_0^\infty x^n = 1 + x + x^2 + \cdots + x^n + \cdots,$$

converges for $|x| < 1$ and diverges for all other x's.

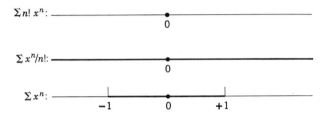

$\Sigma n!\, x^n$:

$\Sigma x^n/n!$:

Σx^n:

The diagram represents graphically the convergence behavior of the three examples we have just examined.

Now it turns out that these examples are typical of the behavior of a power series. It either converges only for $x = 0$ or for all x's, or in an interval centered at $x = 0$ (or centered at x_0, in the case of powers of $x - x_0$). The following theorems make this clear.

16.1a   Theorem. If $\Sigma a_n x^n$ converges for $x = x_0$, then it is absolutely convergent for all values of x for which $|x| < |x_0|$. If it diverges for $x = x_1$, it is divergent for all values of x such that $|x| > |x_1|$.

Proof. Since $\Sigma a_n x_0^n$ converges, the sequence $\{a_n x_0^n\}$ converges to zero and hence is bounded (Theorem 2.3b). Thus there is an M such that

$$|a_n x_0^n| < M \qquad \text{all } n = 0, 1, 2, \ldots.$$

Choose any x such that $|x| < |x_0|$. Then

$$r \equiv \left| \frac{x}{x_0} \right| < 1.$$

Thus $\qquad \left| a_n x^n \right| = \left| a_n x_0^n \cdot \dfrac{x^n}{x_0^n} \right| = |a_n x_0^n| \cdot \left| \dfrac{x}{x_0} \right|^n \leqslant M r^n.$

Then the series converges by comparison with a geometric series with $r < 1$.

From this the second part follows easily. We assume that $\Sigma a_n x_1{}^n$ diverges and that there is another value of x, say $x = x_0$, with $|x_0| > |x_1|$ for which $\Sigma a_n x_0{}^n$ converges. If this could happen, we would be in the following situation: there is an x_0 for which the series converges and an x_1 with $|x_1| < |x_0|$ for which it diverges. But this contradicts the first part of the theorem. ∎

It seems clear from this theorem that a power series has the property of converging in an interval, if it converges at all. To make this precise, we make the following definition.

Given a power series $\Sigma a_n x^n$, let S be the set of x's for which this series converges. Then the number R, defined below, will be called the **radius of convergence** of $\Sigma a_n x^n$:

$R = 0$ if $\Sigma a_n x^n$ converges only for $x = 0$

$R = +\infty$ if $\Sigma a_n x^n$ converges for all x's.

$R = \sup_S |x|$ if $\Sigma a_n x^n$ converges for some x's and diverges for others.

The interval $\{-R < x < R\}$ will be called the **interval of convergence**.

16.1b Theorem. A power series $\Sigma a_n x^n$ converges absolutely for all x's inside the interval of convergence $\{-R < x < R\}$ and diverges in $\{|x| > R\}$.

This theorem says that the series converges at all points in the interval of convergence and diverges at all points out beyond the ends of the interval of convergence. It makes no statement about the end points $x = \pm R$ themselves. These in general have to have special tests, for it can happen that a series converges at neither point, or at one and not the other, or at both.

Proof. We restrict ourselves to the last case, for clearly if $R = 0$ or $R = \infty$ we have nothing to prove. This proof is more semantical than mathematical in character. Mostly we examine the meaning of the concept of supremum. (You should review that definition.)

Now let any x in $\{|x| < R\}$ be given. Then there is an x_0,

$$|x| < |x_0| < R$$

for which the series converges. (This is by the definition of supremum.) By the previous theorem, it converges absolutely at x. Hence it converges for all such x—that is, all for which $|x| < R$.

Suppose now that the series does not diverge for some x_0, $|x_0| > R$. This means it converges for x_0. But then we have found a member of the set S larger than the supremum. This is a contradiction. ∎

In the study of power series, it is convenient to know R exactly. Of course we can get bounds on R if we know a point x_0 for which $\Sigma a_n x^n$ converges and a point x_1 for which it diverges. Then it is clear that

$$|x_0| \leqslant R \leqslant |x_1|.$$

In extreme cases, we might have to be satisfied with such bounds, but we would accept this situation only reluctantly.

We can give certain criteria for determining R. The following test is simple, useful, and frequently easy to apply.

16.1c   Theorem. Let $\Sigma a_n x^n$ be a given series for which $\lim a_{n+1}/a_n \equiv q$ exists. Then $R = 1/q$.

Proof. Applying the ratio test,

$$\lim \left| \frac{a_{n+1}x^{n+1}}{a_n x^n} \right| = \lim \left| \frac{a_{n+1}}{a_n} x \right| = q|x|$$

we see that the series converges if $|x| < 1/q$ and diverges if $|x| > 1/q$. ∎

There is another test which always gives the exact value of R. It is sometimes cumbersome to apply because of the difficulty involved in actually carrying out the necessary calculations. The result is called the **Cauchy-Hadamard formula.**

16.1d   Theorem. For any power series $\Sigma a_n x^n$, the radius of convergence R is given by

$$R = 0 \qquad \text{if } \overline{\lim} \sqrt[n]{|a_n|} = \infty$$
$$R = \infty \qquad \text{if } \overline{\lim} \sqrt[n]{|a_n|} = 0$$
$$R = 1/\overline{\lim} \sqrt[n]{|a_n|} \qquad \text{if } 0 < \overline{\lim} \sqrt[n]{|a_n|} < \infty.$$

Proof. This theorem is a consequence of Theorem 14.3b. We test $\Sigma |a_n x^n|$ by that theorem. Let $q = \overline{\lim} \sqrt[n]{|a_n|}$. Then

$$\overline{\lim} \sqrt[n]{|a_n x^n|} = \overline{\lim} |x| \sqrt[n]{|a_n|} = |x| \overline{\lim} \sqrt[n]{|a_n|} = |x|q.$$

Now we get convergence if $|x|q < 1$, which is so for all x's if $q = 0$. If $q = +\infty$, it holds only for $x = 0$; if q is neither 0 nor ∞, it holds only if $|x| < 1/q$. ∎

16.1e   Corollary. For a power series $\Sigma a_n x^n$ if $q = \lim \sqrt[n]{|a_n|}$ exists, then

$$R = 0 \qquad \text{if } q = \infty$$
$$R = \infty \qquad \text{if } q = 0$$
$$R = 1/q \qquad \text{if } 0 < q < \infty.$$

Proof. If $\lim \sqrt[n]{|a_n|}$ exists, then $\overline{\lim} \sqrt[n]{|a_n|} = \lim \sqrt[n]{|a_n|}$. ∎

We will determine the interval of convergence of the following series and investigate the convergence at the end points.

EXAMPLE 1. $1 + \left(\dfrac{x}{2}\right) + \left(\dfrac{x}{4}\right)^2 + \left(\dfrac{x}{2}\right)^3 + \left(\dfrac{x}{4}\right)^4 + \cdots$, where $a_{2n-1} = \left(\dfrac{1}{2}\right)^{2n-1}$ and $a_{2n} = \left(\dfrac{1}{4}\right)^{2n}$.

Solution. $\lim \left|\dfrac{a_n}{a_{n+1}}\right|$ does not exist. Let us examine the sequence

$$\{\sqrt[n]{|a_n|}\}: \quad 1, \tfrac{1}{2}, \tfrac{1}{4}, \tfrac{1}{2}, \tfrac{1}{4}, \tfrac{1}{2}, \tfrac{1}{4}, \ldots.$$

It is clear that $\overline{\lim} \sqrt[n]{|a_n|} = \tfrac{1}{2}$. Hence $R = 2$. Thus we know the series converges in $\{-2 < x < 2\}$.

What about $x = \pm 2$? At either of these values, all the odd terms have absolute value 1. That is,

$$\lim a_n \neq 0.$$

Hence the series diverges at each end.

EXAMPLE 2. $1 + \displaystyle\sum_1^\infty \dfrac{x^n}{n^2} = 1 + x + \dfrac{x^2}{4} + \dfrac{x^3}{9} + \dfrac{x^4}{16} + \cdots$.

Solution. We try the ratio determination of R:

$$\lim \dfrac{1}{n^2} \Big/ \dfrac{1}{(n+1)^2} = \lim \left(\dfrac{n+1}{n}\right)^2 = 1 = R.$$

Thus our series converges in $\{-1 < x < 1\}$. At the ends we have $1 + \displaystyle\sum_1^\infty \dfrac{1}{n^2}$ and $1 + \displaystyle\sum_1^\infty \dfrac{(-1)^n}{n^2}$. In either case we have absolute convergence, since the series are k series with $k > 1$.

EXAMPLE 3. $\displaystyle\sum_1^\infty \dfrac{10^n}{n} x^n = 10x + 50x^2 + 333\tfrac{1}{3}x^3 + \cdots$.

Solution. Again we apply the ratio test:

$$\left|\dfrac{a_n}{a_{n+1}}\right| = \dfrac{10^n}{n} \Big/ \dfrac{10^{n+1}}{n+1} = \dfrac{n+1}{n} \cdot \dfrac{1}{10} \to \dfrac{1}{10} = R.$$

Hence the series converges in $\{-1/10 < x < 1/10\}$. At $x = +1/10$, the harmonic series diverges; at $x = -1/10$, the alternating harmonic converges.

A EXERCISES

1. Determine the radius of convergence of $\Sigma a_n x^n$, where a_n is given below. Investigate the convergence at each end of the interval of convergence.

(a) $1/[n(n + 1)(n + 2)]$ (b) $(n - 1)/n!$ (c) $(2n)!/(n!)^2$

(d) $1/n^k$ (e) $(3^n + 2n)/(4^n + 5)$ (f) $a_{2n} = e^{-2n}$; $a_{2n+1} = e^{2n}$

2. Determine the interval of convergence of each of the following series:

(a) $\Sigma(1 + 1/n)^{n^2}(x - 10)^n$ (b) $\Sigma(x/2 - 1)^n$

(c) $\Sigma(n^2/2^n)(x - 3)^n$ (d) $\Sigma(\cos n\pi/2)(x - \pi)^n$

B EXERCISES

1. Discuss the following problems as in A1 above.

(a) $\dfrac{1 \cdot 2 \cdot 3 \cdots n}{3 \cdot 5 \cdot 7 \cdots (2n + 1)}$ (b) $\dfrac{1 \cdot 3 \cdot 5 \cdots (2n - 1)}{2 \cdot 4 \cdot 6 \cdots (2n)}$ (c) $\left(1 + \dfrac{1}{n}\right)^{-n^2}$

2. Prove that if the sequence $\{a_n\}$ is bounded away from both 0 and ∞, then $\Sigma a_n x^n$ has radius of convergence equal to 1.

3. Let $\Sigma a_n x^n$ and $\Sigma b_n x^n$ have radii of convergence R and R', respectively. What can you say about the radii of convergence of the following?

(a) $\Sigma(a_n \pm b_n)x^n$ (b) $\Sigma a_n b_n x^n$ (c) $\Sigma(a_n/b_n)x^n$

16.2 PROPERTIES OF POWER SERIES

A power series $\Sigma a_n x^n$ which has a non-zero radius of convergence R converges for each x in the interval $\{-R < x < R\}$, and thus defines a function in that interval. If we are to use this function in any calculations, we need to know some of its properties. In particular we need to know if it is continuous, integrable, differentiable. If it is differentiable, we want to know how many derivatives it has. These are questions which can be easily answered by the uniform convergence criteria of the last chapter.

16.2a Theorem. Let $\Sigma a_n x^n$ have a non-zero radius of convergence R, and let a and b be any two numbers which satisfy the condition $-R < a < b < R$. Then $\Sigma a_n x^n$ converges uniformly in the closed interval $I: \{a \leqslant x \leqslant b\}$.

Proof. Let $r = \max\{|a|, |b|\}$. If x is in I, then $|x| \leqslant r$. And r is a point in the interval of convergence, so that $\Sigma|a_n r^n|$ converges. Hence,

$$|a_n x^n| \leqslant |a_n r^n|, \qquad x \text{ in } I.$$

If we choose $M_n = |a_n r^n|$, we see that the Weierstrass M test applies. ∎

Immediately we have the following corollary.

16.2b Corollary. If $\Sigma a_n x^n$ has a non-zero radius of convergence, then the function it represents is continuous at each point x in the interval $\{-R < x < R\}$. Furthermore, for any a, b for which $-R < a < b < R$,

$$\int_a^b \left(\sum_0^\infty a_n x^n \right) dx = \sum_0^\infty \frac{a_n}{n+1} (b^{n+1} - a^{n+1}) = \sum_0^\infty \frac{a_n \cdot b^{n+1}}{n+1} - \sum_0^\infty \frac{a_n \cdot a^{n+1}}{n+1}$$

Proof. Let x_0 be any point in $\{-R < x < R\}$. Then there is a positive number a for which the interval $I: (x_0 - a \leqslant x \leqslant x_0 + a)$ is contained in the interval of convergence. (Why?) By the previous theorem, the convergence is uniform in I. Hence, by Theorem 15.3a, the sum is continuous in I; in particular, it is continuous at x_0. But since x_0 was an arbitrary point in the interval of convergence, the sum is continuous at all such points.

To prove the second part, we write

$$\int_a^b (\Sigma a_n x^n)\, dx = \int_0^b (\Sigma a_n x^n)\, dx - \int_0^a (\Sigma a_n x^n)\, dx.$$

Now since the convergence is uniform in the closed interval from 0 to b,

$$\int_0^b \Sigma a_n x^n\, dx = \Sigma a_n \int_0^b x^n\, dx = \Sigma a_n \left. \frac{x^n}{n+1} \right]_0^b = \Sigma \frac{a_n \cdot b^{n+1}}{n+1},$$

the interchange of Σ and $\int$ being permissible by Theorem 15.3c. Similarly, the other integral can be computed and the results combined to give the statement asserted in the theorem. ∎

EXAMPLE 1. $\dfrac{1}{1+x} = 1 - x + x^2 - + \cdots = \sum_0^\infty (-x)^n \qquad \{|x| < 1\}.$

Solution:

$$\log(1 + a) = \int_0^a \frac{dx}{1+x} = \sum_0^\infty \int_0^a (-x)^n dx = \sum_0^\infty \frac{(-1)^n a^{n+1}}{n+1} = \sum_1^\infty \frac{(-1)^{n+1} a^n}{n}.$$

Now we raise another question. The original series $\Sigma(-x)^n$ does not converge at $x = 1$. However, the integrated series $-\sum_1^\infty (-1)^n a^n/n$ does converge there. Our information enables us to assert that

$$\log(1 + a) = - \sum_1^\infty (-a)^n/n!$$

only for $|a| < 1$. The question is whether it continues to hold for $a = +1$? (There is no question at $a = -1$, since the series diverges there.) Again we see that this resolves itself into a question of the continuity of the function represented by the series. If the series is continuous at 1, then the equality continues to hold; if not, the equality does not hold.

We could handle this question much as we did the example of the arc tangent in the last chapter. But there is a general theorem, **Abel's theorem**, which covers the situation for all power series at once.

16.2c   Theorem. If a power series $\Sigma a_n x^n$ has a finite non-zero radius of convergence, and if it converges at $x = R$—that is, if $\Sigma a_n R^n$ converges then it converges uniformly in $\{0 \leqslant x \leqslant R\}$. If it converges at $-R$, then it converges uniformly in $\{-R \leqslant x \leqslant 0\}$.

Proof. It is convenient to carry out the proof for $R = 1$, and this is sufficient to effect the complete proof. For the substitution $x = Ry$ carries $\Sigma a_n x^n$ into

$$\Sigma(a_n R^n)y^n = \Sigma b_n y^n,$$

where $b_n = a_n R^n$ and where the new series has a radius of convergence equal to 1. Hence we will assume that $R = 1$. Our assumption that $\Sigma a_n x^n$ converges at $x = R$ becomes an assumption that Σa_n converges.

We apply Dirichlet's test, Theorem 15.4b, with

$$u_n(x) = a_n, \qquad v_n(x) = x^n.$$

Let us verify the hypotheses:

(i) $\Sigma u_n(x)$ converges uniformly means Σa_n converges, which is an explicit assumption.

(ii)   If $x \neq 1$, then

$$\sum_1^\infty |v_k - v_{k-1}| = \sum_1^\infty |x^k - x^{k-1}| = \sum_1^\infty x^{k-1}|x - 1|$$

$$= (1 - x) \sum_1^\infty x^{k-1} = (1 - x) \sum_0^\infty x^k = (1 - x)/(1 - x) = 1,$$

If $x = 1$, then

$$\sum_1^\infty |v_k - v_{k-1}| = 0.$$

(iii) $|v_0(x)| = 1$.

Hence (ii) and (iii) are satisfied with $K = 1$.   ∎

If we return to our example, we see that the convergence of the series for $a = 1$, namely $\sum_1^\infty (-1)^{n+1}/n$, enables us to assert that $\Sigma(-1)^{n+1}a^n/n$ converges uniformly in $\{0 \leqslant a \leqslant 1\}$, and hence represents a continuous function there. Then, since

$$\log(1 + a) = \sum_1^\infty \frac{(-1)^{n+1}a^n}{n} \qquad \text{for } |a| < 1,$$

we have on taking limits,

$$\log 2 = \sum_1^\infty \frac{(-1)^{n+1}}{n} = 1 - \frac{1}{2} + \frac{1}{3} - \frac{1}{4} + \frac{1}{5} - + \cdots.$$

We have yet to discuss the differentiability of power series, but before we get to this question we consider a preliminary one. If $\Sigma a_n x^n$ converges in an interval $\{|x| < R\}$, then the formal derivative (that is, the result of performing termwise differentiation without asking if it is permissible) is $\Sigma n a_n x^{n-1}$. We first ask about the convergence of this series. It turns out that it has the same radius of convergence.

16.2d   Theorem. If $\Sigma a_n x^n$ converges for $|x| < R$, then $\Sigma n a_n x^{n-1}$ also converges for $|x| < R$.

Proof. We recall that $nr^n \to 0$ as $n \to \infty$ for $r < 1$. Hence, for any fixed $x_0 \neq 0$, $nr^n/|x_0| \leqslant 1$ for n sufficiently large.

Let x_0 be any point for which $|x_0| < R$, and let x_1 be so chosen that $|x_0| < |x_1| < R$. Then set $r = |x_0/x_1|$ and calculate

$$|na_n x_0^{n-1}| = \left| \frac{na_n x_1^n}{x_0} \left(\frac{x_0}{x_1} \right)^n \right| = \frac{nr^n}{|x_0|} \cdot |a_n x_1^n| \leqslant |a_n x_1^n|$$

for n sufficiently large.

We see, then, that $\Sigma n a_n x_0^{n-1}$ converges by the comparison test. ∎

Now we can easily settle the question of differentiability.

16.2e   Theorem. Let $\Sigma a_n x^n$ have a non-zero radius of convergence R. Denote its sum by $f(x)$. Then f is differentiable for $\{-R < x < R\}$ and

$$f'(x) = \sum_0^\infty a_n \frac{d}{dx} (x^n) = \sum_1^\infty na_n x^{n-1} \qquad \{|x| < R\}.$$

Proof. Let x_0 be any point in $\{-R < x < R\}$. Then there is an $a > 0$ for which the interval $I: \{x_0 - a \leqslant x \leqslant x_0 + a\}$ is in the interval of convergence. Hence both $\Sigma a_n x^n$ and $\Sigma n a_n x^{n-1}$ are uniformly convergent in I, so that by Theorem 15.3g the termwise differentiation is justified in I, in particular at x_0. Since x_0 is an arbitrary point in $\{-R < x < R\}$, the differentiation is justified for all points in the interval of convergence. ∎

16.2f   Corollary. Under the above hypotheses $f(x)$ has derivatives of all orders and

$$f^{(k)}(x) = \sum_{n=0}^\infty a_n \frac{d^k}{dx^k} x^n = \sum_{n=k}^\infty a_n n \cdot (n-1) \cdots (n-k+1) x^{n-k}$$

$$= \sum_{n=k}^\infty a_n \frac{n!}{(n-k)!} x^{n-k}$$

$$= \sum_{n=0}^\infty \frac{a_{n+k}(n+k)!}{n!} x^n \qquad \{-R < x < R\}.$$

Proof. An induction argument based on Theorem 16.2e effects the proof. ∎

Example 2. Differentiate

$$\frac{1}{1-x} = \Sigma x^n = 1 + x + x^2 + \cdots \qquad \{|x| < 1\}.$$

Solution. By termwise differentiation,

$$\frac{1}{(1-x)^2} = 1 + 2x + 3x^2 + 4x^3 + \cdots \qquad \{|x| < 1\},$$

$$\frac{2}{(1-x)^3} = 2 \cdot 1 + 3 \cdot 2x + 4 \cdot 3x^2 + \cdots \qquad \{|x| < 1\},$$

and in general

$$\frac{1}{(1-x)^k} = (1-x)^{-k} = 1 + kx + \frac{k(k+1)}{1 \cdot 2}x^2 + \cdots$$

$$+ \frac{(n+k-1)!}{n!\,(k-1)!}x^n + \cdots \qquad \{|x| < 1\}.$$

We know that a power series represents an infinitely differentiable function on its interval of convergence and that all the derivatives can be computed by termwise differentiation. We can express the coefficients in terms of these derivatives. This result follows as a corollary of the previous theorem.

16.2g   Corollary. Let $\Sigma a_n x^n$ have a radius of convergence $R > 0$. Denote its sum by $f(x)$. Then

$$a_k = \frac{f^{(k)}(0)}{k!}$$

Proof. Set $x = 0$ in the formula of the previous theorem.   ∎

As a corollary of 16.2g, we get the uniqueness of a power series representation. That is, if a function f is representable in an interval $\{-R < x < R\}$ by two power series, then they must be identical. The precise statement follows.

16.2h   Corollary. Let $f(x) = \Sigma a_n x^n$ and $f(x) = \Sigma b_n x^n$, in $\{-R < x < R\}$. Then

$$a_n = b_n \qquad n = 0, 1, 2, \ldots.$$

Proof. By Theorem 16.2g,

$$a_n = f^{(n)}(0)/n! = b_n.$$ ∎

Example 3. Sum the series and obtain f in finite form, where

$$f(x) = 1 + \sum_1^\infty \frac{x^n}{n^2} = 1 + x + \frac{x^2}{4} + \cdots \qquad \{-1 \leqslant x \leqslant 1\}.$$

Solution. Now in $\{-1 < x < 1\}$

$$f'(x) = \sum_1^\infty \frac{x^{n-1}}{n} = 1 + \frac{x}{2} + \frac{x^2}{3} + \cdots$$

$$xf'(x) = x + \frac{x^2}{2} + \frac{x^3}{3} + \cdots .$$

(Why can we multiply termwise? See Exercise B2, Section 14.1.) Then

$$\frac{d}{dx}\left[xf'(x)\right] = 1 + x + x^2 + \cdots = \frac{1}{1-x}.$$

Hence
$$xf'(x) = \int_0^x \frac{dt}{1-t} = -\log(1-x),$$

so that
$$f'(x) = \frac{-\log(1-x)}{x}$$

and
$$f(x) = -\int_0^x \frac{\log(1-t)}{t}\,dt + 1.$$

(Why do we have $+1$ on the end?) By Abel's theorem, this evaluation is valid in $\{-1 < x \leqslant 1\}$.

A EXERCISES

1. Compute $f'(x)$ in each of the following and give the interval of convergence in each case:

(a) $f(x) = \sum_1^\infty \dfrac{x^n}{n^n}$

(b) $f(x) = \sum_0^\infty \dfrac{(n!)^2 x^n}{(2n)!}$

(c) $f(x) = \sum_1^\infty \dfrac{x^n}{n}$

(d) $f(x) = \sum_2^\infty \dfrac{x^n}{n(n-1)}$

2. Compute $\displaystyle\int_0^x f(t)\,dt$ for each part of Exercise 1.

3. Evaluate $\displaystyle\lim_{x\to 1} f(x)$ for each of the following:

(a) $f(x) = \sum_1^\infty \dfrac{x^n}{n(n+1)}$

(b) $f(x) = \sum_2^\infty \dfrac{x^n}{n(n-1)}$

B EXERCISE

1. Sum the following series:

(a) $\displaystyle\sum_2^\infty \frac{x^n}{n(n-1)}$

(b) $\displaystyle\sum_1^\infty \frac{x^n}{n(n+1)}$

(c) $\displaystyle\sum_1^\infty nx^n$

(d) $\displaystyle\sum_1^\infty \frac{nx^n}{(n+1)(n+2)}$

(e) $\displaystyle\sum_0^\infty n^2 x^n$

(f) $\displaystyle\sum_0^\infty x^{5k+1}$

C EXERCISES

I. Let $f(x) = 1 + x + \dfrac{x^2}{2!} + \cdots + \dfrac{x^n}{n!} + \cdots$ $\{-\infty < x < \infty\}$. Show that

for all x's $f'(x) = f(x)$ and $f(0) = 1$, and deduce that $f(x) = e^x$. Be careful; there may be points where f vanishes.

2. Let $f(x) = \Sigma a_n x^n$, with $a_n \geqslant 0$ have radius of convergence 1. Show that if $\lim\limits_{x \to 1-0} f(x) = \sigma$, then Σa_n converges and $\sigma = \Sigma a_n$. (This is a converse of Abel's theorem under the additional hypothesis that $a_n \geqslant 0$. The exact converse is not true.)

16.3   THE TAYLOR AND MACLAURIN SERIES

We want to consider here the question of expanding a given function in terms of a power series. From our previous work, we can see that the series must possess certain properties. Perhaps the most striking of these is that the function must possess derivatives of all orders. By Corollary 16.2f, we have seen that any power series has this property. Hence if a function is to be representable as such a series, it too must have this property.

You might reasonably ask if this is sufficient. That is, you might ask if every function which is infinitely differentiable in an interval $\{-R < x < R\}$ is representable by a power series in that interval. The answer is "No." This can be seen by means of examples.

Before giving such an example, let us observe that we can write down right away what the series is, if the function is so representable. Let $f(x)$ be a given function, infinitely differentiable on $\{-R < x < R\}$. If there are coefficients a_n for which

$$f(x) = \Sigma a_n x^n \qquad \{-R < x < R\},$$

then $a_n = f^{(n)}(0)/n!$ (Why?)

This means that, for any given function f, we know what the only possible power series expansion must be. The question to face is this: Is it really an answer? That is, does it do what we ask: does it converge in $\{-R < x < R\}$? And if it does converge, is its sum the function we want it to be, namely f?

As we pointed out, the answer is "No". We can see this by means of the following example:

$$f(x) = \begin{cases} e^{-1/x^2} & x \neq 0 \\ 0 & x = 0. \end{cases}$$

It is clear that f has derivatives of all orders, except possibly at $x = 0$, which has to be handled separately. First let us compute $f'(0)$. We examine the difference quotient:

$$\frac{\Delta f}{\Delta x} = \frac{f(x) - f(0)}{x - 0} = \frac{f(x)}{x} = \frac{1}{x} e^{-1/x^2}.$$

We want to know the limit of this as $x \to 0$. Substituting $x = 1/t$, we get

$$\frac{\Delta f}{\Delta x} = t e^{-t^2} \to 0 \qquad \text{as } x \to 0 \text{ (i.e. as } t \to \infty\text{)}.$$

Hence $f'(0) = 0$, and for $x \neq 0$ we can compute

$$f'(x) = \frac{2}{x^3} e^{-1/x^2}.$$

In general, we see that for $x \neq 0$, $f^{(k)}(x)$ is of the form

$$e^{-1/x^2} P\left(\frac{1}{x}\right),$$

where P is a polynomial in $1/x$. By induction, we conclude that $f^{(k)}(0) = 0$ for all k. The details of this argument are left to the exercises.

This means that all our coefficients in the series we wrote down are zero. In other words, for every x the sum of the series is 0. But the function we are trying to represent by that series is zero at only one point. Hence our series fails to represent the function.

Let us see now under what conditions on f we might expect our series to represent (that is, converge to) the function f. We have indicated occasionally that the fact that we work with series centered at $x = 0$ was a matter of choice, because any series in powers of say $(x - a)$ (that is, centered at $x = a$) could be brought into our standard form by a translation $z = x - a$. We now choose to work about an arbitrary point $x = a$.

We turn to Taylor's formula with remainder as the means of investigating this question. If we have a function f which is infinitely differentiable on an interval $\{-R < x - a < R\}$, we can apply Taylor's formula for any x in our interval and for any n

$$f(x) = f(a) + f'(a)(x - a) + \frac{f''(a)}{2!}(x - a)^2 + \cdots$$
$$+ \frac{f^{(n)}(a)(x - a)^n}{n!} + R_{n+1}(x),$$

and we have any of several forms in which to express $R_{n+1}(x)$. Let $S_n(x)$ denote the sum of the terms up to $R_{n+1}(x)$. Then we have

$$f(x) - S_n(x) = R_{n+1}(x).$$

It should now be clear that what we have to examine is the behavior of this remainder.

16.3a   Theorem. Let $f(x)$ be infinitely differentiable in

$$\{-R < x - a < R\}.$$

If $R_{n+1}(x) \to 0$ as $n \to \infty$, then for this x

$$f(x) = \sum_{0}^{\infty} \frac{f^{(n)}(a)}{n!} (x - a)^n.$$

Proof. The proof of this theorem is immediate from the previous equation.   ∎

This series is called the **Taylor series** of the function f. If $a = 0$, it is sometimes called the **Maclaurin Series**. However, we will always refer to it as a Taylor series whether or not $a = 0$.

16.3b   Theorem. Any power series is the Taylor series of its sum.

Proof. Prove by Corollary 16.2g.   ∎

This explains the title of this chapter.

EXAMPLE. Expand e^x in a Taylor series about $x = 0$.

Solution:

$$\begin{array}{ll} f(x) = e^x & f(0) = 1 \\ f'(x) = e^x & f'(0) = 1 \\ f''(x) = e^x & f''(0) = 1 \\ \quad \cdot & \quad \cdot \\ \quad \cdot & \quad \cdot \\ \quad \cdot & \quad \cdot \\ f^{(n)}(x) = e^x & f^{(n)}(0) = 1 \\ \quad \cdot & \quad \cdot \\ \quad \cdot & \quad \cdot \\ \quad \cdot & \quad \cdot \end{array}$$

Hence the formal series expansion is given by

$$\sum_{0}^{\infty} \frac{1}{n!} x^n = 1 + x + \frac{x^2}{2!} + \frac{x^3}{3!} + \cdots + \frac{x^n}{n!} + \cdots$$

To know whether the series converges to e^x, we have to examine the remainder. Let x be any fixed number. Then

$$|e^x - S_n(x)| = |R_{n+1}(x)| = \frac{1}{(n+1)!} e^{\xi} |x|^{n+1},$$

where ξ is some number between 0 and x. Thus if x is negative $e^\xi < 1$; if x is positive, $e^\xi < e^x$. In either case $e^\xi < e^{|x|}$. Hence

$$|e^x - S_n(x)| \leqslant e^{|x|} \cdot |x|^{n+1}/(n+1)!$$

Now choose $N > 2|x|$ so that $|x|/N < 1/2$. Then for $n \geqslant N$,

$$\frac{e^{|x|}|x|^{n+1}}{(n+1)!} = \frac{e^{|x|}|x|^N}{N!} \frac{|x|^{n+1-N}}{(N+1)(N+2)\cdots(n+1)}$$

$$= \frac{e^{|x|}|x|^N}{N!} \cdot \frac{|x|}{N+1} \cdot \frac{|x|}{N+2} \cdots \frac{|x|}{n+1} \leqslant \frac{e^{|x|}|x|^N}{N!}\left(\frac{1}{2}\right)^{n+1-N}$$

$$= \frac{2^N e^{|x|}|x|^N}{N!} \cdot \left(\frac{1}{2}\right)^{n+1}.$$

Now keep N fixed and x fixed, and let $n \to \infty$. We see then that the factor $(1/2)^n \to 0$, while the others remain unchanged. Hence $R_{n+1} \to 0$, and therefore we have proved that

$$e^x = 1 + x + x^2/2! + x^3/3! + \cdots + x^n/n! + \cdots \qquad \{-\infty < x < \infty\}.$$

Similarly we find that

$$\sin x = \sum_0^\infty \frac{(-1)^n x^{2n+1}}{(2n+1)!} = x - \frac{x^3}{3!} + \frac{x^5}{5!} - + \cdots \frac{(-1)^{n+1}x^{2n+1}}{(2n+1)!} + \cdots$$

$$\{-\infty < x < \infty\},$$

and

$$\cos x = \sum_0^\infty \frac{(-1)^n x^{2n}}{(2n)!} = 1 - \frac{x^2}{2!} + \frac{x^4}{4!} - \frac{x^6}{6!} - + \cdots \frac{(-1)^n x^{2n}}{(2n)!} + \cdots$$

$$\{-\infty < x < \infty\}.$$

It is possible to write the Taylor series as a very compact and easy-to-remember notation. You are familiar with the differential operator $D = d/dx$, from its use in differential equations. For example, we would write $D^2 = d^2/dx^2 \cdots$, so that an expression like

$$a\frac{d^2y}{dx^2} + b\frac{dy}{dx} + cy$$

can be written as

$$(aD^2 + bD + c)y.$$

We have to be careful though, in the handling of D. For example,

$$x\,Dy \neq D(xy). \qquad \text{(Why?)}$$

Let us write the Taylor series in the form obtained by replacing a by x and x by $x + h$. Then $x - a$ becomes h, and the series takes the form

$$f(x + h) = \sum_0^\infty \frac{h^n}{n!} f^{(n)}(x) = \sum_0^\infty \frac{h^n}{n!} \frac{d^n f(x)}{dx^n}.$$

In terms of the operator D, this becomes

$$f(x + h) = \sum_0^\infty \frac{h^n}{n!} D^n f(x) = \left[\sum_0^\infty \frac{(hD)^n}{n!} \right] f(x).$$

The formal sum in the brackets is the formal expansion of e^{hD}, so that

$$f(x + h) = e^{hD} f(x).$$

You have to realize that e^{hD} represents an operation and not a number, and the operation it represents is defined by the previous expansions.

A EXERCISES

1. Expand the following functions in Taylor series centered at the points indicated. Determine the radius of convergence in each case:

(a) $\sin x$, $\pi/4$ (b) $\cos x$, $3\pi/4$ (c) $\log(1 + x)$, 0

(d) a^x, 0   (e) $\sqrt{1 + x}$, 0   (f) $\log(1 - x)$, 0

(g) $\sqrt{x}$, 4   (h) e^x, 1   (i) $\displaystyle\int_0^x \frac{e^t - 1}{t} dt$, 0

(j) $\displaystyle\int_0^x e^{-t^3} dt$, 0   (k) $\displaystyle\int_0^x \sin t^2 \, dt$, 0   (l) $\displaystyle\int_0^x \frac{1 - \cos t}{t^2} dt$, 0.

2. Evaluate $\displaystyle\int_0^1 e^{-x^2} dx$ correct to three decimal places.

3. Expand $(1 + x)^\alpha$ in a power series about $x = 0$. Observe that the convergence of this series has already been discussed in Exercise B2 of Section 14.6.

4. Show that if f is odd, the Taylor series about the origin can be written in the form

$$f(h) = \sinh(hD) f(0);$$

that if f is even, it can be written in the form

$$f(h) = \cosh(hD) f(0).$$

16.4 THE ARITHMETIC OF POWER SERIES

In their intervals of convergence, power series represent functions. It is sometimes necessary to perform the elementary operations of arithmetic (addition, subtraction, multiplication, division) on these functions. In so far as addition and subtraction are concerned, the situation is very simple and is handled in the problems (see Exercise B1). Multiplication and division are more complicated, however. We first prove a general theorem on multiplication of series, which was postponed until now because of the fact that its primary application is to power series.

16.4a Theorem. Let $\sum_0^\infty a_n$ and $\sum_0^\infty b_n$ be absolutely convergent series with sums A and B respectively. Define $c_n = \sum_0^n a_k b_{n-k}$. Then $\sum_0^\infty c_n$ is absolutely convergent, and its sum is $C = A \cdot B$.

Proof. Before giving details of the proof, note that all possible terms of the form $a_j b_k$ can be arranged as follows:

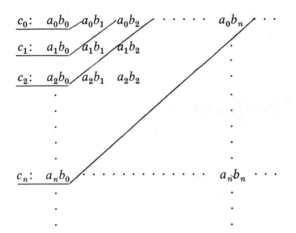

We see that c_n is just exactly the sum of all the terms for which the sum of the indices is n—that is, the sum of all the terms lying on the nth diagonal line. Hence $\sum_0^n c_k$ is the sum of all the terms on or above the nth diagonal.

Now we set up some notation:

$$A_n = \sum_0^n a_k \qquad B_n = \sum_0^n b_k \qquad C_n = \sum_0^n c_k$$

$$A_n' = \sum_0^n |a_k| \qquad B_n' = \sum_0^n |b_k|$$

$$A' = \sum_0^\infty |a_k| \qquad B_j' = \sum_0^\infty |b_k|.$$

We assume that neither A' nor B' vanishes. (Why?) Observe that $A_n \cdot B_n$ is the sum of all terms in a square of side n cornering at the $a_0 b_0$ term. Since $A_n \to A$ and $B_n \to B$, $A_n B_n \to AB$. Hence for each $\epsilon > 0$ there is an $N_1(\epsilon)$ such that

$$|A_n B_n - AB| < \epsilon \qquad \text{if } n > N_1.$$

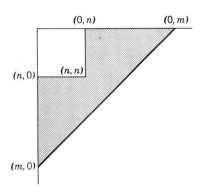

We now consider $|C_m - A_n B_n|$. This is the sum of all the terms above the mth diagonal minus the sum of the terms in the nth square. If $m > 2n$, then this difference is just precisely the sum of those terms which occur in the shaded area in the first diagram.

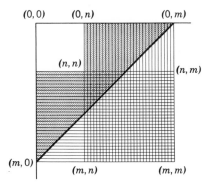

We estimate this sum from above by replacing each term by its absolute value, which yields a larger sum. We get a still larger sum if we replace this sum by the sum of absolute values of all the terms in the shaded area in the second diagram. Again, we get a still larger sum by adding the absolute values of all the terms in the rectangle with vertical shading to those in the rectangle with horizontal shading, thus taking those terms in the cross-hatched area twice. The sum of those terms in the rectangle with

vertical shading is $\displaystyle\sum_{j=0}^{m} \sum_{k=n+1}^{m} |a_j b_k|$, and the sum of those in the other one is
$\displaystyle\sum_{k=0}^{m} \sum_{j=n+1}^{m} |a_j b_k|$. Hence if $m > 2n$,

$$|C_m - A_n B_n| \leqslant \sum_{n+1}^{m} |a_j| \cdot \sum_{0}^{m} |b_k| + \sum_{0}^{m} |a_j| \sum_{n+1}^{m} |b_k|$$

$$= B_m{}' \sum_{n+1}^{m} |a_j| + A_m{}' \sum_{n+1}^{m} |b_k| \leqslant B' \sum_{n+1}^{m} |a_j| + A' \sum_{n+1}^{m} |b_k|$$

$$= B'(A_m{}' - A_n{}') + A'(B_m{}' - B_n{}').$$

The sequences $A_n{}'$ and $B_n{}'$ converge. Hence, given $\epsilon > 0$, there is an $N_2(\epsilon)$ for which

$$|A_m{}' - A_n{}'| < \epsilon \qquad \text{and} \qquad |B_m{}' - B_n{}'| < \epsilon \qquad \text{if } n > N_2.$$

If $n > N_2$ and $m > 2n$, then

$$|C_m - A_n \cdot B_n| < \epsilon B' + \epsilon A'.$$

We can now piece our estimates together to complete the proof. Choose $m > N(\epsilon) \equiv$ twice the larger of $N_1(\epsilon)$ and $N_2(\epsilon)$. Choose n larger than $(1/2)N(\epsilon)$ and smaller than $(1/2)m$. Then

$$|C_m - AB| \leqslant |C_m - A_n B_n| + |A_n B_n - AB|$$
$$\leqslant B'\epsilon + A'\epsilon + \epsilon$$
$$= \epsilon(A' + B' + 1).$$

This proves that $\Sigma c_n = AB$. Now we must show that $\Sigma |c_n|$ converges. We observe that the part of the theorem completed applies to the series $\Sigma |a_n|$ and $\Sigma |b_n|$. Hence if

$$c_n{}' = \sum_{k=0}^{n} |a_k b_{n-k}|,$$

then by the proof already completed $\Sigma c_n{}'$ converges. But

$$|c_n| = \left| \sum_{k=0}^{n} a_k b_{n-k} \right| \leqslant \sum_{k=0}^{n} |a_k b_{n-k}| = c_n{}',$$

so by the comparison test Σc_n converges absolutely.   ∎

As previously indicated, the main application of this general theorem is to power series, as shown in the following theorem.

16.4b Theorem. Let $f_1(x) = \Sigma a_n x^n$ have radius of convergence R_1, and $f_2(x) = \Sigma b_n x^n$ radius of convergence R_2. Then the product $f(x) = f_1(x) \cdot f_2(x)$ is represented by a power series $\Sigma c_n x^n$, where $c_n = \sum_{k=0}^{n} a_k b_{n-k}$ in the interval $\{-R < x < R\}$, where $R = \min(R_1, R_2)$.

Actually, it is possible that the radius of convergence might be greater than both R_1 and R_2. However, the proper interpretation in that case must await the study of analytic function theory. We now prove the theorem.

Proof. Let x be any point in the interval $\{-R < x < R\}$. Then both $\Sigma a_n x^n$ and $\Sigma b_n x^n$ are absolutely convergent, so that the previous theorem applies. ∎

EXAMPLE. Expand $\dfrac{\log(1+x)}{1+x}$ in a power series.

Solution:

$$\log(1+x) = -\sum_{1}^{\infty}(-1)^n \frac{x^n}{n}.$$

$$\frac{1}{1+x} = \sum_{0}^{\infty}(-1)^n x^n.$$

$$\frac{\log(1+x)}{1+x} = -\sum_{1}^{\infty} x^n \sum_{k=1}^{n} \frac{(-1)^k}{k} \cdot (-1)^{n-k}$$

$$= -\sum_{1}^{\infty}(-1)^n x^n \sum_{k=1}^{n} \frac{1}{k}.$$

Let $H_n = \sum_{1}^{n} \frac{1}{k}$. Then

$$\frac{\log(1+x)}{1+x} = -\sum_{1}^{\infty}(-x)^n H_n.$$

We come now to the division of power series. Clearly, it is sufficient to study the case of dividing a power series into 1, since

$$(\Sigma b_n x^n)/(\Sigma a_n x^n) = (\Sigma b_n x^n) \cdot (1/\Sigma a_n x^n).$$

It is also clear that we can assume the leading coefficient to be 1; that is, $a_0 = 1$. We will not consider the case $a_0 = 0$ (see Exercise B2). For any other a_0, we simply divide it out, leaving the leading coefficient equal to 1:

$$\frac{1}{a_0 + a_1 x + a_2 x^2 + \cdots} = \frac{1}{a_0} \cdot \frac{1}{1 + (a_1/a_0)x + (a_2/a_0)x^2 + \cdots}.$$

These comments should explain the somewhat special looking form of the theorem.

16.4c Theorem. Let $\Sigma a_n x^n$ be a series in which $a_0 = 1$ and having a non-zero radius of convergence R. Then $1/(\Sigma a_n x^n) = \Sigma b_n x^n$ with a non-zero radius of convergence. The b's are determined recursively (one after the other) by

$$b_0 = 1$$
$$b_1 = -a_1 b_0$$
$$b_2 = -(a_1 b_1 + a_2 b_0)$$
$$\cdot$$
$$\cdot$$
$$\cdot$$
$$b_n = -\sum_{k=1}^{n} (a_k b_{n-k})$$
$$\cdot$$
$$\cdot$$

You will recall that it was said earlier we might sometimes have to be satisfied with merely an estimate for the radius of convergence. This is such a case. The proof is typical of certain classes of proofs in analysis.

Proof. If there is a solution, then

$$(\Sigma a_n x^n)(\Sigma b_n x^n) = 1.$$

But $$(\Sigma a_n x^n)(\Sigma b_n x^n) = \Sigma c_n x^n,$$

where $$c_n = \sum_{0}^{n} a_k b_{n-k}.$$

Hence, by the uniqueness of a power-series expansion,

$$c_0 = 1, c_n = 0, n = 1, 2, \ldots . \qquad \text{(Why?)}$$

That is, $$a_0 b_0 = 1, \sum_{k=0}^{n} a_k b_{n-k} = 0 \qquad n = 1, 2, \ldots$$

or $$a_0 b_n = -\sum_{k=1}^{n} a_k b_{n-k}.$$

Since $a_0 = 1$, this completes the determination of the b's.

We must now show that the series $\Sigma b_n x^n$ has a non-zero radius of convergence. To do this, we estimate the b's. We observe that if r is any number $0 < r < R$, then $\Sigma a_n r^n$ converges. Hence there is a constant $M \geqslant 1$ for which

$$|a_n r^n| \leqslant M \qquad n = 0, 1, 2, \ldots$$

or $$|a_n| \leqslant \frac{M}{r^n} \qquad n = 0, 1, 2, \ldots .$$

Then

$$|b_0| = 1 = |a_0| \leqslant M$$

$$|b_1| = |a_1 b_0| = |a_1| \leqslant \frac{M}{r}.$$

$$|b_2| \leqslant |a_1 b_1| + |a_2 b_0| \leqslant \frac{M}{r} \cdot \frac{M}{r} + \frac{M}{r^2} M \leqslant \frac{2M^2}{r^2},$$

$$|b_3| \leqslant |a_1 b_2| + |a_2 b_1| + |a_3 b_0| \leqslant \frac{M}{r} \cdot \frac{2M^2}{r^2} + \frac{M}{r^2} \cdot \frac{M}{r} + \frac{M}{r^3}$$

$$\leqslant \frac{M^3}{r^3}(2 + 1 + 1) = 4\frac{M^3}{r^3} = 2^2 \frac{M^3}{r^3}.$$

By induction, we get

$$|b_n| \leqslant 2^{n-1}M^n/r^n \leqslant 2^n M^n/r^n.$$

Thus $$\sqrt[n]{|b_n|} \leqslant 2M/r \qquad n = 1, 2, \dots,$$

and so $$\overline{\lim} \sqrt[n]{|b_n|} \leqslant 2M/r.$$

Hence the radius of convergence is

$$1/\overline{\lim} \sqrt[n]{|b_n|} \geqslant \frac{r}{2M} > 0. \qquad \blacksquare$$

It turns out that the coefficients b_n are precisely those obtained by long division.

EXAMPLE. Compute $1/\left(\sum_0^\infty x^n/n!\right) = 1/\left(1 + x + \frac{x^2}{2!} + \cdots + \frac{x^n}{n!} + \cdots\right).$

Solution:

$$
1 + x + \frac{x^2}{2!} + \cdots \overline{\smash{\big)}\begin{array}{l} 1 - x + x^2/2! - \cdots \\ 1 \\ \overline{1 + x + x^2/2! + \cdots} \\ \quad - x - x^2/2! - x^3/3! \cdots \\ \overline{\quad - x - x^2 - x^3/2! -} \\ \qquad\qquad \vdots \end{array}}
$$

A EXERCISES

I. By squaring both sides of $(1 - x)^{-1} = \Sigma x^n$, show that

$$(1 - x)^{-2} = \sum_0^\infty (n + 1)x^n.$$

2. By power-series multiplication, compute the first few terms in the expansions about $x = 0$ of:

(a) $\sin x \cos x$ (b) $e^x \sin x$

(c) $\sin x \, \text{arc} \sin x$ (d) $e^x \cos x$ (e) $(e^x)^2$

3. By division of power series, compute the first few terms in the expansions about $x = 0$ of:

(a) $\dfrac{1}{\cos x}$ (b) $\dfrac{\sin x}{\cos x}$ (c) $\dfrac{1}{\cosh x}$

(d) $\dfrac{\sinh x}{\cosh x}$ (e) $\dfrac{1}{\sin x}$ (f) $\dfrac{1}{e^x + 1}$

B EXERCISES

1. Derive a general formula for the coefficients b_n, as defined by

$$\left(\frac{1}{1-x}\right)\Sigma a_n x^n = \Sigma b_n x^n.$$

2. Suppose $f(x) = x^p \sum_0^\infty a_n x^n$, where p is a positive integer and $a_0 \neq 0$. Let $g(x) = \sum_0^\infty b_n x^n$, and suppose that both series have non-zero radii of convergence. Show that for some deleted neighborhood of 0 (that is, punctured at $x = 0$), $\dfrac{g(x)}{f(x)} = \dfrac{c_{-p}}{x^p} + \dfrac{c_{-p+1}}{x^{p-1}} + \cdots + \dfrac{c_1}{x} + c_0 + c_1 x + \cdots$.

3. Compute the first few terms of expansions of the type considered in Exercise 2 for $\csc x$ and $\cot x$.

4. Verify that $d/dx \cot x = -\csc^2 x$ holds for the first few terms of the series calculated in Exercise 3.

C EXERCISES

1. Verify by multiplying series that $\sin 2x = 2 \sin x \cos x$. (*Hint:*

$$(1 + 1)^n = 1 + n + \frac{n(n-1)}{2!} + \cdots + 1 = 2^n$$

$$(1 - 1)^n = 1 - n + \frac{n(n-1)}{2!} + \cdots + (-1)^n = 0.)$$

2. The **Bernoulli numbers** B_n are defined by $\dfrac{x}{e^x - 1} = \sum_0^\infty \dfrac{B_n}{n!} x^n$. Prove that $B_{2k+1} = 0$ for $k = 1, 2, 3, \ldots$ and that $B_1 = -1/2$, $B_2 = 1/6$, $B_4 = -1/30$, $B_6 = -1/42$, $B_8 = -1/30$.

3. Show that $\dfrac{1}{e^x + 1} = -\sum_0^\infty B_n (2^n - 1) \dfrac{x^{n-1}}{n!}$, where the B's are defined as in Exercise 2 above.

4. Prove that $e^x \cdot e^y = e^{x+y}$ by multiplication of power series. Use the hint given in Exercise 1 above.

16.5 SUBSTITUTION AND INVERSION

We will now state without proof two theorems on power series. The first of these is a substitution theorem. The proofs are best given within the framework of analytic function theory. Any proof we might give here would be difficult and cumbersome.

16.5a Theorem. Let $g(y) = \sum_{0}^{\infty} a_n(y - y_0)^n$ converge in $\{-R_1 < y - y_0 < R_1\}$ and $f(x) = b_0 + \sum_{1}^{\infty} b_n(x - x_0)^n$ converge in $\{-R_2 < x - x_0 < R_2\}$. If $y_0 = b_0$, then there is an interval $\{-R_3 < x - x_0 < R_3\}$ in which $|f(x) - y_0| < R_1$. The composite function given by $h(x) = g[f(x)]$ is expansible in a Taylor expansion $h(x) = \sum_{0}^{\infty} c_n(x - x_0)^n$ in $\{-R_3 < x - x_0 < R_3\}$, where the c's are determined by the identity

$$\sum_{0}^{\infty} c_n(x - x_0)^n = \sum_{0}^{\infty} a_n \left[\sum_{1}^{\infty} b_k(x - x_0)^k \right]^n.$$

Let the function f be given by a power series $f(x) = \Sigma a_n(x - x_0)^n$ on an interval $\{-R < x - x_0 < R\}$. If $f'(x_0) \neq 0$ (that is, if $a_1 \neq 0$), then by continuity there is an interval $I : \{-r_1 < x - x_0 < r_1\}$ in which $f'(x)$ has the same sign as $f'(x_0)$. We see then that, in the interval I, the function f is monotone-increasing or decreasing according as $f'(0) > 0$ or $f'(0) < 0$. Under these conditions, Theorem 3.4a guarantees the existence of an inverse function in a neighborhood of the point $y_0 = a_0$. That is, there is an $r_2 > 0$ and a function ϕ defined on $\{-r_2 < y - a_0 < r_2\}$ which is inverse to f. It is natural, then, to ask if ϕ can be represented in powers of $y - a_0$. The answer is given by the following theorem.

16.5b Theorem. Let $f(x) = \sum_{0}^{\infty} a_n(x - x_0)^n$ converge in $\{-R < x - x_0 < R\}$, and let $a_1 \neq 0$. Then there is an r and an inverse function ϕ defined by

$$x = \phi(y) = x_0 + \sum_{1}^{\infty} b_n(y - a_0)^n \qquad \{|y - a_0| < r\},$$

where the coefficients b_n are given by

$$x = x_0 + \sum_{1}^{\infty} b_n \left[\sum_{k=1}^{\infty} a_k(x - x_0)^k \right]^n.$$

EXAMPLE 1. Compute the first few terms of the expansion of $e^{\sin x}$ about $x = 0$.

Solution:

$$e^{\sin x} = \sum_0^\infty \frac{(\sin x)^n}{n!} = \sum_0^\infty \frac{1}{n!}\left(x - \frac{x^3}{3!} + \frac{x^5}{5!} \cdots\right)^n$$

$$= 1 + \left(x - \frac{x^3}{3!} + \cdots\right) + \frac{1}{2!}\left(x - \frac{x^3}{3!} + \cdots\right)^2 + \frac{1}{3!}(x - \cdots)^3$$

$$= 1 + x + \frac{x^2}{2!} + 0 \cdot \frac{x^3}{3!} + \cdots.$$

EXAMPLE 2. Compute the first few terms of arc sin y from the expansion for sin x.

Solution. Let arc sin $y = \sum_1^\infty b_n y^n$. Then

$$x = \sum_1^\infty b_n y^n = \sum_1^\infty b_n\left(x - \frac{1}{3!}x^3 + \cdots\right)^n$$

$$= b_1\left(x - \frac{1}{3!}x^3 + \cdots\right) + b_2\left(x - \frac{1}{3!}x^3 + \cdots\right)^2$$

$$+ b_3\left(x - \frac{1}{3!}x^3 - \cdots\right)^3 + \cdots$$

$$= b_1 x + b_2 x^2 + x^3\left(-\frac{1}{3!}b_1 + b_3\right) + \cdots.$$

Hence $\qquad\qquad b_1 = 1, \ b_2 = 0, \ b_3 = \dfrac{1}{3!}, \ldots.$

Thus $\qquad\qquad$ arc sin $y = y + \dfrac{1}{3!}y^3 + \cdots.$

16.6 COMPLEX SERIES

Let us recall the basic facts about complex numbers.

The letter i represents the imaginary unit which is characterized by the relation

(1) $\qquad\qquad\qquad i^2 = -1.$

If x and y are real numbers, the expression $z = x + iy$ is called a **complex number**; x is its **real part** and y its **imaginary part**. The addition, subtraction, multiplication, and division of complex numbers are described by the following. Here $z_1 = x_1 + iy_1$ and $z_2 = x_2 + iy_2$.

(2) $\qquad z_1 \pm z_2 = (x_1 \pm x_2) + i(y_1 \pm y_2)$.

(3) $\qquad z_1 z_2 = (x_1 x_2 - y_1 y_2) + i(x_1 y_2 + x_2 y_1)$.

(4) $\qquad \dfrac{z_1}{z_2} = \dfrac{(x_1 x_2 + y_1 y_2) + i(-x_1 y_2 + x_2 y_1)}{x_2^2 + y_2^2} \qquad z_2 \neq 0$.

The complex number $z = x + iy$ can be represented graphically by the point or vector (x, y). The length of the vector (x, y) (or equivalently the distance of the point (x, y) from the origin) is called the **absolute value** of z and is written $|z|$. Thus $|z| = \sqrt{x^2 + y^2}$. Sometimes $|z|$ is also called the **modulus** of z.

If we introduce polar coordinates (ρ, θ), then the relations $x = \rho \cos \theta$, $y = \rho \sin \theta$ enable us to express the complex number $z = x + iy$ in the form

(5) $\qquad\qquad\qquad z = \rho(\cos \theta + i \sin \theta)$.

Clearly $|z| = \rho$. The angle θ, called the **argument** of z, is sometimes written $\theta = \arg z$. Clearly, θ is determined only up to an additive multiple of 2π.

If $z = x + iy$, the number $x - iy$ is called the **complex conjugate** of z and is denoted by $\bar{z}$. Note that $\overline{z_1 z_2} = \bar{z}_1 \bar{z}_2$, $\overline{z_1 + z_2} = \bar{z}_1 + \bar{z}_2$ and $\bar{\bar{z}} = z$, and $|z|^2 = z\bar{z}$.

We turn now to some simple but important inequalities.

16.6a.   Theorem:

(i) If $z = x + iy$, where x and y are real, then
$$|x| \leqslant |z| \qquad \text{and} \qquad |y| \leqslant |z|.$$

(ii) If z_1 and z_2 are complex numbers, then
$$|z_1 + z_2| \leqslant |z_1| + |z_2|.$$

Proof:

(i) $|x| = |\rho \cos \theta| \leqslant \rho = |z|$.

(ii) This follows from the triangle inequality for vectors. It can also be seen directly by
$$|z_1 + z_2|^2 = (z_1 + z_2)(\overline{z_1} + \overline{z_2}) = |z_1|^2 + (z_1 \bar{z}_2 + \bar{z}_1 z_2) + |z_2|^2.$$

Now $\bar{z}_1 z_2 = \overline{z_1 \bar{z}_2}$, so the quantity in parentheses is twice the real part of $\bar{z}_1 z_2$, which by part (i) of this theorem is smaller than $2|\bar{z}_1 z_2| = 2|z_1| \cdot |z_2|$. Thus
$$|z_1 + z_2|^2 \leqslant |z_1|^2 + 2|z_1| \cdot |z_2| + |z_2|^2 = (|z_1| + |z_2|)^2. \qquad \blacksquare$$

Suppose we have a sequence $\{a_n\}$ of complex numbers. The limit is defined exactly as for real numbers: The number A is the limit of the sequence if for each $\epsilon > 0$ there is an $N(\epsilon)$ such that

$$|a_n - A| < \epsilon \qquad \text{if } n > N.$$

The terminology, notation, and many proofs concerning limits of sequences can be taken over bodily from the real case, since they depend primarily upon the definition of a limit and on the triangle inequality, both of which have the same form in the two cases.

In particular, the Cauchy criterion for the convergence of complex sequences carries over unchanged. This, however, is not a completely trivial transcription but is a consequence of Theorem 9.2c, on the Cauchy criterion in higher dimensional spaces.

The following theorem is concerned with the relation between the limit of a complex sequence and the limits of its real and imaginary parts.

16.6b Theorem. In order that a complex sequence $\{a_n\}$, where $a_n = \alpha_n + i\beta_n$, shall have a limit $A = \alpha + i\beta$, it is necessary and sufficient that $\alpha_n \to \alpha$ and $\beta_n \to \beta$.

Proof. Suppose, first, that $a_n \to A$. Then for each $\epsilon > 0$ there is an $N(\epsilon)$ such that

$$|a_n - A| < \epsilon \qquad \text{if } n > N.$$

But by Theorem 16.6a (i),

$$|\alpha_n - \alpha| \leqslant |a_n - A| < \epsilon \qquad \text{if } n > N$$

and

$$|\beta_n - \beta| \leqslant |a_n - A| < \epsilon \qquad \text{if } n > N.$$

Thus $\alpha_n \to \alpha$ and $\beta_n \to \beta$.

Suppose now that $\alpha_n \to \alpha$ and $\beta_n \to \beta$. We want to show that $a_n \to A$. Let $\epsilon > 0$ be given. There is an $N_1(\epsilon)$ and an $N_2(\epsilon)$ such that

$$|\alpha_n - \alpha| < \epsilon/2 \qquad \text{if } n > N$$

and

$$|\beta_n - \beta| < \epsilon/2 \qquad \text{if } n > N_2.$$

Let $N = \max{(N_1, N_2)}$. Then for $n > N$ we have

$$|a_n - A| = |(\alpha_n - \alpha) + i(\beta_n - \beta)| \leqslant |\alpha_n - \alpha| + |\beta_n - \beta| < \epsilon \qquad \blacksquare$$

If $\{a_n\}$ is a sequence of complex numbers, we define the expression $\sum_{n=0}^{\infty} a_n$ to be an infinite series of complex numbers. The convergence of the series is defined just as in the real case, namely Σa_n converges if the sequence of partial sums converges. The concepts of absolute and conditional convergence carry over without change.

A power series $\Sigma a_n z^n$ in a complex variable converges in a **circle of convergence** given by

$$|z| < R,$$

where the radius of convergence R is given by the **Cauchy-Hadamard** formula

$$R = 1/\limsup \sqrt[n]{|a_n|}.$$

By DeMoivre's theorem from trigonometry (Exercise A4),

$$(\cos \theta + i \sin \theta)^n = \cos n\theta + i \sin n\theta,$$

complex formulas can sometimes be used to sum certain trigonometric expressions.

EXAMPLE. Sum $S = \sum_{1}^{n} \cos k\theta$.

Solution. Let $z = \cos \theta + i \sin \theta$. Then

$$S = Re\left(\sum_{1}^{n} z^k\right),$$

where $Re(\ )$ denotes the real part of whatever occurs in the parentheses. Now

$$\sum_{1}^{n} z^k = \frac{1 - z^{n+1}}{1 - z} = \frac{1 - \cos(n+1)\theta - i \sin(n+1)\theta}{1 - \cos \theta - i \sin \theta}.$$

By means of a little trigonometry, we deduce

$$S = Re\left(\sum_{1}^{n} z^k\right) = \frac{\sin(n + 1/2)\theta}{2 \sin 1/2\theta} - \frac{1}{2}.$$

Hence $\dfrac{1}{2} + \cos \theta + \cos 2\theta + \cdots + \cos n\theta = \dfrac{\sin(n + 1/2)\theta}{\sin 1/2\theta}.$

16.7 REAL ANALYTIC FUNCTIONS

A function of a real or complex variable is said to be **analytic** at a point a in its domain if it is expansible in a power series centered at a. The study of analytic functions is most easily carried out for complex variables, it being soon evident that the restriction of reality is awkward and indeed unnatural. The theorem we want to prove here is as simple in real as in complex cases; as a matter of fact, the proof we give is equally valid for complex functions.

We have seen that a necessary condition that a (real) function be analytic is that it be infinitely differentiable. We have also seen that this condition is not sufficient—there are infinitely differentiable functions which cannot be expanded in a power series. We want now to give a set of conditions which is necessary and sufficient for a function to be analytic. For simplicity, we assume that the center of the power series is at the origin.

16.7a   Theorem. Let f be defined in a neighborhood of the origin. In order that f be analytic at the origin, it is necessary and sufficient that f be infinitely differentiable and that there exist two constants r and K such that

$$|f^{(n)}(x)| \leqslant \frac{rKn!}{(r - |x|)^{n+1}} \qquad \text{in } \{-r < x < r\}.$$

Proof. Necessity. We have already seen the necessity of the infinite differentiability. It remains to obtain the estimates. Suppose

$$f(x) = \sum_{k=0}^{\infty} a_k x^k \qquad \{-R < x < R\}.$$

By Corollary 16.2f,

$$f^{(n)}(x) = \sum_{k=n}^{\infty} \frac{a_k k!}{(k - n)!} x^{k-n}.$$

Choose any $r < R$. There is a K for which

$$|a_k r^k| < K \qquad \text{for } k = 0, 1, 2, \ldots.$$

Then for $|x| < r$,

$$|f^{(n)}(x)| \leqslant \sum_{k=n}^{\infty} |a_k r^k| \frac{k!}{(k - n)! \, r^n} \left(\frac{|x|}{r}\right)^{k-n}$$

$$\leqslant \frac{K}{r^n} \sum_{k=n}^{\infty} \frac{k!}{(k - n)!} \left(\frac{|x|}{r}\right)^{k-n}$$

$$= \frac{K}{r^n} \frac{n!}{\left(1 - \dfrac{|x|}{r}\right)^{n+1}}$$

$$= \frac{rKn!}{(r - |x|)^{n+1}},$$

where the series is summed by Example 2 of Section 16.2.

Sufficiency. We now suppose that f is infinitely differentiable and that the estimate of the theorem is satisfied. Then, by Taylor's formula with remainder,

$$f(x) - S_n(x) = R_{n+1}(x),$$

where S_n and R_{n+1} have their usual meaning. Choose x with $|x| < r/2$ and keep it fixed. Then

$$|R_{n+1}(x)| = \frac{|f^{(n+1)}(\bar{x})|\, |x|^{n+1}}{(n+1)!}$$

$$\leqslant \frac{rK(n+1)!}{(r-|x|)^{n+2}} \frac{|x|^{n+1}}{(n+1)!}$$

$$= \frac{rK}{(r-|x|)}\left(\frac{|x|}{r-|x|}\right)^{n+1} \to 0 \qquad \text{as } n \to \infty,$$

since $|x| < r/2$. ∎

A EXERCISES

1. By substitution, compute the first few terms of the Taylor expansions of the following functions about 0:
   (a) $e^{\cos x}$ (b) $e^{\tan x}$ (c) $\log \cos x$

2. By inversion compute the first few terms of the Taylor expansions of the following functions:
   (a) $\tan y$ about 0 from arc tan x
   (b) arc cos y about 0 from cos x
   (c) arc sinh y about 0 from sinh x.

3. Prove DeMoivre's theorem for integer n:
   $$(\cos \theta + i \sin \theta)^n = \cos n\theta + i \sin n\theta.$$

4. From $\Sigma z^n = 1/(1-z)$, with $|z| < 1$, deduce the sums of $\Sigma r^n \cos n\theta$ and $\Sigma r^n \sin n\theta$, where $0 \leqslant r < 1$.

5. Show that sin x and cos x are analytic for all x's.

17

Improper Integrals

17.1 IMPROPER INTEGRALS. CONDITIONAL AND ABSOLUTE CONVERGENCE

Our definition of an integral required that the interval I of integration be bounded, and also that the function f being integrated be bounded on I. There are certain extensions of the concept of integral which permit us to remove one or both of these requirements in some cases. These extensions are called improper integrals. They were briefly defined in Chapter 4. We now want to rephrase those definitions and study improper integrals systematically.

The theory of improper integrals bears considerable resemblance to that of infinite series, and our treatment of them in this chapter will be quite analogous to our earlier study of infinite series. We begin by formulating the definitions of improper integrals.

Let f be defined on an interval $\{a \leqslant x \leqslant b\}$. Suppose further that f is integrable on $\{a \leqslant x \leqslant c\}$ for every c between a and b, and that f is not bounded in any neighborhood of b; that is, there is a sequence $\{x_n\}$ of points approaching b for which $|f(x_n)| \to +\infty$. The point b will be called a **singular point** or a **singularity** of the function f. The symbol $\int_a^b f(x)\, dx$ will be called the **improper integral** of f from a to b. We will say that the improper integral **converges** or **exists** if

$$\lim_{c \to b-0} \int_a^c f(x)\, dx$$

exists, and this limit will be called the **value** of the integral. If the limit does not exist, we will say that the integral **diverges,** or does not exist.

The improper integral is defined in an analogous fashion if the singular point is at the lower limit:

$$\int_a^b f(x)\,dx = \lim_{c \to a+0} \int_c^b f(x)\,dx.$$

Also a singular point c may occur as an interior point of an interval $\{a \leqslant x \leqslant b\}$. In this case, before we say that $\int_a^b f(x)\,dx$ exists, both improper integrals $\int_a^c f(x)\,dx$ and $\int_c^b f(x)\,dx$ must exist. We say the value of the first integral is the sum of the second and third. And if both upper and lower limits are singular points, then before we say that $\int_a^b f(x)\,dx$ exists, both $\int_a^c f(x)\,dx$ and $\int_c^b f(x)\,dx$ must both exist; and again we say the value of the first integral is the sum of the second and third. You might convince yourself that the value of this sum is independent of the choice of the intermediate point c.

Let $f(x)$ be defined in $\{a \leqslant x\}$ and be integrable (that is, properly integrable) in $\{a \leqslant x \leqslant b\}$ for every $b > a$. Then the symbol $\int_a^\infty f(x)\,dx$ will be called the **improper integral** of f from a to ∞. We say the integral **converges** or **exists** if

$$\lim_{b \to \infty} \int_a^b f(x)\,dx$$

exists, and the limit will be called the **value** of the integral. In this case we will say that the "point ∞" is a singular point, whether or not f becomes unbounded as $x \to \infty$. If the limit does not exist, we will say the integral **diverges,** or does not exist.

EXAMPLE 1. Investigate the convergence or divergence of $\int_1^\infty \dfrac{dx}{x^2}$

Solution:

$$\int_1^b \frac{dx}{x^2} = -\frac{1}{x}\Big|_1^b = 1 - \frac{1}{b} \to 1 \qquad \text{as } b \to \infty$$

Hence

$$\int_1^\infty \frac{dx}{x^2} = 1.$$

EXAMPLE 2. Investigate $\int_0^1 \dfrac{dx}{x^2}$.

Solution:

$$\int_a^1 \frac{dx}{x^2} = -\frac{1}{x}\Big|_a^1 = \frac{1}{a} - 1 \to +\infty \qquad \text{as } a \to 0.$$

Hence $\int_0^1 \dfrac{dx}{x^2}$ diverges.

EXAMPLE 3. Investigate $\int_0^\infty \dfrac{\sin x}{x}\, dx.$

Solution. First we note that $\dfrac{\sin x}{x} \to 1$ as $x \to 0$. Hence the integrand is not singular at $x = 0$. The singularity is at the upper limit.

Choose any $b > 0$. Then there is an n such that $b = n\pi + r_n$, where $0 \leqslant r_n \leqslant \pi$. Clearly, then, $n \to \infty$ as $b \to \infty$.

Hence we can write

$$\int_0^b \frac{\sin x}{x}\, dx = \int_0^{n\pi} \frac{\sin x}{x}\, dx + \int_{n\pi}^{n\pi + r_n} \frac{\sin x}{x}\, dx \equiv I_1 + I_2,$$

respectively.

Let us examine I_2:

$$\left| \int_{n\pi}^{n\pi + r_n} \frac{\sin x}{x}\, dx \right| \leqslant \int_{n\pi}^{n\pi + r_n} \left| \frac{\sin x}{x} \right| dx \leqslant \int_{n\pi}^{n\pi + r_n} \frac{1}{n\pi}\, dx \leqslant \frac{\pi}{n\pi} = \frac{1}{n}.$$

Hence $I_2 \to 0$ as $b \to \infty$. It is therefore sufficient to prove that I_1 has a limit as $b \to \infty$.

Now

$$I_1 = \sum_{k=1}^n \int_{(k-1)\pi}^{k\pi} \frac{\sin x}{x}\, dx = \sum_{k=1}^n b_k,$$

where

$$b_k = \int_{(k-1)\pi}^{k\pi} \frac{\sin x}{x}\, dx.$$

Clearly the signs of b's alternate. They are decreasing (why?), and $b_k \to 0$ (for the same reason that $I_2 \to 0$). Therefore I_1 is a partial sum of a convergent alternating series. We have thus shown that

$$\int_0^\infty \frac{\sin x}{x}\, dx = \lim_{b \to \infty} \int_0^b \frac{\sin x}{x}\, dx$$

converges. We will evaluate it in the next chapter.

The last example helped point up the analogy between series and integrals—an analogy which will guide our development throughout this chapter. We must be careful, however; for this analogy has its limits: it is an analogy and not an isomorphism. For example, since $a_n \to 0$ in any convergent series Σa_n, we might be led to think that, if $\int_a^\infty f(x)\, dx$

converges, then $f(x) \to 0$ *as* $x \to \infty$. To see that this is not so, let us examine the function f given by

$$f(x) = \begin{cases} 1 & \text{if } n \leqslant x \leqslant n + 1/n^2 \quad n = 1, 2, 3, \ldots \\ 0 & \text{otherwise.} \end{cases}$$

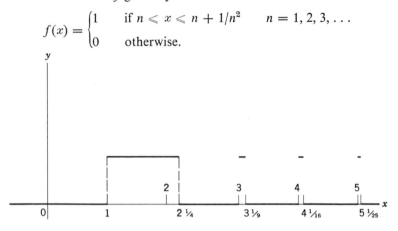

Then clearly for $n \leqslant a \leqslant n + 1$,

$$\sum_1^n \frac{1}{k^2} \leqslant \int_0^a f(x)\, dx \leqslant \sum_1^{n+1} \frac{1}{k^2},$$

so that

$$\lim_{a \to \infty} \int_0^a f(x)\, dx = \int_0^\infty f(x)\, dx = \sum_1^\infty \frac{1}{k^2},$$

while obviously $\lim_{x \to \infty} f(x)$ does not exist.

There is a **Cauchy criterion** for convergence of improper integrals. The diagram will help illustrate the wording of the theorem.

17.1a   Theorem. Let b be either a finite number or the symbol ∞, and let f be defined on $\{a \leqslant x < b\}$ and integrable on $\{a \leqslant x \leqslant c\}$ for every c between a and b. A necessary and sufficient condition that

$$\int_a^b f(x)\, dx$$ exists is that for each $\epsilon > 0$ there is an $X(\epsilon)$ such that

$$\left| \int_c^d f(x)\, dx \right| < \epsilon \quad \text{for } X < c < d < b.$$

Proof. Let

$$F(y) = \int_a^y f(x)\, dx.$$

The theorem is then precisely a restatement of the Cauchy criterion for existence of the limit of the function $F(y)$. (See Theorem 6.2b.)   ∎

Clearly, a similar criterion holds for the existence of an improper integral when the singularity is at the lower limit.

We distinguish absolutely and conditionally convergent integrals. We say that $\int_a^b f(x)\,dx$ (again b may be finite or ∞) is **absolutely convergent** if $\int_a^b |f(x)|\,dx$ is convergent. But if the first integral converges and the second diverges, then we say that $\int_a^b f(x)\,dx$ is **conditionally convergent.**

EXAMPLE 4. Test $\int_0^1 \dfrac{1}{\sqrt{x}} \sin \dfrac{1}{x}\,dx$ for absolute convergence.

Solution. Let $f(x) = \dfrac{1}{\sqrt{x}} \sin \dfrac{1}{x}$.

Then
$$|f(x)| \leqslant \frac{1}{\sqrt{x}},$$

and
$$\int_c^d |f(x)|\,dx \leqslant \int_c^d x^{-\frac{1}{2}}\,dx = 2x^{\frac{1}{2}}\Big|_c^d = 2(\sqrt{d} - \sqrt{c}) < 2\sqrt{d}.$$

Given $\epsilon > 0$, we choose $X(\epsilon) = \epsilon^2/4$. Then for $0 < c < d < X(\epsilon)$,

$$\int_c^d |f(x)|\,dx < 2\sqrt{d} < \epsilon.$$

Hence the integral converges absolutely.

Just as in the case of series, absolute convergence implies ordinary convergence.

17.1b Theorem. If $\int_a^b f(x)\,dx$ is an absolutely convergent improper integral, it is convergent.

Proof. In the theorem b can be a finite point or ∞. The proof follows from the inequality $\left| \int_c^d f(x)\,dx \right| \leqslant \int_c^d |f(x)|\,dx$, with a two-way use of the Cauchy criterion. (See the proof of the analogous theorem for series.) ∎

EXAMPLE 5. Evaluate $\int_0^\infty xe^{-x}\,dx$.

Solution:

$$\int_0^a xe^{-x}\,dx = -xe^{-x}\Big|_0^a + \int_0^a e^{-x}\,dx.$$

$$= -ae^{-a} + 1 - e^{-a} \to 1 \qquad \text{as } a \to \infty$$

Hence $\int_0^\infty xe^{-x} = 1$.

EXAMPLE 6. Show that $\displaystyle\int_0^\infty e^{-x^2}\,dx = \tfrac{1}{2}\sqrt{\pi}.$

Solution. Let $I = \displaystyle\int_0^\infty e^{-x^2}\,dx.$ First we work quite formally, and then return to justify our calculations:

$$I^2 = \int_0^\infty e^{-x^2}\,dx \int_0^\infty e^{-y^2}\,dy = \int_0^\infty \int_0^\infty e^{-x^2-y^2}\,dx\,dy$$
$$= \int_0^{\pi/2}\int_0^\infty e^{-r^2} r\,dr\,d\theta = \frac{\pi}{2}\int_0^\infty e^{-r^2} r\,dr = \frac{\pi}{4}.$$

Whence
$$I = \tfrac{1}{2}\sqrt{\pi}.$$

This simple calculation makes it easy to recall the value of the integral. However, a good deal has to be added before it can be called a proof. First we observe that

$$I^2 = \lim_{R\to\infty}\left(\int_0^R e^{-x^2}\,dx\right)\left(\int_0^R e^{-y^2}\,dy\right),$$

and we now proceed to work with the product of these two proper integrals. Clearly

$$\left(\int_0^R e^{-x^2}\,dx\right)\left(\int_0^R e^{-y^2}\,dy\right) = \int_0^R\left(\int_0^R e^{-x^2-y^2}\,dx\right)dy,$$

and the iterated integral may be written as a double integral:

$$\int_0^R\left(\int_0^R e^{-x^2-y^2}\,dx\right)dy = \iint_{S_R} e^{-x^2-y^2}\,dx\,dy \equiv J_R,$$

where S_R is a square of side R in the first quadrant, as shown in the accompanying figure. We have thus shown that $J_R \to I^2$ as $R \to \infty$.

Let c_R be the quarter circle $\{0 \leqslant x^2 + y^2 \leqslant R, x \geqslant 0, y \geqslant 0\}$ inscribed in S_R. Then $S_{R/\sqrt{2}}$ is contained in c_R. Since the integrand is positive,

$$\iint_{S_{R/\sqrt{2}}} e^{-x^2-y^2}\,dx\,dy \leqslant \iint_{c_R} e^{-x^2-y^2}\,dx\,dy \leqslant \iint_{S_R} e^{-x^2-y^2}\,dx\,dy.$$

Now the integrals on the ends are $J_{R/\sqrt{2}}$ and J_R, respectively. As $R \to \infty$, each of these tends to I^2. Hence so does the integral in the middle.

In this integral we introduce polar coordinates and write the resulting double integral again as an iterated integral in r and θ:

$$\iint_{c_R} e^{-x^2-y^2}\,dx\,dy = \iint_{c_R} e^{-r^2} r\,dr\,d\theta = \int_0^R \int_0^{\pi/2} e^{-r^2} r\,dr\,d\theta$$

$$= \int_0^R e^{-r^2} r\,dr \int_0^{\pi/2} d\theta = -(\pi/2)\tfrac{1}{2}e^{-r^2}\Big|_0^R = (\pi/4)[1 - e^{-R^2}].$$

Letting $R \to \infty$, we get the desired result.

A EXERCISES

1. Test the following integrals for convergence and absolute convergence. Evaluate the convergent ones when you can:

(a) $\displaystyle\int_0^1 \frac{dx}{x^k}, k \geqslant 1.$

(b) $\displaystyle\int_0^1 \frac{dx}{x^k}, k < 1$

(c) $\displaystyle\int_1^\infty \frac{dx}{x^k}, k > 1$

(d) $\displaystyle\int_1^\infty \frac{dx}{x^k}, k \leqslant 1$

(e) $\displaystyle\int_0^1 \csc x\,dx$

(f) $\displaystyle\int_0^1 \sqrt{x}\,\csc x\,dx$

(g) $\displaystyle\int_0^\infty e^{-x^2}\,dx$

(h) $\displaystyle\int_0^\infty x^2 e^{-x}\,dx$

(i) $\displaystyle\int_0^\infty \cos x\,dx$

(j) $\displaystyle\int_0^\infty e^{-x}\cos x\,dx$

(k) $\displaystyle\int_1^\infty \frac{\sin x}{x^2}\,dx$

(l) $\displaystyle\int_0^\infty e^{-x^2}\sin x\,dx$

(m) $\displaystyle\int_0^\infty e^{-x} x^n\,dx$

(n) $\displaystyle\int_1^\infty e^{-x^2} x^4\,dx$

(o) $\displaystyle\int_0^\infty e^{-x^2} x^3\,dx$

(p) $\displaystyle\int_0^\infty e^{-x^2} x^{2n}\,dx$

(q) $\displaystyle\int_0^\infty e^{-x^2} x^{2n+1}\,dx$

B EXERCISES

1. Let $\displaystyle\int_a^b f(x)\,dx$ be an absolutely convergent improper integral and ϕ be a bounded integrable function. Show that $\displaystyle\int_a^b f(x)\phi(x)\,dx$ converges absolutely.

2. Prove that $\displaystyle\int_0^\infty \cos x^2\,dx$ and $\displaystyle\int_0^\infty \sin x^2\,dx$ converge. (*Hint:* Make the substitution $y = x^2$.)

3. We saw that for $\displaystyle\int_a^\infty f(x)\,dx$ to exist it was not necessary for $\displaystyle\lim_{x\to\infty} f(x) = 0$. Show, however, that for any positive constant c

$$\lim_{y\to\infty} \int_y^{y+c} f(x)\,dx = 0.$$

Need c be constant?

4. Evaluate $\displaystyle\int_0^{\pi/2} \log \sin x\,dx$. (*Hint:* Use the identity $\sin 2x = 2 \sin x \cos x$.)

5. Show that $\displaystyle\int_0^\infty \frac{\sin^2 x}{x^2}\,dx = \int_0^\infty \frac{\sin x}{x}\,dx$.

C EXERCISE

1. Show that $f(x) = \displaystyle\int_x^1 \frac{\cos t}{t}\,dt$ diverges logarithmically as $x \to 0$. In particular, show that $\displaystyle\lim_{x\to 0+} [-\log x - f(x)] = a$ exists and that $23/96 < a < 1/4$.

17.2 IMPROPER INTEGRALS WITH NON-NEGATIVE INTEGRANDS

The following theorems about improper integrals are analogous to those on series given in Section 14.2. Since the proofs are quite similar for both cases, they are given here in somewhat abbreviated form.

17.2a   Theorem. Let b be a finite point or ∞ and f a non-negative function on I: $\{a \leqslant x < b\}$, integrable on $\{a \leqslant x \leqslant c\}$ for every c, $a < c < b$, with a singularity at b. Then $\displaystyle\int_a^b f(x)\,dx$ exists if, and only if, $\displaystyle\int_a^x f(t)\,dt$ is bounded for x in I.

Proof. This is so because $\displaystyle\int_a^x f(t)\,dt$ is non-decreasing. ∎

Here, as in all the theorems of this section, we assume that the singular point is at the upper limit of the integral, which may be finite or infinite.

You should realize, of course, that these tests apply equally well to integrals in which the singularity occurs at the lower limit.

17.2b   Theorem. Let f and g be non-negative functions on $I : \{a \leqslant x < b\}$, integrable on $\{a \leqslant x \leqslant c\}$ for every c, $a < c < b$. Suppose, further, that each has a singularity at b and that $f(x) \leqslant g(x)$ on I. Then

(i)   if $\displaystyle\int_a^b g(x)\,dx$ converges, so does $\displaystyle\int_a^b f(x)\,dx$;

(ii)   if $\displaystyle\int_a^b f(x)\,dx$ diverges, so does $\displaystyle\int_a^b g(x)\,dx$.

Proof. Both conclusions follow from $\displaystyle\int_a^x f(t)\,dt \leqslant \int_a^x g(t)\,dt$ and Theorem 17.2a. ∎

17.2c   Theorem. Let f and g be positive functions on $\{a \leqslant x < b\}$ and integrable on $\{a \leqslant x \leqslant c\}$ for every c between a and b, and suppose

$$0 < \lim_{x \to b} \frac{f(x)}{g(x)} < \infty.$$

Then either both $\displaystyle\int_a^b f(x)\,dx$ and $\displaystyle\int_a^b g(x)\,dx$ converge, or they both diverge.

Proof. Let $q = \displaystyle\lim_{x \to b} \frac{f(x)}{g(x)}$. Then there is an X such that

$$q/2 < \frac{f(x)}{g(x)} < 2q \qquad \text{if } X < x < b. \qquad \text{(Why?)}$$

Hence

$$\frac{q}{2} \int_c^d g(x)\,dx \leqslant \int_c^d f(x)\,dx \leqslant 2q \int_c^d g(x)\,dx \qquad \text{for } X < c < d < b.$$

By the Cauchy criterion, the theorem follows. ∎

A useful function to use for comparison is the power function given by $1/x^k$. By Exercises A1(*a*), (*b*), (*c*), and (*d*) of the last set of exercises we see that

$$\int_a^\infty \frac{dx}{x^k} \quad \text{for} \quad a > 0 \quad \text{converges if, and only if,} \quad k > 1$$

and

$$\int_0^a \frac{dx}{x^k} \quad \text{for} \quad a > 0 \quad \text{converges if, and only if,} \quad k < 1.$$

By the same arguments,

$$\int_a^\infty \frac{dx}{(x - x_0)^k} \quad \text{for} \quad a > x_0 \quad \text{converges if, and only if,} \quad k > 1$$

and

$$\int_{x_0}^a \frac{dx}{(x - x_0)^k} \quad \text{for} \quad a > x_0 \quad \text{converges if, and only if,} \quad k < 1.$$

EXAMPLE 1. Test $\displaystyle\int_0^1 \frac{dy}{\sqrt{1 - y^2}}$ (see Section 5.3).

Solution. The singularity is at $y = 1$. Now

$$\frac{1}{\sqrt{1 - y^2}} = \frac{1}{\sqrt{(1 - y)(1 + y)}} < \frac{1}{\sqrt{1 - y}} = \frac{1}{(1 - y)^{1/2}}$$

Thus the integral converges by the comparison test.

EXAMPLE 2. Test $\displaystyle\int_0^\infty e^{-t} t^\alpha \sin t \, dt$ for absolute convergence if $\alpha \geq 0$.

Solution. Now $|e^{-t} t^\alpha \sin t| \leq e^{-t} t^\alpha = e^{-t/2} e^{-t/2} t^\alpha$.

We see that $e^{-t/2} t^\alpha$ is bounded for $t \geq 0$, since it is 0 at $t = 0$, small for large t, and continuous in between. In fact, we can compute the maximum value by the methods of Section 7.4.

Let M be that maximum. Then

$$|e^{-t} t^\alpha \sin t| \leq M e^{-t/2},$$

and $M e^{-t/2}$ is integrable. That is, $\displaystyle\int_0^\infty M e^{-t/2} \, dt$ converges (and equals $2M$ in fact), so that by the comparison test

$$\int_0^\infty e^{-t} t^\alpha \sin t \, dt$$

converges absolutely, and hence converges.

EXAMPLE 3. Prove that $\displaystyle\int_0^\infty \frac{\sin x}{x} \, dx$ does not converge absolutely.

Solution. In $\{[k + (1/6)]\pi \leq x \leq [k + (5/6)]\pi\}$ we have

$$\left| \frac{\sin x}{x} \right| > \frac{1}{2x} > \frac{1}{2(k + 1)\pi} .$$

So

$$\int_{k\pi}^{(k+1)\pi} \left| \frac{\sin x}{x} \right| dx \geq \int_{k\pi + \pi/6}^{k\pi + 5\pi/6} \left| \frac{\sin x}{x} \right| dx \geq \frac{1}{2\pi(k + 1)} \cdot \frac{2\pi}{3} = \frac{1}{3(k + 1)} .$$

Summing from $k = 0$ to $n - 1$, we get

$$\int_0^{n\pi} \left| \frac{\sin x}{x} \right| dx \geqslant \frac{1}{3} \sum_0^{n-1} \frac{1}{k+1} = \frac{1}{3} \sum_1^n \frac{1}{k} \to +\infty \qquad \text{as } n \to \infty.$$

17.3 THE CAUCHY PRINCIPAL VALUE

We have pointed out that for an integral with a singularity at an interior point c of $\{a < x < b\}$ to be admitted as a convergent improper integral, both improper integrals $\int_a^c f(x)\, dx$ and $\int_c^b f(x)\, dx$ must exist. The sum of these is defined as the value of the improper integral from a to b:

$$\int_a^b f(x)\, dx = \int_a^c f(x)\, dx + \int_c^b f(x)\, dx.$$

There are circumstances when it is possible to define a value for the integral on the left when neither of the ones on the right exists. The idea is that certain $+\infty$'s cancel with certain $-\infty$'s to leave a finite sum. The precise definition follows.

Let f be defined on $\{a \leqslant x \leqslant b\}$, except possibly at an interior point c, which is a singular point of f. If $\int_a^b f(x)\, dx$ does not exist, but

$$\lim_{\epsilon \to 0} \left[\int_a^{c-\epsilon} f(x)\, dx + \int_{c+\epsilon}^b f(x)\, dx \right]$$

does exist, we call this the **Cauchy principal value** of $\int_a^b f(x)\, dx$ and write it as

$$P_c \int_a^b f(x)\, dx = \lim_{\epsilon \to 0} \left[\int_a^{c-\epsilon} f(x)\, dx + \int_{c+\epsilon}^b f(x)\, dx \right].$$

Do not interpret the P_c as a numerical factor. It is a red flag, warning us that we are not dealing with a proper integral nor even with an ordinary or garden-variety improper one. By putting the P_c in front of the integral, we call attention to the fact that it is a principal value. The c gives the location of the bad or singular point.

EXAMPLE. Compute $P_0 \int_{-1}^2 \frac{dx}{x}$.

Solution. Clearly $\int_{-1}^0 \frac{dx}{x}$ and $\int_0^2 \frac{dx}{x}$ both diverge, the one to $-\infty$ and the other to $+\infty$, so that the integral $\displaystyle\int_{-1}^{2}\frac{dx}{x}$ does not exist as an ordinary improper integral. However,

$$\int_{-1}^{-\epsilon}\frac{dx}{x}+\int_{\epsilon}^{2}\frac{dx}{x}=\int_{1}^{2}\frac{dx}{x}=\log 2.$$

Thus

$$P_0\int_{-1}^{2}\frac{dx}{x}=\log 2.$$

17.4   AN ALTERNATION TEST

The following test is a generalization of the idea we used earlier in the chapter when we examined $\displaystyle\int_{0}^{\infty}\frac{\sin x}{x}\,dx$. The proof is quite similar to the arguments used in the example.

17.4a   Theorem. Let f be a function defined for $\{x \geqslant a\}$ and properly integrable on $\{a \leqslant x \leqslant b\}$ for every $b > a$. Suppose there is a sequence of numbers $\{a_n\}$ with the properties $a_0 = a$, $a_{n+1} > a_n$, $a_n \to +\infty$, so that

(i) $f(x)$ has constant sign in each interval $\{a_n \leqslant x \leqslant a_{n+1}\}$,

(ii) $f(x)$ changes sign from $\{a_{n-1} \leqslant x \leqslant a_n\}$ to $\{a_n \leqslant x \leqslant a_{n+1}\}$,

(iii) $\left| \displaystyle\int_{a_{n-1}}^{a_n} f(x)\,dx \right| \geqslant \left| \displaystyle\int_{a_n}^{a_{n+1}} f(x)\,dx \right|$,

(iv) $\displaystyle\int_{a_{n-1}}^{a_n} f(x)\,dx \to 0$ as $n \to \infty$.

Then $\displaystyle\int_{a}^{\infty} f(x)\,dx$ converges.

Proof. Let $c_n = \displaystyle\int_{a_{n-1}}^{a_n} f(x)\,dx$. Then $\displaystyle\sum_{1}^{\infty} c_n$ converges, by the alternating series test. And given any $b > a$, there is an n for which $b = a_n \pm r_n$, where $0 \leqslant r_n < (a_{n+1} - a_n)$. Then

$$\int_{a}^{b} f(x)\,dx = \sum_{1}^{n} c_k + \int_{a_n}^{r_n} f(x)\,dx.$$

Now

$$\left| \int_{a_n}^{r_n} f(x)\,dx \right| \leqslant \left| \int_{a_n}^{a_{n+1}} f(x)\,dx \right| \to 0 \qquad \text{as } n \to \infty. \qquad \blacksquare$$

Explain carefully the inequality in the previous line.

There are other more delicate tests similar to Abel's and Dirichlet's tests for series. These will be discussed in the next chapter. Certain other tests will be explored in the problems.

A EXERCISES

I. Test the following integrals for convergence.

(a) $\displaystyle\int_0^\infty \cos x^3\, dx$

(b) $\displaystyle\int_0^\infty \sin x^\alpha\, dx,\ \alpha \geqslant 1.$

(c) $\displaystyle\int_0^\infty t^{-t}\, dt$

(d) $\displaystyle\int_{7532}^\infty \frac{e^{1/x}}{1 + x^2}\sin x\, dx$

(e) $\displaystyle\int_{351}^\infty \frac{1}{t^{1/2}}\sin\frac{1}{t}\, dt$

(f) $\displaystyle\int_e^\infty \frac{1}{t^{1/2}}\cos\frac{1}{t}\, dt$

(g) $\displaystyle\int_0^{15} \frac{1}{t^{3/2}}\sin\frac{1}{t}\, dt$

(h) $\displaystyle\int_0^\infty \frac{dx}{\sqrt{1 + x^3}}$

(i) $\displaystyle\int_0^\infty \frac{dx}{\sqrt{1 + x^2}}$

(j) $\displaystyle\int_0^1 \log x\, dx$

(k) $\displaystyle\int_1^\infty \frac{dx}{x(\log x)^p}$

(l) $\displaystyle\int_1^\infty \frac{(\log x)^{365}}{x^{35/34}}\, dx$

(m) $\displaystyle\int_0^\infty e^{\cos x}\frac{dx}{x}$

(n) $\displaystyle\int_0^1 \frac{x^{\alpha-1}}{\sqrt{1 - x}}\, dx,\ \alpha > 0$

(o) $\displaystyle\int_0^1 \frac{\log(1 - x)}{x^{3/2}}\, dx$

(p) $\displaystyle\int_0^{1/75} \frac{x - \sin x}{x^{5/2}}\cot x\, dx$

(q) $\displaystyle\int_0^\infty \frac{1}{x^{95}}e^{-1/x}\, dx$

(r) $\displaystyle\int_0^\pi \frac{x}{\sin x}\, dx$

2. Test the following principal value integrals for existence.

(a) $\displaystyle P_0\int_{-1}^{75} \frac{dx}{x^2}$

(b) $\displaystyle P_0\int_{-1}^1 \frac{dx}{x^3}$

(c) $\displaystyle P_0\int_{-1}^1 \frac{\operatorname{sgn} x}{x}\, dx$

B EXERCISES

I. Show that the integrals in Exercises $A1(a)$ and (b) are not absolutely convergent.

2. Test $\displaystyle\int_0^{\pi/2} \frac{d\theta}{\sqrt{1 - \sin^2\theta}}$ for convergence.

3. Let f be a non-negative function defined in $\{x \geqslant a\}$ and integrable on $\{a \leqslant x \leqslant b\}$ for every $b > a$. Show that if there is an $r < 1$ and an $X \geqslant a$ for which $[f(x)]^{1/x} \leqslant r$ for all $x \geqslant X$, then $\displaystyle\int_a^\infty f(x)\, dx$ converges.

4. Let f be a positive continuous function in $\{x \geqslant a\}$. Show that $\displaystyle\int_a^\infty f(x)\, dx$ converges if $\displaystyle\lim_{x\to\infty} \frac{f(x + 1)}{f(x)} < 1.$

5. Let f and g be two differentiable functions defined on $\{a \leqslant x < b\}$, where as usual b can be either finite or infinite. Let f' and g' be integrable on $\{a \leqslant x \leqslant c\}$ for every c between a and b. Show that if $\displaystyle\int_a^b f(x)g'(x)\,dx$ is a convergent improper integral and $\displaystyle\lim_{x \to b} f(x)g(x)$ exists, then $\displaystyle\int_a^b f'(x)g(x)\,dx$ exists either as a proper integral or a convergent improper one, and

$$\int_a^b f(x)g'(x)\,dx = \lim_{x \to b} f(x)g(x) - f(a)g(a) - \int_a^b f'(x)g(x)\,dx.$$

C EXERCISES

1. Let f and g be defined on $I: \{a \leqslant x < b\}$, where b is finite or infinite, and let $\displaystyle\int_a^b f^2(x)\,dx$ and $\displaystyle\int_a^b g^2(x)\,dx$ exist as proper integrals or as convergent improper integrals. Show that:

(a) $\displaystyle\int_a^b f(x)g(x)\,dx$ and $\displaystyle\int_a^b [f(x) + g(x)]^2\,dx$

exist as proper or convergent improper integrals.

(b) $\left| \displaystyle\int_a^b f(x)g(x)\,dx \right| \leqslant \tfrac{1}{2}\displaystyle\int_a^b f^2(x)\,dx + \tfrac{1}{2}\displaystyle\int_a^b g^2(x)\,dx$

(c) $\left(\displaystyle\int_a^b f(x)g(x)\,dx \right)^2 \leqslant \left(\displaystyle\int_a^b f^2(x)\,dx \right)\left(\displaystyle\int_a^b g^2(x)\,dx \right)$

(d) $\left[\displaystyle\int_a^b [f(x) + g(x)]^2\,dx \right]^{1/2} \leqslant \left[\displaystyle\int_a^b f^2(x)\,dx \right]^{1/2} + \left[\displaystyle\int_a^b g^2(x)\,dx \right]^{1/2}$

2. Let a and b be finite points, and let $\displaystyle\int_a^b f(x)\,dx$ be absolutely convergent. Then $\displaystyle\int_a^b |f(x)|^{1/2}\,dx$ converges and

$$\int_a^b |f(x)|^{1/2}\,dx \leqslant \sqrt{b - a}\,\sqrt{\int_a^b |f|\,dx}.$$

3. State and prove an alternation theorem similar to 17.4a for the case of a finite singular point.

17.5 IMPROPER MULTIPLE INTEGRALS

As in the case of single integrals, the definition of multiple integrals requires that both the function f and the domain of f be bounded. We can extend the definition by relaxing either or both of these restrictions. Again the extensions will be called improper integrals when they exist.

Because of the varied circumstances under which a multiple integral may be improper, we will not attempt an exhaustive study of these situations. It is better to wait with this until you come to the Lebesgue theory of integration. The distinctions necessitated by the different types of singularities are all absorbed in the general theory of the Lebesgue integral. We will content ourselves here with a discussion of two cases, namely a single singularity at a finite point and an infinite domain of integration. Also, we will work only in two dimensions, although clearly an analogous treatment is possible for the higher dimensions.

Before beginning our definitions, we recall a bit of nomenclature which we will use again. A region is an open-connected set. A closed region is a region together with its boundary. The diameter d of a set S is given by

$$d = \sup |P - Q|,$$

where P and Q are points in S. A bounded set is quadrable if it has an area.

Let f be bounded and continuous in a bounded quadrable region R, except at a point P_0, where it becomes unbounded. Let R' be a bounded quadrable region containing P_0 in its interior. Let R'' be the set consisting of those points of R which are not in R'. Then R'' is quadrable (why?) and f is integrable on R''. Let d be the diameter of R'.

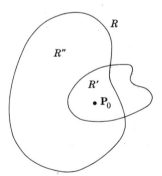

If $\displaystyle \lim_{d \to 0} \iint_{R''} f(P) \, dA = J$ exists, then we say that f is **improperly integrable** over R. The value of the **improper integral** is J. We use the same symbol to represent an improper integral that is used for a proper one:

$$J = \iint_{R} f(P) \, dA.$$

The precise meaning of the limit involved in the definition is that, for each $\epsilon > 0$, there is a $\delta(\epsilon)$ for which $\left| \int\!\!\int_{R''} f(\mathbf{P})\, dA - J \right| < \epsilon$ for all R'''s for which $d < \delta$.

Absolute and conditional convergence are defined as before. There is a Cauchy criterion for this type of limit, and we deduce that any absolutely convergent integral of the type defined above is convergent. We have also the same comparison tests as in the case of integrals of one variable. Instead of exploring these things in detail, we content ourselves with proving one theorem, basically a comparison theorem. It is the most used theorem for dealing with integrals of the type defined above. We assume the Cauchy criterion.

17.5a   Theorem. Let f be a function continuous in a bounded quadrable region R except at $\mathbf{P}_0$, where it becomes unbounded. Suppose f satisfies an inequality of the form

$$|f(\mathbf{P})| \leqslant \frac{C}{|\mathbf{P} - \mathbf{P}_0|^\alpha} \qquad \mathbf{P} \text{ in } R,$$

where $\alpha < 2$. (In general, $\alpha < n =$ dimension of the space.) Then $\int\!\!\int_R f(\mathbf{P})\, dA$ converges absolutely in R.

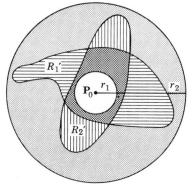

Proof. Let R_1' and R_2' be two bounded open regions, both containing $\mathbf{P}_0$. Then R_1'' and R_2'' are respectively the points of R not in R_1' and R_2'. Let D be the sets of those points of R_1' not in R_2', together with those points of R_2' not in R_1'. Then

$$\left| \int\!\!\int_{R_1''} f(\mathbf{P})\, dA - \int\!\!\int_{R_2''} f(\mathbf{P})\, dA \right| \leqslant \int\!\!\int_D |f(\mathbf{P})|\, dA \leqslant \int\!\!\int_D \frac{C\, dA}{|\mathbf{P} - \mathbf{P}_0|^\alpha}.$$

Now since R_1' and R_2' are open, there are two circles with radius r_1 and r_2 such that D is contained in the ring $\{r_1 < |\mathbf{P} - \mathbf{P}_0| < r_2\}$. This last integral is then bounded by $\displaystyle\int\int_{r_1\leqslant|\mathbf{P}-\mathbf{P}_0|\leqslant r_2} \frac{C\,dA}{|\mathbf{P}-\mathbf{P}_0|^\alpha}$. If we introduce

polar coordinates centered at $\mathbf{P}_0$, then $|\mathbf{P}-\mathbf{P}_0| = r$, and the last integral becomes

$$\int_{r_1}^{r_2}\int_0^{2\pi} Cr^{-\alpha}r\,dr\,d\theta = \frac{2\pi Cr^{2-\alpha}}{2-\alpha}\bigg|_{r_1}^{r_2} = \frac{2\pi C}{2-\alpha}[r_2^{2-\alpha} - r_1^{2-\alpha}] \leqslant \frac{2\pi C}{2-\alpha}r_2^{2-\alpha}.$$

But $\alpha < 2$. Hence this difference can be made as small as we please by making r_2 small—that is, by making the diameters of R_1' and R_2' small. Thus by the Cauchy criterion the limit exists and the integral converges. ∎

A similar definition and theorem holds for integrals with unbounded domains of integration. Let R be an unbounded region with the property that, if R' is any quadrable region, then the common part R'' of R and R' is also quadrable. Let f be continuous and bounded in R. Let the **inner radius** r of a set R' be the radius of the largest circle centered at the origin which is contained in the set. We then say that $J = \displaystyle\int\int_R f(\mathbf{P})\,dA$

exists if $\displaystyle\lim_{r\to\infty}\int\int_{R''} f(\mathbf{P})\,dA = J$, where the precise meaning of the limit is that for each $\epsilon > 0$ there is an r_0 such that

$$\left|\int\int_{R''} f(\mathbf{P})\,dA - J\right| < \epsilon \qquad \text{if } r > r_0.$$

The theorem is then as follows.

17.5b **Theorem.** Let R and f be as described above. If there are three constants $r_1 > 0$, $C > 0$, and $\alpha > 2$, such that

$$|f(\mathbf{P})| \leqslant C/|\mathbf{P}|^\alpha \qquad \text{if } |\mathbf{P}| > r_1,$$

then $\displaystyle\int\int_R f(\mathbf{P})\,dA$ exists.

Proof. The proof is similar to the previous one and is left as an exercise (B1). ∎

A EXERCISES

I. Let $\mathbf{P}$ have rectangular coordinates (x, y) and polar coordinates (r, θ), and let R be the set $\{|\mathbf{P}| \leqslant 1\}$. Test for convergence:

(a) $\displaystyle\int\int_R \log\frac{1}{r}\,dA$

(b) $\displaystyle\int\int_R \frac{x^2 y}{r^4}\,dA$

(c) $\displaystyle\int\int_R \frac{\cos\theta}{r}\,dA$

(d) $\displaystyle\int\int_R \frac{x^2 + y^4}{r^{5/2}}\,dA$

2. Let R be the set $\{|\mathbf{P}| \geqslant 1\}$. Test for convergence:

(a) $\displaystyle\iint\limits_R \frac{x^2 y}{r^8}\, dA$

(b) $\displaystyle\iint\limits_R \frac{x^2 + y^4}{r^3}\, dA$

(c) $\displaystyle\iint\limits_R \frac{x^2 + y^4}{r^{9/2}}\, dA$

(d) $\displaystyle\iint\limits_R \frac{x^2 y^4 z^4}{r^{13}}\, dA$

B EXERCISES

1. Prove Theorem 17.5b.

2. In the case of triple integrals, show that Theorem 17.5a remains true if $\alpha < 2$ is replaced by $\alpha < 3$, and that Theorem 17.5b remains true if $\alpha > 2$ is replaced by $\alpha > 3$.

C EXERCISES

1. Let D be a standard region in E_3 (see Chapter 13), S its boundary, and D' the exterior of S. Let $\mathbf{F}$ be continuously differentiable in D', and suppose $|\mathbf{P}|^2|\mathbf{F}| \to 0$ uniformly as $|\mathbf{P}| \to \infty$. Show that the divergence theorem holds for $\mathbf{F}$ in D':

$$\iiint\limits_{D'} \nabla \cdot \mathbf{F}\, dV = \iint\limits_S \mathbf{F} \cdot \mathbf{n}\, d\sigma,$$

where $\mathbf{n}$ is the interior normal of D.

2. Let D be a standard region in E_3, and let $\mathbf{F}$ be continuously differentiable in D except at one point $\mathbf{P}_0$ in the interior, where $\mathbf{F}$ may become unbounded. If $|\mathbf{F}|\, |\mathbf{P} - \mathbf{P}_0|^2 \to 0$ uniformly as $\mathbf{P} \to \mathbf{P}_0$, show that the divergence theorem holds for $\mathbf{F}$ in D.

3. Let R be a bounded quadrable region in E_2 and $\mathbf{Q} = (\alpha, \beta)$. Define f in R by

$$f(\mathbf{Q}) = \iint\limits_R \log\left(1/|\mathbf{P} - \mathbf{Q}|\right) dA_{\mathbf{P}}.$$ Show that f has both partials in R and

that they can be computed by differentiation under the integral sign, for example,

$$\frac{\partial f}{\partial \alpha}(\mathbf{Q}) = \iint\limits_R [(x - \alpha)/|\mathbf{P} - \mathbf{Q}|^2]\, dA_{\mathbf{P}}.$$

(*Hint:* Show that the second integral converges and that the difference quotient $\Delta f/\Delta\alpha$ tends to it as $\Delta\alpha \to 0$.)

18

Integral Representations
of Functions

18.1 INTRODUCTION. PROPER INTEGRALS

As we pointed out at the beginning of Chapter 15, there are relatively few functions which can be expressed in simple terms. Many require rather esoteric expressions for their representations, such as integrals, or series of one kind or another. The class of functions we want to discuss in this chapter are those which may be represented by an integral depending on a parameter.

Let us suppose that F is defined on the rectangle R: $\{a \leqslant x \leqslant b; \; \alpha \leqslant y \leqslant \beta\}$, and that for each x, F is an integrable function of y. Then the integral $\int_\alpha^\beta F(x, y)\, dy$ defines a function of x in $\{a \leqslant x \leqslant b\}$. If we denote this function by f, its values are then given by

$$f(x) = \int_\alpha^\beta F(x, y)\, dy \qquad \{a \leqslant x \leqslant b\}.$$

It is natural to inquire about the properties of f. Is it continuous? Differentiable? Integrable? The answers to these questions depend, of course, on the properties of F. A discussion of these problems will be the object of this chapter. First we will discuss proper integrals.

18.1a Theorem. Let F be a continuous function of (x, y) on the rectangle R: $\{a \leqslant x \leqslant b, \; \alpha \leqslant y \leqslant \beta\}$. Then f defined on I: $\{a \leqslant x \leqslant b\}$ by

$$f(x) = \int_\alpha^\beta F(x, y)\, dy$$

427

is continuous on I. It is therefore integrable on I, and

$$\int_a^b f(x)\,dx = \int_\alpha^\beta dy \int_a^b F(x, y)\,dx.$$

Proof. For x_1 and x_2 in I, we examine $f(x_1) - f(x_2)$. By Theorem 9.6d, F is uniformly continuous in the rectangle R. Thus for each $\epsilon > 0$ there is a $\delta(\epsilon)$ such that

$$|F(x_1, y) - F(x_2, y)| < \epsilon \qquad \text{if } |x_1 - x_2| < \delta.$$

Thus
$$|f(x_1) - f(x_2)| = \left| \int_\alpha^\beta [F(x_1, y) - F(x_2, y)]\,dy \right|$$

$$\leqslant \int_\alpha^\beta |F(x_1, y) - F(x_2, y|\,dy$$

$$\leqslant \epsilon(\beta - \alpha) \qquad \text{if } |x_1 - x_2| < \delta.$$

This proves the continuity. The second conclusion follows from Theorem 12.3a on the evaluation of a double integral as an iterated integral. ∎

The continuity of the integral as a function of x permits the interchange of limit and integration. We can see this as follows. Let x_0 be any point in I. Then the continuity of f is expressed as

$$\lim_{x \to x_0} f(x) = f(x_0).$$

In terms of the integral representation, this becomes

$$\lim_{x \to x_0} \int_\alpha^\beta F(x, y)\,dy = \int_\alpha^\beta F(x_0, y)\,dy.$$

And since F is continuous, this is equivalent to

$$\lim_{x \to x_0} \int_\alpha^\beta F(x, y)\,dy = \int_\alpha^\beta \lim_{x \to x_0} F(x, y)\,dy.$$

We now turn to the question of differentiability of a function f defined as in the last theorem. The result follows.

18.1b Theorem. Let $F(x, y)$ and $\dfrac{\partial F}{\partial x}(x, y)$ both be continuous in the rectangle R: $\{a \leqslant x \leqslant b,\ \alpha \leqslant y \leqslant \beta\}$. Then f, as given by

$$f(x) = \int_\alpha^\beta F(x, y)\,dy,$$

is differentiable in $I:\{a \leqslant x \leqslant b\}$ and furthermore the derivative may be computed by differentiation under the integral sign

$$f'(x) = \int_{\alpha}^{\beta} \frac{\partial F}{\partial x}(x, y)\, dy.$$

That is, $$\frac{d}{dx} \int_{\alpha}^{\beta} F(x, y)\, dy = \int_{\alpha}^{\beta} \frac{\partial F}{\partial x}(x, y)\, dy.$$

Proof. Let the function g be defined by

$$g(x) = \int_{\alpha}^{\beta} \frac{\partial}{\partial x} F(x, y)\, dy.$$

Then, by the previous theorem,

$$\int_{a}^{x} g(t)\, dt = \int_{\alpha}^{\beta} dy \int_{a}^{x} \frac{\partial}{\partial t} F(t, y)\, dt = \int_{\alpha}^{\beta} [F(x, y) - F(a, y)]\, dy$$

$$= \int_{\alpha}^{\beta} F(x, y)\, dy - \int_{\alpha}^{\beta} F(a, y)\, dy = f(x) - f(a).$$

Differentiating the two ends of this string of equalities, we get

$$g(x) = f'(x). \qquad \blacksquare$$

A EXERCISES

1. For any fixed positive a, let f be defined on

$$I:\{-a \leqslant x \leqslant a\} \text{ by } f(x) = \int_{0}^{1} e^{-xt}\, dt$$

(a) Show that f is continuous on I.

(b) Evaluate the integral to obtain an explicit formula for f. Does this formula define a continuous function at $x = 0$?

(c) Differentiate f by differentiating the integral. Evaluate the resulting integral and verify that you get the same result by differentiating the formula found in (b).

(d) Integrate f from 0 to a by integrating under the integral sign. Evaluate the inner integral. Is the resulting integrand continuous?

(e) Expand the integrand in a power series in (xt). Show that you can integrate termwise and that the resulting power series in x is the same as the one obtained directly from the formula in part (b).

2. Examine the functions defined on $\{-a \leqslant x \leqslant a\}$ by $\int_{0}^{1} \sin xt\, dt$ and $\int_{0}^{1} \cosh xt\, dt$, by means of the procedure used in Exercise 1.

3. Study the function f defined by $f(x) = \int_0^1 e^{-xt^2}\, dt$.

(a) For what values of x is f defined?

(b) Where is the function continuous?

(c) Compute $\int_0^x f(y)\, dy$ and $f'(x)$ by operating under the integral sign.

(d) Show that f is a strictly decreasing function of x.

(e) Is $f(x)$ large or small when x is large and > 0?

(f) Is $f(x)$ large or small when x is large and < 0?

4. Let $f(x) = \int_0^\pi \dfrac{dy}{(1 + x\cos y)^2}$.

(a) For what values of x is f defined?

(b) Compute $f'(x)$.

5. Use the result of Exercise B2 to calculate f' where f is given by

(a) $\displaystyle\int_0^x \tan(x - y)\, dy.$ (b) $\displaystyle\int_0^{x^2} \tan\frac{t}{x^2}\, dt.$

For what values of x is f defined in each case?

6. Verify that $y = \displaystyle\int_0^x \phi(t)\sin(x - t)\, dt$ is a solution of the problem

$$y'' + y = \phi(x) \qquad y(0) = 0,$$

if ϕ is continuous.

B EXERCISES

I. Let b be either a finite point or the symbol ∞. Suppose F is continuous in $R: \{a \leqslant x < b,\ \alpha \leqslant y \leqslant \beta\}$ and f is defined on $I: \{a \leqslant x < b\}$ by $f(x) = \displaystyle\int_\alpha^\beta F(x, y)\, dy$.

(a) Show that $f(x)$ is continuous in I.

(b) Show that $\displaystyle\int_a^x f(t)\, dt = \int_\alpha^\beta dy \int_a^x F(t, y)\, dt$ for x in I.

(c) If $\dfrac{\partial F}{\partial x}(x, y)$ is continuous in R, show that f is differentiable in I and that

$$f'(x) = \int_a^b (\partial F/\partial x)(x, y)\, dy.$$

(d) Give an example to show that $\lim_{x \to b} f(x)$ need not exist.

(e) Show that if b is finite, the additional requirement that F be uniformly continuous implies that $\lim_{x \to b} f(x)$ exists.

(f) Let $b = \infty$. Give an example to show that if F is uniformly continuous and bounded, $\lim_{x \to \infty} f(x)$ need not exist.

2. Let F be continuous in $R: \{a \leqslant x \leqslant b, \alpha \leqslant y \leqslant \beta\}$, and let $\dfrac{\partial F}{\partial x}$ also be continuous in R. Let u and v be differentiable functions of x defined on $I: \{a \leqslant x \leqslant b\}$ with values in $J: \{\alpha \leqslant y \leqslant \beta\}$—that is, $\alpha \leqslant u(x) \leqslant \beta$, $\alpha \leqslant v(x) \leqslant \beta$. Derive Leibnitz' rule

$$\frac{d}{dx} \int_{u(x)}^{v(x)} F(x, y)\, dy = \int_{u(x)}^{v(x)} \frac{\partial F}{\partial x}(x, y)\, dy + F[x, v(x)]v'(x) - F[x, u(x)]u'(x).$$

3. Show that if f is continuous in $I: \{a \leqslant x \leqslant b\}$, then

$$\int_a^x dx_2 \int_a^{x_2} f(x_1)\, dx_1 = \int_a^x f(t)(x - t)\, dt.$$

4. Show that if f is continuous in $I: \{a \leqslant x \leqslant b\}$, then

$$\int_a^x dx_n \cdots \int_a^{x_3} dx_2 \int_a^{x_2} f(x_1)\, dx_1$$

$$= \frac{1}{(n-1)!} \int_a^x f(t)(x - t)^{n-1}\, dt \qquad \text{for all } x\text{'s in } I.$$

18.2 UNIFORM CONVERGENCE

It is of course true that if $\displaystyle\int_a^b F(x, y)\, dy$ is an improper integral it still defines a function, assuming that it is convergent. Again, as in the previous section, we will be concerned with applying the operations of analysis to such a function. There are, however, certain difficulties inherent in the fact that the integral is an improper one. As in the case of infinite series depending on a parameter, we will overcome these difficulties with aid of the concept of uniform convergence. We now define uniform convergence for integrals.

Let F be defined in $R: \{a \leqslant x \leqslant b, \alpha \leqslant y < \beta\}$, where β is finite or $+\infty$; and suppose that for each x in $I: \{a \leqslant x \leqslant b\}$ the integral $\displaystyle\int_\alpha^\beta F(x, y)\, dy$ exists as a proper or improper integral. (It is entirely permissible, if β is finite, for the integral to be improper for certain values of x in I and proper for others.) If for each $\epsilon > 0$ there is a $Y(\epsilon)$, independent of x, for which $\left| \displaystyle\int_\eta^\beta F(x, y)\, dy \right| < \epsilon$ for every $\eta > Y(\epsilon)$, then we say that $\displaystyle\int_\alpha^\beta F(x, y)\, dy$ **converges uniformly** with respect to x in $\{a \leqslant x \leqslant b\}$.

There is an M test for the uniform convergence of such integrals.

18.2a   Theorem. Suppose F is defined in $R: \{a \leqslant x \leqslant b, \alpha \leqslant y < \beta\}$, where β may be finite or $+\infty$; and suppose that $\int_\alpha^\beta F(x, y)\, dy$ converges for each x in $I: \{a \leqslant x \leqslant b\}$. Suppose further that there is a function M on $\{\alpha \leqslant y < \beta\}$ for which $|F(x, y)| \leqslant M(y)$ and $\int_\alpha^\beta M(y)\, dy$ converges. Then $\int_\alpha^\beta F(x, y)\, dy$ converges uniformly for x in I.

Proof. Let $\epsilon > 0$ be given. Then there is a $Y(\epsilon)$ such that

$$0 \leqslant \int_\eta^\beta M(y)\, dy < \epsilon \qquad \text{if } \eta > Y(\epsilon). \qquad \text{(Why?)}$$

Then if $\eta > Y$,

$$\left| \int_\eta^\beta F(x, y)\, dy \right| \leqslant \int_\eta^\beta |F(x, y)|\, dy \leqslant \int_\eta^\beta M(y)\, dy < \epsilon, \qquad \blacksquare$$

Again we remind you that although this theorem is stated for the singularity at the upper limit, it applies equally well to integrals with the singularity at the lower limit.

EXAMPLE 1. $\displaystyle\int_0^\infty \frac{\sin xt}{1 + t^2}\, dt$ converges uniformly for all x's.

Solution:

$$\left| \frac{\sin xt}{1 + t^2} \right| \leqslant \frac{1}{1 + t^2} = M(t) \text{ and } \int_0^\infty M(t)\, dt \text{ converges.}$$

EXAMPLE 2.   For any c, $\displaystyle\int_0^i \frac{1}{\sqrt{1 - z}}\, e^{zv}\, dz$ converges uniformly with with respect to v in $\{v \leqslant c\}$.

Solution:

$$\left| \frac{1}{\sqrt{1 - z}}\, e^{zv} \right| < \frac{1}{\sqrt{1 - z}}\, e^{|c|} = M(z)$$

and $\displaystyle\int_0^1 M(z)\, dz$ converges.

We also need the concept of the uniform convergence of a function depending on a parameter. Let F be a function defined on $R: \{a \leqslant x < b, \alpha \leqslant y \leqslant \beta\}$, where b may be finite or infinite. We can look upon F as defining a function of y for each x, the variable x playing the role of a parameter. We can then inquire as to the convergence of F as $x \to b$. If there is a function ϕ defined in $\{\alpha \leqslant y \leqslant \beta\}$ such that for each such y we have $F(x, y) \to \phi(y)$ as $x \to b$, we say that F converges **pointwise** to

ϕ as $x \to b$. This means that for each ϵ and each y there is a $X(\epsilon, y)$ for which

$$|F(x, y) - \phi(y)| < \epsilon \qquad \text{if } X < x < b.$$

If X can be chosen so as to be independent of y, although it may depend on the interval $\{\alpha \leqslant y \leqslant \beta\}$, we say that F **tends uniformly** to ϕ as $x \to b$. The term "uniform" refers of course to the fact that the same X works for all y's in the interval.

In such convergence we are primarily concerned with the case where b is infinite. If b is finite, we can define $F(b, y) = \phi(y)$; and F then becomes continuous in the closed rectangle, $\{a \leqslant x \leqslant b, \alpha \leqslant y \leqslant \beta\}$. This point is discussed in the exercises. (See Exercise B2 in Section 18.3.)

EXAMPLE 3.   Let $F(x, y) = e^y(1 + e^{-x}) + \sin y + \dfrac{1}{x} \cos y$ in $\{x > 0,$ $0 \leqslant y \leqslant 1\}$. Investigate the convergence of F as $x \to \infty$.

Solution. Since $e^{-x} \to 0$ and $\dfrac{1}{x} \to 0$ as $x \to \infty$, we are led to consider $\phi(y) = e^y + \sin y$. Then

$$|F(x, y) - \phi(y)| = \left| e^{y-x} + \frac{1}{x} \cos y \right| \leqslant e \cdot e^{-x} + \frac{1}{x}.$$

This last expression is independent of y, and it clearly $\to 0$ as $x \to \infty$. Hence F tends uniformly to ϕ.

The M test, while very useful, suffers from the same drawback in its integral setting as in its application to series, namely its demand for absolute as well as uniform convergence. Hence more delicate tests are desirable. Analogues of the Dirichlet and Abel tests can be proved for integrals. The critical point in the proof is integration by parts which is the analogue of Abel's identity. However, in many instances it is as easy to prove uniform convergence directly as it is to verify the hypotheses of the one or the other theorems. The following example will illustrate the method.

EXAMPLE 4.   Show that $\displaystyle\int_0^\infty e^{-xt} \frac{\sin t}{t} \, dt$ converges uniformly in $\{x > 0\}$.

Solution. We integrate by parts, integrating $\sin t$ and differentiating e^{-xt}/t. For $x > 0$, we get

$$\int_\tau^\infty e^{-xt} \frac{\sin t}{t} \, dt = \frac{e^{-x\tau} \cos \tau}{\tau} - \int_\tau^\infty \frac{(1 + xt)e^{-xt} \cos t \, dt}{t^2}.$$

Now $|(1 + xt)e^{-xt} \cos t| \leqslant e^{xt} \cdot e^{-xt} |\cos t| \leqslant 1,$

so that

$$\left| \int_\tau^\infty e^{-xt} \frac{\sin t}{t} \, dt \right| \leqslant \frac{1}{\tau} + \int_\tau^\infty \frac{dt}{t^2} = \frac{2}{\tau}.$$

Thus

$$\left| \int_{\tau}^{\infty} e^{-xt} \frac{\sin t}{t} \, dt \right| < \epsilon \qquad \text{if } \tau > \frac{2}{\epsilon}. \qquad \blacksquare$$

We state the Cauchy criterion on which the proofs of the Abel and Dirichlet theorems are based.

18.2b   Theorem. Let F be continuous in $\{a \leqslant x \leqslant b, \ \alpha \leqslant y < \beta\}$, where β may be finite or infinite. In order that $\int_{\alpha}^{\beta} F(x, y) \, dy$ converge uniformly in $I : \{a \leqslant x \leqslant b\}$, it is necessary and sufficient that for each $\epsilon > 0$ there be a $Y(\epsilon)$ independent of x, in I, for which

$$\left| \int_{y_1}^{y_2} F(x, y) \, dy \right| < \epsilon \qquad \text{if } Y < y_1 < y_2 < \beta.$$

Proof. Sufficiency. For each fixed x, the ϵ condition is merely the statement of the Cauchy criterion for the convergence of the integral. Hence the integral converges for each x. Keeping y_1 fixed and letting $y_2 \to \beta$, we then get

$$\left| \int_{y_1}^{\beta} F(x, y) \, dy \right| \leqslant \epsilon \qquad \text{if } Y < y_1 < \beta.$$

Necessity. See Exercise B5. $\blacksquare$

The **modified Abel's test** is given by the following theorem.

18.2c   Theorem. Let u, v, and $\partial v / \partial y$ be continuous in $\{a \leqslant x \leqslant b, \ \alpha \leqslant y < \beta\}$, where β may be finite or infinite. Suppose also that
(i)   there is a constant M for which

$$\left| \int_{\alpha}^{\tau} u(x, y) \, dy \right| \leqslant M \qquad \text{in } \{\alpha \leqslant \tau < \beta, a \leqslant x \leqslant b\},$$

(ii) $\int_{\alpha}^{\beta} \left| \frac{\partial v}{\partial y} (x, y) \right| dy$ converges uniformly in $\{a \leqslant x \leqslant b\}$,

(iii) $v(x, t)$ converges uniformly to zero as $y \to \beta$.

Then $\int_{\alpha}^{\beta} u(x, y) \, v(x, y) \, dy$ converges uniformly for x in $\{a \leqslant x \leqslant b\}$.

Proof. Set

$$\phi(x, \tau) = \int_{\alpha}^{\tau} u(x, y) \, dy.$$

By hypothesis (i), $\phi(x, \tau)$ is bounded in $\{a \leqslant x \leqslant b, \alpha \leqslant \tau < \beta\}$. Integrating by parts, we get

$$\int_{y_1}^{y_2} u(x, y)v(x, y)\, dy = \phi(x, y_2)v(x, y_2) - \phi(x, y_1)v(x, y_1)$$
$$- \int_{y_1}^{y_2} \phi(x, y) \frac{\partial}{\partial y} v(x, y)\, dy.$$

From here on, the proof is similar to that for series: use the boundedness of ϕ and the smallness of v and $\int_{y_1}^{y_2} \left| \dfrac{\partial v}{dy} \right| dy$. The details are left as an exercise. ∎

The next theorem gives the **modified Dirichlet test**.

18.2d   Theorem. Let u, v and $\partial v/\partial y$ be continuous in $\{a \leqslant x \leqslant b, \alpha \leqslant y < \beta\}$, where β may be finite or infinite. Suppose also that

(i) $\displaystyle\int_\alpha^\beta u(x, y)\, dy$ converges uniformly in $\{a \leqslant x \leqslant b\}$,

(ii) there is a constant M for which $\displaystyle\int_\alpha^\beta \left| \frac{\partial y}{\partial y}(x, y) \right| dy \leqslant M$ in $\{a \leqslant x \leqslant b\}$.

(iii) $|v(x, \alpha)| \leqslant M$ in $\{a \leqslant x \leqslant b\}$.

Then $\displaystyle\int_\alpha^\beta u(x, y)v(x, y)\, dy$ converges uniformly in $\{a \leqslant x \leqslant b\}$.

Proof. The proof is left as an exercise (B4). Integrate by parts as in Theorem 18.2c, but replace ϕ by ψ, where ψ is defined by

$$\psi(x, \tau) = \int_\alpha^\tau u(x, y)\, dy - \int_\alpha^\beta u(x, y)\, dy = -\int_\tau^\beta u(x, y)\, dy. ∎$$

A   EXERCISES

I. Show that the following integrals converge uniformly in the stated intervals:

(a) $\displaystyle\int_0^\infty \frac{\cos xt}{t^2 + x^2}\, dt \qquad \{x \geqslant 1\}$

(b) $\displaystyle\int_0^\infty e^{-xt}(1 + t^3)\, dt \qquad \{x \geqslant a\}$, where $a > 0$.

(c) $\displaystyle\int_0^1 \log \frac{x}{t}\, dt \qquad \{a \leqslant x \leqslant b\}$, where $a > 0$, $b < +\infty$

(d) $\displaystyle\int_0^1 \frac{\sin t}{t^y}\, dt \qquad \{0 \leqslant y \leqslant 2 - a\}$, where $0 < a < 2$

(e) $\displaystyle\int_0^1 \frac{e^{-xy}\,dy}{\sqrt{y}(1+y)}$ $\{x \geqslant c\}$, where c is any constant

(f) $\displaystyle\int_0^\infty e^{-t(x+1)}\cos xt\,\frac{t}{t+x^2}\,dt$ $\{x \geqslant 0\}$

B EXERCISES

1. Show that the following limits are attained uniformly in the indicated intervals:

(a) $e^{-xy}\,\dfrac{1}{1+y} \to \dfrac{1}{1+y}$ as $x \to 0$ in $\{-\tfrac{1}{2} \leqslant y \leqslant 1\}$

(b) $t^2 e^{-xt}\cos xt \to 0$ as $x \to \infty$ in $\{t \geqslant 0\}$.

2. Test the following integrals for uniform convergence in the indicated interval:

(a) $\displaystyle\int_0^\infty \frac{\sin xt}{t}\,dt$ $\{x \geqslant c > 0\}$.

(b) $\displaystyle\int_0^\infty \frac{\cos y}{x+y}\,dy$ $\{x \geqslant c > 0\}$.

(c) $\displaystyle\int_0^\infty \frac{t\sin t}{x^2+t^2}\,dt$ $\{x \geqslant c > 0\}$.

(d) $\displaystyle\int_0^\infty x^{y-1}\sin x\,dx$ $\{-1 + \delta \leqslant y \leqslant 1 - \delta\}$, where $0 < \delta < 1$.

(e) $\displaystyle\int_{-\infty}^\infty \sin xy^2\,dy$ $\{x \geqslant 0\}$.

3. Let F be defined in $\{a \leqslant x < b,\ \alpha \leqslant y \leqslant \beta\}$, and let ϕ be defined in $\{\alpha \leqslant y \leqslant \beta\}$. State and prove the Cauchy criterion for the uniform convergence of F to ϕ as $x \to b$.

4. Show that the uniform convergence of an integral depending on a parameter is a special case of the uniform convergence of a function and that the Cauchy criterion for the convergence of integrals follows from Exercise 3 above.

5. Complete the proofs of Theorems 18.2b, c, and d.

6. Show that $e^{-t(x+1)}\cos xt\,\dfrac{t}{t+x^2} \to e^{-t}$ uniformly in $\{y \geqslant 0\}$ as $x \to 0$.

18.3 CONSEQUENCES OF UNIFORM CONVERGENCE

The main object of this section is to discuss the continuity, integrability, and differentiability of functions defined by improper integrals depending on a parameter. We first prove a preliminary theorem dealing with passing to the limit under the integral sign of proper integrals.

18.3a   Theorem. Let F be continuous in $\{x \geqslant a,\, \alpha \leqslant y \leqslant \beta\}$, and let f be defined in $I\colon \{x \geqslant a\}$ by

$$f(x) = \int_\alpha^\beta F(x, y)\, dy.$$

Suppose there is a function ϕ defined in $\{\alpha \leqslant y \leqslant \beta\}$ such that F tends uniformly to ϕ as $x \to \infty$. Then $\lim\limits_{x \to \infty} f(x)$ exists and

$$\lim_{x \to \infty} f(x) = \int_\alpha^\beta \phi(y)\, dy.$$

Proof. The integrability of ϕ is covered by Exercise B1. Consider:

$$\Delta = f(x) - \int_\alpha^\beta \phi(y)\, dy = \int_\alpha^\beta F(x, y)\, dy - \int_\alpha^\beta \phi(y)\, dy = \int_\alpha^\beta [F(x, y) - \phi(y)]\, dy.$$

By the uniform convergence, for each $\epsilon > 0$ there is an $X(\epsilon)$ such that $|F(x, y) - \phi(y)| < \epsilon$ if $x > X$. For such x's,

$$|\Delta| \leqslant \int_\alpha^\beta |F(x, y) - \phi(y)|\, dy < \epsilon \cdot (\beta - \alpha). \qquad \blacksquare$$

Actually we did not use the full power of continuity here. We used it to deduce the integrability of ϕ via Exercise B1. However, it should be clear that what we really used was the integrability of F and ϕ, and the uniform convergence of F to ϕ.

We now turn to the study of improper integrals.

18.3b   Theorem. Let F be continuous in $R\colon \{a \leqslant x \leqslant b,\, \alpha \leqslant y < \beta\}$, where β may be finite or infinite; but we assume that β is a singular point for F. And suppose that f is defined in $I\colon \{a \leqslant x \leqslant b\}$ by

$$f(x) = \int_\alpha^\beta F(x, y)\, dy,$$

where the integral is uniformly convergent. Then f is continuous in I and

$$\int_a^b f(x)\, dx = \int_\alpha^\beta dy \int_a^b F(x, y)\, dx.$$

Proof. Let x_1 and x_2 be any two points in I, and let $\epsilon > 0$ be given. There is then a $Y(\epsilon)$ such that

$$\left| \int_\eta^\beta F(x, y)\, dy \right| < \epsilon \qquad \text{for } Y < \eta < \beta$$

for all x's in I. (Why?) Choose such an η and keep it fixed. Then in the closed bounded rectangle $R:\{a \leqslant x \leqslant b, \alpha \leqslant y \leqslant \eta\}$, the function F is uniformly continuous. Thus there is a $\delta(\epsilon)$ such that

$$|F(x_1, y) - F(x_2, y)| < \frac{\epsilon}{\eta - \alpha} \qquad \text{if } |x_1 - x_2| < \delta.$$

We then have

$$|f(x_1) - f(x_2)| = \left| \int_\alpha^\beta [F(x_1, y) - F(x_2, y)] \, dy \right|$$

$$\leqslant \int_\alpha^\eta |F(x_1, y) - F(x_2, y)| \, dy + \left| \int_\eta^\beta F(x_1, y) \, dy \right| + \left| \int_\eta^\beta F(x_2, y) \, dy \right|$$

$$\leqslant \epsilon + \epsilon + \epsilon = 3\epsilon \qquad \text{if } |x_1 - x_2| < \delta.$$

This proves the continuity. By the same argument as in Theorem 18.1a, this implies that we can interchange limit and integration.

Since f is continuous, it is certainly integrable, so that

$$J_1 = \int_a^b f(x) \, dx = \int_a^b \int_\alpha^\beta F(x, y) \, dy \, dx$$

exists. We need only show that

$$J_2 = \int_\alpha^\beta dy \int_a^b F(x, y) \, dx$$

exists and equals J_1.

Now if J_2 exists, it is defined by

$$J_2 = \lim_{\eta \to \beta} \int_\alpha^\eta dy \int_a^b F(x, y) \, dx.$$

β infinite β finite

Let us therefore consider the difference Δ given by

$$\Delta = J_1 - \int_\alpha^\eta dy \int_a^b F(x, y) \, dx.$$

The integral tends to J_2 as $\eta \to \beta$, if J_2 exists. Hence if we can show that $\Delta \to 0$ as $\eta \to \beta$, we will have shown that J_2 exists and equals J_1, which is our aim. Now we can interchange the order in this proper integral so as to write

$$\Delta = J_1 - \int_a^b dx \int_\alpha^\eta F(x, y) \, dy.$$

Thus

$$\Delta = \int_a^b dx \int_\eta^\beta F(x, dy) \, dy.$$

Now as in the first part of the proof, if $\eta > Y$ we have

$$|\Delta| \leqslant \int_a^b \left| \int_\eta^\beta F(x, y)\, dy \right| dx < \int_a^b \epsilon\, dx = \epsilon(b - a).$$

Thus $\Delta \to 0$ as $\eta \to \beta$, as was required.   ∎

EXAMPLE 1. Show that $\int_0^1 t^{-\frac{1}{2}} e^{-xt}\, dt$ converges uniformly on any bounded closed interval $I: \{a \leqslant x \leqslant b\}$.

Solution. Let $m = \max(|a|, |b|)$. Then

$$|t^{-\frac{1}{2}} e^{-xt}| = t^{-\frac{1}{2}} e^{-xt} \leqslant t^{-\frac{1}{2}} e^m = M(t),$$

and $\int_0^1 M(t)\, dt$ converges. This establishes uniform convergence on I. We can therefore integrate under the integral sign as follows:

$$\int_0^b dx \int_0^1 t^{-\frac{1}{2}} e^{-xt}\, dt = \int_0^1 dt \int_0^b t^{-\frac{1}{2}} e^{-xt}\, dx = \int_0^1 t^{-\frac{3}{2}}(1 - e^{-bt})\, dt.$$

There is no need to discuss the convergence of this last integral. We know that it converges because Theorem 18.3a insures this fact. But the presence of the factor $t^{-\frac{3}{2}}$ casts suspicion on the convergence. By examining the integrand, explain why the integral converges.

EXAMPLE 2. Let $f(s) \equiv \int_0^\infty e^{-st} \dfrac{dt}{1 + t^2}$. Show that the integral converges uniformly in $\{s \geqslant 0\}$.

Solution. Now

$$\left| \frac{e^{-st}}{1 + t^2} \right| = \frac{e^{-st}}{1 + t^2} \leqslant \frac{1}{1 + t^2} = M(t)$$

and $\int_0^\infty M(t)\, dt$ converges. Hence we have uniform convergence in $\{s \geqslant 0\}$. We can therefore integrate over any bounded closed sub-interval of this half line:

$$\int_0^b f(s)\, ds = \int_0^b ds \int_0^\infty e^{-st} \frac{dt}{1 + t^2} = \int_0^\infty \frac{dt}{1 + t^2} \int_0^b e^{-st}\, ds = \int_0^\infty \frac{1 - e^{bt}}{1 + t^2} \frac{dt}{t}.$$

Again, as in the preceding example the convergence of this integral is guaranteed by Theorem 18.3a.

Since the convergence is uniform in $\{s \geqslant 0\}$, Theorem 18.3a guarantees the continuity of f in each bounded closed interval of that half line, and hence the continuity in $\{s \geqslant 0\}$.

The uniform convergence of this improper integral in $\{s \geqslant 0\}$ guarantees the continuity in $\{s \geqslant 0\}$, but it does not guarantee the existence of a limit as $s \to \infty$. Nor does it guarantee that the integral $\int_0^\infty f(s)\, ds$ exists. Even if the integral existed, we would not know that we could interchange the order of the integration. We first discuss the question of taking limits under the integral sign.

18.3c Theorem. Let F be continuous in $\{a \leqslant x < b,\ \alpha \leqslant y < \beta\}$, where either or both b and β may be infinite; and let f be defined in $I : \{a \leqslant x < b\}$ by

$$f(x) = \int_\alpha^\beta F(x, y)\, dy,$$

where the integral converges uniformly in I. Suppose also that there is a function defined in $\{\alpha \leqslant y < \beta\}$ such that F converges uniformly to ϕ in $\{\alpha \leqslant y \leqslant \eta\}$ for each η between α and β as $x \to \infty$. Then $\int_\alpha^\beta \phi(y)\, dy$ converges and

$$\lim_{x \to \infty} f(x) = \int_\alpha^\beta \phi(y)\, dy.$$

Proof. Again by Exercise B1, ϕ is continuous in $\{\alpha \leqslant y < \beta\}$. Thus ϕ is integrable on any closed sub-interval of J. By the uniform convergence of the integral defining f, there is a $Y(\epsilon)$ such that, for x in I,

$$(1) \qquad \left| \int_\eta^\beta F(x, y)\, dy \right| < \epsilon \qquad \text{if} \quad Y < \eta < \beta.$$

Then for $Y < \eta_1 \leqslant \eta_2 < \beta$,

$$\left| \int_{\eta_1}^{\eta_2} F(x, y)\, dy \right| = \left| \int_{\eta_1}^\beta F(x, y)\, dy - \int_{\eta_2}^\beta F(x, y)\, dy \right|$$

$$\leqslant \left| \int_{\eta_1}^\beta F(x, y)\, dy \right| + \left| \int_{\eta_2}^\beta F(x, y)\, dy \right| \leqslant 2\epsilon.$$

As $x \to \infty$, we take limits under the integral sign in the first integral, by Theorem 18.3a:

$$\left| \int_{\eta_1}^{\eta_2} \phi(y)\, dy \right| \leqslant 2\epsilon \qquad \text{if} \quad Y < \eta_1 \leqslant \eta_2 < \beta.$$

By the Cauchy criterion, $\int_\alpha^\beta \phi(y)\, dy$ converges. Then, since the integral converges, we can keep η_1 fixed and let $\eta_2 \to \beta$ in the previous inequality to get

$$(2) \qquad \left| \int_{\eta_1}^\beta \phi(y)\, dy \right| \leqslant 2\epsilon \qquad \text{if} \quad Y < \eta_1 < \beta.$$

To see that $\lim\limits_{x \to b} f(x)$ exists and is equal to $\int_\alpha^\beta \phi(y)\, dy$, we consider the difference between $f(x)$ and the integral

$$(3) \quad \left| f(x) - \int_\alpha^\beta \phi(y)\, dy \right| = \left| \int_\alpha^\beta F(x, y)\, dy - \int_\alpha^\beta \phi(y)\, dy \right|$$

$$= \left| \int_\alpha^\beta [F(x, y) - \phi(y)]\, dy \right|$$

$$\leqslant \left| \int_\alpha^\eta [F(x, y) - \phi(y)]\, dy \right|$$

$$+ \left| \int_\eta^\beta F(x, y)\, dy \right| + \left| \int_\eta^\beta \phi(y)\, dy \right|.$$

We choose η between Y and β, and keep it fixed. We know that F converges uniformly to ϕ in $\{\alpha \leqslant y \leqslant \eta\}$. Thus for each $\epsilon > 0$ there is an $X(\epsilon)$ such that

(4) $|F(x, y) - \phi(y)| < \epsilon/(\eta - \alpha)$ $\quad$ if $X < x < b$ for all y in $\{\alpha \leqslant y \leqslant \eta\}$.

From (1), (2), (3), and (4) we get

$$\left| f(x) - \int_\alpha^\beta \phi(y)\, dy \right| \leqslant \epsilon + \epsilon + 2\epsilon = 4\epsilon, \quad \text{if } X < x < b. \quad \blacksquare$$

The problem of interchange of order of integration when both integrals involved are improper is a difficult one, and is best handled in terms of Lebesgue's definition of an intergral. Many different sufficient conditions could be given. We content ourselves by proving the following theorem.

18.3d **Theorem.** Let F be continuous in $\{a < x < b,\, \alpha < y < \beta\}$, where any or all of a, b, α, β may be infinite. Suppose both the iterated integrals

$$\int_a^b dx \int_\alpha^\beta |F(x, y)|\, dy \quad \text{and} \quad \int_\alpha^\beta dy \int_a^b |F(x, y)|\, dx$$

exist. Then both of the following integrals exist and

$$\int_a^b dx \int_\alpha^\beta F(x, y)\, dy = \int_\alpha^\beta dy \int_a^b F(x, y)\, dx.$$

Proof. By writing $F = F^+ - F^-$ (see Section 4.4), where

$$F^+(x, y) = \begin{cases} F(x, y) & \text{if } F(x, y) \geqslant 0 \\ 0 & \text{if } F(x, y) < 0. \end{cases}$$

and $\quad$ $$F^-(x, y) = \begin{cases} 0 & \text{if } F(x, y) \geqslant 0 \\ -F(x, y) & \text{if } F(x, y) < 0, \end{cases}$$

we see that it is sufficient to prove the theorem for F non-negative. We therefore assume that F is non-negative throughout the rest of the proof.

Let
$$I = \int_a^b dx \int_\alpha^\beta F(x, y)\, dy.$$

and
$$J = \int_\alpha^\beta dy \int_a^b F(x, y)\, dx.$$

For all $c < d$ between a and b, and all $\xi < \eta$ between α and β,

$$I \geqslant \int_c^d dx \int_\alpha^\eta F(x, y)\, dy = \int_\xi^\eta dy \int_c^d F(x, y)\, dx,$$

the interchange here being permissible by Theorem 18.1a.

Since this inequality must hold for every $c < d$ between a and b,

$$I \geqslant \int_\xi^\eta dy \int_a^b F(x, y)\, dx. \qquad \text{(Why?)}.$$

Then,
$$I \geqslant \int_\alpha^\beta dy \int_a^b F(x, y)\, dx = J.$$

But the argument is completely symmetrical, so that also $J \geqslant I$. Hence $I = J$. ∎

Actually the theorem is true if we only assume that one of the two integrals is absolutely convergent. But our assumptions enable us to avoid the necessity of proving the existence of the other integral.

We now consider the problem of differentiating an improper integral under the integral sign.

18.3e Theorem. Let F and $\partial F/\partial x$ be continuous in $\{a \leqslant x \leqslant b,\ \alpha \leqslant y < \beta\}$, where β can be finite or infinite. Suppose there is an x_0 in $\{a \leqslant x \leqslant b\}$ for which $\int_\alpha^\beta F(x_0, y)\, dy$ converges and $\int_\alpha^\beta \frac{\partial F}{\partial x}(x, y)\, dy$ converges uniformly in $\{a \leqslant x \leqslant b\}$. Then $\int_\alpha^\beta F(x, y)\, dy$ converges uniformly in $\{a \leqslant x \leqslant b\}$. And if we denote its value $f(x)$, then f is a differentiable function and

$$f'(x) = \int_\alpha^\beta \frac{\partial F}{\partial x}(x, y)\, dy.$$

Proof. Let $g(x) = \int_\alpha^\beta \frac{\partial F}{\partial x}(x, y)\, dy.$

Then, by Theorem 18.3b,

$$\int_{x_0}^{x} g(t)\, dt = \int_{\alpha}^{\beta} dy \int_{x_0}^{x} \frac{\partial F}{\partial t}(t, y)\, dt = \int_{\alpha}^{\beta} [F(x, y) - F(x_0, y)]\, dy$$

$$= \int_{\alpha}^{\beta} F(x, y)\, dy - \int_{\alpha}^{\beta} F(x_0, y)\, dy = f(x) - f(x_0).$$

By the fundamental theorem of calculus, we differentiate this equation and get

$$f'(x) = \frac{d}{dx} \int_{x_0}^{x} g(t)\, dt = g(x) = \int_{\alpha}^{\beta} \frac{\partial F}{\partial x}(x, y)\, dy.$$

This shows that $f(x)$ exists—that is, $\int_{\alpha}^{\beta} F(x, y)\, dx$ exists—that it is differentiable, and that the derivative can be computed by differentiating under the integral sign. To complete the proof, we must show that the convergence is uniform. We choose $Y(\epsilon)$ so that

$$\left| \int_{\eta}^{\beta} \frac{\partial F}{\partial x}(x, y)\, dy \right| < \frac{\epsilon}{(b - a)} \qquad \text{if } Y < \eta < \beta$$

uniformly for all x in $\{a \leqslant x \leqslant b\}$. Consider

$$(1) \quad \left| \int_{\eta}^{\beta} F(x, y)\, dy \right| = \left| \int_{\eta}^{\beta} \left[\int_{x_0}^{x} \frac{\partial F}{\partial t}(t, y)\, dt - F(x_0, y) \right] dy \right|$$

$$\leqslant \left| \int_{\eta}^{\beta} dy \int_{x_0}^{x} \frac{\partial F}{\partial t}(t, y)\, dt \right| + \left| \int_{\eta}^{\beta} F(x_0, y)\, dy \right|.$$

Since $\int_{\alpha}^{\beta} F(x_0, y)\, dy$ exists, there is a $Y_1(\epsilon)$ such that

$$(2) \quad \left| \int_{\eta}^{\beta} F(x_0, y)\, dy \right| < \epsilon \qquad \text{if } Y_1 < \eta < \beta.$$

Combining (1) and (2), we get for $\beta > \eta > Y_2 = \max (Y, Y_1)$,

$$\left| \int_{\eta}^{\beta} F(x, y)\, dy \right| \leqslant \left| \int_{x_0}^{x} dt \int_{\eta}^{\beta} \frac{\partial F}{\partial t}(t, y)\, dy \right| + \epsilon$$

$$\leqslant \int_{a}^{b} \left| \int_{\eta}^{\beta} \frac{\partial F}{\partial t}(t, y)\, dy \right| dt + \epsilon \leqslant \int_{a}^{b} \frac{\epsilon}{b - a}\, dt + \epsilon$$

$$= 2\epsilon \qquad \blacksquare$$

EXAMPLE 3. Evaluate $\int_{0}^{\infty} e^{-t^2} \cos xt\, dt.$

Solution. We denote the value of this integral by $f(x)$. Clearly $f(x)$ exists and is continuous for all x, since the integral is easily seen to converge uniformly for all x by the M test:

$$|e^{-t^2} \cos xt| \leqslant e^{-t^2} = M(t),$$

and $\int_0^\infty M(t) \, dt$ converges.

By differentiation under the integral sign, we get

$$f'(x) = -\int_0^\infty te^{-t^2} \sin xt \, dt,$$

which is valid if this integral converges uniformly. Again the M test applies:

$$|-te^{-t^2} \sin xt| \leqslant te^{-t^2} = M(t)$$

and $\int_0^\infty M(t)$ converges.

Integrating by parts, we then get

$$f'(x) = -\int_0^\infty te^{-t^2} \sin xt \, dt = -\frac{x}{2} \int_0^\infty e^{-xt} \cos xt \, dt = -\frac{x}{2} f(x).$$

We observe that

$$f(0) = \int_0^\infty e^{-t^2} \, dt = \tfrac{1}{2}\sqrt{\pi},$$

so that f satisfies the conditions

$$f'(x) = -\frac{x}{2} f(x) \qquad f(0) = \tfrac{1}{2}\sqrt{\pi}.$$

Let I be the maximal interval about $x = 0$ in which $f(x) > 0$. We know that there is at least a small interval in which $f(x) > 0$, since f is continuous and $f(0) > 0$. Then in I

$$\frac{f'(x)}{f(x)} = -\frac{x}{2}.$$

So

$$\log f(x) = -\frac{x^2}{4} + C_0$$

or

$$f(x) = Ce^{-x^2/4},$$

where

$$C = f(0) = \tfrac{1}{2}\sqrt{\pi}$$

Thus in I

$$f(x) = \tfrac{1}{2}\sqrt{\pi}e^{-x^2/4}.$$

Now that this evaluation is established in interval I, we go on to show that I is the entire x-axis. Suppose it were not. Then there would be a finite point x_0 at which f vanishes. Taking limits as $x \to x_0$, we get (since both sides are continuous)

$$0 = f(x_0) = \tfrac{1}{2}\sqrt{\pi}\, e^{-x_0^2/4}.$$

But the right-hand side is not zero. This contradiction shows that I is the entire x-axis, and hence that

$$\int_0^\infty e^{-t^2} \cos xt \, dt = \tfrac{1}{2}\sqrt{\pi}\, e^{-x^2/4}$$

for all x's.

18.3f Theorem. $\displaystyle \int_0^\infty \frac{\sin t}{t} \, dt = \frac{\pi}{2}.$

We dignify this example by calling it a theorem because it is important in later work on Fourier series, and because it is a little difficult to establish.

Proof. To evaluate the integral, we consider the function f defined in $\{x \geqslant 0\}$ by

$$f(x) = \int_0^\infty e^{-xt} \frac{\sin t}{t} \, dt.$$

By Example 4 of Section 18.2, this integral converges uniformly in $\{x \geqslant 0\}$, and therefore f is continuous there.

Formally differentiating under the integral, we get

$$f'(x) = -\int_0^\infty e^{-xt} \sin t \, dt.$$

Now $\qquad |e^{-xt} \sin t| \leqslant e^{-xt} \leqslant e^{-ct} = M(t) \qquad \{x \geqslant c\}$

Hence the integral converges uniformly in $\{x \geqslant c\}$ for every $c > 0$. By Theorem 18.3e, the differentiation is therefore valid for $\{x \geqslant c\}$. But any given $x > 0$ can be caught in such an interval so that the differentiation is valid for all $x > 0$.

We now evaluate $f'(x)$ by elementary means. Integration by parts establishes

$$\int_0^T e^{-xt} \sin t \, dt = \frac{e^{-xt}(-x \sin t - \cos t)}{1 + x^2} \bigg|_0^T,$$

so that $\qquad \displaystyle f'(x) = -\int_0^\infty e^{-xt} \sin t \, dt = -\frac{1}{1 + x^2}.$

Thus $\qquad f(x) = C - \arctan x \qquad x > 0.$

To evaluate C, we compute $\displaystyle \lim_{x \to \infty} f(x)$. As noted, the integral defining $f(x)$ converges uniformly for $\{x \geqslant 0\}$. But as $x \to \infty$, the integrand does not converge uniformly to zero in $\{t \geqslant 0\}$. However, for each $\alpha > 0$, it does converge uniformly to zero in $\{t \geqslant \alpha\}$, since

$$\left| e^{-xt} \frac{\sin t}{t} \right| \leqslant e^{-x\alpha} \to 0 \qquad \text{as } x \to \infty.$$

Then for each fixed $\epsilon > 0$ we write $f(x)$ in the form

$$f(x) = \int_0^\epsilon e^{-xt} \frac{\sin t}{t} \, dt + \int_\epsilon^\infty e^{-xt} \frac{\sin t}{t} \, dt$$

$$= f_1(x) + f_2(x), \quad \text{respectively.}$$

Since $\left| e^{-xt} \dfrac{\sin t}{t} \right| < 1$ for $x > 0$, we have $|f_1(x)| \leqslant \epsilon$ for all $x > 0$. The integral defining $f_2(x)$ converges uniformly for $\{x \geqslant \epsilon\}$, and furthermore its integrand converges uniformly to zero as $x \to \infty$. Then, by Theorem 18.3c, we have that $f_2(x) \to 0$ as $x \to \infty$. Thus there is an $X(\epsilon)$ such that $|f_2(x)| < \epsilon$ if $x > X$. We have then that for each $\epsilon > 0$,

$$|f(x)| \leqslant |f_1(x)| + |f_2(x)| < \epsilon + \epsilon = 2\epsilon \qquad \text{if } x > X.$$

This means that $f(x) \to 0$ as $x \to \infty$. Since

$$f(x) = C - \text{arc tan } x \qquad x > 0,$$

we conclude that

$$0 = \lim_{x \to \infty} (C - \text{arc tan } x) = C - \pi/2,$$

So that

$$C = \pi/2.$$

Thus we have

$$f(x) = \pi/2 - \text{arc tan } x \qquad x > 0.$$

It is important to remember that f is defined by the integral and that this evaluation of f has been established only for $x > 0$. But we can extend the evaluation to include $x = 0$ quite easily. As noted at the beginning of the proof, f is continuous in $\{x \geqslant 0\}$. Taking right-hand limits, we then get

$$\int_0^\infty \frac{\sin t}{t} \, dt = f(0) = \lim_{x \to 0+} f(x) = \lim_{x \to 0+} \left(\frac{\pi}{2} - \text{arc tan } x \right) = \frac{\pi}{2}. \quad \blacksquare$$

EXAMPLE 4. Evaluate $f(x) = \displaystyle\int_0^\infty \frac{\sin xt}{t} \, dt$.

Solution. Clearly $f(0) = 0$. For $x > 0$, we make the substitution $xt = y$. Then

$$f(x) = \int_0^\infty \frac{\sin xt}{t} \, dt = \int_0^\infty \frac{\sin y}{y} \, dy = \frac{\pi}{2}.$$

For $x < 0$

$$f(x) = \int_0^\infty \frac{\sin xt}{t} = -\int_0^\infty \frac{\sin(-x)t}{t}\,dt = -\frac{\pi}{2}.$$

Thus

$$f(x) = \begin{cases} \pi/2 & \text{if } x > 0 \\ 0 & \text{if } x = 0 \\ -\pi/2 & \text{if } x < 0 \end{cases} = \frac{\pi}{2}\operatorname{sgn} x$$

EXAMPLE 5. Evaluate $f(x, y) = \displaystyle\int_0^\infty \frac{\sin xt \cos yt}{t}\,dt$.

Solution:

$$f(x, y) = \int_0^\infty \frac{\sin xt \cos yt}{t}\,dt = \frac{1}{2}\int_0^\infty \frac{\sin(x+y)t}{t}\,dt + \frac{1}{2}\int_0^\infty \frac{\sin(x-y)t}{t}\,dt.$$

Since $y = |y|$ or $-y = |y|$,

$$f(x, y) = \frac{1}{2}\int_0^\infty \frac{\sin(x+|y|)t}{t}\,dt + \frac{1}{2}\int_0^\infty \frac{\sin(x-|y|)t}{t}\,dt$$

$$= \begin{cases} \dfrac{\pi}{2} & x > |y| \\[2mm] \dfrac{\pi}{4} & x = |y| \\[2mm] 0 & -|y| < x < |y| \\[2mm] -\dfrac{\pi}{4} & x = -|y| \\[2mm] -\dfrac{\pi}{2} & x < -|y| \end{cases}$$

A EXERCISES

I. Carefully justify the following:

(a) $\displaystyle\int_0^1 e^{-xy}\frac{dy}{1+y} \to \log 2 \qquad$ as $x \to 0$

(b) $\displaystyle\int_1^\infty e^{-xz}\frac{dz}{1+z} \to 0 \qquad$ as $x \to \infty$

(c) $\displaystyle\int_0^\infty e^{-t(x+1)}\cos xt\,\frac{t}{t+x^2}\,dt \to 1 \qquad$ as $x \to 0$
(*Hint:* Use B6 of Section 18.2.)

(d) $\displaystyle\int_0^\infty t^2 e^{-xt}\cos xt\,dt \to 0 \qquad$ as $x \to \infty$

(e) $\displaystyle\int_0^2 dx \int_0^1 y^{-\frac12} \cos\frac{x}{y}\frac{x-y}{x+y}\,dy = \int_0^1 dy \int_0^2 y^{-\frac12}\cos\frac{x}{y}\frac{x-y}{x+y}\,dx$

(f) $\displaystyle\int_1^2 dx \int_0^\infty \sin\frac{y}{x} e^{-xy}y^{\frac12}\cos^2 y\,dy = \int_0^\infty dy \int_1^2 \sin\frac{y}{x} e^{-xy}y^{\frac12}\cos^2 y\,dx$

(g) $\displaystyle\int_0^1 dx \int_0^\infty \frac{1}{\sqrt{x}} e^{-(x+1)y}\cos\sqrt{y}\,dy = \int_0^\infty dy \int_0^1 \frac{1}{\sqrt{x}} e^{-(x+1)y}\cos\sqrt{y}\,dx$

(h) $\displaystyle\frac{d}{dx}\int_0^1 \frac{e^{-xy}\,dy}{1+y} = -\int_0^1 \frac{e^{-xy}y\,dy}{1+y}$ for all x

(i) $\displaystyle\frac{d}{dx}\int_0^1 \frac{e^{-xy}}{\sqrt{y}(1+y)}\,dy = -\int_0^1 \frac{e^{-xy}\sqrt{y}\,dy}{(1+y)}$ for all x

(j) $\displaystyle\frac{d}{dx}\int_0^\infty \frac{dy}{x+y^3} = -\int_0^\infty \frac{dy}{x^2+2xy^3+y^6}$ $x>0$

2. Although the integrand does not converge uniformly to zero, show that:

(a) $\displaystyle\int_0^1 e^{-xy}\frac{dy}{1+y} \to 0$ as $x\to\infty$

(b) $\displaystyle\int_0^\infty e^{-xy}\frac{dy}{1+y^2} \to 0$ as $x\to\infty$

3. Evaluate $f(z) = \displaystyle\int_0^\infty xe^{-zx^2}\,dx$. For what z's is this valid?

4. (a) Show that $\displaystyle\int_0^\infty e^{-xt}\,dt = \frac{1}{x}$ and hence that $\displaystyle\int_0^\infty e^{-xt}t^n\,dt = (n!)/x^{n+1}$

(b) Deduce the value of $\displaystyle\int_0^\infty t^n e^{-t}\,dt$.

5. Show formally, without justifying your steps, that $\displaystyle\int_0^\infty \frac{x^2\,dx}{e^x-1} = \sum_1^\infty \frac{1}{n^3}$.

B   EXERCISES

1. Suppose F is continuous in $\{a \leqslant x < b,\ \alpha \leqslant y \leqslant \beta\}$, where b is finite or infinite. Suppose also that there is a function ϕ in $\{\alpha \leqslant y \leqslant \beta\}$ such that F tends uniformly to ϕ as $x \to b$. Show that ϕ is continuous.

2. In Exercise 1 above, if b is finite define $F(b, y) = \phi(y)$. Show then that F is continuous in $\{a \leqslant x \leqslant b,\ \alpha \leqslant y \leqslant \beta\}$.

3. Evaluate the integrals $\displaystyle\int_0^1 dy \int_0^1 \frac{(x-y)}{(x+y)^3}\,dx$ and $\displaystyle\int_0^1 dx \int_0^1 \frac{(x-y)\,dy}{(x+y)^3}$, and hence show that inversion of the order of integration is not always permissible.

4. Show that $\displaystyle\int_0^\infty dy \int_0^\infty e^{-xy-1/y}\frac{\sin x}{1+x}\,dx = \int_0^\infty dx \int_0^\infty e^{-xy-1/y}\frac{\sin x}{1+x}\,dy$.

5. Show that $\displaystyle\int_0^1 \frac{\log x}{1-x}\,dx = -\sum_1^\infty \frac{1}{n^2}$.

6. Show rigorously that if f is a continuous bounded function on $\{-\infty < x < \infty\}$, then the function u, defined in $\{0 < t < \infty,\; -\infty < x < \infty\}$ by the formula

$$u(x, t) = \frac{1}{\sqrt{4\pi t}} \int_{-\infty}^\infty e^{-\frac{(x-y)^2}{4t}} f(y)\,dy$$

satisfies the equation $u_{xx} = u_t$.

7. Let $\displaystyle f(x) = \int_0^\infty e^{-y^2 - \frac{x^2}{y^2}}\,dy$.

    (a) Show that for $x > 0$, $f'(x) = -2f(x)$. (*Hint:* Make the substitution $y = x/t$.)

    (b) Deduce $f(x) = (1/2)\sqrt{\pi}\,e^{-|x|}$.

8. Evaluate $\displaystyle\int_0^\infty \frac{\cos ax - \cos bx}{x^2}\,dx$. (*Hint:* $\cos ax - \cos bx = -x\int_a^b \sin xt\,dt$.)

9. Evaluate $\displaystyle\int_0^\infty \frac{\sin xt \sin yt}{t^2}\,dt$.

10. Evaluate $\displaystyle\int_0^\infty \frac{\sin xt \cos yt \cos zt}{t}\,dt$.

11. Evaluate $\displaystyle\int_0^\infty \frac{\sin xt \sin yt \cos zt}{t^2}\,dt$.

12. Evaluate $\displaystyle\int_0^\infty \frac{\sin xt \sin yt \sin zt}{t^3}\,dt$.

C EXERCISES

1. Let $\displaystyle f(x) = \sum_0^\infty a_n x^n$, where the radius of convergence is infinite and where the a's are all non-negative. Suppose also that $\sum_0^\infty a_n n!$ converges. Show then that $\int_0^\infty e^{-x} f(x)\,dx$ converges and that $\int_0^\infty e^{-x} f(x)\,dx = \Sigma a_n n!$.

2. Show rigorously that $\displaystyle\int_0^\infty \frac{x^2\,dx}{e^x - 1} = \sum_1^\infty \frac{1}{n^3}$.

3. Show that if g is continuous in $I: \{a \leqslant x \leqslant b\}$ and x_0 is a point in I, then

$$f'(x) = g(x)f(x) + h(x) \qquad f(x_0) = c$$

can have at most one solution in I. (*Hint:* Suppose there were two solutions. Show that the difference is everywhere positive in I if it is greater than zero at one point in I.) Deduce the value of $\displaystyle\int_0^\infty e^{-t^2} \sin xt\,dt$.

4. Evaluate $\displaystyle\int_0^\infty \frac{\sin^2 xy}{x^2}\, dx.$

5. Evaluate $f(y) = \displaystyle\int_0^\infty \frac{\sin xy}{x(a^2 + x^2)}\, dx.$ (*Hint:* Show that $f''(y) - a^2 f(y)$ is constant.)

6. Evaluate $\displaystyle\int_0^\infty \frac{\sin xt \sin yt}{t}\, dt.$ (*Hint:* Set $f(z) = \displaystyle\int_0^\infty e^{-zt}\, \frac{\sin xt \sin yt}{t}\, dt$ and proceed as in Theorem 18.3f.

7. From Exercise 6 above, deduce the value of $\displaystyle\int_0^\infty \frac{\sin xt\,(1 - \cos at)}{t^2}\, dt.$

8. From Exercise 6, deduce the value of $\displaystyle\int_0^\infty \frac{\cos at - \cos bt}{t}\, dt.$

19

Gamma and Beta Functions.
Laplace's Method and
Stirling's Formula

19.1 THE GAMMA FUNCTION

An important function defined by means of an integral depending on
a parameter is the **Gamma function** given by

$$\Gamma(x) = \int_0^\infty e^{-t} t^{x-1}\, dt \qquad \{x > 0\}.$$

The integrand is singular at $t = 0$ if $x < 1$. We proceed to establish a few
simple properties of Γ.

19.1a Theorem. Γ is continuous and infinitely differentiable in $\{x > 0\}$.

Proof. Let x_0 be an arbitrary point in $\{x > 0\}$. Choose a and b so that
$0 < a < x_0 < b$. We now examine Γ in $I: \{a \leqslant x \leqslant b\}$. Let $\Gamma =
\Gamma_1 + \Gamma_2$, where Γ_1 and Γ_2 are defined by

$$\Gamma_1(x) = \int_0^1 e^{-t} t^{x-1}\, dt$$

and
$$\Gamma_2(x) = \int_1^\infty e^{-t} t^{x-1}\, dt.$$

For x in I and $0 \leqslant t \leqslant 1$,

$$|e^{-t} t^{x-1}| = e^{-t} t^{x-1} \leqslant t^{a-1} \equiv M_1(t);$$

and for $t \geqslant 1$,

$$|e^{-t} t^{x-1}| \leqslant e^{-t} t^{b-1} \equiv M_2(t).$$

Since $\int_0^1 M_1(t)\,dt$ and $\int_1^\infty M_2(t)\,dt$ converge, the integrals defining Γ_1 and Γ_2 converge uniformly for x in I, and consequently these functions are continuous in I. Γ is then continuous in I, since it is the sum of two continuous functions there; in particular, Γ is continuous at x_0. Since x_0 was an arbitrary positive number, Γ is continuous in $\{x > 0\}$.

Similarly, we can show that repeated differentiation under the integral sign is permissible in $\{x > 0\}$. The details are left to the exercises. ∎

A formula which is sometimes quite useful is given next.

19.1b Corollary. For any $a > 0$,

$$\int_0^\infty e^{-at}t^{x-1}\,dt = \frac{\Gamma(x)}{a^x}.$$

Proof. Prove by making the substitution $at = \tau$. ∎

An important functional equation satisfied by Γ is given in the following theorem.

19.1c Theorem. $\Gamma(x + 1) = x\Gamma(x)$ $\{x > 0\}$.
  Proof. For $x > 0$,

$$\Gamma(x+1) = \int_0^\infty e^{-t}t^x\,dt = e^{-t}t^x\Big|_0^\infty + x\int_0^\infty e^{-t}t^{x-1}\,dt = x\Gamma(x). \quad ∎$$

19.1d Corollary. For all integer $n \geq 1$ and all $x > 0$,

$$\Gamma(x + n) = (x + n - 1)\cdots(x + 1)x\Gamma(x).$$

Proof. Prove by induction from Theorem 19.1c. ∎

19.1e Corollary. $\Gamma(n + 1) = n!$ $n = 0, 1, 2, \ldots.$
  Proof. By Theorem 19.1d, it suffices to prove that $\Gamma(1) = 1$. But

$$\Gamma(1) = \int_0^\infty e^{-t}\,dt = -e^{-t}\Big|_0^\infty = 1. \quad ∎$$

The preceding corollary points up one of the most important properties of Γ, namely that it interpolates between the factorials. It is perhaps unfortunate that the traditional notation is $\Gamma(n + 1) = n!$ rather than $\Gamma(n) = n!$ However tempting it may be to use the latter, we will not depart from the standard notation because of the vast literature in which $\Gamma(x)$ stands for the function we have defined here. Sometimes $x!$ or $\pi(x)$ is used for $\Gamma(x + 1)$.

The integral defining Γ diverges for $x \leqslant 0$. Consequently Γ is defined only for $x > 0$. We could therefore choose to define Γ for $x < 0$ in any one of many different ways. There is, however, a manner of defining Γ for negative values of x which is "most natural" in a sense which you will understand after studying complex function theory, namely, in the sense of analytic continuation. This leads to the same definition which we get by using the formulas of Theorems 19.1c and 19.1d.

For example, from Theorem 19.1c we have

$$\Gamma(x) = \Gamma(x + 1)/x \qquad \text{in } \{x > 0\}.$$

But the right-hand side of this equation is defined for all $x > -1$ except $x = 0$. We take this to be the definition of Γ in $\{-1 < x < 0\}$. Similarly, from Theorem 19.1d, we have for $n = 2$ that

$$\Gamma(x) = \Gamma(x + 2)/x(x + 1).$$

The right-hand side here makes sense for all $x > -2$ except $x = 0$ and $x = -1$. It therefore provides a definition of Γ in $\{-2 < x < -1\}$ and $\{-1 < x < 0\}$.

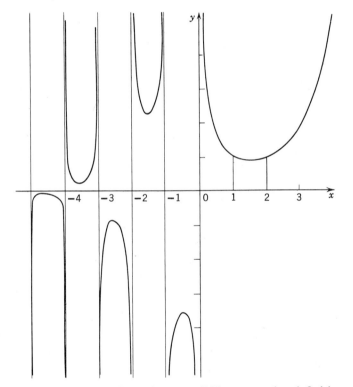

We now face the question of compatibility: are the definitions of Γ in $\{-1 < x < 0\}$ given by these two different-looking formulas compatible? The answer is an easy "Yes," and the proof is left to the problems.

By induction, we extend the definition of Γ to all x except 0 and the negative integers. The behavior of the function is indicated by the accompanying graph.

19.2   THE BETA FUNCTION

A function closely related to Γ is the **Beta function** B given by

$$B(x, y) = \int_0^1 t^{x-1}(1 - t)^{y-1}\, dt.$$

19.2a   Theorem. $B(x, y)$ is continuous in $\{x > 0, y > 0\}$.

Proof. The proof of this theorem is given as an exercise (B2).

Though at first glance B seems to have little connection with Γ, they are intimately related in a rather surprising manner. Before we investigate this connection, we need a new formula for B.

19.2b   Lemma. $B(x, y) = \displaystyle\int_0^\infty \frac{\tau^{x-1}}{(1 + \tau)^{x+y}}\, d\tau \qquad \{x > 0, y > 0\}.$

Proof. Set $t = \tau/1 + \tau$, $dt = d\tau/(1 + \tau)^2$. ∎

We now establish the relationship of B and Γ.

19.2c   Theorem. $B(x, y) = \Gamma(x)\Gamma(y)/\Gamma(x + y) \qquad \{x > 0, y > 0\}.$

Proof. By Theorem 19.1b,

$$\Gamma(x) = t^x \int_0^\infty \tau^{x-1}e^{-t\tau}\, d\tau = \int_0^\infty t^x \tau^{x-1}e^{-t\tau}\, d\tau.$$

Multiplying both sides by $t^{y-1}e^{-t}$ and integrating, we get

$$\Gamma(x)\int_0^\infty e^{-t}t^{y-1}\, dt = \int_0^\infty t^{y-1}e^{-t}\, dt \int_0^\infty t^x \tau^{x-1}\, e^{-t\tau}\, d\tau$$

or $\qquad \Gamma(x)\Gamma(y) = \displaystyle\int_0^\infty dt \int_0^\infty t^{x+y-1}\tau^{x-1}e^{-t}e^{-t\tau}\, d\tau.$

By Theorem 18.3d, interchanging the order of integration is permissible if both iterated integrals converge (since the integrands are positive). But the order we have certainly converges. And in the other order we have

$$\int_0^\infty d\tau \int_0^\infty t^{x+y-1}\tau^{x-1}e^{-t(1+\tau)}\, dt = \int_0^\infty \tau^{x-1}\, d\tau \int_0^\infty t^{x+y-1}e^{-t(1+\tau)}\, dt.$$

By Theorem 19.1b, the inner integral can be evaluated so that the iterated integral reduces to

$$\int_0^\infty \frac{\tau^{x-1}}{(1 + \tau)^{x+y}}\, \Gamma(x + y)\, dt = \Gamma(x + y)\int_0^\infty \frac{\tau^{x-1}}{(1 + \tau)^{x+y}}\, dt$$
$$= \Gamma(x + y)B(x, y)$$

Since both iterated integrals converge, they are equal. Thus $\Gamma(x)\Gamma(y) = \Gamma(x + y)B(x, y)$, and since $\Gamma(x + y) \neq 0$ (why?) we can divide by it to complete the proof. ∎

A EXERCISES

1. Show that $\Gamma(x) > 0$ in $\{x > 0\}$, and sgn $\Gamma(x) = (-1)^n$ in $\{-n < x < -n + 1\}$.

2. Show that $\Gamma(x) = \int_0^1 \left(\log \frac{1}{t}\right)^{x-1} dt$.

3. It is clear from Theorem 19.2c that $B(x, y) = B(y, x)$. Show this directly from the definition of B by substituting $t = 1 - \tau$.

4. Show that $\Gamma(x) \to \pm \infty$ as $x \to \pm 0$.

5. Evaluate $B(x, 1)$.

6. Show that $B(x, y) = 2 \int_0^{\pi/2} \sin^{2x-1} \theta \cos^{2y-1} \theta \, d\theta$.

7. Show that $\Gamma(\frac{1}{2}) = \sqrt{\pi}$. (*Hint:* Set $t = \tau^2$.)

8. Evaluate $\Gamma(-\frac{1}{2})$, $\Gamma(-\frac{3}{2}), \ldots$, $\Gamma(-n + \frac{1}{2})$ and $\Gamma(\frac{3}{2})$, $\Gamma(\frac{5}{2}), \ldots$, $\Gamma(n + \frac{1}{2})$.

9. Define ψ by $\psi(x) = \dfrac{d}{dx} \log \Gamma(x) = \dfrac{\Gamma'(x)}{\Gamma(x)}$ and show that $\psi(x + 1) = \psi(x) + \dfrac{1}{x}$.

B EXERCISES

1. Complete the proof of Theorem 19.1a, and hence establish that

$$\Gamma^{(n)}(x) = \int_0^\infty e^{-t} t^{x-1} (\log t)^n \, dt \qquad \{x > 0\}.$$

2. Prove Theorem 19.2a. Apply the Weierstrass M test.

3. Show that Γ has a single minimum in $\{x > 0\}$ which lies between 1 and 2.

4. From the formula for $\Gamma(n + \frac{1}{2})$, obtained in Exercise A8 of this section, deduce
$$\sqrt{\pi}\,\Gamma(2n) = 2^{2n-1} \Gamma(n) \Gamma(n + \tfrac{1}{2}).$$

5. Use Exercise A6 to show that

$$\int_0^{\pi/2} \sin^{2n} \theta \, d\theta = \int_0^{\pi/2} \cos^{2n} \theta \, d\theta = \frac{1 \cdot 3 \cdots (2n - 1)}{2 \cdot 4 \cdots (2n)} \frac{\pi}{2}$$

and $\quad \displaystyle\int_0^{\pi/2} \sin^{2n-1} \theta \, d\theta = \int_0^{\pi/2} \cos^{2n-1} \theta \, d\theta = \frac{2 \cdot 4 \cdots (2n - 2)}{1 \cdot 3 \cdots (2n - 1)}$.

6. (a) Observe that
$$\int_0^{\pi/2} \sin^{2n+1} \theta \, d\theta < \int_0^{\pi/2} \sin^{2n} \theta \, d\theta < \int_0^{\pi/2} \sin^{2n-1} \theta \, d\theta$$

(b) Deduce from Exercise 5 above that
$$\frac{\pi}{2} = \lim_{n \to \infty} \left[\frac{2 \cdot 4 \cdots (2n)}{1 \cdot 3 \cdots (2n - 1)}\right]^2 \frac{1}{2n + 1}.$$

7. Give formal proofs (that is, manipulation without justification) of Theorem 19.2c by writing

$$\Gamma(a)\Gamma(b) = \int_0^\infty \int_0^\infty e^{-t-\tau} t^{a-1}\tau^{b-1}\, dt\, d\tau.$$

(a) Introduce $t = x^2$ and $\tau = y^2$, convert to polar coordinates, and evaluate.

(b) Set $t + \tau = \xi$ and $\tau = \xi\eta$, and evaluate.

C EXERCISES

1. Evaluate $\displaystyle\int_0^\infty \frac{1 - e^{-x}}{x^{1+\alpha}}\, dx \qquad 0 < \alpha < 1.$

2. Evaluate:

(a) $\displaystyle\int_0^\infty \frac{(1 - e^{-x})^2}{x^{2+\alpha}} \qquad \{-1 < \alpha < 1\}$ (b) $\displaystyle\int_0^\infty \frac{(1 - e^{-x})^3}{x^{3+\alpha}} \qquad \{-2 < \alpha < 1\}$

3. Let ψ be the function defined in Exercise A9.

(a) Show that $\displaystyle \psi(x + n) = \psi(x) + \sum_{k=0}^{n-1} \frac{1}{x + k}.$

(b) Deduce

$$\lim_{n\to\infty} (\psi(x + n) - \log n) = \psi(x) + \gamma + \frac{1}{x} - \sum_1^\infty\left(\frac{1}{k} - \frac{1}{x + k}\right),$$

where γ is the Euler-Mascheroni constant. (See Exercise C2, Section 14.2.)

4. Suppose in Exercise 3(b) above it is known that $\lim_{n\to\infty} [\psi(x + n) - \log n] = 0$. Then show that

$$\psi(x) = -\gamma - \frac{1}{x} + \sum_0^\infty \left(\frac{1}{n} - \frac{1}{x + n}\right).$$

Deduce

$$\frac{1}{\Gamma(x)} = e^{\gamma x}\, x \prod_{k=1}^\infty \left\{\left(1 + \frac{x}{k}\right)e^{-x/k}\right\}.$$

(An **infinite product** $\displaystyle\prod_{k=1}^\infty a_k$ is defined as $\displaystyle\lim_{n\to\infty}\prod_{k=1}^n a_k$ if the limit exists, and $\displaystyle\prod_{k=1}^n a_k$ is defined as $a_1 \cdot a_2 \cdots a_n$.)

5. From Exercise 4 above and from the definition of Γ, deduce

$$\Gamma'(1) = \psi(1) = \int_0^\infty e^{-t} \log t\, dt = -\gamma.$$

19.3 LAPLACE'S METHOD

A method due to the French mathematician Laplace enables us to estimate the size of certain types of integrals depending on a parameter. In particular, we are interested in estimating $\Gamma(x)$ when x is large, and hence obtaining information about the size of $n!$ when n is large.

In Chapter 7 we were introduced to the symbol $\sim$, which we read as "has the same limit as." We now want to extend the meaning of this symbol. We will write

$$A \sim B \qquad \text{as } x \to \infty,$$

if

$$\lim_{x \to \infty} \frac{A(x)}{B(x)} = 1.$$

The expression "$A \sim B$" will now be read as "A is **asymptotic** to B." We are interested in applying this concept where we know something about the size or behavior of B and can thereby infer something about the behavior of A. Note that we make no assumption about the existence of either $\lim_{x \to \infty} A(x)$ or $\lim_{x \to \infty} B(x)$. In general, we will be concerned with situations where these limits do not exist.

EXAMPLE. Show that $x^2 + x \cos x \sim x^2$ as $x \to \infty$.

Solution:

$$\frac{x^2 + x \cos x}{x^2} = 1 + \frac{\cos x}{x} \to 1 \qquad \text{as } x \to \infty.$$

19.3a   Lemma. If $a > 0$, $b > 0$, and f is defined by

$$f(x) = \int_0^a e^{-xbt^2}\, dt,$$

then

$$f(x) \sim \frac{1}{2}\sqrt{\frac{\pi}{bx}} \qquad \text{as } x \to \infty.$$

Proof. Set $\sqrt{bx}\, t = u$, so that

$$f(x) = \int_0^{\sqrt{bx}\,a} e^{-u^2}\, \frac{du}{\sqrt{bx}}\,.$$

Then

$$\sqrt{bx}\, f(x) = \int_0^{\sqrt{bx}\,a} e^{-u^2}\, du \to \int_0^\infty e^{-u^2}\, du = \tfrac{1}{2}\sqrt{\pi}. \qquad \blacksquare$$

The procedure known as **Laplace's method** is presented in the following theorem.

19.3b   Theorem. Suppose
(i) f has two continuous derivatives in $\{0 \leqslant t < a\}$, where a may be finite or infinite,
(ii) f is increasing in $\{0 \leqslant t < a\}$,
(iii) $f(0) = f'(0) = 0$ $f''(0) > 0$,
(iv)   there is an x_0 for which

$$I(x) = \int_0^a e^{-xf(t)}\, dt \qquad \text{exists.}$$

Then $I(x)$ exists for all $x > x_0$ and

$$I(x) \sim \sqrt{\pi/2xf''(0)} \qquad \text{as } x \to \infty.$$

Proof. First we note that, for $x > x_0$,

$$e^{-xf(t)} \leqslant e^{-x_0 f(t)}.$$

Thus $I(x)$ exists by the comparison test.

Let ϵ, $0 < \epsilon < f''(0)$, be chosen. By the continuity of f'', there is a $\delta < a$ for which

$$(1) \qquad 0 < f''(0) - \epsilon \leqslant f''(t) \leqslant f''(0) + \epsilon \qquad \text{in } \{0 \leqslant t \leqslant \delta\}.$$

Then

$$I(x) = \int_0^a e^{-xf(t)} \, dt = \int_0^\delta e^{-xf(t)} \, dt + \int_\delta^a e^{-xf(t)} \, dt \equiv I_1(x) + I_2(x)$$

respectively. First we examine I_2. In $\{\delta \leqslant t < a\}$, we have $f(t) \geqslant f(\delta)$, since f is monotone Thus

$$e^{-xf(t)} = e^{-xf(t)/2} e^{-xf(t)/2} \leqslant e^{-xf(t)/2} e^{-xf(\delta)/2} \leqslant e^{-x_0 f(t)} e^{-xf(\delta)/2}$$

if $x \geqslant 2x_0$. Consequently

$$I_2 = \int_\delta^a e^{-xf(t)} \, dt \leqslant e^{-xf(\delta)/2} \int_\delta^a e^{-x_0 f(t)} \, dt \leqslant e^{-xf(\delta)/2} \int_0^a e^{-x_0 f(t)} \, dt,$$

or

$$(2) \qquad 0 \leqslant I_2 \leqslant e^{-xf(\delta)/2} I(x_0) \qquad \{x \geqslant 2x_0\}.$$

Now in $\{0 \leqslant t \leqslant \delta\}$ we have

$$f(t) = f(0) + f''(0)t + f''(\tau)t^2/2,$$

where $0 \leqslant \tau \leqslant t \leqslant 0$. But $f(0) = f'(0) = 0$, so

$$f(t) = f''(\tau)t^2/2.$$

From this last formula and from (1), we get

$$[f''(0) - \epsilon]t^2/2 \leqslant f(t) \leqslant [f''(0) + \epsilon]t^2/2,$$

so that

$$e^{-x[f''(0) + \epsilon]t^2/2} \leqslant e^{-xf(t)} \leqslant e^{-x[f''(0) - \epsilon]t^2/2}.$$

We integrate this inequality to get

$$(3) \qquad \int_0^\delta e^{-x[f''(0) + \epsilon]t^2/2} \, dt \leqslant I_1(x) \leqslant \int_0^\delta e^{-x[f''(0) - \epsilon]t^2/2} \, dt.$$

Combining (2) and (3) above,

$$(4) \quad \int_0^\delta e^{-x[f''(0)+\epsilon]t^2/2}\, dt \leqslant I(x) \leqslant \int_0^\delta e^{-x[f''(0)-\epsilon]t^2/2}\, dt + e^{-xf(\delta)/2}I(x_0),$$

for $x \geqslant 2x_0$.

If we multiply (4) through by $\sqrt{x}$ and let $x \to \infty$, we get a contribution from the integrals by Lemma 19.3a, while

$$\sqrt{x}e^{-xf(\delta)/2}I(x_0) \to 0.$$

This yields

$$\tfrac{1}{2}(2\pi/[f''(0)+\epsilon])^{1/2} \leqslant \varliminf_{x\to\infty} \sqrt{x}I(x) \leqslant \varlimsup_{x\to\infty} \sqrt{x}I(x) \leqslant \tfrac{1}{2}(2\pi/[f''(0)-\epsilon])^{1/2}.$$

This inequality holds for every positive $\epsilon < f''(0)$. Letting $\epsilon \to 0$, we get

$$\lim_{x\to\infty} \sqrt{x}I(x) = \sqrt{\pi/2f''(0)}. \qquad \blacksquare$$

EXAMPLE. Study the asymptotic behavior of the function I given by

$$I(x) = \int_0^1 e^{x\cos t}\, dt \qquad \text{as } x \to \infty.$$

Solution. Taking the most obvious choice for f, namely $f(t) = -\cos t$, we see that Theorem 19.3b does not apply since $f(0) \neq 0$. Since this is the only condition of the theorem which is not fulfilled here, we write the integral in the form

$$I(x) = e^x \int_0^1 e^{x(\cos t - 1)}\, dt = e^x \int_0^1 e^{-x(1-\cos t)}\, dt$$

and apply Theorem 19.3b to the integral on the right with $f(t) = 1 - \cos t$. Then we see that

$$e^{-x}I(x) = \int_0^1 e^{-x(1-\cos t)}\, dt \sim \sqrt{\frac{\pi}{2x}}$$

or

$$I(x) \sim e^x \sqrt{\frac{\pi}{2x}}.$$

19.3c Corollary. Let f satisfy the conditions of Theorem 19.3b, and let g be continuous in $\{0 \leqslant t < a\}$. If

$$I(x) = \int_0^a g(t)e^{-xf(t)}\, dt$$

converges absolutely for x_0, then $I(x)$ converges absolutely for $x > x_0$ and

$$I(x) \sim g(0)\sqrt{\pi/2xf''(0)}.$$

Proof. For $x > x_0$,

$$|g(t)|e^{-xf(t)} \leqslant |g(t)|e^{-x_0 f(t)},$$

so that $I(x)$ converges absolutely by the comparison test.

Again we break up the integral

$$I(x) = \int_0^\delta g(t)e^{-xf(t)}\, dt + \int_\delta^a g(t)e^{-xf(t)}\, dt \equiv I_1(x) + I_2(x)$$

respectively, where δ will be specified later. Now for any fixed δ we compute, for $x \geqslant 2x_0$,

$$(1) \qquad |I_2(x)| \leqslant e^{-xf(\delta)/2}\int_\delta^a |g(t)|e^{-x_0 f(t)}\, dt \leqslant C_0 e^{-xf(\delta)/2},$$

where C_0 is a constant, namely

$$C_0 = \int_0^a |f(t)|e^{-x_0 f(t)}\, dt.$$

Let $\epsilon > 0$ be given, and choose δ so that (and this is possible by continuity)

$$g(0) - \epsilon \leqslant g(t) \leqslant g(0) + \epsilon \qquad \text{in } \{0 \leqslant t \leqslant \delta\}.$$

Multiplying this by $e^{-xf(t)}$ and integrating, we get

$$(2) \qquad [g(0) - \epsilon]\int_0^\delta e^{-xf(t)}\, dt \leqslant I_1 \leqslant [g(0) + \epsilon]\int_0^\delta e^{-xf(t)}\, dt.$$

Now

$$(3) \qquad I - |I_2| \leqslant I = I_1 + I_2 \leqslant I_1 + |I_2|,$$

so that from (1), (2), and (3) we get

$$[g(0) - \epsilon]\int_0^\delta e^{-xf(t)}\, dt - C_0 e^{-xf(\delta)/2} \leqslant I(x)$$

$$\leqslant [g(0) + \epsilon]\int_0^\delta e^{-xf(t)}\, dt + C_0 e^{-xf(\delta)/2}.$$

We multiply by $\sqrt{x}$, let $x \to \infty$, and use Theorem 19.3b on the integrals to get

$$[g(0) - \epsilon]\sqrt{\pi/2f''(0)} \leqslant \varliminf_{x \to \infty} \sqrt{x}I(x) \leqslant \varlimsup_{x \to \infty} \sqrt{x}I(x)$$

$$\leqslant [g(0) + \epsilon]\sqrt{\pi/2f''(0)},$$

for every $\epsilon > 0$. Letting $\epsilon \to 0$,

$$\lim_{x \to 0} \sqrt{x}I(x) = g(0)\sqrt{\pi/2f''(0)}. \qquad \blacksquare$$

Note that we have proved a little more than we have asserted. For if $g(0) = 0$, the preceding limit is zero, which is not possible to express in the form

$$I(x) \sim g(0)\sqrt{\pi/x2f''(0)}. \quad \text{(Why?)}$$

19.4 STIRLING'S FORMULA

We will now apply Laplace's method to the Gamma function to obtain the result known as **Stirling's formula**:

19.4a Theorem. $\Gamma(x + 1) \sim \sqrt{2\pi}\, x^{x+\frac{1}{2}}e^{-x}$ as $x \to \infty$.

Proof. In the integral formula for $\Gamma(x + 1)$, namely

$$\Gamma(x + 1) = \int_0^\infty e^{-u}u^x \, du,$$

we substitute $u = x(1 + t)$ to get

$$\Gamma(x + 1) = \int_{-1}^\infty e^{-x(1+t)}[x(1 + t)]^x x \, dt = x^{x+1}e^{-x}\int_{-1}^\infty e^{-xt}(1 + t)^x \, dt$$

or $\quad x^{-x-1}e^x\Gamma(x + 1) = \int_{-1}^\infty e^{-xt}(1 + t)^x \, dt$

$$= \int_{-1}^0 e^{-xt}(1 + t)^x \, dt + \int_0^\infty e^{-xt}(1 + t)^x \, dt \equiv I_1(x) + I_2(x)$$

respectively.

We first consider I_1:

$$I_1(x) = \int_{-1}^0 e^{-xt}(1 + t)^x \, dt = \int_0^1 e^{xt}(1 - t)^x \, dt = \int_0^1 e^{-x[-t-\log(1-t)]} \, dt.$$

We then apply Theorem 19.3b with $f(t) = -t - \log(1 - t)$.

Now $\quad f'(t) = -1 + \dfrac{1}{1 - t} = \dfrac{t}{1 - t} > 0$ in $\{0 \leqslant t < 1\}$.

and $\qquad\qquad f''(t) = \dfrac{1}{(1 - t)^2}$ $\{0 \leqslant t < 1\}$,

and in particular $f''(0) = 1$. Thus Theorem 19.3b applies and yields

$$I_1(x) \sim \sqrt{\pi/2x}.$$

We now apply the same theorem to $I_2(x)$ with $f(t) = t - \log(1 + t)$ to get

$$I_2(x) \sim \sqrt{\pi/2x}.$$

Thus $\qquad\qquad I(x) \sim 2\sqrt{\pi/2x} = \sqrt{2\pi/x},$

from which $\qquad \Gamma(x + 1) \sim \sqrt{2\pi}\, x^{x+\frac{1}{2}}e^{-x}.$ ∎

A EXERCISES

1. Investigate the asymptotic behavior of the following integrals as $x \to \infty$.

(a) $\int_0^1 (\cos t)^x \, dt$.   [*Hint:* $(\cos t)^x = e^{x \log \cos t}$.]

(b) $\int_0^{\pi/2} e^{-x \sec t} \, dt$.   (c) $\int_0^1 (1 - t^2)^x \cos t \, dt$.   (d) $\int_0^1 (2 - t^2)^x \, dt$.

2. Show that $[\Gamma(x + 1)]^{1/x} \sim x/e$ as $x \to \infty$.

B EXERCISES

1. Show that:

(a) $\Gamma(a + x) \sim \sqrt{2\pi} x^{x+a-\frac{1}{2}} e^{-x}$.   (b) $\Gamma(a + x)/\Gamma(b + x) \sim x^{a-b}$.

2. In the expansion of $(1 + x)^\alpha$, examine the asymptotic behavior of the coefficient of x^n as $n \to \infty$.

C EXERCISES

1. Using Exercise B1(b) of this section, show that for all x's, except for 0 and the negative integers,

$$\Gamma(x) = \lim_{n \to \infty} \frac{n! \, n^x}{x(x + 1) \cdots (x + n)}.$$

2. (a) Use Exercise C1 above to show that $1/\Gamma(x) = e^{\gamma x} x \prod_1^\infty (1 + x/k) e^{-x/k}$. (See Exercise C4 of Section 19.2.)

(b) Deduce $\lim_{n \to \infty} [\psi(x + n) - \log n] = 0$.

3. Suppose f has two continuous derivatives in $\{a < t < b\}$, and that there is a c between a and b such that f is decreasing in $\{a < t \leqslant c\}$ and increasing in $\{c \leqslant t < b\}$. Finally, suppose that $f'(c) = 0$ and $f''(c) > 0$. Show that if $I(x) = \int_a^b e^{-xf(t)} \, dt$ exists for $x = x_0$, then it exists for $x > x_0$ and $I(x) \sim e^{-xf(c)} \sqrt{2\pi/xf''(c)}$.

4. Suppose f satisfies the conditions of Exercise C3 above and that g is continuous in $\{a < t < b\}$. If $I(x) = \int_a^b g(t) e^{-xf(t)} \, dt$ converges absolutely for $x = x_0$, then it converges absolutely for $x > x_0$ and $I(x) \sim g(c) e^{-xf(c)}/\sqrt{2\pi/xf''(c)}$.

5. Suppose f has four continuous derivatives in $\{0 \leqslant t < a\}$, that it is increasing there, and that $f(0) = f'(0) = f''(0) = f'''(0) = 0$ and $f^{(iv)}(0) > 0$. If $I(x) = \int_0^a e^{-xf(t)} \, dt$ exists for $x = x_0$, then $I(x)$ exists for $x > x_0$ and $I(x) \sim \frac{1}{2} [4!/xf^{(iv)}(0)]^{1/4} \Gamma(\frac{1}{4})$.

20

Fourier Series

The question of representing a function by a trigonometrical series of the form

(1) $$\frac{1}{2} a_0 + \sum_{n=0}^{\infty} (a_n \cos nx + b_n \sin nx)$$

arises naturally in many problems. For example, it comes up in the solution of certain partial differential equations by the method of separation of variables. We will not pursue these applications, but mention them here merely to point out that the study of trigonometric series has intimate connections with many branches of mathematics.

As you will see, a trigonometrical series has some advantages over a power series for the representation of functions. For example, the condition of infinite differentiability that was required in the case of power series will not be needed. Also, it is possible sometimes to integrate or differentiate termwise without having satisfied the uniform convergence criteria which form the usual requirements for such operations (see Chapter 15).

Before beginning our discussion of the series (1), we note that if it converges or diverges at a point x_0, then it converges or diverges at $x_0 + 2\pi$, since each term has period 2π; for periodicity implies that the partial sums at x_0 are identical with the partial sums at $x_0 + 2\pi$, or for that matter at $x_0 + 2n\pi$, where n is any integer, positive or negative. Thus whenever the series (1) represents a function, it represents a **periodic function** with period 2π; that is, the function f must satisfy the functional equation $f(x + 2\pi) = f(x)$.

This requirement seems at first glance to place a rather heavy restriction on the class of functions with which we can deal. However, the situation

463

is not as serious as it might seem; for if we have a function f, defined in $\{-\pi < x < \pi\}$, we can define the so-called **periodic extension** of f. This is indicated pictorially in the figure and is obtained by shifting the graph of f in $\{-\pi < x < \pi\}$ by 2π, 4π, ... to the right and to the left.

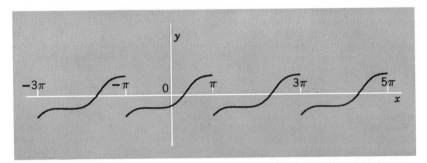

Formally, the periodicity formula provides the definition of f outside $\{-\pi < x < \pi\}$. Thus for x in $\{-3\pi < x < -\pi\}$, f is defined by $f(x) = f(x + 2\pi)$, and for x in $\{\pi < x < 3\pi\}$, f is defined by $f(x) = f(x - 2\pi), \ldots$. This leaves the value of f undetermined at odd multiples of π. There it can be defined in any manner whatever, for that will not affect the form of the series (1) associated with it, as we will see.

We turn now to simple preliminary calculations which will be useful throughout the chapter. In these calculations m and n are non-negative integers, not necessarily different. We first recall the following trigonometric formulas:

$$\sin \alpha \cos \beta = [\sin(\alpha + \beta) - \sin(\alpha - \beta)]/2$$

$$\sin \alpha \sin \beta = [\cos(\alpha - \beta) - \cos(\alpha + \beta)]/2$$

$$\cos \alpha \cos \beta = [\cos(\alpha + \beta) + \cos(\alpha - \beta)]/2.$$

From these, we get immediately

(2) $\displaystyle \int_{-\pi}^{\pi} \sin mx \cos nx \, dx = \frac{1}{2} \int_{-\pi}^{\pi} \sin(m+n)x \, dx$

$$ - \frac{1}{2} \int_{-\pi}^{\pi} \sin(m-n)x \, dx = 0$$

(3) $\displaystyle \int_{-\pi}^{\pi} \sin mx \sin nx \, dx = \begin{cases} 0 & m \neq n \\ \pi & m = n > 0 \end{cases}$

(4) $\displaystyle \int_{-\pi}^{\pi} \cos mx \cos nx \, dx = \begin{cases} 0 & m \neq n \\ \pi & m = n > 0 \\ 2\pi & m = n = 0. \end{cases}$

These integral formulas (2), (3), and (4) will be called the **orthogonality formulas**, for reasons which we will make clear later.

Now let us suppose a trigonometrical series of the form (1) converges. Its sum will therefore be a function of x, given by

$$f(x) = \frac{a_0}{2} + \sum_0^\infty (a_n \cos nx + b_n \sin nx).$$

We want to inquire first of all into the relations between f and the coefficients $\{a_n\}$, $\{b_n\}$. If the convergence of the series is such as to permit termwise integration (for example, uniform convergence would be sufficient), then we get

$$\int_{-\pi}^{\pi} f(x)\, dx = \frac{1}{2} a_0 \int_{-\pi}^{\pi} dx$$

$$+ \sum_1^\infty \left(a_n \int_{-\pi}^{\pi} \cos nx\, dx + b_n \int_{-\pi}^{\pi} \sin nx\, dx \right) = \pi a_0.$$

Thus

(5) $$a_0 = \frac{1}{\pi} \int_{-\pi}^{\pi} f(x)\, dx.$$

For $k \geqslant 1$,

$$\int_{-\pi}^{\pi} f(x) \cos kx\, dx = \int_{-\pi}^{\pi} \frac{1}{2} a_0 \cos kx\, dx$$

$$+ \sum_1^\infty \left(a_n \int_{-\pi}^{\pi} \cos nx \cos kx\, dx + b_n \int_{-\pi}^{\pi} \sin nx \sin kx\, dx \right).$$

By the orthogonality formulas, there is only one non-vanishing term in this series, and it comes when $n = k$. Thus

$$\int_{-\pi}^{\pi} f(x) \cos kx\, dx = a_k \pi$$

or

(6) $$a_k = \frac{1}{\pi} \int_{-\pi}^{\pi} f(x) \cos kx\, dx.$$

Note that (5) arises from (6) by setting $k = 0$. This is the reason for taking the constant term as $a_0/2$ rather than a_0, for now (6) covers both cases. Similarly, we compute

(7) $$b_k = \frac{1}{\pi} \int_{-\pi}^{\pi} f(x) \sin kx\, ds.$$

Let us point out that since f, by its very definition, is periodic, the integrals in (6) and (7) could equally well be taken over any interval of length 2π. In particular, this will be a useful comment when we come to discuss the convergence of trigonometrical series.

Turning the problem around, we can ask how to choose a_n and b_n so that for a given function f we have

$$f(x) = \frac{a_0}{2} + \sum_1^\infty a_n \cos nx + b_n \sin nx,$$

and we see that if they can be so chosen that term-by-term integration is permissible, then they are determined by formulas (6) and (7).

In general, if f is only integrable on $\{-\pi < x < \pi\}$, the coefficients $\{a_n\}$ and $\{b_n\}$ can be computed by formulas (6) and (7). In this case the resulting series (1) is called the **Fourier series** of f, and the numbers are called the **Fourier coefficients**. They take their names from the French mathematician J. B. J. Fourier, whose studies of heat conduction led him to consider such series.

Now a Fourier series may converge or it may diverge, and where it converges it may not converge to the function f which generated it. The remainder of this chapter will be largely devoted to discussing the convergence of Fourier series, and to the question of differentiating and integrating a Fourier series termwise.

We have as an immediate consequence of the definition the following theorem.

20.1a   Theorem. Any uniformly convergent trigonometrical series is the Fourier series of its sum.

To indicate that a Fourier series arises from a function f, we need another symbol than $=$, for the equality sign carries with it the connotation of convergence. The most common symbol is $\sim$, which we used before to indicate asymptotic equality. Therefore we will now use this symbol in a new sense.

$$f(x) \sim \frac{a_0}{2} + \sum_1^\infty (a_n \cos nx + b_n \sin nx)$$

means that the a's and b's are computed by formulas (6) and (7). The symbol $\sim$ is read "generates."

EXAMPLE 1. Calculate the Fourier series of x.

Solution. Now

$$a_n = \frac{1}{\pi} \int_{-\pi}^{\pi} x \cos nx \, dx = 0,$$

since $x \cos nx$ is an odd function. Also

$$b_n = \frac{1}{\pi} \int_{-\pi}^{\pi} x \sin nx \, dx = \frac{2}{\pi} \int_{-\pi}^{\pi} x \sin nx \, dx,$$

since $x \sin nx$ is even. Thus

$$b_n = \frac{2}{\pi} \int_0^\pi x \sin nx \, dx = -\frac{2}{n\pi} x \cos nx \Big|_0^\pi + \frac{1}{n\pi} \int_0^\pi \cos nx \, dx$$

$$= -\frac{2}{n} \cos n\pi = (-1)^{n+1} \frac{2}{n}.$$

Thus $$x \sim \sum_1^\infty \frac{2}{n} (-1)^{n+1} \sin nx.$$

EXAMPLE 2. Compute the Fourier series of f defined by

$$f(x) = \begin{cases} 0 & \{-\pi < x < 0\} \\ 1 & \{0 \leqslant x \leqslant \pi\}. \end{cases}$$

Solution:

$$a_0 = \frac{1}{\pi} \int_{-\pi}^\pi f(x) \, dx = \frac{1}{\pi} \int_0^\pi 1 \cdot dx = 1.$$

For $n \geqslant 1$,

$$a_n = \frac{1}{\pi} \int_0^\pi \cos nx \, dx = \frac{1}{n\pi} \sin nx \Big|_0^\pi = 0$$

$$b_n = \frac{1}{\pi} \int_0^\pi \sin nx \, dx = -\frac{1}{n\pi} \cos nx \Big|_0^\pi$$

$$= -\frac{1}{n\pi} [\cos n\pi - \cos 0] = -\frac{1}{n\pi} [(-1)^n - 1]$$

$$= \begin{cases} 0 & \text{if } n \text{ is even} \\ \dfrac{1}{n\pi} & \text{if } n \text{ is odd.} \end{cases}$$

Then $$f(x) \sim \frac{1}{2} + \frac{1}{\pi} \sum_0^\infty \frac{\sin (2k+1)x}{2k+1}.$$

A EXERCISES

I. Obtain the Fourier series for the following functions:

(a) $f(x) = \begin{cases} 0 & \{-\pi < x < 0\} \\ x & \{0 \leqslant x \leqslant \pi\} \end{cases}$ (b) $f(x) = \begin{cases} 0 & \{-\pi < x < 0) \\ \sin x & \{0 \leqslant x \leqslant \pi\} \end{cases}$

(c) x^2 (d) e^x

(e) $x^2 \operatorname{sgn} x$ (f) $\sin x \operatorname{sgn} x$

2. Show that if f is even, $b_n = 0$; and that if f is odd, $a_n = 0$.

B EXERCISES

I. (a) If f' is continuous in $\{-\pi \leqslant x \leqslant \pi\}$, show that there is a constant C_1, independent of n, for which $|a_n| \leqslant C_1/n$.

(b) If in addition $f(\pi) = f(-\pi)$, show that $|b_n| \leqslant C_1/n$.

(c) If in addition f'' is continuous in $\{-\pi \leqslant x \leqslant \pi\}$, show that there is a constant C_2, independent of n, for which $|b_n| \leqslant C_2/n^2$.

(d) If in addition $f'(\pi) = f'(-\pi)$, show that $|a_n| \leqslant C_2/n^2$.

2. If f is periodic of period 2π and $f^{(k)}$ is continuous, show that there is a constant C_k such that $|a_n| \leqslant C_k/n^k$, $|b_n| \leqslant C_k/n^k$.

3. Show that if t is not an integer, then

$$\cos tx \sim \frac{2t \sin \pi t}{\pi} \left(\frac{1}{2t^2} + \sum_1^\infty \frac{(-1)^k \cos kx}{t^2 - k^2} \right)$$

$$\sin tx \sim \frac{2 \sin \pi t}{\pi} \sum_1^\infty \frac{(-1)^k k \sin kx}{t^2 - k^2}.$$

C EXERCISE

I. If f is monotone and f' is integrable in $\{-\pi < x < \pi\}$, show that there is a constant C such that $|a_k| < C/k$, $|b_k| < C/k$.

20.2 APPROXIMATION IN THE MEAN. BESSEL'S INEQUALITY

In this section, we investigate the problem of "best" approximating on integrable function f in $\{-\pi \leqslant x \leqslant \pi\}$ by a trigonometric polynomial in the form of a partial sum of a trigonometric series:

$$(1) \qquad S_n(x) = \frac{c_0}{2} + \sum_1^n (c_k \cos kx + d_k \sin kx).$$

(We use c's and d's for the coefficients here, since a's and b's denote Fourier coefficients.) We now ask, for each n, how to choose the c's and d's so that S_n given by (1) will be the "best" approximation to f.

There are many ways of measuring the closeness of the approximation. For example, we might say that S_n approximates f best if the c's and d's are chosen so that $\sup_{\{-\pi \leqslant x \leqslant \pi\}} |f(x) - S_n(x)|$ is the smallest. This is in fact the sort of criterion one uses in discussing uniform convergence. Another criterion for measuring the closeness of approximation of S_n to f is the area trapped between the curves given by $y = f(x)$, $y = S_n(x)$, $x = -\pi$, $x = \pi$. This area is $\int_{-\pi}^{\pi} |f(x) - S_n(x)| \, dx$.

Still another measure of the degree of approximation, and the one which seems best suited for the discussion of Fourier series, is

$$(2) \qquad \Delta_n = \int_{-\pi}^{\pi} |f(x) - S_n(x)|^2 \, dx.$$

It should be clear that, for a given n, the S_n which is "best" in one sense probably would not be best in another. For example, if S_n fits closely to f except near one point, then the integral measures of approximation would be small, while the supremum measure could be relatively large.

Having chosen our measure of approximation, namely the Δ_n defined by (2), we can now sensibly ask what choice of c's and d's lead to the best approximation.

20.2a   Theorem. Let f be an integrable function on $\{-\pi \leqslant x \leqslant \pi\}$. Then for each n, in order that

$$\Delta_n = \int_{-\pi}^{\pi} [f(x) - S_n(x)]^2 \, dx,$$

where $\qquad S_n(x) = \dfrac{c_0}{2} + \displaystyle\sum_{k=1}^{n} (c_k \cos kx + d_k \sin kx),$

be the smallest, we must choose $c_k = a_k$ and $d_k = b_k$, where the a_k's and b_k's are the Fourier coefficients of f.

Proof. In the expression for Δ_n, we substitute for S_n, expand, and use the orthogonality formulas and the definitions of the a's and b's as Fourier coefficients:

$$\Delta_n = \int_{-\pi}^{\pi} \left[f(x) - \frac{c_0}{2} - \sum_{1}^{n} (c_k \cos kx + d_k \sin kx) \right]^2 dx$$

$$= \int_{-\pi}^{\pi} f^2(x) \, dx - 2 \int_{-\pi}^{\pi} f(x) \left[\frac{c_0}{2} + \sum_{1}^{n} (c_k \cos kx + d_k \sin kx) \right] dx$$

$$+ \int_{-\pi}^{\pi} \left[\frac{c_0}{2} + \sum_{1}^{n} (c_k \cos kx + d_k \sin kx) \right]^2 dx$$

$$= \int_{-\pi}^{\pi} f^2(x) \, dx - \pi \left[a_0 c_0 + 2\sum_{1}^{n} (a_k c_k + b_k d_k) \right] + \pi \left[\frac{c_0^2}{2} + \sum_{1}^{n} (c_k^2 + d_k^2) \right]$$

$$= \int_{-\pi}^{\pi} f^2(x) \, dx + \pi \left[\frac{1}{2} c_0^2 - a_0 c_0 + \sum_{1}^{n} (c_k^2 - 2a_k c_k) + (d_k^2 - 2b_k d_k) \right].$$

If we complete the square in each group of c's and d's, we get

$$\Delta_n = \int_{-\pi}^{\pi} f^2(x)\, dx + \pi\left[\frac{(c_0 - a_0)^2}{2} + \sum_1^n (c_k - c_k)^2 + (d_k - b_k)^2\right]$$
$$- \pi\left[\frac{a_0^2}{2} + \sum_1^n (a_k^2 + b_k^2)\right].$$

From this last formula, it is clear that the choice of c's and d's which makes Δ_n the smallest is the choice which makes the middle term the smallest. But this middle term can be made zero by choosing $c_k = a_k$ and $d_k = b_k$. ∎

Since $\Delta_n \geqslant 0$ (why?), we get as a corollary the result known as **Bessel's inequality**.

20.2b   Corollary. If f is integrable on $\{-\pi \leqslant x \leqslant \pi\}$, then

$$\frac{a_0^2}{2} + \sum_1^\infty (a_k^2 + b_k^2) \leqslant \frac{1}{\pi} \int_{-\pi}^{\pi} f^2(x)\, dx.$$

Proof. If $S_n(x) = a_0/2 + \sum_1^n (a_k \cos kx + b_k \sin kx)$, then, by the previous calculation,

$$\Delta_n = \int_{-\pi}^{\pi} f^2(x)\, dx - \pi\left[\frac{a_0^2}{2} + \sum_1^n (a_k^2 + b_k^2)\right] \geqslant 0.$$

Hence, for every n,

$$\frac{a_0^2}{2} + \sum_1^n (a_k^2 + b_k^2) \leqslant \frac{1}{\pi} \int_{-\pi}^{\pi} f^2(x)\, dx.$$

Then, by Theorem 14.2a, the result of the lemma follows. ∎

20.2c   Corollary. If f is integrable on $\{-\pi \leqslant x \leqslant \pi\}$, then $a_n \to 0$ and $b_n \to 0$.

Proof. By Theorem 14.1a, $a_n^2 + b_n^2 \to 0$ and $a_n^2 \leqslant a_n^2 + b_n^2$. Hence $a_n^2 \to 0$ and, by Theorem 2.3i, so does a_n. Similarly $b_n \to 0$. ∎

20.3   SOME USEFUL LEMMAS

We will go about building up to a convergence theorem for Fourier series. It is convenient to collect here certain useful preliminary results, and thus avoid interruption of the main argument to supply proofs of these supplementary lemmas.

We begin by summing a certain trigonometric polynomial (compare the example in Section 16.6), namely

$$D_n(\theta) = 1/2 + \cos\theta + \cos 2\theta + \cdots + \cos n\theta.$$

Multiplying by sin $\tfrac{1}{2}\theta$ and using the identity

$$\cos \alpha \sin \beta = \frac{1}{2} [\sin (\alpha + \beta) - \sin (\alpha - \beta)],$$

we get

$$\sin \tfrac{1}{2}\theta\, D_n(\theta) = \tfrac{1}{2} \sin \tfrac{1}{2}\theta + \frac{1}{2} [\sin \tfrac{3}{2}\theta - \sin \tfrac{1}{2}\theta] + \cdots$$

$$\cdots + \frac{1}{2} [\sin (n + \tfrac{1}{2})\theta - \sin (n - \tfrac{1}{2})\theta] = \frac{1}{2} \sin (n + \tfrac{1}{2})\theta$$

or, if θ is not an integral multiple of 2π, then

(1) $$D_n(\theta) = \sin (n + \tfrac{1}{2})\theta/2 \sin \tfrac{1}{2}\theta.$$

This ratio is sometimes called the **Dirichlet kernel.**

20.3a Lemma. $\dfrac{2}{\pi} \displaystyle\int_0^\pi D_n(\theta)\, d\theta = 1.$

Proof:

$$\int_0^\pi D_n(\theta)\, d\theta = \int_0^\pi \left(\frac{1}{2} + \cos \theta + \cdots + \cos n\theta\right) d\theta = \frac{\pi}{2}. \qquad \blacksquare$$

A result which is very fundamental for Fourier series will now be established. It is known as the **Riemann-Lebesgue Lemma.**

20.3b Lemma. If f is integrable on I: $\{a \leqslant x \leqslant b\}$, then

$$\lim_{t \to \infty} \int_a^b f(x) \sin tx\, dx = 0$$

and $$\lim_{t \to \infty} \int_a^b f(x) \cos tx\, dx = 0.$$

Proof. Before we begin the proof, let us note that if $a = -\pi$, $b = \pi$, and $t = n$, the result coincides with Corollary 20.2c. Thus we may consider this a generalization of that result.

We divide the proof into three parts (A), (B) and (C):

(A) Suppose, first, that f is a constant C in a subinterval of I and zero outside that interval:

$$f(x) = \begin{cases} C & \{a \leqslant \alpha \leqslant x \leqslant \beta \leqslant b\} \\ 0 & \text{otherwise.} \end{cases}$$

Then

$$\int_a^b f(x) \sin tx\, dx = C \int_\alpha^\beta \sin tx\, dx = -\frac{C}{t} \cos tx \bigg|_\alpha^\beta = C\, \frac{\cos \alpha t - \cos \beta t}{t}.$$

Thus

$$\left| \int_a^b f(x) \sin tx \, dx \right| \leqslant \frac{2|C|}{t} \to 0 \qquad \text{as } t \to \infty.$$

(*B*) Suppose f is a step function; that is, there is a partition of I such that $f(x)$ is a constant C_k in the kth subinterval I_k of the partition:

$$f(x) = C_k \qquad \text{for } x \text{ in } I_k.$$

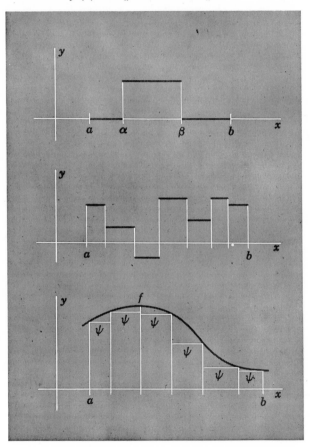

Such functions can be written as a sum of functions of the type in part (*A*):

$$\text{Set } f_k(x) = \begin{cases} C_k & x \text{ in } I_k \\ 0 & \text{otherwise.} \end{cases}$$

Then clearly
$$f(x) = \sum_1^n f_k(x)$$

so that

$$\int_a^b f(x) \sin tx \, dx = \sum_{k=1}^n \int_a^b f_k(x) \sin tx \, dx \to 0.$$

The limit is zero by part (*A*).

(*C*) Now let *f* be an arbitrary integrable function on *I*, and let $\epsilon > 0$ be given.

Since *f* is integrable, there is a lower sum which approximates the integral arbitrarily closely. But a lower sum is just the integral of a step function. For it is of the form

$$\sum_1^n m_k \Delta_k x = \sum_1^n \int_{x_{k-1}}^{x_k} m_k \, dx = \int_a^b \psi(x) \, dx,$$

where $\psi(x) = m_k$ in I_k, since a lower sum can be chosen to approximate the integral of *f* to within $\epsilon/2$. This means that there is a step function ψ, with $\psi(x) \leqslant f(x)$ in *I*, for which

$$0 \leqslant \int_a^b [f(x) - \psi(x)] \, dx = \int_a^b |f(x) - \psi(x)| \, dx \leqslant \epsilon/2.$$

Let us denote $\int_a^b f(x) \sin tx \, dx$ by I_t. Then

$$I_t = \int_a^b f(x) \sin tx \, dx = \int_a^b [f(x) - \psi(x)] \sin tx \, dx + \int_a^b \psi(x) \sin tx \, dx.$$

Thus

$$|I_t| \leqslant \int_a^b |f(x) - \psi(x)| \, dx + |\int_a^b \psi(x) \sin tx \, dx \,|.$$

The first integral is $\leqslant \epsilon/2$ and the second goes to zero as $t \to \infty$. There is then a *T* such that

$$|I_t| < \epsilon \qquad \text{if } t > T,$$

or

$$I_t \to 0 \qquad \text{as } t \to \infty.$$

Our proof has been for the integral involving the sine. It is clear that the same proof goes for the other one. ∎

20.4 CONVERGENCE THEOREMS

We want to investigate conditions under which the Fourier series of a function *f* will converge to $f(x)$ at a point *x*. At present we assume that *f* is integrable in $\{-\pi < x \leqslant \pi\}$ and is extended periodically so as to be defined for all *x*. Under these conditions we can form the Fourier series.

Our first aim is to write the nth partial sum in a suitable form:

$$S_n(x) = \frac{a_0}{2} + \sum_1^n (a_k \cos kx + b_k \sin kx)$$

$$= \frac{1}{2\pi} \int_{-\pi}^{\pi} f(t)\, dt + \frac{1}{\pi} \sum_1^n \left[\cos kx \int_{-\pi}^{\pi} f(t) \cos kt\, dt \right.$$

$$\left. + \sin kx \int_{-\pi}^{\pi} f(t) \sin kt\, dt \right]$$

$$= \frac{1}{\pi} \int_{-\pi}^{\pi} f(t) \left[\frac{1}{2} + \sum_1^n (\cos kx \cos kt + \sin kx \sin kt) \right] dt$$

$$= \frac{1}{\pi} \int_{-\pi}^{\pi} f(t) \left[\frac{1}{2} + \sum_1^n \cos k(t - x) \right] dt$$

$$= \frac{1}{\pi} \int_{-\pi}^{\pi} f(t) D_n(t - x)\, dt = \frac{1}{\pi} \int_{-\pi - x}^{\pi - x} f(x + u) D_n(u)\, du.$$

Since both f and D_n have period 2π, we can put this in the form

$$S_n(x) = \frac{1}{\pi} \int_{-\pi}^{\pi} f(x + u) D_n(u)\, du$$

$$= \frac{1}{\pi} \int_0^{\pi} f(x + u) D_n(u)\, du + \frac{1}{\pi} \int_0^{\pi} f(x - u) D_n(u)\, du$$

$$= \frac{2}{\pi} \int_0^{\pi} \frac{f(x + u) + f(x - u)}{2} D_n(u)\, du.$$

Now, by Lemma 20.3a,

$$f(x) = \frac{2}{\pi} f(x) \int_0^{\pi} D_n(u)\, du = \frac{2}{\pi} \int_0^{\pi} f(x) D_n(u)\, du$$

Thus

(1) $$S_n(x) - f(x) = \frac{2}{\pi} \int_0^{\pi} \left[\frac{f(x + u) - f(x - u)}{2} - f(x) \right] D_n(u)\, du.$$

If we set

(2) $$g(x, u) = \frac{f(x + u) - f(x - u)}{2} - f(x),$$

we get from (1)

(3) $$S_n(x) - f(x) = \frac{2}{\pi} \int_0^{\pi} g(x, u) D_n(u)\, du.$$

Thus it is clear that in order to discuss the convergence of $S_n(x)$ to $f(x)$, it is sufficient to discuss the convergence of the integral on the right side of (3). Now it turns out that the values of f which affect the convergence of $S_n(x)$ to $f(x)$ are those near the value x—that is, in an arbitrarily small neighborhood of x. This is known as the **localization principle.** If x is kept fixed and u is small, then the behavior of $g(x, u)$ near $u = 0$ is really the critical issue; in fact, the rate at which $g \to 0$ as $u \to 0$ is very important. If for some fixed x there is a $\delta_1 > 0$ such that

$$(4) \qquad \int_0^{\delta_1} \left| \frac{g(x, u)}{u} \right| du$$

exists, possibly as a convergent improper integral, we say that f satisfies the **Dini condition.** The convergence of this integral is a measure of the rate at which $g(x, u) \to 0$.

20.4a Theorem. Let f be integrable on $\{-\pi < x \leqslant \pi\}$, and let it be continued periodically outside that interval. Suppose there is an x at which f satisfies the Dini condition (4). Then for that value of x

$$S_n(x) \to f(x).$$

Proof. Let $\epsilon > 0$ be given. Choose any $\delta < \delta_1$ and compute, starting with (3):

$$|S_n(x) - f(x)| = \left| \frac{2}{\pi} \int_0^{\pi} g(x, u) D_n(u) \, du \right|$$

$$= \frac{2}{\pi} \int_0^{\delta} |g(x, u)| \, |D_n(u)| \, du + \left| \frac{2}{\pi} \int_\delta^{\pi} g(x, u) D_n(u) \, du \right|$$

$$\equiv I_1 + I_2, \quad \text{respectively.}$$

Consider first I_1:

$$I_1 = \frac{2}{\pi} \int_0^{\delta} \left| \frac{g(x, u)}{u} \right| \left| \frac{u}{2 \sin 1/2u} \right| \left| \sin \left(n + \frac{1}{2} \right) u \right| \, du.$$

Now $|u/2 \sin \tfrac{1}{2}u|$ is bounded on $\{0 < u \leqslant \pi\}$; in fact, it is non-decreasing there, so that

$$\left| \frac{u}{2 \sin 1/2u} \right| \leqslant \frac{\pi}{2}.$$

And clearly

$$\left| \sin \left(n + \frac{1}{2} \right) u \right| \leqslant 1,$$

so that

$$I_1 \leqslant \int_0^{\delta} \left| \frac{g(x, u)}{u} \right| \, du.$$

Since the integral converges, we can take δ so small that $I_1 \leqslant \epsilon/2$. Having so chosen δ, we keep it fixed and turn to I_2.

In $\{\delta \leqslant u \leqslant \pi\}$, the function $g(x, u)/2 \sin \frac{1}{2}u$ is properly integrable. Hence, by the Riemann-Lebesgue lemma $I_2 \rightarrow 0$ as $n \rightarrow \infty$. Thus there is an N so large that

$$I_2 < \epsilon/2 \qquad \text{if } n > N.$$

Thus

$$|S_n(x) - f(x)| \leqslant I_1 + I_2 \leqslant \frac{\epsilon}{2} + \frac{\epsilon}{2} = \epsilon \qquad \text{if } n > N,$$

that is

$$S_n(x) \rightarrow f(x). \qquad \blacksquare$$

This theorem gives conditions at a point x under which the Fourier series of an integrable function f will converge to $f(x)$. Of course if f satisfies this condition at each point x, then the Fourier series will converge to $f(x)$ for all x's.

It is perhaps not immediately clear whether or not a given function satisfies the Dini criterion (4) for convergence of the Fourier series. We will therefore describe a large class of functions which do satisfy this condition.

A function f is said to be **piecewise continuous** on an interval $I : \{a \leqslant x \leqslant b\}$ if there is a partition Δ of I for which f is continuous in each sub-interval, if $f(x_k + 0)$ and $f(x_k - 0)$ exist at each partition point of Δ, and finally if $f(a + 0)$ and $f(b - 0)$ both exist.

In dealing with a function which is piecewise continuous on $\{-\pi \leqslant x \leqslant \pi\}$ we will assume without further comment that the function is extended by periodicity. Also, we will normalize the value of the function at points of discontinuity—that is, the partition points of Δ—by

$$f(a_k) = \frac{1}{2}[f(a_k + 0) + f(a_k - 0)]$$

By periodicity, this implies

$$f(\pi) = f(-\pi) = \frac{1}{2}[f(-\pi + 0) + f(\pi - 0)].$$

At all other points f is continuous, so that the equation

$$f(x) = \frac{1}{2}[f(x + 0) + f(x - 0)]$$

holds for all points. This involves changing the values of f at most on a finite number of points, so that the Fourier coefficients are not altered by this normalization.

A function defined on an interval $I : \{a \leqslant x \leqslant b\}$ will be called **quasi-differentiable** there if:

(1) f is piecewise continuous on I.

(2) At each interior point x the one-sided derivatives

$$f'(x + 0) = \lim_{h \to 0+} \frac{f(x + h) - f(x + 0)}{h}$$

and

$$f'(x - 0) = \lim_{h \to 0+} \frac{f(x - h) + f(x - 0)}{h}$$

both exist. At a the right, and at b the left derivative exists. Note that condition (2) applies at jump points and at points of continuity. Thus, for example, a corner would be permitted at a point of continuity.

20.4b   Theorem. Suppose f is quasi-differentiable on $\{-\pi \leqslant x \leqslant \pi\}$ and is extended by periodicity. Then the Fourier series of f converges to the value

$$f(x) = \frac{1}{2} [f(x + 0) + f(x - 0)]$$

at each point x. In particular, at π and $-\pi$ it converges to

$$f(\pi) = f(-\pi) = \frac{1}{2} [f(-\pi + 0) + f(\pi - 0)].$$

Proof. We show that the Dini condition is satisfied at each point.

$$g(x, u) = \frac{f(x + u) + f(x - u)}{2} - f(x)$$

$$= \frac{f(x + u) - f(x + 0)}{2} + \frac{f(x - u) - f(x - 0)}{2},$$

so that

$$\left| \frac{g(x, u)}{u} \right| \leqslant \frac{1}{2} \left| \frac{f(x + u) - f(x + 0)}{u} \right| + \frac{1}{2} \left| \frac{f(x - u) - f(x - 0)}{u} \right|.$$

Now since the one-sided derivatives exist, each of these quotients is continuous and bounded for $u > 0$. Thus

$$\left| \frac{g(x, u)}{u} \right| \leqslant \frac{1}{2} M + \frac{1}{2} M = M.$$

So

$$\int_0^{\delta_1} \left| \frac{g(x, u)}{u} \right| du \text{ exists.} \qquad \blacksquare$$

Note that the class of quasi-differentiable functions includes the

piecewise smooth ones—that is, those which are constructed by piecing together differentiable functions, as for example

$$f(x) = \begin{cases} 0 & \left\{-\pi < x < \dfrac{\pi}{2}\right\} \\[2mm] x & \left\{-\dfrac{\pi}{2} < x < \dfrac{\pi}{2}\right\} \\[2mm] x^2 & \left\{\dfrac{\pi}{2} < x < \pi\right\} \end{cases}$$

Complete the definition by supplying the value of f at the partition points by the rule

$$f(x) = \frac{1}{2}\left[f(x+0) + f(x-0)\right],$$

assuming that f is extended periodically.

EXAMPLE 1. In Section 20.1, we derived the Fourier series for x. We can now assert that this series,

$$2[\sin x - \frac{1}{2}\sin 2x + \frac{1}{3}\sin 3x - \frac{1}{4}\sin 4x + - \cdots]$$

converges to x in $\{-\pi < x < \pi\}$ and to 0 at π and $-\pi$. For other values of x, it converges to the periodic extension.

Each partial sum

$$S_n(x) = 2\sum_{1}^{n}(-1)^{k+1}(\sin kx)/k$$

is continuous and has the value 0 at π. Hence the graph of S_n is a smooth curve passing through $(\pi, 0)$. The figure illustrates the behavior of S_n for $n = 1, 4, 5, 6$.

EXAMPLE 2. Let

$$f(x) = \begin{cases} 0 & -\pi < x < 0 \\ \pi & 0 < x < \pi \end{cases}$$

and be defined by periodicity outside the basic interval. Then the Fourier series of f is

$$\frac{\pi}{2} + 2\left[\sin x + \frac{1}{3}\sin 3x + \frac{1}{5}\sin 5x + \cdots\right].$$

This converges to $f(x)$ for $x \neq n\pi$ and to $\pi/2$ for $x = n\pi$. The figure illustrates the behavior of the partial sums.

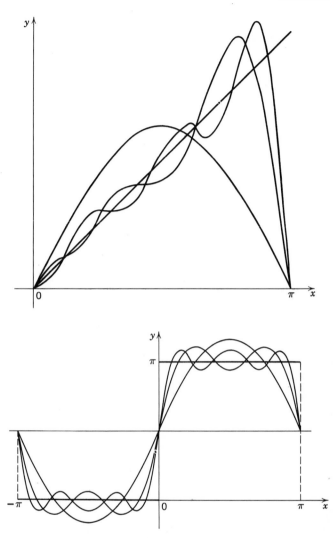

In neither of these examples does the series converge uniformly in $\{-\pi \leqslant x \leqslant \pi\}$. Why?

A EXERCISES

1. Show that all the functions in the A Exercises of Section 20.1 satisfy the conditions of Theorem 20.4b, so that their Fourier series converge. Find the sums of these series at any points of discontinuity.

2. Sketch the graphs of the first few approximating sums of the Fourier series for x^2 and e^x.

B EXERCISES

1. Let f be continuous in $\{-\pi \leqslant x \leqslant \pi\}$ and f' be integrable there. Show that

$$ka_k \to 0 \qquad (-1)^k kb_k \to \frac{f(-\pi) - f(\pi)}{\pi}.$$

2. Using the Fourier series for x^2, deduce

(a) $\displaystyle\sum_1^\infty \frac{1}{k^2} = \frac{\pi^2}{6}$
  (b) $\displaystyle\sum_1^\infty \frac{(-1)^{k+1}}{k^2} = \frac{\pi^2}{12}$

(c) $\displaystyle\sum_1^\infty \frac{1}{(2k-1)^2} = \frac{\pi^2}{8}$

20.5 DIFFERENTIATION AND INTEGRATION. UNIFORM CONVERGENCE

We have seen conditions under which a function f defined on $\{-\pi \leqslant x \leqslant \pi\}$ is representable as a Fourier series. We now want to investigate conditions under which the operations of analysis can be performed termwise on this series. Of course you recall that we have general theorems under which we may differentiate or integrate a series termwise, conditions which involve uniform convergence. It turns out that, in the case of Fourier series, these operations can be performed under considerably weaker conditions, and it is these weaker conditions we now establish.

Before we begin let us comment about integration by parts. The integration by parts formula

$$(1) \qquad \int_a^b f'g \, dx = fg \Big|_a^b - \int_a^b fg' \, dx$$

was proved under the hypothesis that f' and g' exist everywhere in $\{a \leqslant x \leqslant b\}$ and are integrable. If f' exists except at a finite number of points and is a piecewise continuous function, the same formula still applies. For suppose f' has a discontinuity at c between a and b; then we can write

$$\int_a^b f'g \, dx = \int_a^c f'g \, dx + \int_c^b f'g \, dx.$$

We can integrate each of these latter integrals by parts:

$$\int_a^c f'g \, dx = f(c)g(c) - f(a)g(a) - \int_a^c fg' \, dx.$$

and

$$\int_c^b f'g \, dx = f(b)g(b) - f(c)g(c) - \int_c^b fg' \, dx.$$

By adding, we see that the contribution arising from the point c cancels out, leaving the regular formula (1) for integration by parts. We can clearly carry the proof over to the case of a finite number of discontinuities in f'.

20.5a   Theorem. Let f be a continuous function in $\{-\pi \leqslant x \leqslant \pi\}$ and let $f(\pi) = f(-\pi)$, so that the periodic extension of f is continuous. Suppose further that f' is sectionally continuous. Thus, by Theorem 20.4b, f is represented by its Fourier series

$$f(x) = \frac{1}{2} a_0 + \sum_1^\infty (a_n \cos nx + b_n \sin nx),$$

where a_n and b_n have their usual definitions. Then, at each point x where $f''(x)$ exists, $f'(x)$ can be computed by termwise differentiation—that is

$$f'(x) = \sum_1^\infty (nb_n \cos nx - na_n \sin nx).$$

Proof. At such a·point, f' satisfies the conditions of our convergence theorem (20.4a), so that the Fourier series for f' converges at the point x. Thus for this point

$$f'(x) = \frac{a_0'}{2} + \sum_1^\infty (a_n' \cos nx + b_n' \sin nx),$$

where a_n' and b_n' are the Fourier coefficients of f'. Thus we have only to show that $a_0' = 0$, $a_n' = nb_n$, and $b_n' = -na_n$.

Since f' is sectionally continuous, integrals involving it can be integrated by parts. Thus

$$a_0' = \frac{1}{\pi} \int_{-\pi}^\pi f'(x)\,dx = \frac{1}{\pi} f(x) \Big|_{-\pi}^\pi = \frac{1}{\pi} [f(\pi) - f(-\pi)] = 0.$$

Further,

$$a_n' = \frac{1}{\pi} \int_{-\pi}^\pi f'(x) \cos nx\,dx = \frac{1}{\pi} f(x) \cos nx \Big|_{-\pi}^\pi + \frac{n}{\pi} \int_{-\pi}^\pi f(x) \sin nx\,dx$$

$$= \frac{1}{\pi} [f(\pi) - f(-\pi)] + nb_n = nb_n.$$

Similarly, $\qquad\qquad\qquad b_n' = -na_n.$ ∎

In the proof of this theorem we did not demand uniform convergence of either the original or the differentiated series. Similarly, in discussing termwise integration, we can get along without uniform convergence. In fact, we don't ask that the original series converge at all!

20.5b   Theorem. Suppose f is piecewise continuous on $\{-\pi \leqslant x \leqslant \pi\}$ and that its Fourier series is

$$f(x) \sim \frac{a_0}{2} + \sum_1^{\infty} (a_n \cos nx + b_n \sin nx).$$

Then

$$\int_{-\pi}^{x} f(x)\, dx = \frac{a_0}{2}(x + \pi) + \sum_1^{\infty} \frac{1}{n}(a_n \sin nx + b_n[\cos nx - (-1)^n])$$

in $\{-\pi \leqslant x \leqslant \pi\}$.

Proof. Define F by

$$F(x) = \int_{-\pi}^{x} f(t)\, dt - \frac{1}{2} a_0 x$$

Then F is continuous; and furthermore $F' = f - a_0/2$, and so is sectionally continuous. Also F has left- and right-hand derivatives at the points of discontinuity of f and $F(\pi) = F(-\pi)$ (why?). Then F is represented by its Fourier series:

$$F(x) = \int_{-\pi}^{x} f(t)\, dt - \frac{1}{2} a_0 x = \frac{1}{2} A_0 + \sum_1^{\infty} A_n \cos nx + B_n \sin nx,$$

where A_n and B_n are the Fourier coefficients of F. Thus for $n \geqslant 1$,

$$A_n = \frac{1}{\pi} \int_{-\pi}^{\pi} F(x) \cos nx\, dx$$

$$= \frac{1}{n\pi} F(x) \sin nx \Big|_{-\pi}^{\pi} - \frac{1}{n\pi} \int_{-\pi}^{\pi} F'(x) \sin nx\, dx$$

$$= -\frac{1}{n\pi} \int_{-\pi}^{\pi} \left[f(x) - \frac{a_0}{2} \right] \sin nx\, dx = -\frac{1}{n} b_n$$

Similarly,
$$B_n = \frac{1}{n} a_n.$$

Thus
$$F(x) = \frac{1}{2} A_0 + \sum_1^{\infty} \left(\frac{1}{n} a_n \sin nx - \frac{1}{n} b_n \cos nx \right).$$

But $F(\pi) = \pi a_0/2$, so by the previous equation

$$\frac{1}{2} a_0 \pi = \frac{1}{2} A_0 - \sum_1^{\infty} \frac{1}{n} b_n \cos n\pi = \frac{1}{2} A_0 + \sum_1^{\infty} (-1)^n \frac{b_n}{n}.$$

This evaluates A_0. Substituting the value for A_0 into the Fourier series for F, we get the result.   ∎

As the two previous theorems show, it is not necessary to demand uniform convergence in order to permit termwise integration or differentiation of a Fourier series. However, uniform convergence is convenient if it does occur. We give one criterion for the uniform convergence of Fourier series.

20.5c   Theorem. Let f be continuous, have $f(\pi) = f(-\pi)$, and have a piecewise continuous derivative in $\{-\pi \leqslant x \leqslant \pi\}$. Then the Fourier series converges uniformly and absolutely to f in that interval. Furthermore,

$$|f(x) - S_n(x)| \leqslant \frac{C}{\sqrt{n}},$$

where $\qquad S_n(x) = \dfrac{a_0}{2} + \sum_1^n (a_k \cos kx + b_k \sin kx)$

and $\qquad C^2 = \dfrac{1}{\pi} \displaystyle\int_{-\pi}^{\pi} f'(x)^2 \, dx.$

Proof. Let us denote the Fourier coefficients of f by a_n and b_n, and those of f' by a_n' and b_n'. Then

(1) $\qquad\qquad a_n' = nb_n \quad \text{and} \quad b_n' = -na_n,$

and, by Corollary 20.2b,

(2) $\qquad \dfrac{a_0'^2}{2} + \sum_1^\infty (a_n'^2 + b_n'^2) \leqslant \dfrac{1}{\pi} \displaystyle\int_{-\pi}^{\pi} f'(x)^2 \, dx,$

since f' is integrable.

Let us consider

$$|S_m(x) - S_n(x)| = \sum_{n+1}^m (a_k \cos kx + b_k \sin kx).$$

Then (see Exercise A3),

$$|S_m(x) - S_n(x)| \leqslant \sum_{n+1}^m \sqrt{a_k^2 + b_k^2} = \sum_{n+1}^m \frac{1}{k}\sqrt{a_k'^2 + b_k'^2}.$$

Now, by the Cauchy-Schwarz inequality,

(3) $\qquad |S_m(x) - S_n(x)| \leqslant \left(\sum_{n+1}^m \dfrac{1}{k^2} \right)^{1/2} \left(\sum_{n+1}^m (a_k'^2 + b_k'^2) \right)^{1/2}$

But

(4) $\qquad \displaystyle\sum_{n+1}^m (a_k'^2 + b_k^2) \leqslant \dfrac{1}{\pi} \displaystyle\int_{-\pi}^{\pi} f'(x)^2 \, dx$

and

(5) $\qquad \displaystyle\sum_{n+1}^m \dfrac{1}{k^2} \leqslant \sum_{n+1}^\infty \dfrac{1}{k^2} \leqslant \int_n^\infty \dfrac{dx}{x^2} = \dfrac{1}{n}\,.$

Thus from (3), (4), and (5) we get

(6) $$|S_m(x) - S_n(x)| \leqslant C/\sqrt{n},$$

where $$C^2 = \frac{1}{\pi} \int_{-\pi}^{\pi} f'(x)^2 \, dx.$$

This proves uniform convergence by the Cauchy criterion. If we note that by Theorem 20.4b $S_m(x) \to f(x)$ at each point we get immediately from (6), if we let $m \to \infty$,

$$|f(x) - S_n(x)| \leqslant C/\sqrt{n}. \qquad \blacksquare$$

20.6 SINE AND COSINE SERIES. CHANGE OF SCALE

We have noted in an earlier exercise (A2 of Section 20.1) that if f is even, its Fourier series consists only of cosine terms and the constant term; and that if f is odd, its Fourier series consists only of sine terms. We will now examine this phenomenon a little more closely.

Let f be given in $\{0 < x < \pi\}$. If we define f in $\{-\pi < x < 0\}$ to be an even function—that is, by $f(x) = f(-x)$—we say we have an **even extension** of f. If we define f in $\{-\pi < x < 0\}$ to be an odd function— that is, by $f(x) = -f(-x)$—we say we have an **odd extension** of f. If we then extend f by periodicity to have a period of 2π, these two extensions give rise respectively, to the **even periodic extension** and the **odd periodic extension** of f. In all cases we normalize by

$$f(x) = \frac{1}{2}[f(x+0) + f(x-0)]$$

at points of discontinuity, and at zero and the multiples of π.

In the case of the even extension, the Fourier series for f reduces to a series involving only the constant term and the cosine terms:

$$f(x) \sim \frac{a_0}{2} + \sum_1^\infty a_n \cos nx \qquad b_n = 0.$$

This is called the **cosine series** for f, and

$$a_n = \frac{1}{\pi} \int_{-\pi}^{\pi} f(x) \cos nx \, dx = \frac{2}{\pi} \int_0^{\pi} f(x) \cos nx \, dx. \qquad \text{(How?)}$$

In the case of the odd extension, the Fourier series for f reduces to a series involving only the sine terms:

$$f(x) \sim \sum_1^\infty b_n \sin nx \qquad a_n = 0$$

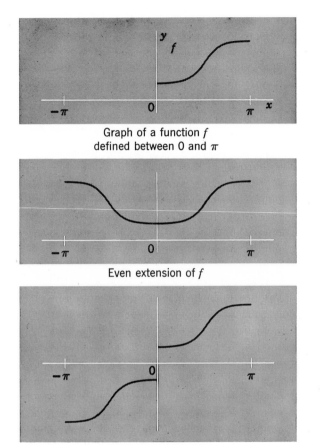

Graph of a function f
defined between 0 and π

Even extension of f

Odd extension of f

This is called the **sine series** for f and

$$b_n = \frac{1}{\pi} \int_{-\pi}^{\pi} f(x) \sin nx \, dx = \frac{2}{\pi} \int_{0}^{\pi} f(x) \sin nx \, dx. \qquad \text{(How?)}$$

EXAMPLE. Since x is odd, the complete Fourier series for x is a sine series. We now compute the cosine series.

Solution:

$$a_0 = \frac{2}{\pi} \int_{0}^{\pi} x \, dx = \frac{2}{\pi} \frac{\pi^2}{2} = \pi,$$

and for $n > 0$

$$a_n = \frac{2}{\pi} \int_{0}^{\pi} x \cos nx \, dx = \frac{2}{\pi} \frac{1}{n^2} [(-1)^n - 1] = \begin{cases} 0 & n \text{ even} \\ \dfrac{-4}{\pi n^2} & n \text{ odd}. \end{cases}$$

Thus

$$|x| = \pi - \frac{4}{\pi} \sum_1^\infty \frac{\cos(2k+1)x}{(2k+1)^2}.$$

We can have Fourier series over other intervals than $\{-\pi \leqslant x \leqslant \pi\}$. Let $\phi(y)$ be integrable over $\{-L \leqslant y \leqslant L\}$. If we substitute $y = Lx/\pi$ and let $f(x) = \phi(Lx/\pi)$, we get

(1) $$f(x) \sim \frac{a_0}{2} + \sum_1^\infty (a_n \cos nx + b_n \sin nx),$$

where

(2) $$a_n = \frac{1}{\pi} \int_{-\pi}^\pi f(x) \cos nx \, dx = \frac{1}{L} \int_{-L}^L \phi(y) \cos \frac{n\pi y}{L} \, dy$$

and

(3) $$b_n = \frac{1}{\pi} \int_{-\pi}^\pi f(x) \sin nx \, dx = \frac{1}{L} \int_{-L}^L \phi(y) \sin \frac{n\pi y}{L} \, dy.$$

Now (1) becomes

$$\phi(y) \sim \frac{a_0}{2} + \sum_1^\infty a_n \cos \frac{n\pi y}{L} + b_n \sin \frac{n\pi y}{L},$$

where a_n and b_n are given by (2) and (3).

Evidently no new problems arise in discussing convergence. We have simply made a change of scale taking $\{-\pi \leqslant x \leqslant \pi\}$ into $\{-L \leqslant y \leqslant L\}$. It is clear that there are sine and cosine series for this new interval. By translation, we could consider Fourier series over any interval $\{a \leqslant x \leqslant b\}$ not centered at the origin.

A EXERCISES

1. Compute the sine and cosine series for the following functions on $\{0 \leqslant x \leqslant \pi\}$:

    (a) $\sin x$ (b) $\cos x$ (c) 1   (d) e^x

2. Compute the Fourier series of the following functions on the interval $\{-L \leqslant x \leqslant L\}$:

    (a) x^2 (b) $x^2 + x$ (c) 1

3. Show that $|a_k \cos kx + b_k \sin kx| \leqslant \sqrt{a_k^2 + b_k^2}$.

4. Write out the form of the Fourier series over $\{a \leqslant x \leqslant b\}$ and give formulas for the coefficients.

B EXERCISES

1. Let f satisfy the conditions of Theorem 20.5c. Show that

    (a) $$\frac{a_0^2}{2} + \sum^\infty (a_k^2 + b_k^2) = \frac{1}{\pi} \int_{-\pi}^\pi f^2(x) \, dx.$$

(b) If g is integrable then

$$\frac{1}{\pi} \int_{-\pi}^{\pi} f(x)g(x) \, dx = \frac{1}{2} a_0 \alpha_0 + \sum_1^{\infty} (a_n \alpha_n + b_n \beta_n),$$

where α_n and β_n are the Fourier coefficients of g.

2. Suppose f is periodic and has m continuous derivatives in $\{-\pi \leqslant x \leqslant \pi\}$. Show that

$$|f(x) - S_n(x)| \leqslant \frac{C}{n^{m-\frac{1}{2}}},$$

where

$$C^2 = \frac{1}{(2m-1)\pi} \int_{-\pi}^{\pi} [f^{(m)}(x)]^2 \, dx.$$

20.7 THE FOURIER INTEGRAL

Suppose f is bounded, integrable, and absolutely integrable from $-\infty$ to $+\infty$; that is, suppose both

$$\int_{-\infty}^{\infty} f(x) \, dx \quad \text{and} \quad \int_{-\infty}^{\infty} |f(x)| \, dx$$

exist (see Exercises B3 and B4). Then for any interval $\{-L \leqslant x \leqslant L\}$ the Fourier series for f is

$$f(x) \sim \frac{a_0}{2} + \sum_1^{\infty} \left(a_n \cos \frac{n\pi x}{L} + b_n \sin \frac{n\pi x}{L} \right),$$

where the coefficients are given by (2) and (3) of Section 20.6. We want to examine, quite heuristically, the behavior of this series as $L \to \infty$.

First we note that

$$|a_0| = \left| \frac{1}{L} \int_{-L}^{L} f(t) \, dt \right| \leqslant \frac{1}{L} \int_{-L}^{L} |f(t)| \, dt \leqslant \frac{1}{L} \int_{-\infty}^{\infty} |f(t)| \, dt \to 0.$$

We also have

$$\sum_1^{\infty} \left(a_n \cos \frac{n\pi x}{L} + b_n \sin \frac{n\pi x}{L} \right)$$

$$= \sum_1^{\infty} \frac{1}{L} \int_{-L}^{L} f(t) \left[\cos \frac{n\pi t}{L} \cos \frac{n\pi x}{L} + \sin \frac{n\pi t}{L} \sin \frac{n\pi x}{L} \right] dt$$

$$= \sum_1^{\infty} \frac{1}{L} \int_{-L}^{L} f(t) \cos \left(\frac{n\pi}{L} (x - t) \right) dt.$$

Now we set $n\pi/L = u_n$, $\Delta_n u = \pi/L$, so that our sum becomes

$$\frac{1}{\pi} \sum_1^\infty \Delta_n u \int_{-L}^L f(t) \cos \left[u_n(x - t) \right] dt.$$

This looks somewhat like a Riemann sum of a function F, defined by

$$F(u) = \frac{1}{\pi} \int_{-L}^L f(t) \cos u(x - t) \, dt.$$

So as $L \to \infty$, our sum seems to converge to

$$\frac{1}{\pi} \int_0^\infty du \int_{-\infty}^\infty f(t) \cos u(x - t) \, dt.$$

We write

$$f(x) \sim \frac{1}{\pi} \int_0^\infty du \int_{-\infty}^\infty f(t) \cos u(x - t) \, dt,$$

where, as in the case of Fourier series, we read the symbol $\sim$ as "corresponds to."

The above argument is an outline of Fourier's original discussion. Although it is no longer considered an acceptable proof, it is interesting historically and enables us to write down the formula. Our aim in this section is to give a convergence proof of this formula and to indicate something of its utility.

20.7a   Theorem. Suppose f is bounded and $\displaystyle\int_{-\infty}^\infty f(x) \, dx$ and $\displaystyle\int_{-\infty}^\infty |f(x)| \, dx$ both exist, and that f satisfies the Dini condition at a point x— that is, there is a $\delta_1 > 0$ such that $\displaystyle\int_0^{\delta_1} \left| \frac{g(x, y)}{y} \right| dy$ exists, where

$$g(x, y) = \frac{f(x + y) + f(x - y)}{2} - f(x).$$

Then for that x we have

$$f(x) = \frac{1}{\pi} \int_0^\infty du \int_{-\infty}^\infty f(t) \cos u(x - t) \, dt.$$

Proof. The integral we want to evaluate is the limit as $a \to \infty$ of

$$I_a(x) \equiv \frac{1}{\pi} \int_0^a du \int_{-\infty}^\infty f(t) \cos u(x - t) \, dt.$$

Now the inner integral converges uniformly with respect to u by the M test for

$$|f(t) \cos u(x - t)| \leqslant |f(t)|.$$

Hence we can interchange the order of integration,

$$I_a(x) = \frac{1}{\pi} \int_{-\infty}^{\infty} f(t) \left[\int_0^a \cos u(x - t) \, du \right] dt$$

$$= \frac{1}{\pi} \int_{-\infty}^{\infty} f(t) \frac{\sin a(x - t)}{x - t} \, dt$$

$$= \frac{1}{\pi} \int_{-\infty}^{\infty} f(x - y) \frac{\sin ay}{y} \, dy$$

$$= \frac{1}{\pi} \int_0^{\infty} f(x - y) \frac{\sin ay}{y} \, dy + \frac{1}{\pi} \int_{-\infty}^0 f(x - y) \frac{\sin ay}{y} \, dy.$$

We replace y by $-y$ in the second integral and combine it with the first one to get

$$I_a(x) = \frac{2}{\pi} \int_0^{\infty} \frac{f(x + y) + f(x - y)}{2} \frac{\sin ay}{y} \, dy.$$

Now, by Theorem 18.3f, we have for $a > 0$,

$$1 = \frac{2}{\pi} \int_0^{\infty} \frac{\sin ay}{y} \, dy,$$

so that

$$f(x) = \frac{2}{\pi} \int_0^{\infty} f(x) \frac{\sin ay}{y} \, dy.$$

Thus

$$I_a(x) - f(x) = \frac{2}{\pi} \int_0^{\infty} \left[\frac{f(x + y) + f(x - y)}{2} - f(x) \right] \frac{\sin ay}{y} \, dy$$

$$= \frac{2}{\pi} \int_0^{\infty} \frac{g(x, y)}{y} \sin ay \, dy.$$

From now on the proof is similar to that used with Fourier series, except that it is a little more complicated because the upper limit of integration is infinite.

We estimate as follows:

$$I_a(x) - f(x) = \frac{2}{\pi} \int_0^b \frac{g(x,y)}{y} \sin ay \, dy + \frac{2}{\pi} \int_b^{\infty} \frac{f(x + y) + f(x - y)}{2} \frac{\sin ay}{y} \, dy$$

$$- \frac{2}{\pi} \int_b^{\infty} f(x) \frac{\sin ay}{y} \, dy \equiv J_1 + J_2 + J_3 \text{ respectively.}$$

Since the integral J_3 is convergent, we know that for each $\epsilon > 0$ there is a B_1 such that

$$|J_3| \leqslant \frac{2}{\pi} |f(x)| \left| \int_b^{\infty} \frac{\sin ay}{y} \, dy \right| < \epsilon \qquad \text{if } b > B_1.$$

Also

$$|J_2| \leqslant \frac{2}{\pi} \int_b^\infty \frac{|f(x+y)| + |f(x-y)|}{2} \frac{dy}{y}$$

$$\leqslant \frac{1}{\pi b} \int_{-\infty}^\infty [|f(x+y)| + |f(x-y)|] \, dy = \frac{2}{\pi b} \int_{-\infty}^\infty |f(t)| \, dt$$

Thus $|J_2| < \epsilon$ if $b > B_2 \equiv \dfrac{2}{\pi \epsilon} \displaystyle\int_{-\infty}^\infty |f(t)| \, dt$. We now choose $b > \max [B_1, B_2]$ and keep it fixed.

We now return to estimate J_1. We choose $\delta < \delta_1$, and so small that

$$\frac{2}{\pi} \int_0^\delta \left| \frac{g(x,y)}{y} \right| dy < \epsilon.$$

Then
$$J_1 = \left| \frac{2}{\pi} \int_0^b \frac{g(x,y)}{y} \sin ay \, dy \right| \leqslant \frac{2}{\pi} \int_0^\delta \left| \frac{g(x,y)}{y} \right| dy$$

$$+ \frac{2}{\pi} \left| \int_\delta^b \frac{g(x,y)}{y} \sin ay \, dy \right|$$

$$\leqslant \epsilon + \frac{2}{\pi} \left| \int_\delta^b \frac{g(x,y)}{y} \sin ay \, dy \right|.$$

By the Riemann-Lebesgue lemma, this last integral vanishes when $a \to \infty$. Thus there is a $A > 0$

$$\left| \frac{2}{\pi} \int_\delta^b \frac{g(x,y)}{y} \sin ay \, dy \right| < \epsilon \qquad \text{if } a > A.$$

Thus for $a > A$ we have

$$|I_a(x) - f(x)| \leqslant |J_1| + |J_2| + |J_3| \leqslant 4\epsilon. \qquad \blacksquare$$

20.7b Corollary. Suppose f is quasi-differentiable and both $\displaystyle\int_{-\infty}^\infty f(x) \, dx$ and $\displaystyle\int_{-\infty}^\infty |f(x)| \, dx$ exist. Then for every x

$$\frac{1}{2} [f(x+0) + f(x-0)] = \frac{1}{\pi} \int_0^\infty du \int_{-\infty}^\infty f(t) \cos u(x - t) \, dt.$$

Proof. Prove this corollary by Theorem 20.4b. $\qquad \blacksquare$

If f is an odd function, the Fourier integral reduces to

$$\frac{2}{\pi} \int_0^\infty du \int_0^\infty f(t) \sin ux \sin ut \, dt.$$

If f is even, the integral becomes

$$\frac{2}{\pi} \int_0^\infty du \int_0^\infty f(t) \cos ux \cos ut.$$

Thus if f is quasi-differentiable in $\{x > 0\}$ and $\int_0^\infty |f(x)| \, dx$ exists, then f can be extended to be either even or odd. So, by Theorem 20.7b,

(1)
$$\begin{cases} \dfrac{1}{2}[f(x+0) + f(x-0)] = \dfrac{2}{\pi} \displaystyle\int_0^\infty du \int_0^\infty f(t) \sin ux \sin ut \, dt \\[3mm] \qquad\qquad\qquad\quad = \dfrac{2}{\pi} \displaystyle\int_0^\infty du \int_0^\infty f(t) \cos ux \cos ut \, dt. \end{cases}$$

The integrals

$$g(u) = \sqrt{\frac{2}{\pi}} \int_0^\infty f(t) \sin ut \, dt$$

and

$$h(u) = \sqrt{\frac{2}{\pi}} \int_0^\infty f(t) \cos ut \, dt,$$

when they exist, are called respectively the **Fourier sine** and **cosine transform** of f. It it is known, for example, that f satisfies the conditions of Theorem 20.7b, and if g and h are both given for $u \geqslant 0$, then we can use the formulas (1) to recover f. Thus

$$\frac{1}{2}[f(x+0) + f(x-0)] = \sqrt{\frac{2}{\pi}} \int_0^\infty g(u) \sin ux \, du$$

$$= \sqrt{\frac{2}{\pi}} \int_0^\infty h(u) \cos ux \, du.$$

B EXERCISES

1. Use the Fourier cosine integral on f, defined by

$$f(x) = \begin{cases} 1 & \{0 \leqslant x \leqslant 1\} \\ 0 & \{x > 1\}, \end{cases}$$

to evaluate $\displaystyle\int_0^\infty \frac{\sin u \cos ux}{u} \, du$.

2. Use the Fourier sine integral on f, defined by

$$f(x) = \begin{cases} \sin x & \{0 \leqslant x \leqslant \pi\} \\ 0 & \{x > \pi\}, \end{cases}$$

to evaluate $\displaystyle\int_0^\infty \frac{\sin ux \sin \pi u}{1 - u^2} \, du$.

(Is this integral improper at $u = 1$?)

3. Give an example of a function for which $\int_{-\infty}^{\infty} f(x)\,dx$ exists and $\int_{-\infty}^{\infty} |f(x)|\,dx$ does not.

4. Give an example of a function for which $\int_{-\infty}^{\infty} |f(x)|\,dx$ exists and $\int_{-\infty}^{\infty} f(x)\,dx$ does not.

5. Show by use of the cosine integral that

$$\int_0^{\infty} \frac{\cos ux}{a^2 + u^2}\,du = \frac{\pi}{2a}\,e^{-a|x|} \qquad a > 0, \{-\infty < x < \infty\}.$$

6. The existence theorem gave sufficient conditions under which the Fourier integral exists. Prove that the Fourier integral of $(\sin x)/x$ exists, thus showing that the requirement of the existence of $\int_{-\infty}^{\infty} |f(x)|\,dx$ is not a necessary condition.

7. Write out the Fourier integral for f given by

$$f(x) = \begin{cases} 0 & \{x < 0\} \\ e^{-x} & \{x > 0\} \end{cases}$$

and evaluate $\int_0^{\infty} \frac{\cos xt + t \sin xt}{1 + t^2}\,dt.$

8. Let f be given by

$$f(x) = \begin{cases} 0 & \{x < 0\} \\ 1 & \{0 \leqslant x \leqslant 1\} \\ 0 & \{x > 1\}. \end{cases}$$

Evaluate $\int_0^{\infty} \frac{(\sin t \cos xt + \sin xt - \cos t \sin xt)}{t}\,dt.$

20.8 FUNCTION SPACES. COMPLETE ORTHONORMAL SETS

A collection of mathematical objects (such as functions, numbers) which satisfy Theorems 8.1a and b is called a **vector space**. If this collection of objects happens to be a collection of functions defined on a certain interval, it is called a **function space**. For example, the set of functions defined on $\{a \leqslant x \leqslant b\}$ is such a space. So also is the collection of integrable functions, as well as the collection of continuous functions.

We will discuss here the function space which consists of the set of continuous functions defined on $\{-\pi \leqslant x \leqslant \pi\}$. This set of functions will be denoted by $\mathscr{F}$. It will be clear that a translation and a change of scale will reduce any interval to this one, so the considerations are typical.

We define the **inner product** (f, g) of two functions in $\mathscr{F}$ by

$$(f, g) = \int_{-\pi}^{\pi} f(x)g(x) \, dx$$

and the **norm** of f, namely $\|f\|$, by

$$\|f\| = \sqrt{\int_{-\pi}^{\pi} f^2(x) \, dx} = \sqrt{(f, f)}$$

20.8a   Lemma. $\|f\| = 0$ if, and only if, $f(x) \equiv 0$ in $\{-\pi \leqslant x \leqslant \pi\}$.

Proof. Clearly if $f(x) \equiv 0$, then $f^2(x) \equiv 0$ and

$$\|f\| = \sqrt{\int_{-\pi}^{\pi} 0 \, dx} = 0.$$

Conversely, if $\|f\| = 0$, then $\|f\|^2 = 0$,

so that $$\int_{-\pi}^{\pi} f^2(x) \, dx = 0.$$

Suppose there were an x_0 at which $f(x) \neq 0$. Then $f^2(x_0) > 0$ and, by Theorem 3.2c, there is a neighborhood—say $\{x_0 - \delta \leqslant x \leqslant x_0 + \delta\}$—in which $f^2(x) > \frac{1}{2} f^2(x_0)$. Then

$$0 = \int_{-\pi}^{\pi} f^2(x) \, dx > \int_{x_0 - \delta}^{x_0 + \delta} f^2(x) \, dx > \frac{1}{2} f^2(x_0)(2\delta) = \delta f^2(x_0) > 0.$$

This contradiction completes the proof. ∎

This lemma is the analogue of Theorem 8.1c. There is also a Cauchy-Schwarz inequality:

20.8b   Theorem. $(f, g) \leqslant \|f\| \|g\|$ and equality holds if, and only if, one function is a constant multiple of the other.

Proof. In the presence of Lemma 20.8a, the proof is formally identical with that of Theorem 8.2c. ∎

From this we also get the triangle inequality by the same argument as that used with Theorem 8.2e.

20.8c   Theorem. $\|f + g\| \leqslant \|f\| + \|g\|$.

We define **orthogonality** in terms of the inner product; f and g are **orthogonal** if

$$(f, g) = \int_{-\pi}^{\pi} f(x)g(x) \, dx = 0.$$

A set of functions is said to be an **orthogonal set** if any two distinct members are orthogonal, and it is an **orthonormal set** if each function has unit norm. For example, the set of functions

$$\{1, \sin \theta, \cos \theta, \sin 2\theta, \cos 2\theta, \ldots\}$$

is an infinite set of orthogonal functions by formulas (2), (3), and (4) of Section 20.1. They can be normalized by dividing each function by its norm. Thus

$$\left\{\frac{1}{\sqrt{2\pi}}, \frac{1}{\sqrt{\pi}} \sin \theta, \frac{1}{\sqrt{\pi}} \cos \theta, \frac{1}{\sqrt{\pi}} \sin 2\theta, \frac{1}{\sqrt{\pi}} \cos 2\theta, \ldots\right\}$$

form an orthonormal set.

Now let the functions

$$\{\phi_0, \phi_1, \phi_2 \ldots, \phi_n, \ldots\}$$

be an orthonormal set in $\mathscr{F}$. We can inquire about the possibility of representing an arbitrary member of our function space in terms of the ϕ's. We ask whether there are c's such that

(1) $$f = c_0\phi_0 + c_1\phi_1 + c_2\phi_2 + \cdots + c_n\phi_n + \cdots.$$

If it is possible, and if termwise integration is permissible, we can compute

$$(f, \phi_k) = (c_0\phi_0 + c_1\phi_1 + \cdots, \phi_k)$$
$$= c_0(\phi_0, \phi_k) + c_1(\phi_1, \phi_k) + \cdots + c_k(\phi_k, \phi_k) + \cdots$$

(2) $$(f, \phi_k) = c_k.$$

The c_k's so determined are called the **generalized Fourier coefficients** of f with respect to orthonormal system of ϕ's. Thus if f can be expanded in the form (1), then the c_k's are given by (2).

20.8d Theorem. For each n, the choice of a_k's so that $t_n = \sum_0^\infty a_k\phi_k$ best approximates f in norm is $a_k = c_k$.

Proof. The problem is to choose the a's so that $\|f - t_n\|$ is the least. Equivalently, we can make $\|f - t_n\|^2$ a minimum:

$$\|f - t_n\|^2 = (f - t_n, f - t_n) = \left(f - \sum_0^n a_k\phi_k, f - \sum_0^n a_k\phi_k\right)$$
$$= (f, f) - 2\sum_0^n a_k(f, \phi_k) + \sum_0^n \sum_0^n a_k a_j(\phi_k, \phi_j).$$

Using the definition of c_k and the orthonormality of the ϕ's, this reduces to

(3) $$\begin{cases} \|f - t_n\|^2 = \|f\|^2 - 2\sum_0^n a_k c_k + \sum_0^n a_k^2 \\ \qquad = \|f\|^2 + 2\sum_0^n (a_k - c_k)^2 - \sum_0^n c_k^2, \end{cases}$$

which is clearly the smallest when $a_k = c_k$. ∎

We will denote $\sum_{0}^{n} c_k \phi_k$ by S_n. Thus choosing $t_n = S_n$ in the previous theorem yields the following corollary.

20.8e Corollary (Bessel's Inequality). For any f in $\mathscr{F}$,

$$\sum_{0}^{\infty} c_k^2 \leqslant \|f\|^2.$$

Proof. Choose $t_n = S_n$. By (3),

$$\sum_{0}^{n} c_k^2 \leqslant \|f\|^2 \qquad \text{for every } n. \qquad \blacksquare$$

We return to comment very briefly on point sets, mainly to make a definition. Let A be one set of points and B a sub-set of A. We say that B is **dense** in A, if, given any point $\mathbf{P_0}$ in A, there is a sequence of points $\{\mathbf{P_n}\}$ in B with $\mathbf{P_n} \to \mathbf{P_0}$. For example, the rationals are dense in the reals, for the decimal expansion (see Exercises C3 and C4 of Section 2.7) of a real number x represents such a sequence of rationals converging to x.

Now back to function spaces: we say an orthonormal set $\{\phi_n\}$ is **complete** in $\mathscr{F}$ if $\|f - S_n\| \to 0$, where, of course, $S_n = \sum_{0}^{n} c_k \phi_k$ with $c_k = (f, \phi_k)$.

We find viewing $\mathscr{F}$ as a collection of "points"—that is, functions playing the role of points—with the distance between two "points" f and g being given by $\|f - g\|$, to be very illuminating. The reason is that there is a certain formal resemblance between sets of points and sets of functions, since the "distance" (norm of the difference) satisfies the three conditions upon which most geometrical properties of point sets depend, namely,

(1) $\|f\| \geqslant 0$.
(2) $\|f\| = 0$ if, and only if, $f \equiv 0$.
(3) the triangle inequality $\|f + g\| \ \|<f\| + \|g\|$.

Let us denote by L the set of all finite linear combinations of the ϕ's—that is, the set of all functions of the form

$$\sum_{0}^{n} a_k \phi_k.$$

Then the set $\{\phi_n\}$ being complete in $\mathscr{F}$ means that L is dense in $\mathscr{F}$ in a point-set sense: given any "point" f in $\mathscr{F}$, there is a sequence of "points" S_n in L which converge to f, where convergence is in the sense of the norm or "distance" tending to zero. The converse is also true (see Exercise B2).

This type of convergence, namely convergence in norm, does not imply pointwise convergence of the sequence of functions S_n to the function f

on $\{-\pi \leqslant x \leqslant \pi\}$. But for many purposes of advanced analysis it is of equal or greater importance.

Now a consequence of completeness is **Parseval's theorem**, which follows.

20.8f Theorem. If f is in $\mathscr{F}$ and $\{\phi_n\}$ is a complete orthonormal set in $\mathscr{F}$, then

$$\sum_0^\infty c_k^2 = \|f\|^2,$$

where

$$c_k = (f, \phi_k).$$

Proof. From the proof of Bessel's inequality,

$$\|f - S_n\|^2 = \|f\|^2 - \sum_0^n c_k^2 \to 0 \qquad \text{as } n \to \infty. \qquad \blacksquare$$

This theorem strengthens our view of $\mathscr{F}$ as a vector space. The set $\{\phi_n\}$ plays the role of an orthonormal basis, c_k being the projection of f in the "direction" of the basis vector ϕ_k—i.e. the component of the vector in the kth direction. Finally, the norm or length of the vector is the square root of the sum of the squares of the components:

$$\|f\| = \sqrt{c_0^2 + c_1^2 + c_2^2 + \cdots + c_n^2 \cdots}.$$

The analogy, while very useful, cannot be pushed too far. In finite dimensional Euclidean vector spaces, the vector is the sum of its components in the basis directions. The analogue here would be

$$f = \sum_0^\infty c_k \phi_k = c_0 \phi_0 + c_1 \phi_1 + \cdots + c_n \phi_n + \cdots.$$

Equality in the sense of pointwise convergence is not always the case here, however.

It is in fact true that the trigonometric functions

$$\left\{ \frac{1}{\sqrt{2\pi}}, \frac{1}{\sqrt{\pi}} \sin \theta, \frac{1}{\sqrt{\pi}} \cos \theta, \frac{1}{\sqrt{\pi}} \sin 2\theta, \frac{1}{\sqrt{\pi}} \cos 2\theta, \ldots \right\}$$

form a complete orthonormal set in $\mathscr{F}$, though we will not prove it. This, then, implies that the Parseval equation holds for the trigonometric functions. Thus if f is in $\mathscr{F}$,

$$\frac{1}{\pi} \int_{-\pi}^\pi f^2(x) \, dx = \frac{a_0^2}{2} + \sum_0^\infty (a_k^2 + b_k^2).$$

B EXERCISES

1. A set of functions (ϕ_k), finite or infinite in number, is said to be **linearly dependent** if there is a finite linear combination of them without zero coefficients which vanishes identically. Otherwise it is linearly independent. Show that an orthogonal set is linearly independent.

2. Let $\{\phi_n\}$ be an orthonormal set in $\mathscr{F}$, and let L be the set of all finite linear combinations of the ϕ's. Show that if L is dense in $\mathscr{F}$, then $\{\phi_n\}$ is complete.

3. Show that the inner product satisfies Theorem 8.2b: (i) $(f, g) = (g, f)$; (ii) $(f, g + h) = (f, g) + (f, h)$; (iii) $(af, g) = (f, ag) = a(f, g)$; (iv) $(f, f) = \| f \|^2$.

4. If $\{\phi_n\}$ is a complete orthonormal set in $\mathscr{F}$, and if f and g are in $\mathscr{F}$ with $f \sim \sum_0^\infty c_k \phi_k$ and $g \sim \sum_0^\infty b_k \phi_k$, show that:

(a) $f \pm g \sim \sum_0^\infty (c_k \pm b_k)\phi_k$.

(b) $\sum_0^\infty c_k b_k$ converges and $(f, g) = \sum_0^\infty c_k b_k$. (*Hint:* Consider $\| f + g \|^2$.)

5. Let $\{\phi_n\}$ be a complete orthonormal set in $\mathscr{F}$. Suppose $(g, \phi_k) = 0$ for all k implies $g \equiv 0$. Suppose f is in $\mathscr{F}$ and $f \sim \sum_0^\infty c_k \phi_k$ and, finally, suppose $\sum_0^\infty c_k \phi_k$ converges uniformly in $\{-\pi \leqslant x \leqslant \pi\}$. Show that it converges to f. (The condition $(g, \phi_k) = 0$ implies $g = 0$ is true in the case of the trigonometric functions.)

Elementary Differentiation
and Integration Formulas

$$\frac{dx^n}{dx} = nx^{n-1}$$

$$\frac{d}{dx}\log x = \frac{1}{x} \qquad \frac{d}{dx}e^x = e^x$$

$$\frac{d}{dx}\sin x = \cos x$$

$$\frac{d}{dx}\cos x = -\sin x$$

$$\frac{d}{dx}\tan x = \sec^2 x$$

$$\frac{d}{dx}\cot x = -\csc^2 x$$

$$\frac{d}{dx}\sec x = \sec x \tan x$$

$$\frac{d}{dx}\csc x = -\csc x \cot x$$

$$\frac{d}{dx}\arcsin x = \frac{1}{\sqrt{1-x^2}}$$

$$\frac{d}{dx}\arccos x = \frac{-1}{\sqrt{1-x^2}}$$

$$\frac{d}{dx}\arctan x = \frac{1}{1+x^2}$$

$$\frac{d}{dx}\operatorname{arc\,cot} x = \frac{-1}{1+x^2}$$

$$\int x^n \, dx = \frac{x^{n+1}}{n+1} + C, \qquad n \neq -1$$

$$\int \frac{dx}{x} = \log|x| + C$$

$$\int e^x \, dx = e^x + C$$

$$\int \sin x \, dx = -\cos x + C$$

$$\int \cos x \, dx = \sin x + C$$

$$\int \sec^2 x \, dx = \tan x + C$$

$$\int \csc^2 x = -\cot x + C$$

$$\int \sec x \tan x \, dx = \sec x + C$$

$$\int \csc x \cot x \, dx = -\csc x + C$$

$$\int \frac{dx}{x^2 + a^2} = \frac{1}{a}\arctan\frac{x}{a} + C$$

$$\int \frac{dx}{\sqrt{a^2 - x^2}} = \arcsin\frac{x}{a} + C$$

$$\int \frac{dx}{x^2 - a^2} = \frac{1}{2a}\log\left|\frac{x-a}{x+a}\right| + C$$

$$\int \frac{dx}{\sqrt{x^2 \pm a^2}}$$
$$= \log|x \pm \sqrt{x^2 \pm a^2}| + C$$

$$\int \sec x \, dx = \log|\sec x + \tan x| + C$$

$$\int \csc x \, dx = \log|\csc x - \cot x| + C$$

Answers, Hints, and Solutions

SECTION 1.2

B EXERCISES

1. (b) $a + (-a) = 0$, so $ba + b(-a) = 0$ or $ab + b(-a) = 0$. By the definition of negative $b(-a) = -(ab)$.
   (d) $[a + (-a)][b + (-b)] = 0$. Multiply and get result.
   (f) If $a > 0$, multiply by a; if $a < 0$, by $-a$.
   (h) Suppose $b \neq 0$: $a = ab(1/b) = 0(1/b) = 0$.
   (j) $b > 0$: multiply both sides by a.
   (l) $b < 0$: multiply both sides by $-a$.
   (n) $x/y = a$ and $u/v = b$ mean $x = ay$, $u = bv$. $(xu)/(yv) = c$ means $xu = cyv$. The problem reduces to showing $ab = c$. By multiplication we get $xu = (ay)(bv) = (ab)yv$. Therefore, by uniqueness of division we get $ab = c$.

SECTION 1.7

A EXERCISES

1. (a) Add $n + 1$ to both sides: right sides reduces to $(n + 1)(n + 2)/2$.
   (e) Use part (a).
2.

	b	d	f	g	j
sup	$-\frac{11}{2}$	1	$\frac{1}{2}$	—	1
inf	—	—	$-\frac{3}{2}$	-5	0 (in S)

B EXERCISES

4. Except when $x = 0$.

SECTION 2.2

A EXERCISES

1. (b) $\frac{1}{2}$; (d) $+\infty$; (f) diverges: even terms $\to -\infty$.
2. (b) 0 (d) oscillates.

B EXERCISES

1. (b) $\frac{3}{2}$; (d) 10; (f) 0.
2. By induction $|a_n| \leq |a_0|q^n \to 0$.

3.

	b	d
sup	$2\frac{1}{4}\,(n=4)$	$\frac{3}{2}\,(n=2)$
inf	-1	$-\infty$

4.

	a	c	e
sup	1	$\pi/2$	1
inf	0 (att.)	0 (att.)	0

SECTION 2.3

A EXERCISES

1. $(b)\ +\infty$; $(d)\ 1$; $(f)\ -\frac{1}{2}$; $(h)\ 5a^4$.

B EXERCISES

6. $(a)\ a/3$; $(b)\ 0$; $(c)\ 1$.

C EXERCISES

2. $(a)\ x/2^{1/n} < [(x^n + y^n)/2]^{1/n} \leqslant x$, by replacing y by 0 then by x. Thus limit is $x = \max(x, y)$.

$(b)\ \max a_j$; $(c)\ y = \min(x, y)$; $(d)\ \min a_j$.

SECTION 2.5

A EXERCISES

1. $(b)\ m/n$; $(d)\ -2/x^3$; $(f)\ \frac{1}{3}$.

2. $(a)\ 3$; $(c)\ 1$; $(e)\ 0$; $(g)\ 8$; $(i)\ \frac{1}{2}$; $(k)\ 0$.

B EXERCISES

2. 1.

6. $f(0 + 0) = +\infty, f(0 - 0) = 0$.

8. $f(0 + 0) = \pi/2, f(0 - 0) = -\pi/2$.

C EXERCISES

2. $\dfrac{1}{n}\sum a_j$.

SECTION 2.7

A EXERCISES

2. (a) Sub-sequence of $\left(1 + \dfrac{1}{n}\right)^n$ (c) $\left[\left(1 + \dfrac{1}{2n}\right)^{2n}\right]^{\frac{1}{2}} \to e^{\frac{1}{2}}$

(e) Sub-sequence of $\left(1 + \dfrac{1}{n}\right)^n$.

SECTION 3.4

A EXERCISES

2. At the integers.

6. By Theorem 3.3*a*.

8. (*a*) $x = 1 + \sqrt{y - 3}$, $\{y > 3\}$; (*b*) $x = 1 - \sqrt{y - 3}$, $\{y > 3\}$.

B EXERCISES

2. $g(x) = x(1 - x)$, and is continuous throughout *I*.

8. $f(x) = x^2 - 3x + 5$ everywhere in the interval.

10. Define $f(a)$ to be $f(a + 0)$ and $f(b)$ to be $f(b - 0)$.

SECTION 3.6

A EXERCISES

2. (*a*) $-y^{1/2}/x^{1/2}$ (*b*) $-y^{1/3}/x^{1/3}$

4. $x \pm 4\sqrt{6}y = 5$

6. (*a*) $\sqrt{x + h} - \sqrt{x} = h/2\sqrt{x_0}$.

B EXERCISES

2. $f'(0 \pm 0) = 0$.

4. $(f_1 g_2 - f_2 g_1)' = (f_1' g_2 - f_2' g_1) + (f_1 g_2' - f_2 g_1')$.

8. Use induction.

10. To see that $f'(0)$ exists:

$$\frac{f(h) - f(0)}{h} = h \sin \frac{1}{h^2} \to 0.$$

17. $(\alpha - \beta)f'(a)$.

SECTION 4.3

A EXERCISES

1. (*b*) Suppose $a = 0$. Then for P: $0, b/n, 2b/n, \ldots, b$ we get $\bar{S} = \Sigma(jb/n)^2 b/n = (b^3/n^3)\Sigma j^2 = b^3 n(n + 1)(2n + 1)/6n^3 \to b^3/3$.

B EXERCISES

2. -1.

4. $\frac{1}{2} \log 2$.

SECTION 4.6

A EXERCISES

1. (*b*) $(x^2 - 3) \sin x + 2x \cos x + C$.

(*d*) $e^{ax}(a \sin bx - b \cos bx)/(a^2 + b^2) + C$.

(*f*) $\frac{1}{2} \sec x \tan x + \frac{1}{2} \log |\sec x + \tan x| + C$.

(*h*) arc sin $x/a + C$.

(*j*) $-x\sqrt{x^2 - a^2}/2 + a^2[\log |x + \sqrt{x^2 - a^2}|]/2 + C$.

(*l*) Rationalize.

5. $-f(x)$.

SECTION 5.2

A EXERCISES

4. Set $y = x^a$. Then $\log y = a \log x$ so $y'/y = a/x$ or $y' = ay/x = ax^{a-1}$.

B EXERCISES

2. (a) 1, (c) 1, (e) 1, (g) c.

C EXERCISES

1. (b) 0; (d) e^a.

SECTION 5.3

B EXERCISES

2. Replace θ by $(\pi/2 - \theta)$ in $\sin(\pi - \theta) = \sin\theta$, then use the addition formula. Differentiate to get the second formula.

SECTION 6.2

A EXERCISES

1. (b) $-2 - \sqrt{2}/2, -2 + \sqrt{2}/2, -\sqrt{2}/2, 0, \sqrt{2}/2, 1, 2$.
3. (a) All points in $\{-1 \leqslant y \leqslant 1\}$. (c) $\{0 \leqslant y \leqslant 1\}$.

B EXERCISES

2. $|A - x_n| \leqslant cr^n/(1-r)$.
4. By the Cauchy criterion.
6. By the Cauchy criterion.

SECTION 6.3

A EXERCISES

	1b	1d	1f	2b
lim sup	2	∞	∞	1
lim inf	$-1 - \frac{1}{2}\sqrt{2}$	0	0	0

SECTION 6.4

A EXERCISES

1. By Theorem 6.4c.

SECTION 7.2

A EXERCISES

1. (b) $-\pi/2$, (d) 0, (f) 1, for $\alpha = 1$; 0, for $\alpha > 1$, (h) large, (j) -1, (l) 1, (n) 1, (p) $\sqrt{e}$.

C EXERCISES

2. $B = An!$; $f^{(n-k)}(x)/x^{n-k} \to An!/(n-k)!$

SECTION 7.3

A EXERCISES

1. (b) $\cos x = 1 - \dfrac{x^2}{2!} + \dfrac{x^4}{4!} - \dfrac{x^6}{6!} + R_7, \; |R_7| = |R_8| \leqslant \left|\dfrac{x^8}{8!}\right|.$

$$\cos x = \tfrac{1}{2}\sqrt{2}\left[1 - (x - \pi/4) - \dfrac{1}{2!}(x - \pi/4)^2 + \dfrac{1}{3!}\left(x - \dfrac{\pi}{4}\right)^3\right.$$
$$\left. + \dfrac{1}{4!}(x - \pi/4)^4 - \dfrac{1}{5!}\left(x - \dfrac{\pi}{4}\right)^5 - \dfrac{1}{6!}\left(x - \dfrac{\pi}{4}\right)^6\right] + R_7,$$

$|R_7| \leqslant \dfrac{1}{7!}\left|x - \dfrac{\pi}{4}\right|^7.$

(d) $e^x = 1 + x + \dfrac{x^2}{2!} + \dfrac{x^3}{3!} + \dfrac{x^4}{4!} + \dfrac{x^5}{5!} + \dfrac{x^6}{6!} + R_7,$

$|R_7| \leqslant \dfrac{1}{7!}e^{|x|}|x|^7,$

$$e^x = e^a\left[1 + (x - a) + \dfrac{1}{2!}(x - a)^2 + \cdots + \dfrac{1}{6!}(x - a)^6\right] + R_7,$$

$|R_7| \leqslant \dfrac{1}{7!}e^a e^{|x-a|}|x - a|^7.$

(f) $\cosh x = 1 + \dfrac{x^2}{2!} + \dfrac{x^4}{4!} + \dfrac{x^6}{6!} + R_7, \; |R_7| = |R_8| \leqslant \dfrac{1}{8!}e^{|x|}|x|^8.$

(h) $2 + 6(x - 1) + 15(x - 1)^2 + 13(x - 1)^3 + 5(x - 1)^4 + (x - 1)^5,$
  $R_n = 0, n \geqslant 6.$

(j) $108 + 252(x - 2) + 270(x - 2)^2 + 165(x - 2)^3 + 60(x - 2)^4$
  $+ 12(x - 2)^5 + (x - 2)^6, R_n = 0, n \geqslant 7.$

2. (b) $\sin^2 x = x^2 - \tfrac{1}{3}x^4 + \tfrac{2}{45}x^6 \cdots .$

(d) $\tan x = x + \tfrac{1}{3}x^3 + \tfrac{2}{15}x^5 \cdots .$

(f) $\arctan x = x - \tfrac{1}{3}x^3 + \tfrac{1}{5}x^5 \cdots .$

(h) $(1 + x^2)^a = 1 + ax^2 + \dfrac{a(a - 1)}{2}x^4 \cdots .$

(j) $e^{-x^2} = 1 - x^2 + \tfrac{1}{2}x^4 \cdots .$

B EXERCISES

2. $\cot x = \dfrac{1}{x} - \dfrac{x}{3} \cdots .$

C EXERCISES

2. $f(x) = e[1 - \tfrac{1}{2}x + \tfrac{11}{24}x^2 \cdots].$

SECTION 7.4

A EXERCISES

1. (b) $\tfrac{2}{3}$, min; 2, max. (d) 1, max. (f) 0, min; $\sqrt[4]{(n - \tfrac{1}{2})\pi}$: n even, min; n odd, max.
  (h) e, min; (j) n even: 0, min; $\pm\sqrt{n/2}$ max; n odd: 0 neither, $+\sqrt{n/2}$, max,
  $-\sqrt{n/2}$ min; (l) e, max.

B EXERCISES

1. 0, min; 1, min; $\tfrac{1}{2}$ max.   **4.** f: neither; g: min.

SECTION 8.1

A EXERCISES

2. $T = 100$.   **6.** Yes.

B EXERCISES

2. A plane through the origin containing the vectors **a** and **b**.

SECTION 8.3

A EXERCISES

2. (a) $\mathbf{i} - \mathbf{k}$, (d) $2\mathbf{i} - \mathbf{j} + 2\mathbf{k}$, (g) -1, (i) 0, (j) 0.

8. It is normal to the plane through **P**, **Q**, and **R**.

12. $\sqrt{(a_1 + b_1)^2 + (a_2 + b_2)^2 + (a_3 + b_3)^2} \leqslant \sqrt{a_1^2 + a_2^2 + a_3^2} + \sqrt{b_1^2 + b_2^2 + b_3^2}$.

B EXERCISES

4. $[(\mathbf{a} \times \mathbf{b}) \cdot \mathbf{d}]\mathbf{c} - [(\mathbf{a} \times \mathbf{b}) \cdot \mathbf{c}]\mathbf{d} = [(\mathbf{c} \times \mathbf{d}) \cdot \mathbf{a}]\mathbf{b} - [(\mathbf{c} \times \mathbf{d}) \cdot \mathbf{b}]\mathbf{a}$.

SECTION 8.6

A EXERCISES

2. $\mathbf{P}(t) = \mathbf{P}_1 + (\mathbf{P}_2 - \mathbf{P}_1)t$.

4. $5(x - 1) + 2(y - 2) - 2(z + 1) = 0$.

B EXERCISES

2. If **c** is not orthogonal to **a**, there are no such **P**'s.

If **c** is orthogonal to **a**, it is a line parallel to **a** lying a distance $|\mathbf{c}|/|\mathbf{a}|$ units away.

4. If the vectors are $\mathbf{e}_1$, $\mathbf{e}_2$, and $\mathbf{e}_3$ respectively, then $\mathbf{i} = \mathbf{e}_1$, $\mathbf{j} = \mathbf{e}_2 - \mathbf{e}_1$, and $\mathbf{k} = \mathbf{e}_3 - \mathbf{e}_2$. Then $\mathbf{a} = a_1\mathbf{i} + a_2\mathbf{j} + a_3\mathbf{k} = (a_1 - a_2)\mathbf{e}_1 + (a_2 - a_3)\mathbf{e}_2 + a_3\mathbf{e}_3$.

SECTION 8.9

A EXERCISES

5. (a) $\mathbf{v} = \sqrt{1 + c^2}\,\mathbf{T}$, $\mathbf{a} = \mathbf{N}$.

B EXERCISES

2. $\mathbf{v} = \mathbf{T}\dfrac{ds}{dt}$, $\mathbf{a} = \mathbf{N}\kappa\left(\dfrac{ds}{dt}\right)^2 + \mathbf{T}\dfrac{d^2s}{dt^2}$.

SECTION 9.2

A EXERCISES

2. $\left\{\left(\dfrac{1}{n}, 0\right)\right\}$; $\left\{\left(0, \dfrac{1}{m}\right)\right\}$, $\{(0, 0)\}$.

4. S is neither open nor closed since it contains part but not all of its boundary.

SECTION 9.4

A EXERCISES

1. (a) D: $\{x^2 + y^2 > 0\}$, R: $\{-1 \leqslant f \leqslant 1\}$.

(f) D: $\{xy > -1\}$, R: $\{-\infty < f < \infty\}$.

2. (a) D: E_3, R: That part of E_3 for which the last two components are non-negative.

(c) D: $\{x^2 + y^2 = 1\}$, R: $\{(0, 0, 1)\}$.

B EXERCISES

2. (*a*) The closed unit cube in E_3.
(*b*) The surface of the unit sphere in E_3.
6. 1.

SECTION 9.7

A EXERCISES

1. (*b*) 0; (*d*) $\frac{1}{2}$.
4. In the definition of continuity take $\epsilon = f(x_0)/2$.

B EXERCISES

4. Set $g(x, x) = f'(x)$.

SECTION 10.1

A EXERCISES

3. (*b*) $z_1 = -\dfrac{2xz \log z}{ze^z + x^2}$, $z_2 = \dfrac{-z}{ze^z + x^2}$

4. (*a*) $u_1 = \cos v + \sin v$ $v_1 = (\cos v - \sin v)/u$
$u_2 = \sin v$ $v_2 = (\cos v)/u$

SECTION 10.2

A EXERCISES

2. (*a*) $x - y = z - 1$; (*d*) $2x + 4y - z = 3$.
4. Approximate maximum error $= \pi/1600 \sim 0.00196$.

SECTION 10.4

A EXERCISES

1. (*a*) $\alpha \cdot \nabla f = 8/\sqrt{22}$, (*h*) $-446/\sqrt{129}$
2. $\beta \cdot \nabla f$.   **4.** $g_x = f_u + f_v + 2f_w, g_y = -f_u + f_v$.

B EXERCISES

6. $\left(\dfrac{\partial f}{\partial x}\right)^2 + \left(\dfrac{\partial f}{\partial y}\right)^2$
10. $h_x = f'g, h_y = xf'g', h_{xx} = f''g^2$,
$h_{xy} = f'g' + xf''gg', h_{yy} = x^2f''(g')^2 + xf'g''$.

SECTION 10.6

A EXERCISES

1. (*a*) $xy - \dfrac{1}{3!}\left(xy^3 + x^3y\right) + \left(\dfrac{xy^5}{5!} + \dfrac{x^3y^3}{(3!)^2} + \dfrac{x^5y}{5!}\right) + \cdots$
(*h*) $\displaystyle\sum_0^{14} (x + y)^2$.

SECTION 11.2

A EXERCISES

1. (*a*) $(1, 3, 4)$.

B EXERCISES

4. Rotation through $\pi/3$.

SECTION 11.3

A EXERCISES

1. (a) 1, (c) e^{2r}, (d) $\dfrac{1}{n} y^{1/n-1}$

2. (a) The square rotated by $\pi/4$.
(d) A four-sided figure cornering at $(0, 0)$, $(1, 0)$, $(2, 1)$ and $(1, 1)$ with the top and bottom being line segments. The sides are curves: $u = v^n$ and $u - 1 = v^n$.

4. (c) $1/(x^2 + y^2) = e^{2r}$.

6. $\dfrac{\partial f}{\partial x} = \dfrac{\partial f}{\partial r} \cos\theta - \dfrac{\partial f}{\partial \theta} \dfrac{\sin\theta}{r}$, $\dfrac{\partial f}{\partial y} = \dfrac{\partial f}{\partial r} \sin\theta + \dfrac{\partial f}{\partial \theta} \dfrac{\cos\theta}{r}$.

8. $\Delta u = \dfrac{\partial^2 u}{\partial r^2} + \dfrac{1}{r}\dfrac{\partial u}{\partial r} + \dfrac{1}{r^2}\dfrac{\partial^2 u}{\partial \theta^2}$.

10. $\Delta u = e^{4r}\left[\dfrac{\partial^2 u}{\partial r^2} + \dfrac{\partial^2 u}{\partial \theta^2} \right]$

12. $\left(\dfrac{\partial u}{\partial r}\right)^2 + \dfrac{1}{r^2}\left(\dfrac{\partial u}{\partial \theta}\right)^2$

B EXERCISES

4. $\dfrac{\partial z}{\partial x} = \dfrac{\partial h}{\partial u}\dfrac{\partial g}{\partial v}\dfrac{\partial(u, v)}{\partial(x, y)} - \dfrac{\partial h}{\partial v}\dfrac{\partial g}{\partial u}\dfrac{\partial(u, v)}{\partial(x, y)} = \dfrac{\partial(h, g)}{\partial(u, v)}\dfrac{\partial(u, v)}{\partial(x, y)}$.

SECTION 11.6

A EXERCISES

2. (a) Two functions. ± 5, (b) none.

4. Only for $x = y = 0$.

6. u, v are polar coordinates. The coordinates (u, v) and $(u, v + 2\pi)$ describe the same point in the (x, y) plane.

B EXERCISES

4. When the Jacobian of $\mathbf{F}$ with respect to $\mathbf{P}$ is not zero.

8. (c) $\Delta f = \dfrac{1}{u^2 + v^2}\left(\dfrac{\partial^2 f}{\partial u^2} + \dfrac{\partial^2 f}{\partial v^2} \right)$.

SECTION 11.8

A EXERCISES

1. (b) $(0, 0)$ saddle, $(-4, -4)$ max; (d) $(2, -2)$ max; (f) $(\tfrac{1}{2}, \tfrac{1}{2})$ max, $(-\tfrac{1}{2}, -\tfrac{1}{2})$ min.

2. (b) max 28, min: -20. (d) max: $2\sqrt{2}$, min: 0.

4. $(2, \tfrac{2}{3}, 1)$ **6.** $(\tfrac{12}{13}, \tfrac{17}{13}, \tfrac{3}{13})$.

B EXERCISES

4. (a) $(0, 0)$ saddle.
(b) $(0, 0)$ saddle, $(\pm 1/\sqrt{2}, \pm 1/\sqrt{2})$ min.

SECTION 12.3

A EXERCISES

1. (b) 2, (c) 0, (d) $\frac{1}{6}$ [sin 9 + sin 7 − sin 11 − sin 3 − 2 sin 1].

SECTION 12.4

A EXERCISES

2. The integration is over the triangle bounded by $y = 0$, $y = x$, $x = a$.

4. (a) $a^3/6$. (b) $(e − 1)/2$. It's a proper integral since $x > y$.

5. (b) $\int_0^1 dx \int_{x^{3/2}}^x f(x, y)\, dy$.

(d) $c < a$: $\int_c^a dy \int_a^b f(x, y)\, dx + \int_a^b dy \int_y^b f(x, y)\, dx$.

B EXERCISES

2. $6(b^{7/6} − a^{7/6})(d^{5/6} − c^{5/6})/35$.

SECTION 13.1

A EXERCISES

1. (a) $-\frac{3}{5}$, (c) $1 − 2 \cos 1$, (e) $\frac{2}{3}$, (g) $2\pi + \frac{1}{2}$.

2. (a) 2π, (c) $\int_0^{2\pi} \cos^2 \theta\, d\theta = \pi$.

4. $4/\sqrt{17} + \log [4 + (1/\sqrt{17})]$.

7. (c) $\phi = x^2y + xz^3 + 3yz$.

SECTION 13.2

A EXERCISES

1. (b) 0, (d) 0, (f) 0.

C EXERCISES

2. (a) Set $L = -u \dfrac{\partial v}{\partial y}$, $M = u \dfrac{\partial v}{\partial x}$ and note that $dx = n_y\, ds$,

$$dy = n_x\, ds \quad \text{where} \quad \mathbf{n} = \mathbf{i}n_x + \mathbf{j}n_y.$$

(c) Set $u = v$ in (a).

3. (a) Set $\mathbf{F} = M\mathbf{i} − L\mathbf{j}$ and use the differential relations noted in 2a.

SECTION 13.4

A EXERCISES

1. (b) $2\pi\sqrt{2}$, (d) $\frac{2}{3}\pi[2\sqrt{2} − 1]$.

3. (a) π, (b) $81\pi/2$, (d) 2π.

5. (b) 0.

SECTION 13.6

A EXERCISES

1. (a) -4π.

SECTION 13.7

A EXERCISES

2. (a) $D \to D'$: $\{(u + 1)^2 + (v - 1)^2 \leqslant a^2\}$, a circle.

(b) $D \to D'$: $\{(au + bv)^2 + (cu + dv)^2 \leqslant a^2\}$, an ellipse.

4. (a) $\displaystyle\int_{-\frac{1}{2}}^{\frac{1}{2}} \int_{-\sqrt{x-x^2}}^{\sqrt{x-x^2}} \int_{x^2+y^2}^{x} dz \, dy \, dx.$

(b) $\displaystyle\int_{-\pi/2}^{\pi/2} \int_{0}^{\cos\theta} \int_{x}^{r^2} r \, dz \, dr \, d\theta.$

B EXERCISES

2. $2 \log 2 - \frac{1}{2}.$

SECTION 14.1

A EXERCISES

1. (b) $\frac{1}{4}$

2. Converges absolutely.

SECTION 14.2

A EXERCISES

AC = Absolutely convergent.

NAC = Not absolutely convergent.

2. (a) NAC, (c) NAC, (e) NAC, (g) AC (i) NAC, (j) NAC, (l) NAC.

B EXERCISES

2. $x > 0.$

4. First NAC; second AC.

6. $x \neq \pm 1.$

SECTION 14.4

A EXERCISES

C = convergent

CC = Conditionally convergent.

AC = Absolutely convergent.

D = Divergent.

1. (b) CC, (d) CC, (f) CC, (h) CC, (j) D, (l) C (and therefore AC) if and only if $x > 1.$

2. (b) $n \geqslant \exp 10^{10}.$

3. (a) $|x| < 1$, (c) $|x| > 1$, (e) $-1 \leqslant x < 1.$

4. (a) If n is so large that $\left(1 + \dfrac{1}{n}\right)x = r < 1$, then $|S - S_n| \leqslant \dfrac{a_{n-1}|x|^{n+1}}{1 - r}.$

5. (a) C, (c) D, (e) C, (g) C.

6. (a) $0 \leqslant S - S_{100} \leqslant \dfrac{a_{100}\dfrac{101}{201}}{1 - \dfrac{100}{201}} = a_{100}.$

B EXERCISES

2. The k-series, $k > 1$.

3. (a) $a_n = a_{N+1} \dfrac{a_{N+2}}{a_{N+1}} \cdots \dfrac{a_n}{a_{n-1}} \geqslant a_{N+1}.$

C EXERCISES

4. Consider $\displaystyle\sum_{0}^{\infty} (a_n x + b_n)^2$.

SECTION 14.6

A EXERCISES

2. (a) D, (c) D.

B EXERCISES

2. It converges for $|x| < 1$, and diverges for $x > 1$. For $x = -1$ it converges (and hence converges absolutely), for $a \geqslant 0$, and diverges for $a < 0$. For $x = 1$, it converges absolutely for $a \geqslant 0$, conditionally for $-1 < a < 0$, and diverges for $a \leqslant -1$.

C EXERCISES

2. $1 - \dfrac{1}{2} - \dfrac{1}{4} - \dfrac{1}{6} - \dfrac{1}{8} + \dfrac{1}{3} - \cdots - \dfrac{1}{16} + \dfrac{1}{5} - \cdots - \dfrac{1}{24} - \cdots +$

$\dfrac{1}{2k-1} - \cdots - \dfrac{1}{8k} + \cdots$

SECTION 15.2

A EXERCISES

2. If $|x| \leqslant a < 1$, then $M_n = a^n \to 0$.

4. Converges pointwise to zero in (a), (b), (c) uniformly only in (b).

8. Converges uniformly for all x since $\left| \dfrac{x^{2n} - 1}{x^{2n} + 1} \right| \leqslant 1$.

B EXERCISES

4. a can be any number $< b$, where b is defined by $b \log b = 1$.

SECTION 15.3

A EXERCISES

2. $x < 1/2$.

4. $S(x) = 0$, $\{0 \leqslant x < 1\}$; $S(x) = 1$, $\{1 \leqslant x \leqslant 2\}$. If the convergence were uniform S would be continuous.

6. The convergence is not uniform, yet here limit and integration can be interchanged. Uniform convergence is a sufficient, not a necessary, condition for the interchange.

8. f is continuous for $x > 0$.

$\displaystyle\int_{1}^{2} f(x)\, dy = \dfrac{1}{e-1} - \dfrac{1}{e^2 - 1}.$

SECTION 15.5
A EXERCISES

2. We need only show the uniform convergence of the series for f'. Apply Dirichlet's test with $u_n = \dfrac{(-1)^n}{n}$, $v_n = e^{-nx}$.

4. Apply Dirichlet's test with $u_n = \dfrac{(-1)^n}{\log n}$, $v_n = x^n e^{-nx}$.

6. $\Sigma(-1)^n \log\left(1 + \dfrac{x^2}{n}\right)$. It converges uniformly in every finite interval, but not for all x.

B EXERCISES

4. Apply Abel's test with $u_n = \cos nx$, $v_n = n^{-\alpha}$.

Observe $\left| \dfrac{1}{n^\alpha} - \dfrac{1}{(n-1)^\alpha} \right| \leqslant \dfrac{\alpha}{(n-1)^{\alpha+1}}$ by the mean value theorem.

SECTION 16.1
A EXERCISES

1. (b) $R = \infty$, (d) $R = 1$. Converges at $x = 1$ if $k > 1$, converges at $x = -1$ if $k > 0$, absolutely if $k > 1$. (f) $R = 1/e$. Diverges for $x = \pm 1/e$.

2. (b) $0 < x < 4$, (d) $\pi - 1 < x < \pi + 1$.

B EXERCISES

1. (c) e.

3. (a) $\geqslant \min(R, R')$, (b) $\geqslant RR'$, (c) Can say nothing.

SECTION 16.2
A EXERCISES

1. (b) $R = 4$, (d) $R = 1$.

3. (a) $1 = \displaystyle\sum_1^\infty \dfrac{1}{n(n+1)}$.

B EXERCISES

1. (b) $f = -\displaystyle\int_0^x \{[t + \log(1-t)]/t^2\}\, dt \ \{-1 \leqslant x \leqslant 1\}$.

(d) $f = \dfrac{2}{x}\displaystyle\int_0^x \{[t + \log(1-t)]/t^2\}\, dt - \dfrac{1}{x}\log(1-x) \ \{-1 \leqslant x < 1\}$.

(f) $f = \dfrac{x}{1-x^5} \ \{-1 < x < 1\}$

SECTION 16.3
A EXERCISES

1. (b) $-\frac{1}{2}\sqrt{2}\left[1 + (x - 3\pi/4) - \dfrac{1}{2!}(x - 3\pi/4)^2 - \dfrac{1}{3!}(x - 3\pi/4)^3 + + - - \cdots\right]$

(d) $\displaystyle\sum_0^\infty (x \log a)^n/n$ (f) $-\displaystyle\sum_1^\infty x^n/n$ (h) $e\displaystyle\sum_0^\infty (x - 1)^n/n!$

(j) $\displaystyle\sum_0^\infty \dfrac{(-1)^n x^{3n+1}}{n!\,(3n+1)}$ (l) $\displaystyle\sum_1^\infty \dfrac{(-1)^{k+1} x^{2k-1}}{(2k!)(2k-1)}$

2. 0.747.

SECTION 16.4

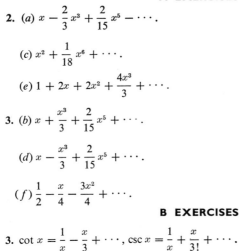

A EXERCISES

2. *(a)* $x - \dfrac{2}{3} x^3 + \dfrac{2}{15} x^5 - \cdots$.

(c) $x^2 + \dfrac{1}{18} x^6 + \cdots$.

(e) $1 + 2x + 2x^2 + \dfrac{4x^3}{3} + \cdots$.

3. *(b)* $x + \dfrac{x^3}{3} + \dfrac{2}{15} x^5 + \cdots$.

(d) $x - \dfrac{x^3}{3} + \dfrac{2}{15} x^5 + \cdots$.

(f) $\dfrac{1}{2} - \dfrac{x}{4} - \dfrac{3x^2}{4} + \cdots$.

B EXERCISES

3. $\cot x = \dfrac{1}{x} - \dfrac{x}{3} + \cdots$, $\csc x = \dfrac{1}{x} + \dfrac{x}{3!} + \cdots$.

SECTION 16.7

A EXERCISES

1. *(b)* $1 + y + \dfrac{y^2}{2!} + \dfrac{y^3}{2!} + \cdots$.

2. *(a)* $y + \dfrac{y^3}{3} + \dfrac{3y^5}{40} + \cdots$.

4. $\Sigma r^n \cos n\theta = \dfrac{1 - r \cos \theta}{1 - 2r \cos \theta + r^2}$.

SECTION 17.1

A EXERCISES

(D = divergent, AC = absolutely convergent.)

1. *(b)* D, *(d)* D for $k = 1$, $1/(k - 1)$ for $k > 1$, *(f)* AC, *(h)* AC : 2, *(j)* AC : $\frac{1}{2}$, *(l)* AC, *(n)* AC : $3\sqrt{\pi}/8$, *(p)* AC : $\frac{1}{2}(n - \frac{1}{2})(n - \frac{3}{2}) \cdots (\frac{1}{2})\sqrt{\pi}$.

B EXERCISES

4. $-\pi \log 2$.

SECTION 17.4

A EXERCISES

(D = divergent, C = convergent.)

1. *(b)* $\alpha = 1$, D; $\alpha > 1$, C; *(d)* C; *(f)* D; *(h)* C; *(j)* C; *(l)* C; *(n)* C; *(p)* D; *(r)* D.

2. *(a)* no, *(c)* no.

B EXERCISES

2. D.

SECTION 17.5
A EXERCISES

1. (b) C, (d) C.
2. (a) C, (c) C.

SECTION 18.1
A EXERCISES

2. (a) By Theorem 18.1a.

(b) $\displaystyle\int_0^t \sin xt\, dt = \begin{cases} \dfrac{1-\cos x}{x} & x \neq 0 \\ 0 & x = 0 \end{cases}$

(c) $\displaystyle\int_0^1 t\cos xt\, dt \begin{cases} = \dfrac{\sin x}{x} + \dfrac{\cos x - 1}{x^2} & x \neq 0 \\ = \frac{1}{2} & x = 0 \end{cases}$

(d) $\displaystyle\int_0^1 \dfrac{1 - \cos at}{t}\, dt$

(e) $\displaystyle f(x) = \sum_0^\infty \dfrac{(-1)^n x^{2n+1}}{(2n+2)!}$

4. (a) $|x| < 1$.

(b) $\displaystyle f'(x) = -2\int_0^\pi \dfrac{\cos y\, dy}{(1 + x\cos y)^3}$

SECTION 18.2
A EXERCISES

1. (b) $e^{-xt}(1 + t^3) \leqslant e^{-at}(1 + t^3)$.

(d) $\left| \dfrac{\sin t}{t^y} \right| \leqslant \left| \dfrac{t}{t^y} \right| = t^{1-y} \leqslant t^{1-a}$.

(f) $\left| e^{-t(x+1)} \cos xt \dfrac{t}{t + x^2} \right| \leqslant e^{-t}$.

B EXERCISES

2. (a) Apply Abel's test with $u(x, t) = \sin xt$.
   (c) Apply Abel's test with $u(x, t) = \sin t$.
   (e) Does not converge uniformly. It is 0 when $x = 0$, and $c/\sqrt{x}$, when $x > 0$.

SECTION 18.3
A EXERCISES

1. (a, b, d) Theorem 18.3c.
   (e, f, g) Theorem 18.3b.
   (h, i, j) Theorem 18.3e

B EXERCISES

8. $\pi(b-a)$.

10.
$$\begin{array}{ll} 0 & x > |y|+|z|. \\ -\pi/8 & x = |y|+|z|. \\ -\pi/4 & \big||y|-|z|\big| < x < |y|+|z|. \\ -\pi/8 & |x| = \big||y|-|z|\big|. \\ 0 & |x| < \big||y|-|z|\big|. \\ \pi/8 & x = -\big||y|-|z|\big|. \\ \pi/4 & -|y|-|z| < x < -\big||y|-|z|\big|. \\ \pi/8 & x = -|y|-|z|. \\ 0 & x < -|y|-|z|. \end{array}$$

11, 12. Integrate the integral in 10 with respect to y and then z.

C EXERCISES

4. $\dfrac{\pi}{2}|y|$.

6. $\frac{1}{2}\log\left|\dfrac{x-y}{x+y}\right|$.

8. $\log|a/b|$.

SECTION 19.2

A EXERCISES

8. $\Gamma(n+\frac{1}{2}) = (n-\frac{1}{2})(n-\frac{3}{2})\cdots(\frac{1}{2})\sqrt{\pi}.$
$\Gamma(-n+\frac{1}{2}) = (-1)^n\sqrt{\pi}/(n-\frac{1}{2})(n-\frac{3}{2})\cdots(\frac{1}{2}).$

C EXERCISES

1. $\dfrac{\Gamma(1-a)}{a}$.

2. (a) $\dfrac{2\Gamma(1-a)(2^a-1)}{(1+a)a}$ $\qquad a \neq 0$

$\qquad 2\log 2 \qquad\qquad\qquad a = 0$

(b) $\dfrac{3\Gamma(1-a)(1-2^{2+a}+3^{1+a})}{(2+a)(1+a)a}$ $\qquad a \neq 0, -1$

$\qquad 3\log\left(\frac{4}{3}\right) \qquad\qquad a = -1$

$\qquad (\frac{3}{2})\log\left(\frac{27}{16}\right) \qquad\quad a = 0.$

SECTION 19.4

A EXERCISES

1. (a) $I(x) \sim \sqrt{\dfrac{\pi}{2x}}$.

(c) $I(x) \sim \sqrt{\dfrac{\pi}{4x}}$.

SECTION 20.1

A EXERCISES

1. (b) $\dfrac{1}{\pi} + \dfrac{1}{2}\sin x - \dfrac{2}{\pi}\sum_{1}^{\infty}\dfrac{\cos 2nx}{4n^2 - 1}$.

(d) $\dfrac{2}{\pi}\sinh\pi\left[\dfrac{1}{2} + \sum_{1}^{\infty}(-1)^n(\cos nx - n\sin nx)/(1 + n^2)\right]$.

(f) $\dfrac{2}{\pi} - \dfrac{4}{\pi}\sum_{1}^{\infty}\dfrac{\cos 2nx}{4n^2 - 1}$

SECTION 20.5

A EXERCISES

1. (a) sine series: $\sin x = \sin x$.

cosine series: $\sin x = \dfrac{2}{\pi} - \dfrac{4}{\pi}\sum_{1}^{\infty}\dfrac{\cos 2nx}{4n^2 - 1}$.

(c) sine series: $1 = \dfrac{2}{\pi}\sum_{0}^{\infty}\dfrac{\sin(2k + 1)x}{(2k + 1)}$.

cosine series: $1 = 1$.

2. (a) $x^2 = \dfrac{L^2}{3} + \dfrac{4L^2}{\pi^2}\sum_{1}^{\infty}(-1)^n\cos\dfrac{n\pi x}{L}$.

(c) $1 = 1$.

4. $f(x) = \dfrac{a_0}{2} + \Sigma\left\{a_n\cos\left[\dfrac{2n\pi}{b - a}\left(x - \dfrac{a + b}{2}\right)\right] + b_n\sin\left[\dfrac{2n\pi}{b - a}\left(x - \dfrac{a + b}{2}\right)\right]\right\}$

$a_n = \dfrac{2}{b - a}\int_{a}^{b}f(x)\cos\left[\dfrac{2n\pi}{b - a}\left(x - \dfrac{a + b}{2}\right)\right]dx$

$b_n = \dfrac{2}{b - a}\int_{a}^{b}f(x)\sin\left[\dfrac{2n\pi}{b - a}\left(x - \dfrac{a + b}{2}\right)\right]dx$

SECTION 20.7

B EXERCISES

2. $\dfrac{\pi}{2}\sin x$ in $\{0 \leqslant x \leqslant \pi\}$, 0 in $\{x > \pi\}$.

6. Since f is even the integral reduces to the cosine integral.

And $h(u) = \sqrt{\dfrac{2}{\pi}}\int_{0}^{\infty}\dfrac{\sin t\cos ut}{t}\,dt = \begin{cases} 1, & 0 < u < 1 \\ \frac{1}{2} & u = 1 \\ 0, & u > 1 \end{cases}$

by example 5 of Section 18.3.

8. π in $\{0 < x < 1\}$, 0 in $\{x < 0\}$ and $\{x > 1\}$.

Index